International Conference on Materials - Properties, Measurements and Applications (ICMPMA 2022)

IOP Conference Series: Materials Science and Engineering
Volume 1263

Online
9 – 13 May 2022

ISBN: 978-1-7138-6423-3
ISSN: 1757-8981

Printed from e-media with permission by:

Curran Associates, Inc.
57 Morehouse Lane
Red Hook, NY 12571

Some format issues inherent in the e-media version may also appear in this print version.

Institute of Physics
Dirac House, Temple Back
Bristol BS1 6BE UK

Phone: 44 1 17 929 7481
Fax: 44 1 17 920 0979

techtracking@iop.org

Additional copies of this publication are available from:

Curran Associates, Inc.
57 Morehouse Lane
Red Hook, NY 12571 USA
Phone: 845-758-0400
Fax: 845-758-2633
Email: curran@proceedings.com
Web: www.proceedings.com

TABLE OF CONTENTS

IOP Conf. Series: Materials Science and Engineering 1263 (2022) 011001 doi:10.1088/1757-899X/1263/1/011001

Proceedings of
International Conference on Materials - Properties, Measurements, and Applications (ICMPMA 2022)

Edited By

Sunil Thomas
Fatima Mata National College, Kollam, Kerala, India

P S Anil Kumar
Indian Institute of Science, Bengaluru, India

C K Jayasankar
Sri Venkateswara University, Tirupati, India

Sajan D George
Manipal Academy of Higher Education, Karnataka, India

Alida Timar-Gabor
Babes-Bolyai University, Cluj-Napoca, Romania

Sheena Mary Y
Fatima Mata National College, Kollam, Kerala, India

Toney Teddy Fernandez
Macquarie University, Australia

About the Conference

ICMPMA primarily aims to bring together the ignited and inquisitive minds of students, researchers, academicians, and scientists, thereby creating a platform where they can exhibit and observe the myriad research works so that a forum is built to share innovative developments in material science. In due course, we intend to be an acknowledged global forum for researchers working in material science by organizing a triennial conference through which we expect to attract a large number of participants.

The first edition of the ICMPMA series was organized by Fatima Mata National College, Kollam, Kerala, India from May 09 to May 13, 2022. The assemblage of ardent scientific minds from all over the world has made this conference series an outstanding scientific program. The leading experts in the domain of materials research engaged us in deliberations that enlightened and enriched our knowledge, and also bestowed on us new perspectives to approach the various allied disciplines of material science. This scientific program was keen on emphasizing the recent developments in material science at an international level and has created an opportunity for the participants to build intellectual associations with researchers across the world. ICMPMA 2022 has been well represented globally as international researchers have held diverse roles in the course of the conference as Editors and Reviewers of the Proceedings, Conference Chairs, Speakers, and Scientific Advisors.

ICMPMA 2022 comprised 6 plenary talks, 21 invited talks, 8 technical sessions, 195 oral presentations, 160 poster presentations, 14 oral presentation sessions, 6 poster sessions, and 6 conference chairs. The active involvement of 856 participants from 33 countries is one of the key highlights of the first edition of the conference. Photonic Materials and Devices, Energy Materials, Electronic Materials, Biomaterials, and Magnetic Materials were the thrust areas of discussion across the course of the conference series.

In the upcoming years, the conference series will indeed be phenomenal in contributing to the development of the various disciplines of material science.

Conference Organizers

Dr. Sunil Thomas* and **Dr. Sachin P C**
Fatima Mata National College, Kollam, Kerala, India
*Email: sunilthomas@fmnc.ac.in ; sunilspap@gmail.com

Conference Convener

Dr. Sheena Mary Y
Fatima Mata National College, Kollam, Kerala, India

Local Organizing Committee

Mr. Ratheesh Kumar R, Mr. Sunil A, Dr. Ben Byju, Dr. Bhagya Uthaman, Dr. Manu Raj R, Ms. Arya Anilkumar, Dr. Soniya S R, Ms. Syama Nath H, Ms. Mary Lizy P, and Mr. Albert R
Fatima Mata National College, Kollam, Kerala, India

IOP Conf. Series: Materials Science and Engineering 1263 (2022) 011001 doi:10.1088/1757-899X/1263/1/011001

Conference Chairs

Primary Conference Chair

Prof. Gin Jose
University of Leeds, UK

Additional Conference Chairs

Prof. Reji Philip
Raman Research Institute, Bengaluru, India

Prof. Kuruvila Joseph
Indian Institute of Space Science and Technology, India

Prof. N V Unnikrishnan
Mahatma Gandhi University, Kerala, India

Prof. Mayeen Uddin Khandaker
Sunway University, Malaysia

Prof. Jojo P J
Fatima Mata National College, Kollam, Kerala, India

Session Chairs

Prof. Nirmala R
Indian Institute of Technology Madras, India
Prof. P R Biju
Mahatma Gandhi University, Kerala, India
Prof. P P Pradyumnan
University of Calicut, Kerala, India
Prof. Cyriac Joseph
Mahatma Gandhi University, Kerala, India
Prof. Riju C Issac
Cochin University of Science and Technology, Kerala, India
Prof. Jayachandran K
Mahatma Gandhi University, Kerala, India
Dr. S N Potty
Centre for Materials for Electronics Technology, Thrissur, India

Oral Presentation Chairs

Prof. Cyriac Joseph
Mahatma Gandhi University, Kerala, India
Dr. Saritha A C
Mahatma Gandhi University, Kerala, India
Dr. Jitumani Kalita
Cotton University, Assam, India
Dr. Suneesh C V
University of Kerala, India
Dr. Sibi K S
University of Kerala, India
Dr. I Hubert Joe
University of Kerala, India
Dr. Savitha Pillai S
University of Kerala, India
Dr. Jayakrishnan R
University of Kerala, India
Dr. Derry Holaday M G
University of Calicut, Kerala, India
Dr. K P Zuhail
University of Calicut, Kerala, India
Dr. Pranay Ranjan
Indian Institute of Technology Jodhpur, India
Dr. Rithesh Raj D
SASTRA Deemed University, Tamil Nadu, India
Dr. Arun Kumar K V
CMS College, Kottayam, Kerala, India
Dr. Ann Mary K A
St. Thomas College, Thrissur, India

Speakers

Plenary Speakers

Prof. C Vijayan
Indian Institute of Technology Madras, India
Prof. Laeticia Petit
Tampere University, Finland
Dr. Aldrin Antony
Cochin University of Science and Technology, Kerala, India
Prof. Saji George
McGill University, Canada
Prof. S M Yusuf
Bhabha Atomic Research Centre, Mumbai, India
Dr. K P Surendran
CSIR - NIIST, Thiruvananthapuram, India

IOP Conf. Series: Materials Science and Engineering 1263 (2022) 011001 doi:10.1088/1757-899X/1263/1/011001

Invited Speakers

Prof. Reji Philip
Raman Research Institute, Bengaluru, India
Prof. Sajan D George
Manipal Academy of Higher Education, Karnataka, India
Dr. Kavita Devi
Indian Institute of Technology Dharwad, India
Prof. M L Chithambo
Rhodes University, Grahamstown, South Africa
Prof. Radhakrishnan Prabhu
Robert Gordon University, Scotland
Prof. Gin Jose
University of Leeds, UK
Prof. Prasanth Ravindran
Pondicherry University, India
Prof. S Assa Aravindh
University of Oulu, Finland
Dr. Libu Manjakkal
University of Glasgow, Scotland
Prof. Biju V
University of Kerala, India
Dr. Rakhi R B
CSIR - NIIST, Thiruvananthapuram, India
Prof. Harikrishna Varma P R
Sree Chitra Tirunal Institute for Medical Sciences and Technology, India
Prof. Virginia Pensabene
University of Leeds, UK
Prof. C. Sudarsanakumar
Mahatma Gandhi University, Kerala, India
Prof. Santhosh P N
Indian Institute of Technology Madras, India
Prof. K G Suresh
Indian Institute of Technology Bombay, India
Prof. P S Anil Kumar
Indian Institute of Science, Bengaluru, India
Dr. Senoy Thomas
Cochin University of Science and Technology, Kerala, India
Dr. Subodh G
University of Kerala, India
Qassim Abdullahi
Heriot-Watt University, UK
Dr. Sheetal Kaushik Bhardwaj
University of Amsterdam, Netherlands

Advisory Committee

Most Rev. Dr. Paul Antony Mullassery
Bishop, Diocese of Quilon (Patron)
Rev. Fr. Anil Jose
Former Manager, Fatima Mata National College, Kollam, Kerala, India
Rev. Fr. (Dr.) Abhilash Gregory
Manager, Fatima Mata National College, Kollam, Kerala, India
Prof. Jojo P J
Former Principal, Fatima Mata National College, Kollam, Kerala, India
Dr. Shaiju P N
IQAC Coordinator, Fatima Mata National College, Kollam, Kerala, India
Prof. Saleh Thaker
United Arab Emirates University, Al Ain, Abu Dhabi, UAE
Prof. C Vijayan
Indian Institute of Technology Madras, India
Prof. C K Jayasankar
Sri Venkateswara University, Tirupati, India
Prof. Alida Timar-Gabor
Babes-Bolyai University, Cluj-Napoca, Romania
Prof. P P Pradyumnan
University of Calicut, Kerala, India
Dr. S N Potty
Centre for Materials for Electronics Technology, Thrissur, India
Dr. Sujin P Jose
Madurai Kamaraj University, Tamil Nadu, India
Prof. N V Unnikrishnan
Mahatma Gandhi University, Kerala, India
Prof. P R Biju
Mahatma Gandhi University, Kerala, India
Prof. Cyriac Joseph
Mahatma Gandhi University, Kerala, India
Prof. Pramod Gopinath
Cochin University of Science and Technology, Kerala, India
Prof. Riju C Issac
Cochin University of Science and Technology, Kerala, India
Dr. Subodh G
University of Kerala, India
Dr. Sibi K S
University of Kerala, India
Prof. Biju V
University of Kerala, India
Prof. K G Gopchandran
University of Kerala, India

IOP Conf. Series: Materials Science and Engineering 1263 (2022) 011001 doi:10.1088/1757-899X/1263/1/011001

Best Oral Presentations

Mrs. Sariga C Lal *(Session - Photonic Materials and Devices)*
Department of Physics, University of Kerala, India
Ms. Devadharshini K *(Session - Energy Materials)*
CSIR-Central Electrochemical Research Institute, Tamil Nadu, India
Mrs. Soumya V S *(Session - Biomaterials)*
St. Stephen's College, Pathanapuram, Kerala, India
Mr. Abinesh A R *(Session - Magnetic Materials)*
St. Joseph's College of Engineering, Chennai, India
Mrs. Dhanya P K *(Session - Electronic Materials)*
University College, Thiruvananthapuram, India
Ms. Nishitha Chandran *(Session - Other Materials)*
The National Institute of Engineering, Mysuru, India

Best Poster Presentations

Mr. Debasish Barman *(Session - Photonic Materials and Devices)*
Indian Institute of Technology Guwahati, India
Mr. Raj Kumar *(Session - Energy Materials)*
Indian Institute of Technology (BHU), Varanasi, India
Mr. Omkar *(Session - Biomaterials)*
CSIR-National Physical Laboratory, New Delhi, India
Mr. Boini Brahmanandam *(Session - Magnetic Materials)*
University College of Science, Osmania University, Hyderabad, India
Mr. Kenneth Lobo *(Session - Electronic Materials)*
Centre for Nano and Soft Matter Sciences, Bengaluru, India
Mr. Puneethkumar M Srinivasappa *(Session - Other Materials)*
Centre for Nano and Materials Science, JAIN University, Bengaluru, India

Reviewers of the Proceedings

Dr. Aldrin Antony
Cochin University of Science and Technology, Kerala, India
Dr. Ann Mary K A
St. Thomas College, Thrissur, Kerala, India
Dr. Bhagya Uthaman
Fatima Mata National College, Kollam, Kerala, India
Prof. C Vijayan
Indian Institute of Technology Madras, India
Prof. Cyriac Joseph
Mahatma Gandhi University, Kerala, India
Dr. Dawam Robert Rangmou
University of Jos, Nigeria
Dr. Deepthy Menon
Amrita Institute of Medical Sciences and Research Centre, Kerala, India
Dr. S N Potty
Centre for Materials for Electronics Technology, Thrissur, India
Dr. Anil Kumar Yadav
Chaudhary Charan Singh University, Meerut, India

IOP Conf. Series: Materials Science and Engineering 1263 (2022) 011001 doi:10.1088/1757-899X/1263/1/011001

Dr. Rithesh Raj D
SASTRA Deemed University, Tamil Nadu, India
Dr. Sachin P C
Fatima Mata National College, Kollam, Kerala, India
Prof. Saji George
McGill University, Canada
Dr. Sameera S
University of Kerala, India
Prof. Santhosh P N
Indian Institute of Technology Madras, India
Dr. Sarathlal Koyiloth Vayalil
University of Petroleum and Energy Studies, Dehradun, India
Dr. Savitha Pillai S
University of Kerala, India
Dr. Senoy Thomas
Cochin University of Science and Technology, Kerala, India
Dr. Shashikant D Shinde
MES's Nowrosjee Wadia College, Pune, India
Dr. Sreeja P B
CHRIST (Deemed to be University), Karnataka, India
Prof. Srinivas Mutalik
Manipal Academy of Higher Education, Karnataka, India
Dr. Subodh G
University of Kerala, India
Dr. Sujin P Jose
Madurai Kamaraj University, Tamil Nadu, India
Dr. Sunil Thomas
Fatima Mata National College, Kollam, Kerala, India
Dr. Suresh Pittala
Dayananda Sagar University, Bengaluru, India
Prof. Virginia Pensabene
University of Leeds, UK
Dr. K P Zuhail
University of Calicut, Kerala, India
Dr. Zuzanna Kabacińska
Babes-Bolyai University, Cluj-Napoca, Romania
Prof. Biju V
University of Kerala, India
Prof. Sanjay J Dhoble
Rashtrasant Tukadoji Maharaj Nagpur University, Maharashtra, India
Prof. Kailasnath Madanan
Cochin University of Science and Technology, Kerala, India
Dr. G Hema Chandra
Visvesvaraya National Institute of Technology, Nagpur, India
Prof. B M Nagabhushana
M.S. Ramaiah Institute of Technology, Bengaluru, India
Prof. Vineet Kumar Rai
Indian Institute of Technology (ISM) Dhanbad, Jharkhand, India
Prof. T S Anirudhan
University of Kerala, India

IOP Conf. Series: Materials Science and Engineering 1263 (2022) 011002 doi:10.1088/1757-899X/1263/1/011002

Peer Review Statement

All papers published in this volume have been reviewed through processes administered by the Editors. Reviews were conducted by expert referees to the professional and scientific standards expected of a proceedings journal published by IOP Publishing.

1. Type of peer review: Single anonymous
2. Conference submission management system: Morressier
3. Number of submissions received: 51
4. Number of submissions sent for review: 39
5. Number of submissions accepted: 36
6. Acceptance Rate (Submissions Accepted / Submissions Received × 100): 70.6 %
7. Average number of reviews per paper: 3
8. Total number of reviewers involved: 60
9. Contact person for queries:
   Name: Dr. Sunil Thomas
   Affiliation: Fatima Mata National College, Kollam, Kerala, India
   Email: sunilspap@gmail.com

* means value has been edited

Investigations on the fluorescence and radiative parameters of Sm^{3+} activated BaO-ZnF_2-K_2O-SiO_2-B_2O_3 glass for laser applications

Adon Jose[1, 2], T Krishnapriya [1], Ani Archa Raju [2], Febina Shah[2], P R Biju[1]
[1] *School of Pure & Applied Physics, Mahatma Gandhi University, Kottayam 686560, India*

[2] *St.Stephen's College, Uzhavoor, Kottayam 686634, India*

E-mail: prb.mgu@gmail.com

Abstract. Present work mainly illustrates the absorbance and fluorescence characteristics of 1 mol% trivalent Samarium ions integrated BaO-ZnF_2-K_2O-SiO_2-B_2O_3 glass to identify its applicability in photonic materials. With the aid of well renowned Judd Ofelt (J-O) analysis, its corresponding parameters were evaluated by using the absorbance spectrum of the prepared host matrix. Fluorescence spectrum recorded under 400 nm excitation epitomizes 4 luminescent transitions and among these the $^4G_{5/2}\rightarrow{}^6H_{7/2}$ transition (598 nm) is observed to be the intense one. Diverse radiative parameters were estimated for that intense emission transition in the Samarium ions integrated $BaO+ZnF_2+K_2O+SiO_2+B_2O_3$ glassy system. Comparatively superior fluorescent and radiative features recommend the prepared glassy system for orange lasing applications.

1. Introduction

Growing technological needs of luminescent materials that found potential applications in diverse optoelectronic devices have been intensified the research in scientific community for the invention of novel rare earth embedded materials[1-3]. Glasses regarded to be the active contenders of host matrices appraised in this context due to their excellent optical transparency, thermal and mechanical stability, large rare earth ion solubility and high luminescence efficiency. Consequently, glassy matrices play a major part in the fabrication of several photonic devices such as lasers, light converters, fiber optic communication devices and solar energy converters etc. Glassy system with enhanced structural, thermal and optical features are very much required for the successful rare earth ion integration and thereby its improved luminescent characteristics. On this context, we have chosen multicomponent borosilicate glassy system (BaO-ZnF_2-K_2O-SiO_2-B_2O_3 glass) as the host material in the present work because of its significant characteristics that we already reported in our previous works. Existence of ZnF_2 in the glassy matrix significantly reduces the non-radiative transitions from the as-prepared glassy system and which in turn boosts the radiative emission and metastable lifetime values whenever the rare earth ions are incorporated with it [4-8].

Among rare earth ions, trivalent Samarium ions are most auspicious one due to their reddish orange fluorescence in the visible region and hence Sm^{3+} doped glasses have found diverse applications in the field of photonic materials. Moreover, the evaluation of radiative properties of Sm^{3+} doped materials will provide detailed information about its suitability in various optoelectronic applications[9-17]. Thus, an investigation reliant on the radiative parameters of Samarium doped $BaO+ZnF_2+K_2O+SiO_2+B_2O_3$ glass is vital for suggesting the material for various lasing applications.

The synthesis of 1 mol% Sm^{3+} activated $BaO\text{-}ZnF_2\text{-}K_2O\text{-}SiO_2\text{-}B_2O_3$ glass and its spectroscopic investigation on the radiative characteristics are mainly focused on the scope of this work. The spectroscopic characterizations were carried out for the as-synthesized glass via absorbance and fluorescence excitation and emission measurements. Moreover, this work gives us an insight into the numerous radiative features (Radiative transition rate (A), branching ratio (β_R), radiative lifetime (τ_R), stimulated emission cross-section (σ_{em})) of Sm^{3+} integrated $BaO\text{-}ZnF_2\text{-}K_2O\text{-}SiO_2\text{-}B_2O_3$ glass by using J–O theory, to find its suitability in diverse photonic applications.

2. Experimental Procedure

1 mol% Sm^{3+} activated multicomponent borosilicate glass (FABS1: $10BaO+10ZnF_2+10K_2O+20SiO_2+49B_2O_3+1Sm_2O_3$) was synthesized by means of melting and quenching technique. Starting chemicals were crushed well and placed in a muffle furnace at 950 ^{0}C for 1 hour via porcelain crucible. The melt was then transferred to a 400 ^{0}C preheated brass mould and annealed at 400 ^{0}C for 10 hours. The Varian Cary-5000 and Horiba fluorolog-3 were used to record the absorbance and fluorescence spectra (photoluminescence emission (PL) and excitation (PLE)) of FABS1 glass.

3. Results and discussions

3.1 Absorbance spectrum

The absorbance spectra of FABS1 glass recorded in the 300-1800 nm wavelength range were shown in Fig. 1 (a & b). The observed absorption transitions are found well matched with that of earlier works and is found comparable with the characteristic absorption bands of Samarium ions [13]. The absorbance spectra exhibit fifteen absorption bands. Among the various absorbance transitions, the bands lies at 402 and 1216 nm are found as more intense. The shielding effect of 4f electrons via the 5s and 5p orbitals and spin allowed ($\Delta S=0$) and orbital angular momentum allowed ($\Delta L=0$) transitions are involved in the appearance of intense peak in the spectrum [14-17].

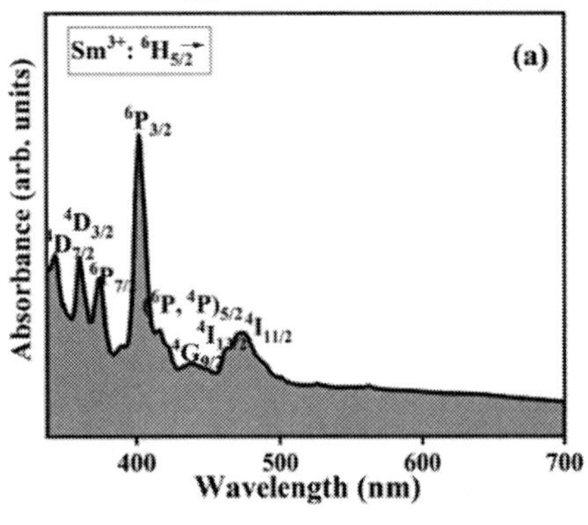

Figure 1(a). Absorbance spectrum of FABS1 in the Ultraviolet-Visible range

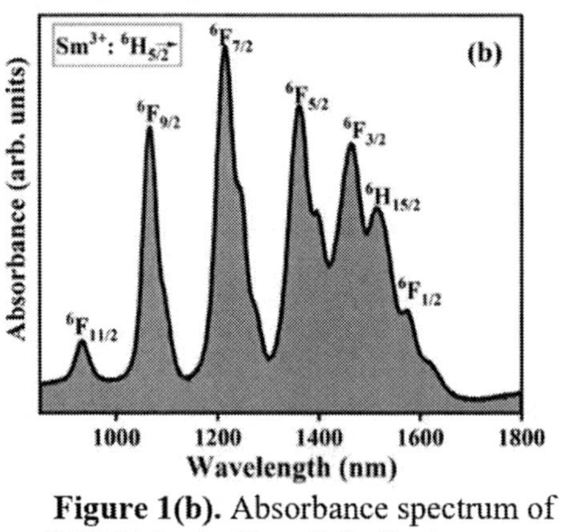

Figure 1(b). Absorbance spectrum of FABS1 in the Near Infra Red range

The information regarding the energy band gap of the material is an essential factor for the development of photonic materials and is estimated for the FABS1 glass with the aid of Tauc's relation. As per Taucs, the correlation between absorption coefficient and photon energy can depicted in diverse regions. The foremost region considered as a steady-absorption region associated with exciton photon coupling. Another section that comprise of inter band electronic transitions and strong absorptions are termed as the Tauc's region where the energy gap is evaluated and the third sector is called as urbach region [2,7]. The Tauc plot for FABS1 glass portrayed as figure 2 and obtained energy bandgap value for the direct allowed transition is E_g= 3.93 eV. Urbach energy of an optical material is defined as the indicator of imperfections or defects present in the matrix [7]. The existence of imperfection in a matrix may guide to the variation in optical band gap via prompting the change in size of localized states. The Urbach energy value of the FABS1 glass is estimated 0.377 eV. The lower value affirms better quality of the FABS1 glass.

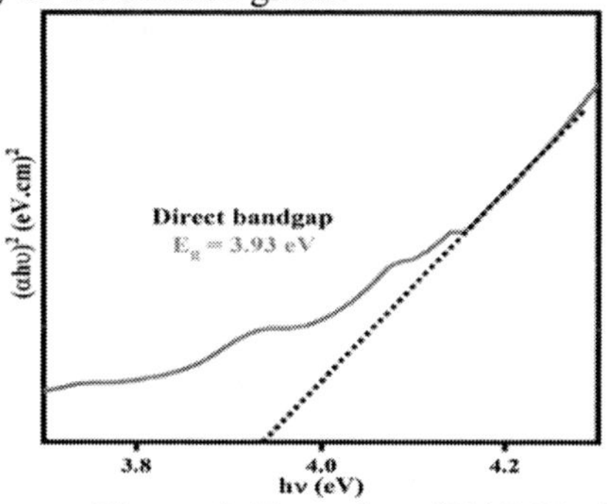

Figure 2. Tauc plot of FABS1 glass.

For estimating the applicability of the prepared glassy system for laser applications, JO analysis is carried out to the optical absorbance spectra of FABS1 glass. The oscillator strength values corresponding to each absorbance bands of FABS1 glassy system are tabulated in table 1. The experimental (f_{exp}) and calculated oscillator strength (f_{cal}) values calculated with the help of equations from the previous work [8]. The evaluated oscillator strength values further carried out for a least square fitting and determined phenomenological J-O intensity parameters of the FABS1 glass. J-O intensity parameters of FABS1 glassy matrix with various reported Samarium doped glasses are enlisted in table 2. The **Ω** values of a rare earth doped host can also provide some vital knowledge about asymmetry of ion sites in the rare earth ion environment. The **Ω** parameters in the FABS1 glass exhibit the trend $\Omega_4 > \Omega_6 > \Omega_2$. Higher Ω_4 and Ω_6 values depict rigid nature of FABS1 glass. Furthermore, the smaller value of Ω_2 specifies the ionic nature and weaker covalent bonding between Sm^{3+} ions and ligands. Moreover, the lesser value of Ω_2 illustrates higher symmetry at trivalent Samarium ion sites vicinity in the FABS1 glassy system [14-17]. The rms deviation measures the precision of least square fitting. The smaller rms value (0.645×10^{-6}) specifies better fitting and correlation amid the f_{exp} and f_{cal} values of FABS1 glass.

Table 1. f_{exp} and f_{cal} values of FABS1 glass

Peaks centered at (nm)	$f_{exp}(\times10^{-6})$	$f_{cal}(\times10^{-6})$
1575	0.1300	0.0068
1517	0.3500	0.0173
1462	0.5700	0.7942
1360	2.0100	1.7699
1216	2.7300	3.1582
1066	2.4900	2.1206
933	1.3700	0.3417
474	1.2500	0.1393
461	0.8300	0.3568
439	0.4700	0.0585
416	1.3000	0.5374
402	3.5100	3.5581
374	1.9000	1.2604
360	1.8300	0.5906
343	1.3600	0.6785
		rms deviation = 0.645×10^{-6}

Table 2. J-O parameters ($\Omega_\lambda \times 10^{-20}$ cm^2, λ =2, 4, 6) of FABS1 glass with other reported glasses

Glass	Ω_2	Ω_4	Ω_6	Reference
FABS1	0.021	3.2	2.3	Present
KTFP	0.156	2.44	1.76	[14]
B4TS	0.066	2.82	1.36	[15]
2SLBTZ	0.232	3.33	3.12	[16]
GlassB	0.47	2.00	1.70	[17]

3.2 Photoluminescence Excitation (PLE) spectrum

The proper assessment of photoluminescence (PL) emission spectrum of rare earth activated optical material can only be conducted with a proper excitation wavelength (λ_{exc}). Thus, in order to find the λ_{exc} for the FABS1 glass, the excitation spectrum is recorded by monitoring the orange emission of Sm^{3+} ions arising through the band $^4G_{5/2} \rightarrow ^6H_{7/2}$. A series of bands from 343 to 472 nm confirms the excitation peaks in the n-UV and blue region of visible spectrum. PLE spectrum of FABS1 glassy system gives eight bands and is depicted in Fig. 3. Among these observed excitation bands, the transition peaks at 400 nm is found as the intense one and hence it was opted as the λ_{exc} for attaining the emission spectrum. Broad excitation wavelength ranges from 325-500 nm specifies that commercial Ultraviolet blue laser diodes can efficiently excite the Samarium ions in the FABS1 glass[14-17].

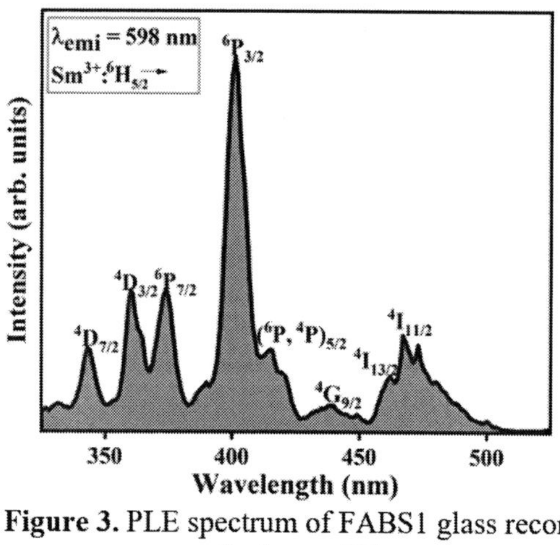

Figure 3. PLE spectrum of FABS1 glass recorded under λ_{emi} = 598 nm

3.3 PL spectrum and radiative parameters

The PL spectra of FABS1 glass under the λ_{exc} of 400 nm is portrayed in Fig. 4. The observed luminescence spectrum gives 4 luminescent bands and is centered at 562, 598, 645 and 707 nm. Among these, the transition peaks at 598 nm is found to be the prominent one and the band centered at 707 nm is found to be weak in intensity. Also, the band at 562 nm lies in the yellow region of the fluorescence spectra is attributed as a magnetic-dipole transition (MD). Additionally, the transition peaks at 645 nm is regarded to be a pure electric-dipole (ED) transition located in the reddish-orange region. The 562 nm band is insensitive to changes for the local crystal fields as it is contributed by the MD transitions and fluorescent bands at 645 and 707 nm due to the electric dipole transitions are subjective to the local environment changes by means of ligand atoms. Whereas, the prominent peak centered at 598 nm is a MD allowed transition, but it is prevailed via an ED transition [14-17].

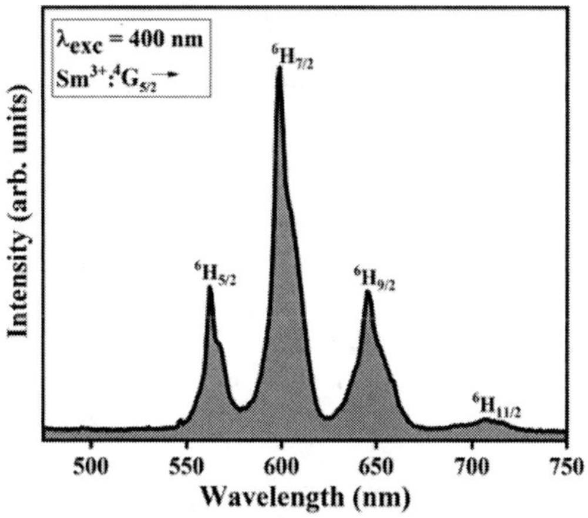

Figure 4. PL spectrum of FABS1 glass under 400 nm excitation

The luminescence intensity ratio termed as the orange to red (O/R) ratio of the FABS1 glass can be studied from $^4G_{5/2}\rightarrow{}^6H_{7/2}$ and $^4G_{5/2}\rightarrow{}^6H_{9/2}$ bands as they give orange and red luminescence in the PL spectra. For the FABS1 glass, it is estimated as 2.70. Higher value of O/R ratio affirms the feasibility of obtaining enhanced orange emission from the Sm^{3+} doped sample. Moreover, the ratio amid emission intensities of ED ($^4G_{5/2}\rightarrow{}^6H_{9/2}$) and MD ($^4G_{5/2}\rightarrow{}^6H_{5/2}$) transition provide information about the asymmetry of host environment around the Sm^{3+} atom. As for FABS1 glass, the asymmetric ratio is calculated as 0.97. Interaction of Samarium ions with lattice vibrations induces more electric dipole transitions which permits higher ED/MD ratio. The symmetric nature of the ligand-ion bond leads if the asymmetry ratio is less than 1[14-17]. The photoluminescence excitation, radiative and non-radiative (NR) emissions of FABS1 glassy system is visualized in Fig. 5. Upon 400 nm pumping, Samarium ions in the FABS1 glass system are pumped to $^6P_{3/2}$ state and via NR relaxation it reaches the $^4G_{5/2}$ level. From $^4G_{5/2}$ state, they finally undertake radiative transitions to ^6H_j (j=5/2, 7/2, 9/2, 11/2) multiplets.

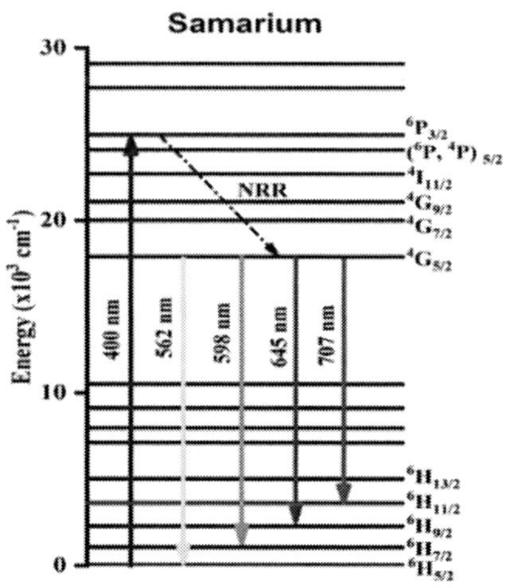

Figure 5. Partial energy level diagram of FABS1 glass

J-O theory is well-known for the estimation of certain significant radiative characteristics of rare-earth activated matrices such as radiative transition rate(A), branching ratio(β_R), radiative lifetime(τ_R) etc. Among these, the radiative transition rate can predict the lasing potentiality of a system. Thus, relying on the J-O analysis, with the help of PL spectrum and Ω values, radiative features of FABS1 glassy system were estimated. The equations used for the calculation were referred from the previous work[8]. The radiative parameters corresponding to each emission transitions are tabulated in table 3 and among these radiative properties owing to the luminescent band observed at 598 nm are found to be more prominent than other observed emission bands. Thus, the evaluated properties such as A, β_R, τ_R, and σ_{em} of the prominent one were listed in table 4 along with that of reported works. Table 4 concludes that, the prepared glassy system have better values than several reported glasses and it confirms the materials applicability in various photonic materials. Earlier works points out the fact that, optical systems with β_R value equal or higher than 50% are well suitable for better laser action [8]. On this context, we can firmly say that FABS1 glass possesses better radiative characteristics.

Table 3. Peak wavelength, A and β_R of observed emission transitions from FABS1 glass under 400 nm excitation wavelength.

Sl. No	Peak wavelength (nm)	A (s^{-1})	β_R
1	562	4.81	0.09
2	598	102	0.50
3	645	44.26	0.19
4	707	27.57	0.12

Table 4. Radiative characteristics ($^4G_{5/2} \rightarrow {}^6H_{7/2}$ band) of FABS1 glass with other reported works.

Glass	Effective bandwidth $\Delta\lambda_{eff}$ (nm)	Radiative transition rate A (s^{-1})	Stimulated emission cross-section, σ_{em} ($\times 10^{-22}$ cm^2)	Branching ratio β_R	Radiative life time τ_R (ms)
FABS1	13	102	5.13	0.50	4.35
[15]	-	122	8.5	0.47	3.89
[17]	-	65	2.83	0.51	2.73
[14]	--	86	4.7	0.48	2.5
[16]	8	206	14	0.60	2.14

4. Conclusions

1 mol% of Sm^{3+} ions activated BaO-ZnF_2-K_2O-SiO_2-B_2O_3 glass was prepared via melting and quenching technique. To study the spectroscopic features of FABS1 glass, absorbance, fluorescence emission and excitation spectra were recorded and analysed. The spectroscopic features of the as-synthesized glassy system was further analysed via J-O analysis and the Ω parameters were observed to follow the trend $\Omega_4 > \Omega_6 > \Omega_2$. Radiative properties and lasing characteristics of FABS1 glass were compared with reported Sm^{3+} activated glassy matrices. Better radiative and luminescence features recommend FABS1 glass for diverse opto-electronic applications.

References

[1] Sundari S S, Marimuthu K, Sivraman M and Babu S S 2010 *J. Lumin.* **130** 1313–9
[2] Jose A, Gopi S, Krishnapriya T, Jose T A, Joseph C, Unnikrishnan N V and Biju P R 2021

Mater. Chem. Phys. **261** 124223
[3] Aryapriya N, Gopi S, Krishnapriya T, Jose A, Saritha A C, Unnikrishnan N V and Joseph C 2020 *J. Electron. Mater.* **49** 3624–33
[4] Jose A, Krishnapriya T, Jose T A, Joseph C, Unnikrishnan N V and Biju P R 2021 *Scr. Mater.* **203** 114088
[5] Jose A, Krishnapriya T, Sreeja E, Rose J, Joseph C and Biju P R 2022 *Vacuum* **199** 110927
[6] Jose A, Mohan R, Jose T A and Joseph C 2020 *J. Mater. Sci.: Mater.* **31** 13531
[7] Jose A, Krishnapriya T, Jose T A, Joseph C, Unnikrishnan N V and Biju P R 2021 *Ceram. Int.* **47** 6790–9
[8] Jose A, Krishnapriya T, Jose J R, Joseph C and Biju P R 2022 *Phys. B Phys. Condens. Matter* **634** 413772
[9] Jose A, Krishnapriya T, Jose T A, Joseph C and Biju P R 2021 *J. Lumin.* **236** 118105
[10] Jose A, Krishnapriya T, George A, Rose J, Vijoy P S, Joseph C and Biju R 2022 *Chem. Phys. Lett.* **792** 139432
[11] Jose A, Krishnapriya T, George A, Jose T A, Joseph C, Unnikrishnan N V and Biju P R 2021 *J. Non. Cryst. Solids* **562** 120775
[12] Jose A, Biju P R, Jose T A and Joseph C 2021 *Luminescence,* **36** 1422
[13] Carnall W T, Fields P R and Rajnak K 1968 *J. Chem. Phys.* **4424**
[14] Jayasimhadri M, Moorthy L R, Saleem S A and Ravikumar R V S S N 2006 *Spectrochim. Acta - A: Mol. Biomol. Spectrosc.* **64** 939–44
[15] Maheshvaran K, Linganna K and Marimuthu K 2011 *J. Lumin.* **131** 2746–53
[16] Selvaraju K and Marimuthu K 2013 *J. Alloys Compd.***553** 273-281
[17] Seshadri M, Rao K V, Rao J L and Ratnakaram Y C 2009 *J. Alloys Compd.***476** 263–70

Tunable Reflection Properties and Photonic Bandgap Behavior of a One-Dimensional Metamaterial-Superconductor-Based Ternary Photonic Crystal

Girijesh Narayan Pandey[1*], Narendra Kumar[2*], Pawan Singh[3], K. B. Thapa[3], Sonika[2], and Vanshika Singhania[2]

[1]Department of Applied Physics, Amity University Uttar Pradesh, Noida 201303, India
[2]Department of Physics, Mody University of Science and Technology, Lakshmangarh 332311, Rajasthan, India
[3]Department of Physics, Babasaheb Bhimrao Ambedkar University, Lucknow 226025, Uttar Pradesh, India

gnpandey@amity.edu; narendrakumar.slas@modyuniversity.ac.in

Abstract. In the present communication, we have investigated the tunable reflection properties and photonic bandgap variation of a one-dimensional metamaterial and superconductor based ternary photonic crystal. To design the 1D ternary photonic crystal, we have taken three alternate layers of metamaterial, superconductor (BSSCO), and silica (SiO_2). Transfer matrix method (TMM) is employed to determine the optical reflection properties of the considered 1DPC for TE-mode by varying five parameters, viz. incident angle, superconductor temperature, thickness and refractive index of dielectric layer, and number of unit cells. It is noted that the ternary PC exhibits the features of tunable narrow band reflector, whose width increases with increase in the incident angle with a blue shift, and decreases with operating temperature of superconductor with red shift. It also enhances with increase in the dielectric layer thickness in low frequency region, and decreases in high frequency regime with red shifts. We obtain only one PBG at $n_3=1.46$ in low frequency regime, while with increase in the refractive index multiple gaps are obtained in different frequency regions having distinct widths at $n_3=2.4$ and 3.4. An increase in the number of unit cells causes increase in the reflectance, wherein no PBG is found below $N=8$. This analysis gives some insights to design tunable devices based on narrowband reflectivity in the terahertz frequency regime, including THz-metadevices, emitters, thermo-optical devices, and security sensors.

Keywords: Double negative (DNG), metamaterial, Superconductor (BSSCO), Multilayer, Transfer matrix method (TMM), Ternary structure, Tunable reflectance

1. Introduction

The two simultaneous researches done by E. Yablonovitch and S. John in 1987 generated a flow in periodic media called photonic crystals (PCs) [1, 2]. PCs are generally artificially created periodic media that offer photonic bandgap (PBG) in analogy with the electronic bandgap used in condensed matter physics. Many literatures are available on one-dimensional (1D) PCs considering as nanolayered media by introducing a variety of materials, including dielectrics, semiconductors, plasma, cold plasma, superconductor, magnetic, polymer, chiral, and liquid crystal [3-8]. Among them, Pandey et al. [9] have reported the omnidirectional reflection (ODR) characteristics of a superconducting binary PC in terahertz (THz) frequency region. The concept of left-handed material (LHM) with simultaneously negative electrical permittivity as well as magnetic permeability in a particular frequency region stems from the idea of Veselago demonstrated in 1968 [10]. Further, the two works of Pendry and his co-workers [11] were reported on experimental models for designing negative permittivity. Hence, many works have been done on metamaterial based binary PC using double negative (DNG) and single negative (SNG) layers in a 1DPC. In recent years, a ternary PC designed with three alternate layers in periodic structures have attracted the interests of many researchers. Kumar et al. [12] have recently reported the features of cold plasma based ternary photonic crystal (TPC). Pandey et al. [13] have studied the optical feature of polymer-based 1D ternary PC. Nowadays, metamaterial based TPCs are showing potential applications in ultra-omnidirectional PBG, optical filters, remote sensing, aerospace, solar power management, lenses, gas sensors, and infrastructure monitoring [2, 3, 14, 15].

In view of the above progress in metamaterial-based ternary PC, we introduce here a 1DTPC comprised of metamaterial/superconductor/dielectric layers, and determine its tunable optical reflection properties with variations in incident angle, operating temperature of superconductor, thickness as well as refractive index of third dielectric layer, and number of unit cells. Focusing our attention towards the completely reflected region with ≈100% reflection termed as PBG in the reflection spectra obtained in various cases, some insights are drawn. Usually DNG materials are artificially created with different novel structures, viz. split ring resonators, mushroom structures, and transmission lines, where refractive index along with permittivity and permeability become negative in certain frequency regions [3]. Although we have considered DNG material as one of the three layers, we have not emphasized on its design as we are interested for the optical characteristics of the ternary structure with DNG metamaterial, whose permittivity and permeability are frequency dependent [15]. As we discussed above that the ternary structures are more advantageous in many ways, where high temperature superconductors are providing marvelous features in optical design. The proposed PC structure is based on ternary structure, and by taking a superconductor layer, it creates a novel kind of tunability that can be applied in designing optical filters, switches, and multichannel devices.

2. Theoretical Design

We take a one-dimensional ternary PC of metamaterial/superconductor/dielectric, whose refractive indices are n_1, n_2 and n_3 and having thicknesses d_1, d_2 and d_3, respectively, with lattice parameter $d = d_1 + d_2 + d_3$, and is shown in Fig.1.

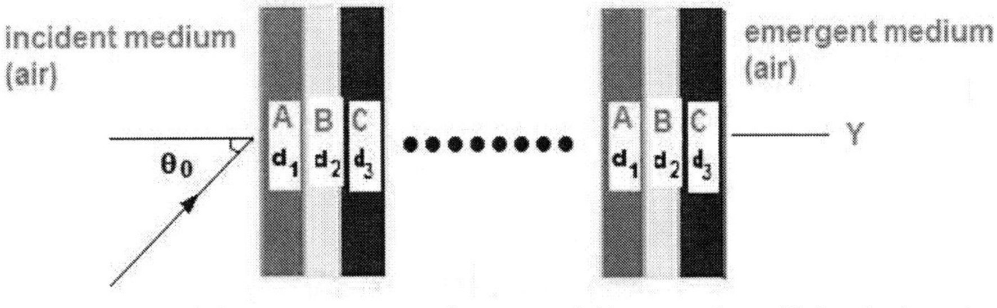

Figure 1. The proposed 1D ternary structure of metamaterial/superconductor/dielectric photonic crystal.

For such TPC, the refractive index is defined as

$$n(y)=\begin{cases} n_1, & 0<x<d_1 \\ n_2, & d_1<x<d_2 \\ n_3, & d_2<x<d_3 \end{cases} \tag{1}$$

With the help of the transfer matrix method (TMM), we calculate the reflectance for such chosen 1DPC, where the total matrix for such ternary structure $(ABC)^N$ with lattice parameter d and the number of unit cells N, is written as [3, 12]

$$M(Nd)=\begin{pmatrix} m_{1,1} & m_{1,2} \\ m_{2,1} & m_{2,2} \end{pmatrix}, \tag{2}$$

where M(Nd) $=\left(\prod_{l=1}^{3} M_l\right)^N$; M_1, M_2 and M_3 are the characteristics matrices for the three layers, respectively; with $l=1, 2$ or 3 layer; and the characteristics matrix for layer-l is written as [3, 6, 16]

$$M_l=\begin{bmatrix} \cos k_l & -\frac{i}{p_l}\sin k_l \\ -ip_l \sin k_l & \cos k_l \end{bmatrix}. \tag{3}$$

Here, $k_l=\left(\frac{\omega n_l d_l}{c}\right)\cos\theta_l$, taking c as the light speed in air, and θ_l is the ray angle in layer l, and $\cos\theta_l=\sqrt{1-\frac{n_0^2\sin^2\theta_0}{n_l^2}}$, where θ_0 is the angle of incidence. Further, the parameter p_l for TE waves is defined as $p_l=\sqrt{\frac{\varepsilon_l}{\mu_l}}\cos\theta_l$.

Hence, the reflection coefficient will be [3, 9]

$$r=\frac{(m_{1,1}+m_{1,2}\,p_e)p_0-(m_{2,1}+m_{2,2}\,p_e)}{(m_{1,1}+m_{1,2}\,p_e)p_0+(m_{2,1}+m_{2,2}\,p_e)}; \tag{4}$$

where p_0 and p_e denote the incident and emergent media parameters. Hence, the reflectance will be

$$R=|r|^2. \tag{5}$$

For the metamaterial, the frequency dependent permittivity and permeability are expressed as [15]

$$\varepsilon=1+\frac{5^2}{0.9^2-f^2}+\frac{10^2}{11.5^2-f^2}, \tag{6a}$$

$$\mu=1+\frac{3^2}{0.902^2-f^2}, \tag{6b}$$

$$and \quad n_1=\sqrt{\mu}\,\sqrt{\varepsilon}, \tag{6c}$$

where f be the wave frequency.

Now, the conductivity of superconductor is given by [2]

$$\sigma = -\left(\frac{i}{\mu_0 \omega}\right)\frac{1}{\lambda_L^{\ 2}}. \qquad 7(a)$$

Here, λ_L denotes the London-penetration depth mentioned as

$$\lambda_L = \sqrt{\frac{m}{\mu_0 n_s e^2}}. \qquad (7b)$$

The Gorter-Casimir relation introduces the ratio: $\frac{n_s}{n_n} = \left(\frac{T_c}{T}\right)^4 - 1$, where n_s and n_n are number of super and normal electrons in which T_C be the critical temperature.

For the superconductor, frequency and temperature dependent refractive index is expressed as [9]

$$n_2 = \sqrt{\cos^2\theta_o - \frac{c^2}{(\omega\ \lambda_L(T))^2}}, \qquad (7c)$$

where London-penetration depth showing variation with temperature is defined as

$$\lambda_L(T) = \frac{\lambda_L(0)}{\sqrt{1 - \left(\frac{T}{T_C}\right)^4}}. \qquad (7d)$$

In high temperature superconductors, the dependence of penteration depth given by equation (7d) depends on pairing mechanism by means of wave, weak/strong coupling. However, in the low temperature supeconductors, the penetration depth is explained with BCS theory [16].
With the help of equations (2), (4), (6), (7c) and (7d), the reflectance spectra in various cases are plotted by using equation (5), and by comparing them some conclusions are drawn.

3. Simulation Results and Discussion

In this section, we study the reflection properties of the ternary structure made of metamaterial, superconductor of Bismuth Strontium Calcium Copper Oxide (BSSCO) and silica (SiO_2). With the help of reflection formula given by equation (5), the reflection spectra are plotted in five different cases, by choosing the fixed value of the following parameters as: $N=10$, $T=70K$, $Tc=95K$, $n_3=1.46$, $d_1=d_2=d_3=10\ \mu m$, in which we take the absolute zero penetration depth $\lambda_L(0)$ as 163 nm.

To study the tunable optical properties, reflection spectra between reflectance and frequency f (THz) are plotted with variations in incident angle, operating temperature T, and thickness as well as refractive index of the third dielectric layer, and the number of unit cells, where the focus of attention is to analyze the completely reflected region with ≈100% reflection conceived as PBG. First, the angle of incidence is varied as 0°, 30°, and 60°, and the reflection spectra so obtained are shown in Fig.2. On the basis of reflection spectra at these angles, we find that the completely reflected bands are obtained at low and high frequency regions, whose width increases considerably with increasing the incident angle and both shows a blue shift with an increase in the incident angle. Such PBG regions are showing the properties of Bragg's gap.

Second, the operating temperature of superconductor is changed as $4.5K$, $75K$, and $85K$, and the reflection spectra are depicted in Fig.3. On the basis of the reflection spectra, it is to note that a single complete narrow PBG is only obtained at all these temperatures and showing red shift with increasing in temperature T, and offering the properties of Bragg's gap.

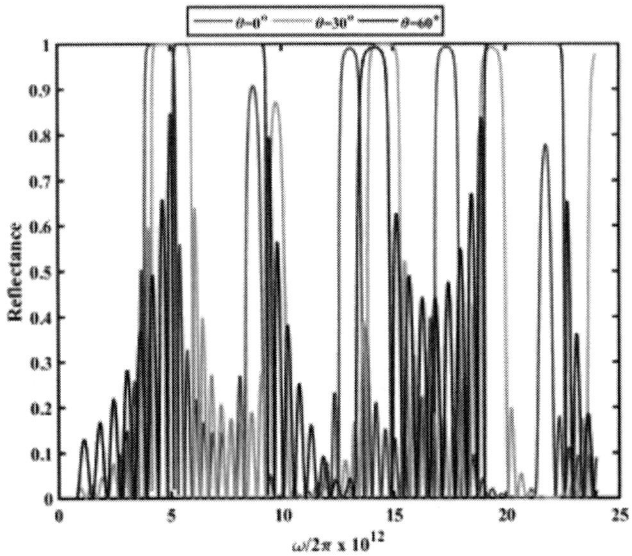

Figure 2. Reflectance spectra of the TPC at three incident angles, 0°, 30°, *and* 60°.

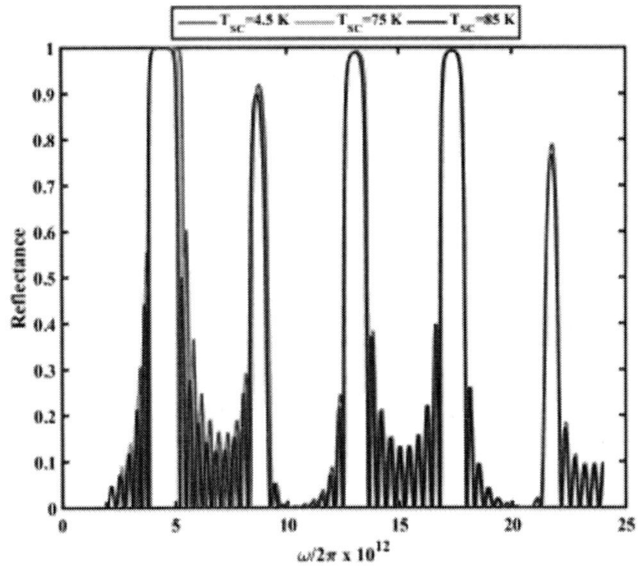

Figure 3. *Reflectance spectra of the TPC at three temperatures of the superconductor,* $4.5K$, $75K$, *and* $85K$.

Third, by changing the thickness of third dielectric layer as $2\mu m$, $4\mu m$, *and* $8\mu m$, the drawn reflection spectra are shown in Fig. 4. Comparing the reflection spectra at various dielectric thicknesses, we note that a complete narrow PBGs are obtained at $2\mu m$, $4\mu m$, *and* $8\mu m$, in different frequency regions and with increase in the dielectric thickness, we get red shifts in their positions.

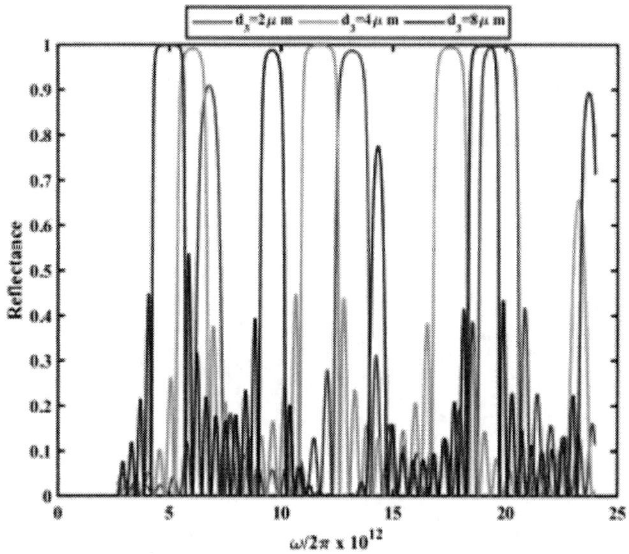

Figure 4. *Plot of reflectance spectra at three thicknesses of third dielectric layer,* $2\mu m$, $4\mu m$, *and* $8\mu m$.

Fourth, we change the refractive index of third dielectric layer as $1.46, 2.4, and\ 3.4,$ and the obtained reflection spectra are shown in Fig. 5. On making comparison of theses reflection spectra at three chosen values of dielectric refractive index, there is only one PBG at n_3=1.46 in low frequency regime, while with increase in the refractive index, more gaps are obtained in different frequency regions, with distinct widths at n_3=2.4 and 3.4. So we can say that an increase in the refractive index of the dielectric layer, the PBG increases in number but decreases in width, and there is only a single PBG at lowest value of the dielectric refractive index.

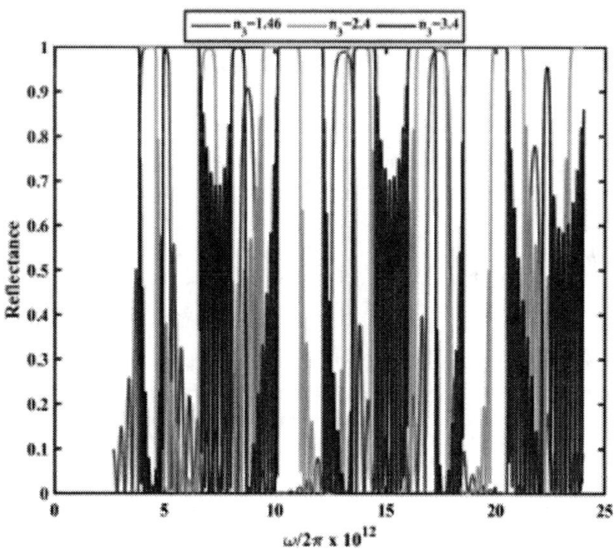

Figure 5. *Plot of reflectance spectra at three refractive indices of third dielectric layer,* 1.46, 2.4, *and* 3.4.

Lastly in the fifth case, on increasing number of unit cells as N=4, 6 and 8, we get a complete reflection is not found at N=4 and 6 (refer Fig. 6) and the reflectance is much less than 100%, for the other fixed parameters. If we increase the number of unit cells, the complete reflectance is obtained in a narrow region at N=8. Thus, with an increase in unit cells, the reflectance increases [17].

On the basis of the outcomes as mentioned in the above paragraphs, there exists the tunability in each of the narrow bands of PBGs with respect to their locations as well as widths. Therefore, insights of this analysis can be employed design while designing terahertz-tunable devices.

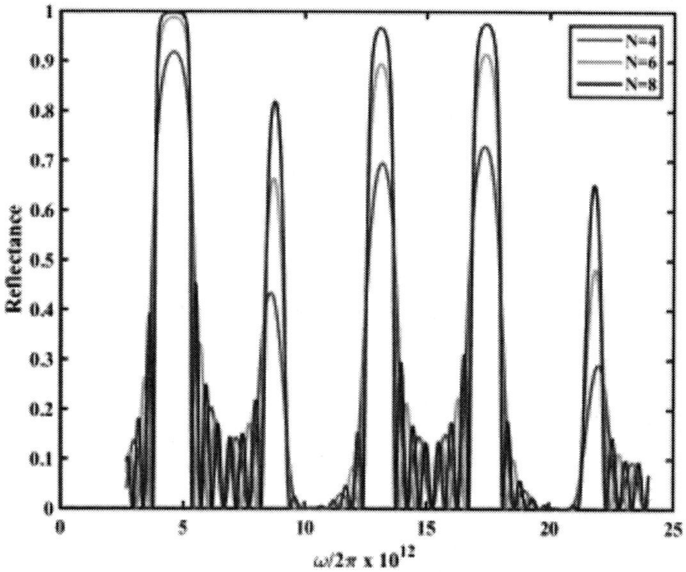

Figure 6. *Plot of reflectance spectra at three values of the number of unit cells,* 2, 4 *and* 8.

In view of seeing the experimental applications of our design, we incorporate some of the advances in metamaterial and superconductor based THz-devices [18-20]. The THz emitters are comparatively beneficial to the presently available sources that have been recently realized by replacing the top layer with high-index dielectric structure in the configuration of metamaterial-based thermal emitters [18]. In our case, the structure is metamaterial-based ternary structure that is working as narrowband tunable reflector, and so can be used in THz emitters, while it requires some changes for the practical realization.

Many metasurface-based devices with different structures have been reported having applications in wavefront shaping and spectrum modulation with tremendous development in THz technology. In this field, metamaterial- and metasurface-based devices are applicable in high-capacity communication, security, etc. [19]. Such designed narrowband reflector in our case can be used for security purpose with narrow band reflection of light waves.

Metamaterials are artificially engineered structures that control the electromagnetic waves, and are resource for designing several THz-metadevices. The tunable THz-metadevices are suggested by tunable structures using thermo-optical materials [20]. In our design, the reflectance is tunable by changing the superconductor temperature that can provide some ideas to make THz-metadevices. Although this article is theoretical in nature, on the basis of above outcomes mentioned in articles [17-

20], we recommend this tunable reflectance based design to be referred in fabricating THz-metadevices, emitters, security sensors, and high capacity communication.

4. Conclusion

In conclusion, we report that, such a metamaterial and superconductor based ternary PC is showing the features of tunable narrow band reflector, whose width increases with increase in the incident angle with a blue shift, decreases with operating temperature of superconductor with a red shift, increases with increase in thickness of dielectric region in low frequency region and decreases in high frequency regime with red shifts. Furthermore, there is only one PBG at n_3=1.46 in low frequency regime, while with increase in the refractive index more gaps are obtained in different frequency regions with distinct narrow widths at n_3=2.4 and 3.4. An increase in number of unit cells, increases the reflectance, but no PBG is found below N=8. Based on the analysis of the dependence of reflection characteristics of the TPC on incident angle, superconductor temperature, thickness of the dielectric layer, refractive index of the dielectric layer, and the number of unit cells; we get tunability in narrow bands called PBGs in their locations as well as widths. This article gives some new insights to design tunable devices in the THz frequency regime, where tunability in narrowband reflection is required. It can be useful in fabricating emitters, security sensors, and temperature dependedent THz devices.

References

[1] John D. Joannopoulos, Steven G. Johnson, et al., Photonic Crystals: Modelling the Flow of Light, Princeton University Press, Second Edition, Princeton, 2008.
[2] Narendra Kumar, Khem. B. Thapa, et al., Photonic Crystals: Features and Applications, Nova Science, Inc., First Edition, New York, 2013.
[3] Narendra Kumar and Bhuvneshwer, Advances in photonic crystals and devices," CRC Press, Taylor & Francis, Boca Raton, 2019. https://doi.org/10.1201/9781351029421
[4] Alok Kumar Pandey, Girijesh Narayan Pandey, et al., Analysis of Multichannel Reflectors Using One-Dimensional Photonic Crystal with Symmetric and Asymmetric Micro-Plasma Defects, OAM – *Rapid Communications,* 2022, 16: 26.
[5] M Inoue, R Fujikawa, A Baryshev, et al., Magnetophotonic crystals, *J. Phys. D: Appl. Phys.* 2006, 39:R151.
[6] N R Ramanujam, Hala J. El-Khozondar, et al., Design of one dimensional defect based photoniccrystal by composited superconducting material for bio sensing applications, Physica B: Physics of Condensed Matter, 2019, 572: 442.
[7] Igor Lyubchanskii, YuliyaDadoenkova, et al., Superconducting Photonic Crystals with Defect Structure, ICTON 2016.
[8] N. N. Dadoenkova, I. L. Lyubchanskii, et al., Dielectric Photonic Crystals with Superconducting Defects, 8th International Congress - Metamaterials 2014.
[9] Girijesh Narayan Pandey, Bhuvneshwer Suthar, et al., Omni directional reflectance property of superconductor-dielectric photonic crystal for reflector application at lower and higher THz frequency, *Journal of Superconductivity and Novel Magnetism, 2021,* 34:2031.
[10] V. G. Veselago, The electrodynamics of substances with simultaneously negative values of permittivity and permeability. Soviet Physics Uspekhi, 1968, 10: 509.
[11] J. B. Pendry, A. J. Holden, et al., Magnetism from conductors and enhanced nonlinear phenomena," IEEE Trans. on Microw. Theory Tech., 1999,. 47: 2075.
[12] Narendra Kumar, Sonu Kaliramna, et al, Design of Cold Plasma Based Ternary Photonic

Crystal for Microwave Applications, ***Silicon*** 2021.https://doi.org/10.1007/s12633-021-01405-9
[13] G.N. Pandey, N., Kumar, P. Singh,. *et al.* Analysis of photonic band structure tunability for te and tm modes in a silicon and polymer based ternary photonic crystal for visible range devices. *Silicon*, 2022. https://doi.org/10.1007/s12633-022-01883-5
[14] Z. Li, Z. Ge, X.Y. Zhang, et al. Analysis of photonic band gaps in metamaterial-based one-dimensional ternary photonic crystals, *Indian J Phys*, 2019, **93**:511. https://doi.org/10.1007/s12648-018-1320-3
[15] A. H. Aly, D. Mohamed, et al., Metamaterial control of hybrid multiunctional high T_C superconducting photonoc crystal for 1-D quasi periodic structure potential applications, Materials Research 2020, 23:1.
[16] S. Karakaya , O. Ozbas, M. Akarsu, The temperature dependence of magnetic penetration depth in superconductor, Journal of Optoelectronics and Advanced Materials 2011, 13: 807.
[17] Wei-Hsiao Lin, Chien-Jang Wu, Tzong-Jer Yang, and Shoou-Jinn Chang, Terahertz multichanneled filter in a superconducting photonic crystal," Opt. Express 2010, 18:27155.
[18] Kaili Sun, Zongshan Zhao, Yangjian Cai, Uriel Levy and Zhanghua Han, Ultra-narrowband and highly-directional THz thermal emitters based on the bound state in the continuum, Nanophotonics 2021; 10: 4035–4043
[19] Jingwen He *et al.*, Recent progress and applications of terahertz metamaterials, *J. Phys. D: Appl. Phys.* 2022, 55:23002
[20] Cheng Xu, Zhihao Ren, Jingxuan Wei, and Chengkuo Lee, Reconfigurable terahertz metamaterials: From fundamental principles to advanced 6G applications, iScience. 2022, 25: 103799.

Theoretical modelling of Au and Ag hollow cylinders for high resolution refractive index sensing of bio-analytes and gases

Devika Mohan[1], Simitha S[2], Vibin Ipe Thomas[2] and Jesly Jacob*[1]

[1]Department of Physics, Assumption College, Changanacherry, Kottayam-686101, Kerala, India.
[2] Department of Chemistry, CMS College, Kottayam-686001, Kerala, India.

E-mail: jeslyjacob@assumptioncollege.edu.in

Abstract. A highly sensitive yet simple plasmonic refractive index (RI) sensor consisting of Au trimer hollow nanocylinders surrounded by an Ag hollow nanocylinder is proposed with a wide range of applications in the near IR range. The plasmonic behaviour of the structure is studied by analysing the absorption cross-section on illumination by electromagnetic (EM) wave using the finite element method (FEM). Nanoscale detections can be realized by using the shift in resonance wavelength of localized surface plasmon resonance (LSPR) in response to the change in RI. The optimized RI sensor gives a maximum sensitivity of 2545.4 nm/RIU, figure of merit (FOM) of 43.90 RIU^{-1} and sensor resolution of the order of 10^{-5} RIU. The proposed sensor can detect even small variations in RI of the order of 10^{-5} RIU with a sensitivity of 1998 nm/RIU. With the observed high sensitivity, resolution and quality, the sensor can contribute a lot to health-care applications and is found highly suitable for multiple detections covering broad range of RI including bio-analytes, chemicals, and gases.

1. Introduction

Among various sensors, the key interest in optical sensors is their high performance and cost-effective settings. Plasmonic nanostructures in sub-wavelength size is of prime importance in sensing and biomedical applications because of their ability of superior light trapping and confinement. It is possible for nano-scaled metallic structures illuminated by appropriate incident wavelength to excite localized oscillation of charges confined to their surface [1]. The resulting coherent localized plasmons oscillate with a resonant frequency that strongly depends on size, shape, composition, refractive index of the surrounding dielectrics, and the particle-to-particle separation distance of the nanoparticles [2]. The optical phenomena resulting from the interactions between incident light and surface electrons in the conduction band is termed LSPR and leads to strong field enhancement in the near field zone. LSPR is a potential candidate for realizing plasmonic biosensors with high sensitivity, where the resonant electromagnetic field is confined to the metallic nanostructure and sensitive to the RI change of the medium surrounding it [3].

Noble metals such as silver (Ag) and gold (Au) with strong and tunable field enhancement and optical signal manipulation are widely used for RI sensing [2, 4]. It is worth mentioning that Ag exhibits the sharpest and strongest bands among all metals and are better for obtaining more local field. While silver-based nano-sensors are known for their narrow spectral width and high detection accuracy, Au is preferred for biological applications [5] as AuNPs are highly stable and sensitive. They are chemically inert and oxidation-free and show high-quality biocompatibility, which is critical for biomedical applications [6]. Varying geometrical parameters of plasmonic nanostructures can easily tune the LSPR wavelength. In contrast to vast majority of biological sensors, LSPR biosensors are label free [7] and offer a wide range of advantages such as low cost, higher surface to volume ratio, facile surface chemistry, detecting several different targets at the same time, and monitoring binding of molecules in real-time [8-11]. Optimizing plasmonic nanostructures to obtain higher sensitivity by changing the RI of the medium is desirable for sensing applications.

In this work, we have designed a highly sensitive yet simple plasmonic refractive index sensor using trimer Au hollow cylinders surrounded by an Ag hollow cylinder. By using FEM through COMSOL Multiphysics 5.1 the absorption cross-section of the structure on illumination with EM radiation is analysed. The strong interactions between Au-Au and Au-Ag enhanced the E-field localization, thereby increasing the sensing performance. Using parameters such as sensitivity, FOM and sensor resolution, quality and the structure's performance are evaluated. A maximum sensitivity of 2545.4 nm/RIU and FOM value of ≈ 43.90 RIU^{-1} is obtained for the RI change from 1.0 – 1.42 RIU. The proposed sensor can detect RI change up to 0.00001 RIU with a sensitivity of 1998.0 nm/RIU, making it highly suitable for multiple detections in a broad range including bio-analytes, chemicals, and gases.

2. Design considerations and simulation

The schematic diagram of the proposed plasmonic sensor is shown in figure 1. The sensor platform consisting of a triangular system of hollow Au nanocylinders surrounded by a hollow Ag nanocylinder has been simulated by the two-dimensional (2D) FEM using COMSOL Multiphysics 5.1. Material parameters of Ag and Au nanocylinders are adopted from Johnson and Christy's wavelength-dependent refractive index values [12].

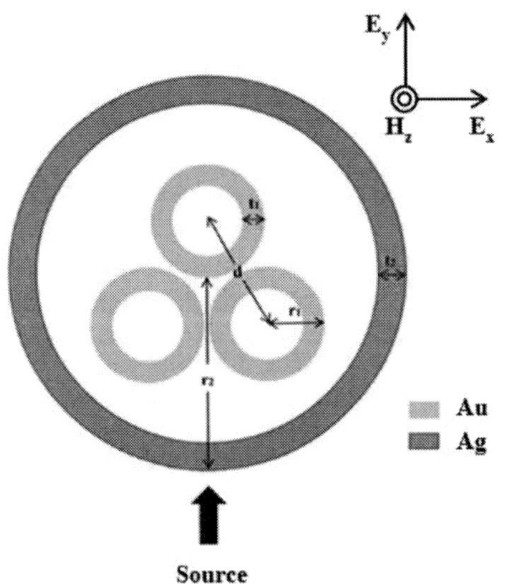

r_1 = Radius of Au nanocylinders
r_2 = Radius of Ag nanocylinders
d = Interparticle distance (centre to centre)
t_1 = Thickness of Au nanocylinders
t_2 = Thickness of Ag nanocylinders

Figure 1. Schematic diagram of the proposed plasmonic sensor. The sensor constitutes a triangular system of hollow Au nanocylinders of radius 'r_1', thickness 't_1', and interparticle distance 'd' arranged at the vertices of an equilateral triangle and a hollow Ag nanocylinder of radius 'r_2' and thickness 't_2' surrounding the Au nanocylinders.

The structure is illuminated by EM wave propagating in the Y direction, having wavelength ranging from 600 nm to 2200 nm. The 2D simulation domain is truncated using perfectly matched layer (PML) which allows waves to be absorbed without reflection [13]. Using the FEM method, the absorption cross-section when the system interacts with the incident EM wave is numerically analysed to characterize the sensor's performance by studying its plasmonic properties. The parameters such as sensitivity (S), FOM, and sensor resolution (S_R) are used for evaluating the quality and performance of the proposed plasmonic sensor.

As the key parameter to describe the performance of RI sensors, sensitivity represents the shift in resonant wavelength (Δλ) for unit RI change of the sensing medium (Δn) expressed as [14]

$$S = \frac{\Delta\lambda}{\Delta n}\ [nm/RIU] \qquad (1)$$

The concept of figure of merit introduced by Sherry et al. [15] which is sensitivity relative to Full Width at Half Maximum (FWHM) [16] is given by,

$$FOM = \frac{S}{FWHM}\ [RIU^{-1}] \qquad (2)$$

Another measuring parameter used for a finer understanding of the sensing performance is the sensor resolution given by [17]

$$S_R = \Delta n \times \frac{\Delta\lambda_{min}}{\Delta\lambda_{peak}}\ [RIU] \qquad (3)$$

where Δn and $\Delta\lambda_{peak}$ represents the change in RI and peak wavelength, respectively, with the minimum spectral resolution $\Delta\lambda_{min}$ assumed as 0.1 nm [18,19].

3. Results and discussion

The absorption cross-section of the structure with air as the sensing medium at standard room temperature of 293 K is shown in figure 2 (a). The designed structure is illuminated by a source of X polarized EM wave propagating in the Y direction with wavelength ranging from 600 nm to 2200 nm. Three distinct peaks corresponding to three different resonance modes are obtained at 824 nm, 1027 nm, and 1442.7 nm. The field distribution representing the norm of E field, $\sqrt{E_x^2 + E_y^2}$ across the surface of the structure, corresponding to the three separate modes shown in figure 2 (b), (c) and (d) reveals that the separation between the trimer Au nanocylinders play a vital role in the localization of electric field and its enhancement.

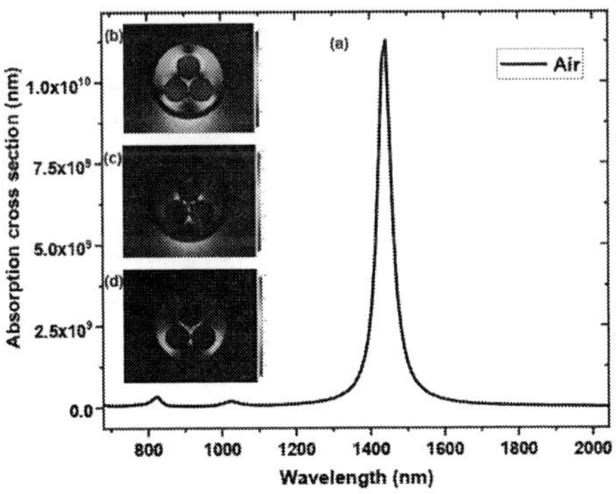

Figure 2. (a) Absorption cross-section of the proposed sensor with air as the sensing medium and electric field distributions at resonant peaks (b) 824 nm, (c) 1027 nm, and (d) 1442.7 nm.

Compared to isolated nanostructures, interacting nanostructures show a considerable field enhancement over a wide range of plasmon wavelengths. Here the first peak observed at 824 nm arises from the interaction between the trimer Au cylinders as well as between Au cylinders and the surrounding Ag cylinder. The second peak at 1027 nm corresponds to the interaction between the hollow Au nanocylinders in the trimer array. The E field intensity corresponding to these two peaks is of the order of 10^7 V/m. The third resonant mode arises from the combined effect of both Au-Au and Au-Ag interactions. From the field distribution plot (figure 2 (d)) it can be seen that the E field is distributed within the inner surface of the hollow Ag cylinder, with an enhanced field localization between the Au cylinders placed at the base vertices of the equilateral triangle. Here the E field intensity is increased to around 4×10^8 V/m. Even though there are multiple interactions (Au-Au and Au-Ag), the field enhancement is depended on the relative positions of the Au hollow cylinders with respect to the outer Ag hollow cylinder. This results in a sharp absorption peak with a rapid increase in intensity in contrast to the first and second peaks. Moreover, compared to the first two peaks the third one gives a good quality factor as the peak becomes intense and sharper. This intense mode of resonance with multiple couplings resulting in sharp absorption peak is considered for optimizing the sensing performance of the structure to bring out its possible applications at the longer wavelengths (near IR) with high resolution.

3.1. Optimization
The localized surface plasmon resonance of metal nanostructures are strongly influenced by the geometry, relative positions, and the RI of the medium [20]. There will be greater polarization of the medium for increased RI, attenuating the accumulated charge in the resonance zone, thereby reducing the restoring force. Therefore, it is evident that the LSPR frequency decreases with an increase in RI, which can be observed as a redshift in resonant wavelength [21]. When it comes to interacting metallic nanostructures, the separation between the particles become significant in tuning the quality and performance of the sensor.

3.1.1. Effect of the gap between Au trimer. We first considered the effect of the separation distance between the trimer Au hollow cylinders on the LSPR sensing capability. The RI of the medium is taken as n = 1.34 RIU. The field distribution corresponding to different plasmon coupling modes in response to the change in d from 170 nm to 110 nm on illumination with EM radiation ranging from 1350 nm to 1600 nm is analysed with r_1 = 50 nm, r_2 = 200 nm, t_1 = 10 nm, and t_2 = 30 nm. Figure 3 (i) a, b, c, d, e, f, and g shows the variation in electric field distribution as d is decreased from 170 nm to 110 nm in steps of 10 nm with n = 1.34 RIU. Figure 3 (ii) shows the corresponding absorption profile as a function of wavelength for different interparticle distances. As shown in figure 3 (i) (a), at d = 170 nm, the E field

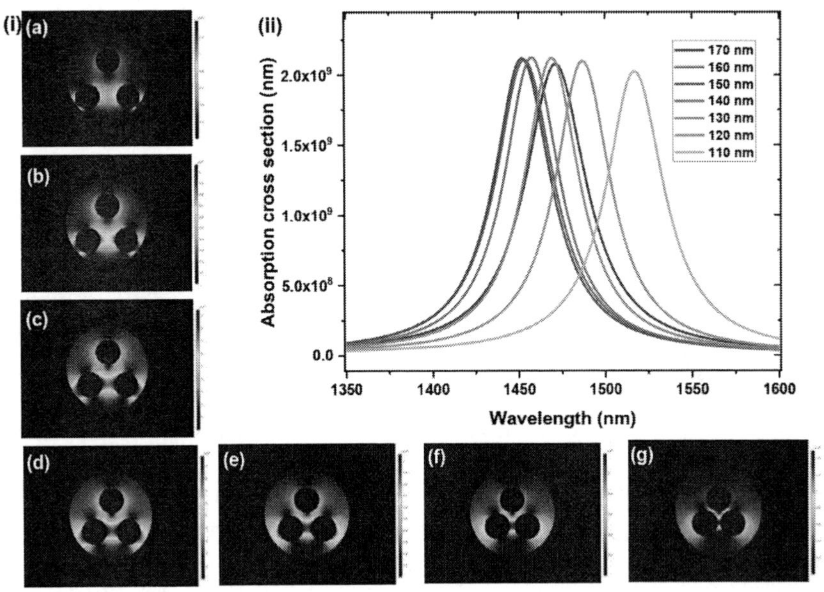

Figure 3. (i) Electric field distribution due to different modes of resonance relative to the position of the hollow Au nanocylinders (a) d = 170 nm, (b) d = 160nm, (c) d = 150 nm, (d) d = 140 nm, (e) d = 130 nm, (f) d = 120 nm, (f) d = 110 nm and (ii) the corresponding absorption cross section as a function of wavelength with n = 1.34 RIU.

is localized at the gap between the outer Ag hollow cylinder and the Au hollow cylinders at the base vertices of the equilateral triangle. Since Au-Au separation is large for d = 170 nm, plasmon coupling between Au-Ag hollow cylinders is dominant and results in the sharp resonant peak at 1471.67 nm. At d = 160 nm (figure 3(i) (b)), it can be seen that the coupling between Au-Ag cylinders is decreasing and as a result the absorption peak is found to be blue shifted with resonant wavelength observed at 1453.33 nm. The same behaviour is observed for d = 150 nm with resonant peak blue-shifted to 1451.66 nm. On further decreasing the separation between Au nanocylinders, it is interesting to observe that the absorption peak gets red-shifted with the E field localized at the gap between Au nanocylinders placed at the base vertices of the equilateral triangle. This change in plasmonic resonant mode can be observed from d = 140 nm (figure 3 (i) (d)), with an absorption peak obtained at 1458.33 nm. Also, it is clear from figure 3 (ii) that as Au-Au coupling becomes stronger, the shift in the resonant position of the absorption peak increases, indicating the highly sensitive nature of the structure. At d = 110 nm (figure 3 (i) (g)), the strong interaction between Au-Au cylinders causes considerable field enhancement at the gap between them. This enhanced plasmon coupling can be clearly understood from the absorption profile which shows the significant red shift in resonant wavelength to 1516.67 nm for d = 110 nm.

To get a fine idea about the capability and quality of the structure in sensing the change in RI, the study was repeated for the same values of d with n = 1.42 RIU. From the absorption cross-section study, the shift in resonant position in response to the change in RI of the medium is noted for each value of d from 170 nm to 110 nm. Table 1 illustrates the calculated sensitivity, FOM, and sensor resolution of the structure. From the table, it is clear that at d = 110 nm (i.e., 10 nm gap between Au trimer), the structure gives a maximum sensitivity of 1091.64 nm/RIU with FOM = 27.29 RIU^{-1} and S_R = 9.160 $\times 10^{-5}$ RIU. Hence for further optimization of the structure, the gap between Au trimer is kept constant at 10 nm.

Table 1. Calculated sensitivity, FOM and sensor resolution values for varying d from 170 nm to 110 nm with n = 1.34 RIU and n = 1.42 RIU (Δn = 0.08 RIU)

d (nm)	$\Delta\lambda$ (nm)	S (nm/RIU)	FOM (RIU^{-1})	S_R (RIU)
170	82.33	1029.12	24.50	9.716×10^{-5}
160	80.66	1008.25	25.21	9.917×10^{-5}
150	82.33	1029.12	25.73	9.716×10^{-5}
140	81.67	1020.87	26.62	9.795×10^{-5}
130	83.67	1045.87	27.28	9.561×10^{-5}
120	83.33	1041.62	26.71	9.600×10^{-5}
110	87.33	1091.62	27.29	9.160×10^{-5}

3.1.2. Effect of the radius of Au nanocylinders. Keeping the gap between the trimer Au cylinders constant at 10 nm, radius r_1 is varied from 50 nm to 70 nm in steps of 5 nm with t_1 = 10 nm and t_2 = 30 nm. To get the effect of radius of Au alone, the gap between Au trimer and Ag is also kept constant by adjusting r_2 accordingly. Separate absorption cross-section studies are carried out with n = 1.34 RIU and n = 1.42 RIU to optimize the sensing performance. Figure 4 (a) gives the resonant wavelength observed for each value of r_1 with n = 1.34 and 1.42 RIU. The resonant wavelength is red shifted as r_1 increases from 50 nm to 65 nm for both RI values. However, for 70 nm, the peak wavelength is decreased (or blue shifted) for n = 1.42 RIU. This aberration is due to the variations in the coupling of dipolar modes on the cylinder surfaces [22]. Initially the dipolar interaction resulted in E field localization with maximum enhancement between Au cylinders at the base vertices of the equilateral triangle. On increasing radius above 65 nm this localized field is found nonuniformly distributed between the trimer Au hollow cylinders with a decrease in the E field intensity and the absorption intensity. Usually on increasing the particle size, peak shifts to longer wavelengths resulting in increased sensing performance. In addition, for Au NPs, it has been verified that this redshift can be observed up to around 60nm for the variation in size between 10 - 100nm [23,24]. Here a maximum shift in resonant wavelength of 122.4 nm is obtained for r_1 = 65 nm.

Using the shift obtained in resonant wavelength on varying r_1, sensitivity and FOM were calculated to optimize the structure. Figure 4 (b) and (c) compare the sensitivity and FOM values obtained for each value of r_1. As the radius of Au cylinders is increased, the sensitivity is also increased and reaches a maximum of 1530.0 nm/RIU for r_1 = 65 nm. On the further increase in the radius sensitivity is found to be decreasing. Figure 4 (c) gives the FOM calculated for each radius. It can be seen that FOM is first decreased on increasing r_1 up to 60 nm, and at 65 nm, it is increased to 22.5 RIU^{-1}. Again at 70 nm FOM is reduced. Thus, a radius of 65 nm with maximum sensitivity and good FOM improves the performance of the sensor.

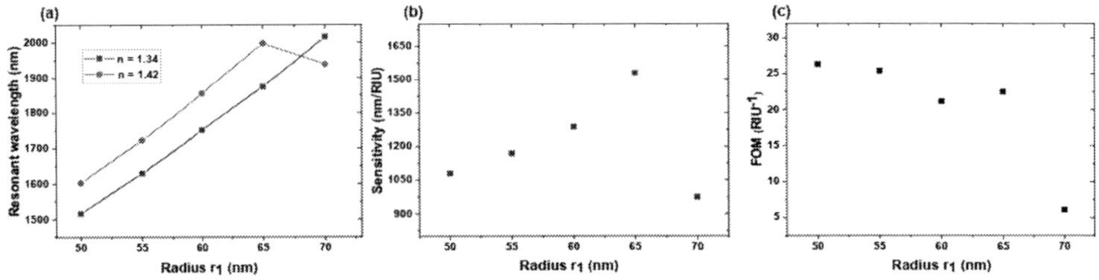

Figure 4. (a) Resonant wavelength as a function of the radius of the hollow Au nanocylinders (r_1 varied from 50 nm to 70 nm) at n = 1.34 RIU and n = 1.42 RIU with t_1 = 10 nm, t_2 = 30 nm, and the gap between Au trimer kept constant at 10 nm. Comparison of (b) Sensitivity and (c) FOM values on varying r_1 from 50 nm to 70 nm.

3.1.3. Effect of thickness of Au nanocylinders. To get an idea of the effect of thickness of Au nanocylinders on the sensing performance of the structure, t_1 is varied from 10 nm to 30 nm keeping all other geometric parameters constant. Absorption cross-section at n = 1.34 RIU and n = 1.42 RIU are studied with r_1 = 65nm, r_2 = 230 nm, t_2 = 30 nm and gap between Au trimer kept constant at 10 nm (i.e., d = 140 nm). The peak position of the absorption profile is noted for both RI values, and the shift obtained in the peak position as a function of thickness is plotted in figure 5 (a). On increasing thickness, the shift in peak position goes on decreasing.

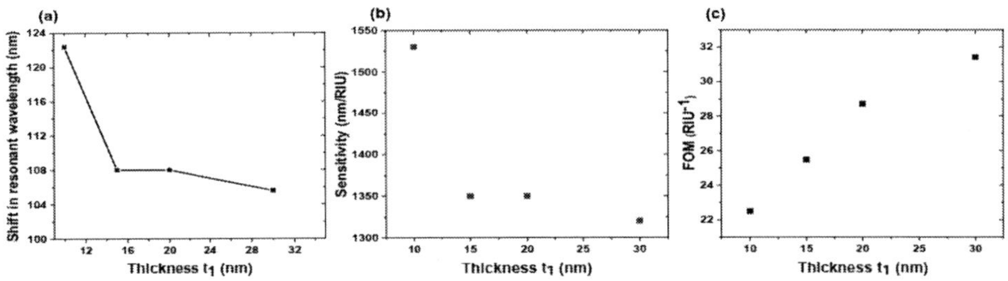

Figure 5. (a) Shift in resonant wavelength as a function of thickness of hollow Au nanocylinders (t_1 varied from 10 nm to 30 nm) for change in refractive index from 1.34 -1.42 RIU with r_1 = 65nm, r_2 = 230 nm, t_2 = 30 nm and d = 140 nm. Comparison of (b) Sensitivity and (c) FOM values on varying t_1 from 10 nm to 30 nm.

If the thickness is decreased below 10 nm shift in peak will increase, but the peak becomes more and more wider with poor FOM, which affects the quality of the sensor. So, the values of t_1 below 10 nm are not considered for the optimization. Figure 5 (b) and (c) compare the sensitivity and FOM obtained for different thicknesses of Au nanocylinders. It is evident from the plot that on increasing t_1, the structure turns less sensitive to the RI change. At the same time, we can observe an increase in FOM for large values of t_1. For t_1 = 30 nm, FOM is increased to 31.42 RIU^{-1} but sensitivity has decreased to 1320.0 nm/RIU. Since we focus more on sensitivity study, t_1 = 10 nm is taken considering its possibility in sensing applications.

3.1.4. Effect of the radius of Ag nanocylinders. To study the effect of radius of Ag nanocylinders on sensing performance r_2 is varied from 210 nm to 240 nm with r_1 = 65 nm, t_1 = 10 nm, d = 140 nm and t_2 = 30 nm. Figure 6 (a) shows the absorption cross-section of the structure as a function of wavelength for varying r_2 from 210 nm to 240 nm with n = 1.34 nm. It is clear that a significant redshift is observed on decreasing the radius, but the peak intensity decreases rapidly and becomes wider. The study is repeated with n = 1.42 RIU, and the peak position is noted for sensitivity and FOM calculations. Figure 6 (b) and (c) show the sensitivity and FOM values as a function of the radius of Ag nanocylinders. The results indicate that increasing or decreasing r_2 from 220 nm causes a decrease in sensitivity and FOM. The designed structure with r_2 = 220 nm gives the maximum sensitivity and FOM values of 1920.0025 nm/RIU and 26.08 RIU^{-1}.

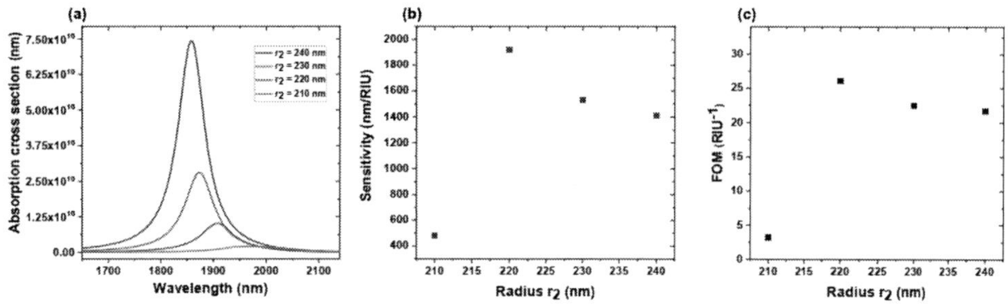

Figure 6. (a) Absorption cross section as a function of wavelength for varying r_2 from 210 nm to 240 nm with r_1 = 65 nm, t_1 = 10 nm, d = 140 nm, t_2 = 30 nm and n = 1.34 RIU. Calculated values of (b) Sensitivity and (c) FOM for varying r_2 from 210 nm to 240 nm.

Table 2. Calculated values of sensitivity, FOM, and sensor resolution of the proposed sensor in response to the change in RI from 1.37-1.40 RIU in steps of 0.005 RIU.

n (RIU)	λ (nm)	S (nm/RIU)	FOM (RIU^{-1})	S_R (RIU)
1.370	1937.499	-	-	-
1.375	1949.545	2409.2	22.31	4.1507×10^{-5}
1.380	1962.272	2545.4	21.05	3.9286×10^{-5}
1.385	1973.409	2227.4	17.26	4.4895×10^{-5}
1.390	1986.136	2545.4	17.67	3.9286×10^{-5}
1.395	1998.863	2545.4	16.49	3.9286×10^{-5}
1.400	2010.000	2227.4	13.42	4.4895×10^{-5}

The absorption cross-section of the optimized sensor is studied by changing refractive index of the medium from 1.37-1.40 RIU in steps of 0.005 RIU with r_1 = 65 nm, r_2 = 220 nm, t_1 = 10 nm, t_2 = 30 nm and d = 140 nm. A distinct red shift in the absorption peak is observed, indicating the highly sensitive nature of the structure to even small variations in the value of n. The calculated values of sensitivity,

FOM, and sensor resolution are illustrated in table 2. The sensor gives an average sensitivity of 2416.7 nm/RIU for the RI change from 1.37-1.40 RIU with a maximum FOM of 22.31 RIU^{-1} and sensor resolution of the order of 10^{-5} RIU.

3.1.5 Refractive index resolution. To evaluate the performance of the proposed sensor more precisely, a close study of the RI sensing is carried out by varying n from 1.33 RIU to 1.299965 RIU, as illustrated in table 3. The change in refractive index is varied from 0.025 RIU to 0.00001 RIU. It is interesting to note that the sensor can detect tiny variations in the RI value. The sensor gives a maximum sensitivity of 2000.67 nm/RIU for $\Delta n = 0.0003$ RIU, and the structure is capable of detecting RI change up to 0.00001 RIU with a sensitivity of 1998.00 nm/RIU. A maximum sensitivity of 1500.00 nm/RIU is obtained for 0.0001 RI change within the range 1 - 1.03 RIU. At smaller RI values, in addition to the high sensitivity and resolution, an increase in FOM to around 43.90 RIU^{-1} is also attained, which contributes to the excellent quality of the sensor. This indicates the highly efficient sensing nature of the proposed sensor with improved resolution and quality in the near IR region.

Table 3. Sensitivity calculation for slight variations in the refractive index of the medium

n (RIU)	Δn (RIU)	λ (nm)	S (nm/RIU)
1.330000	-	1894.00000	-
1.305000	0.025000	1858.60000	1416.00
1.302500	0.002500	1854.99980	1440.08
1.301500	0.001000	1853.80000	1199.80
1.301000	0.000500	1853.19980	1200.40
1.300600	0.000400	1852.60000	1499.50
1.300300	0.000300	1851.99980	2000.67
1.300100	0.000200	1851.90000	499.00
1.300000	0.000100	1851.76000	1400.00
1.299975	0.000025	1851.71998	1600.08
1.299965	0.000010	1851.70000	1998.00

3.2. Practical applications

Based on the sensitivity studies, it is evident that the proposed sensor can find a wide range of applications, including bio-analyte analysis, chemical concentration detection, and gas sensing. The structure is highly sensitive to even small variations of n within the biologically and chemically important RI range 1.30 – 1.40 RIU. The high sensitivity of the optimized sensor can be exploited in the early-stage detection of cancer biomarkers. Some of its potential applications include malignancy development of blood cancer (1.376-1.390 RIU), Adrenal gland cancer (1.381-1.395 RIU), type-I (1.385-1.399 RIU) and type-II (1.387-1.401 RIU) breast cancer [25,26], red blood cells (1.399 ± 0.006 RIU- healthy, 1.395 ± 0.005 RIU-ring stage, 1.383 ± 0.005 RIU- trophozoite stage, 1.373 ± 0.006 RIU-schizont stage) [27]. Platelet cells with refractive index measured as 1.390 RIU in the range of 1.360-1.409 RIU are capable of determining certain diseases such as cerebrovascular disease, ischemic heart disease, and renovascular disease [28–32]. The sensor can also sense the RI range of various gases (n = 1 to n = 1.03), making it a potential candidate for gas sensing with good FOM value. Thus, the designed plasmonic RI sensor with good biocompatibility, high sensitivity, resolution and FOM can be proposed as a promising near IR broad range sensor with less geometrical complexity.

4. Conclusion

In this work, we have designed a highly sensitive plasmonic refractive index sensor using trimer hollow Au nanocylinders surrounded by a hollow Ag nanocylinder. The plasmonic behaviour of the structure is studied by analysing the absorption cross-section when it interacts with EM radiation using the FEM method. The proposed sensor gives a maximum sensitivity of 2545.4 nm/RIU and a maximum FOM of around 43.90 RIU^{-1} for the RI change from 1-1.42 RIU. The detection of changes in RI up to 1×10^{-5} RIU within the biologically and chemically important RI range makes the designed structure a promising sensor for biological, chemical, and gas sensing applications. The optimized RI sensor with less geometrical complexity, biocompatibility, wide range of RI sensing, high sensitivity, high resolution and good FOM can contribute a lot towards health-care applications, including rapid detection of various diseases.

Acknowledgements
The authors acknowledge the computational facility extended by the Department of Physics, Central University of Kerala and thank Prof. Vincent Mathew for the enlightening discussions and helpful suggestions. JJ and DM thank Kerala State Council for Science, Technology and Environment for the approval of financial assistance under Student Project scheme (No. 00857/SPS 65/2021/KSCSTE).

References

[1] Roh S, Chung T and Lee B 2011 *Sensors* **11** 1565–88
[2] Petryayeva E and Krull U J 2011 *Analytica Chimica Acta* **706** 8–24
[3] Shrivastav A M, Cvelbar U and Abdulhalim I 2021 *Communications Biology* **4** 70
[4] Wei H and Xu H 2014 *Materials Today* **17** 372–80
[5] Arya A, Das G M, Dantham V R and Laha R 2019 *Journal of the Optical Society of America B* **36** 235
[6] Kang H *et al.* 2019 *Chemical reviews* **119** 664–699
[7] Dondapati S K, Sau T K, Hrelescu C, Klar T A, Stefani F D and Feldmann J 2010 *ACS Nano* **4** 6318–22
[8] Lee K S and El-Sayed M A 2006 *Journal of Physical Chemistry B* **110** 19220–5
[9] Stewart M E, Anderton C R, Thompson L B, Maria J, Gray S K, Rogers J A and Nuzzo R G 2008 *Chemical Reviews* **108** 494–521
[10] Gómez-Hens A, Fernández-Romero J M and Aguilar-Caballos M P 2008 *TrAC Trends in Analytical Chemistry* **27** 394–406
[11] Lee S W, Lee K S, Ahn J, Lee J J, Kim M G and Shin Y B 2011 *ACS Nano* **5** 897–904
[12] Johnson P B and Christy R W 1972 *Phys. Rev. B* **6** 4370–9
[13] Bérenger J-P 2007 *Synthesis Lectures on Computational Electromagnetics* **8** 1–120
[14] Yu H, Peng Y, Yang Y and Li Z-Y 2019 *NPJ Comput. Mater.* **5** 45–49
[15] Sherry L J, Chang S H, Schatz G C, van Duyne R P, Wiley B J and Xia Y 2005 *Nano Letters* **5** 2034–8
[16] Meng Q Q, Zhao X, Lin C Y, Chen S J, Ding Y C and Chen Z Y 2017 *Sensors* **17** 1846
[17] Sasi S, Francis S M, Jacob J and Thomas V I 2021 *Plasmonics* **16** 1705–17
[18] Rifat A A, Hasan Md R, Ahmed R and Butt H 2017 *Journal of Nanophotonics* **12** 012503
[19] Mollah M A, Razzak S M A, Paul A K and Hasan M R 2019 *Sens Biosensing Res* **24** 100286
[20] Mlayah A, Arbouet A, Girard C, Llado E A, Aizpurua J, Large N, Marty R, Teo S L, Tripathy S and Lin V K 2010 *Optics Express* **18** 22271–82
[21] Shabaninezhad M and Ramakrishna G 2019 *The Journal of Chemical Physics* **150** 144116
[22] Aizpurua J, Hanarp P, Sutherland D S, Käll M, Bryant G W and García de Abajo F J 2003 *Physical Review Letters* **90** 4
[23] Alharbi R, Irannejad M and Yavuz M 2019 *Sensors* **19** 862
[24] Link S and El-Sayed M A 1999 *Journal of Physical Chemistry B* **103** 4212–7
[25] Parvin T, Ahmed K, Alatwi A M and Rashed A N Z 2021 *Optical Review* **28** 134–43

[26] Ramola A, Marwaha A and Singh S 2021 *Applied Physics A: Materials Science and Processing* **127** 643
[27] Park Y, Diez-Silva M, Popescu G, Lykotrafitis G, Choi W, Feld M S and Suresh S 2008 *Proc. Natl. Acad. Sci.* **105** LP – 13735
[28] Kolesnikova I v., Potapov S v., Yurkin M A, Hoekstra A G, Maltsev V P and Semyanov K A 2006 *Journal of Quantitative Spectroscopy and Radiative Transfer* **102** 37–45
[29] McManus D D and Freedman J E 2015 *Nature Reviews Cardiology* **12** 711–7
[30] Vizioli L, Muscari S and Muscari A 2009 *International Journal of Clinical Practice* **63** 1509–15
[31] Daugirdas J T and Bernardo A A 2012 *Kidney International* **82** 147–57
[32] Moskalensky A E *et al.* 2013 *Journal of Biomedical Optics* **18** 017001

Theoretical modelling of a deformation based concave square ring-square disc (SR-SD) silver structure for pressure sensing

Simitha S[1] Shinto M Francis[1,2], Jesly Jacob[2], and Vibin Ipe Thomas[1*]

[1] Department of Chemistry, CMS College Kottayam, Kerala, India- 686001
[2] Department of Physics, Assumption College, Changanacheery, Kerala, India- 686101

* *vibin@cmscollege.ac.in*

Abstract. A compact nanosensor that explores the tie-in between stress-induced deformation and optical resonance characteristics is theoretically proposed for pressure sensing. The structure modeling, electromagnetic (EM) wave simulation, and performance evaluations were carried out using the 2D finite element method (FEM). The proposed surface plasmon resonance (SPR) based metal-insulator-metal (MIM) model responds to the pressure induced on the top-facing side of an Ag concave square ring- square disc arrangement (Concave SR-SD) in terms of a structural curve-in into the insulator cavity. These deformations alter the electromagnetic field distributions and plasmonic resonance conditions, shifting the absorption cross-section profiles towards higher wavelengths. The shift in the resonant wavelength ($\Delta\lambda$) for specific measured deformations (d) exhibited by the normal SR-SD hinds at the application level perspective of the designed system in pressure sensing via its optomechanical correlation. Further, multiple parameters like insulator cavity width (W_I) and structure wise modifications in the outer ring structure are investigated for performance optimization, and subline sensitivity values (maximum) of 24.496 nm/MPa and 40.46 nm/MPa are observed from normal and concave SR-SD systems respectively. The suggested nano pressure sensor of suitable sensitivity and broad sensing range promises strong applicability in biomedicine, health monitoring, nanomechanics, chip-based devices, and nanoelectronics.

Keywords: pressure sensing, structural deformation, square ring disc.

1. Introduction

Micro and nano structure based optical sensors have been desirable and promising candidates for photoelectronic applications in recent years. They meet the demands of ultra-compact volume, low weight, quick response, and precise detection of various substances. These sensors have been efficiently employed in multiple realms for detecting materials like chemicals, gases, bio-analytes, and physical parameters like pressure, temperature, current, refractive index, and magnetic intensity [1]. Among these, the pressure and temperature measurements are quite vital as they are frequently used in automobile industries and petrochemical hazard control, safety monitoring, medical diagnostics, and several other extents of human life [2]. The optical pressure sensors are comparatively more promising because of their safe operation, better efficiency, dynamic sensing range, most minor electromagnetic interference[3], etc. The pressure applied to an optical pressure sensor is effectively transduced into optical responses by exploring the linear relation between stress and the optical resonance properties of the system utilized. Thus, the plasmonic pressure sensor converts applied pressure into an electrical or optical signal. Fabry–Perot interferometers[4], SiO_2 diaphragms, Mach–Zehnder interferometers[5], optical fibers, and other optical pressure sensors have been widely reported. The larger size and less compatibility with optical circuits limit their applicability.

The surface plasmon resonance of a nanostructure is highly sensitive to the embedded medium and its permittivity values[6]. At the same time, size and shape also play crucial roles in their SPR response[7]. Plasmonic pressure sensors have been found to have a more significant quality factor and sensitivity, satisfy low volume requirements, and being compatible with nanodevices [8]. SPR-based pressure sensing is primarily accomplished in two ways: first, the shift in SPR resonance positions with structure deformations. Second is the change in the index of refraction of opto-elastic materials integrated within the nanostructures. In both cases, the optical profiles of the device remain sensitive to the change in stress experienced by its environment.

Recently, optical plasmonic sensors of various geometries, such as nanoparticle array[9], photonic crystal structures[10], dielectric waveguides, MIM structures, and so on, have been investigated for pressure sensor applications[8]. Dinodiya et al. reported a plasmonic sensor of photonic crystal made of Si and GaAs, with a sensing range of 0–5 GPa, and maximum sensitivity values of 1.674 nm/GPa (Si) and 17.00 nm/GPa (GaAs) obtained [3]. Min Suk Oh and his group designed a transparent and capacitive pressuresensor, and achieved the sensitivity of 0.4 kPa^{-1} [11]. Yu et al. reported the highest sensitivity of flexible 2D plasmonic sensors based on layered heterostructures of sensitivity 20.8 kPa^{-1}[12]. A new approach of conductive polymer-based piezoresistive pressure sensor with a sensitivity of 0.79 –1 kPa^{-1} was proposed by Chunguo Liu, where deformation of the polymer by less than 75 Pa pressure was monitored[13]. Nidhi Paliwal and their team presented a lossy-mode, fiber optic based pressure sensor of natural rubber polymer, having a sensitivity of 2 μm/MPa[14]. A nanostructure grating proposed by A Fermani detects pressure ranging from 0–5 kPa [15].

A compact SPR MIM-based pressure sensor of a square ring (SR) and square disc (SD) structure is designed and stimulated through this work. SPR excitations happen as a consequence of imposed deformations (d). When the pressure is applied to an active region of the silver ring, it suppresses the insulator cavity and causes changes in the resonance conditions of the structure. Thus, the pressure level change reflects a shift in resonance frequency and intensity of the absorption cross-section profile. The excellent sensitivity and dynamic sensing range values observed for the basic normal SR-SD structure are further optimized by modifying the ring structure and reducing the insulator cavity region. An enhancement of average pressure-based wavelength sensitivity (WS_{avg}) from 4.677nm/MPa to 18.06 nm/MPa and maximum pressure-based wavelength sensitivity (WS_{max}) from 5.371 nm/MPa to 24.496 nm/MPa is observed for normal SR-SD structure with reduction of insulator cavity from 50 nm to 30 nm. When coming to the concave SR-SD structure, the observed WS_{avg} and WS_{max} increments from 4.271 nm/MPa to 24.86 nm/MPa and from 4.9866 nm/MPa to 40.46 nm/MPa, respectively. Furthermore, when transformed to concave structure from normal, WS_{avg} and WS_{max} show an increment of 37.6% and 65.16%, respectively, when the insulator cavity width is 30 nm.

2. Theoretical modeling and sensor design

As depicted schematically in figure 1a, the initial structural layout proposed for the deformation-based-pressure monitoring nanodevice named normal SR-SD constitutes a concentric arrangement of Ag square disc (SD) and square ring (SR) with an insulator cavity of width (W_I) in between. By default, the side lengths of the SD (l_{sd}), SR (l_{sr}), and width of SR (W_{sr}) are kept fixed at 250 nm, 450 nm, and 50 nm, respectively. Regardless of the potential oxidation effects, the particular choice of Ag as the plasmonic material arises from its lower power drain and as economic feasibility at a hands-on fabrication level. Moreover, the lower ohmic loss of Ag favors sharp spectral response, enhancing the device's efficiency to great extents[7].

The fundamental working principle of the proposed system relays the degree of vertical deformation (d) experienced by the top end of the SR, i.e., the pressure-active region (P_{act}). As shown in figure 1 (inset), when a pressure P is applied on P_{act}, it bends down into the insulator cavity by a vertical

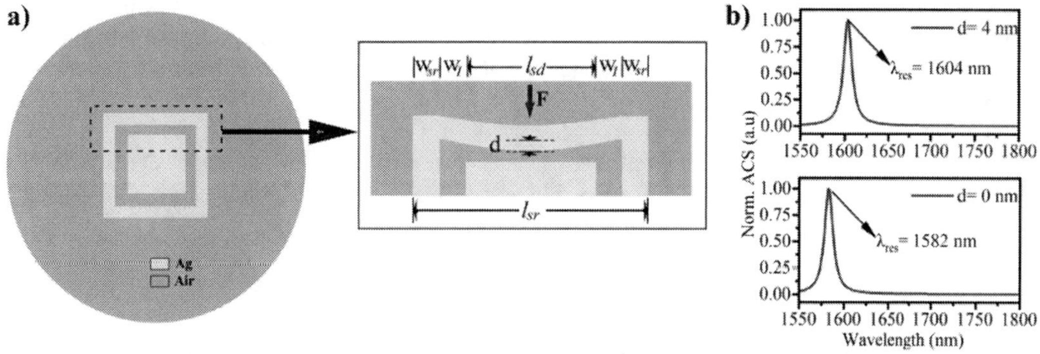

Figure 1. (a) Schematic representation of the suggested normal SR-SD structure with geometric parameters W_{sr}=50 nm, W_I =50 nm, l_{sd}=250 nm, and l_{sr}=450 nm. 'd' denotes the measure of vertical deformation on the P_{act} upon the application of a pressure P. (b) comparison of the normalized absorption cross-sections (ACS) of the designed structure for d=0 nm and d=4 nm.

displacement of d nm pursuant to the standard relation of beam bending. Considering P_{act} as a rectangular slab of length L= 350 nm and thickness W_I =50 nm, the extent of deformation (d) as a result of the pressure applied (P) is expressed as [16]

$$d = \frac{PL^4}{2Y(W_{sr})^3} \quad (1)$$

Where Y denotes the Youngs modulus of Ag (Y=7.5×10^{10} Pa), and L is the inner side length of SR, i.e., L=l_{sr}-2W_{sr}. With the given geometric parameters, a deformation of 4 nm corresponds to the employment of a pressure P≈ 5MPa. Similar to any previously reported SPR-based sensors, wavelength sensitivity (WS) is one of the critical factors determining a plasmonic sensor system's efficiency and practical feasibility. With Δλ representing the resonant wavelength shift for the deformation Δd, the wavelength sensitivity of the designed pressure sensor [17] can be described as

$$WS = \frac{\Delta\lambda}{\Delta P} = \frac{L^4 \Delta\lambda}{2Y(W_{sr})^3 \Delta d} \quad (2)$$

Geometric design and electromagnetic (EM) wave simulation are performed using COMSOL Multiphysics 5.1 via the 2-D finite element approach. Material parameters and dielectric values of silver were adopted from [18]. With mesh size chosen as extra fine, the structure is theoretically simulated for its absorption cross-section (ACS) profile with EM waves propagating in the +Y direction. The whole computational region is terminated by perfectly matching layers (PML, which enhances the computational speed by preventing the simulation across infinite domains, causing a potential running out of memory[19].

3. Results and Discussion

Initially, the structure is simulated with default geometric parameters across a wavelength range of 1.55-1.8 μm with d= 4 nm. From the simulation results plotted in figure 1b, the deformation of 4 nm results in a +20.74 nm resonant wavelength shift in their ACS profile concerning the system simulated under static conditions, i.e., d=0 nm. In both cases, the structure exhibits excellent resonant peaks having full width at half maximum (FWHM) value of 11.51 nm. Thus, the proposed structure can make promising results as a potential nano pressure sensor.

Further, for a detailed investigation of the structure for its dynamic pressure detection range, the deformation is increased to 32 nm in steps of 4 units up from 0 nm, and the EM wave simulation is repeated in each case. The color mapping of the wavelength-Norm. ACS intensity correlation shown in figure 2a reveals the gradual redshift of resonant positions for rising d values. However, it is noted that, toward higher deformations, an enhanced wavelength shift is observed in resonant positions. This can be attributed to the improved plasmonic coupling as the silver disc and ring approach one another very closely. Using equation 2, the normal SR-SD structure's average wavelength density (WS_{avg}) is calculated as 4.677 nm/MPa, a pretty appreciable value. Since there is a minor variation in the resonant shift across higher d values, an additional evaluation term named maximum wavelength sensitivity (WS_{max}) is also considered. With the results in figure 2a, an excellent value of WS_{max} = 5.37 nm/MPa is observed at d=32 nm.

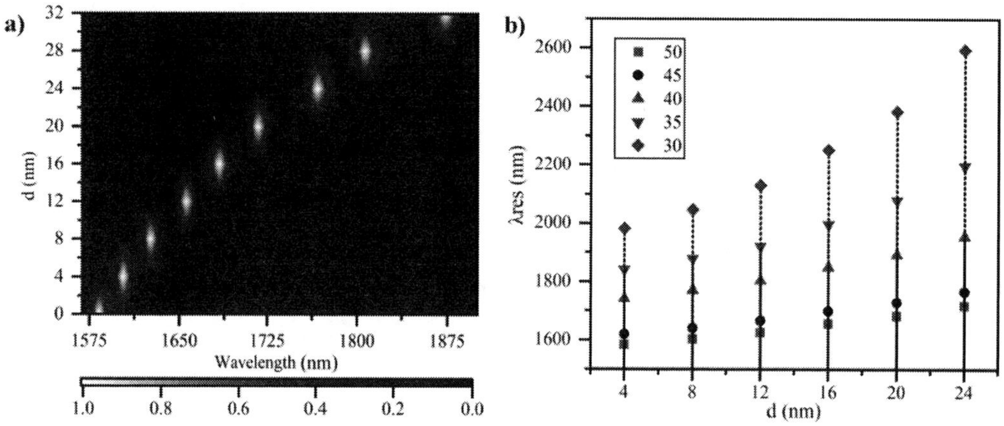

Figure 2. (a) Color mapping of the normalized ACS profiles of the proposed normal SR-SD structure (W_I =50 nm) for deformation values d varying from 0 nm to 32 nm in steps of 4 nm (b) resonance wavelength-deformation (λ_{res}-d) relation of normal SR-SD structure for W_I values varying from 50 nm to 30 nm.

3.1. *Effect of insulator cavity width (W_I)*

As part of the performance optimization, the resonant characteristics of the designed system under varying deformation values are observed for different W_I values. The λ_{res}-d correlation for W_I=50, 45, 40, 35, and 30 nm is plotted in figure 2b. Note that the cavity size is varied by raising the l_{sd} value without affecting SR. Differ from the previous study, d value up to 20 nm is only noted as a sufficient gap of at least 10 nm has to be maintained between SR and SD (in the case of W_I=30 nm) to minimize the error due to coupled plasmonic resonance when they come too closer. As expected, the designed structure exhibits a sublime resonant shift for all observed W_I values. As seen in figure 2, the λ_{res}-d correlation maintains the anticipated linear growth across lower W_I values which eventually assumes an exponential form as d values increase. It can be attributed to the previously discussed field coupling between SD and SR. A profound increase of 13.38 nm/MPa for WS_{avg} and 19.13 nm/MPa for WS_{max}, with result values touching a maximum of 18.06 nm/MPa and 24.49 nm/MPa is observed when W_I is reduced to 30 nm.

3.2. *Sensor performance of Concave-SR-SD structure*

A further crucial structural modification is now introduced into the normal SR-SD structure with a motive of sensitivity enhancement. Keeping the active region (P_{act}) intact, SR at rest three sides is bent into the insulator cavity in a concave shape with a bending value of d_{fix}= 25 nm. The newly formed concave SR-SR structure, as illustrated in figure 3a, is now simulated and analyzed for its deformation-based pressure sensitivity without altering any other parameters. As seen in figures 3b and 3c, while comparing the calculated sensor parameters of concave SR-SD with normal, very close matching results are observed for both WS_{avg} and WS_{max} when W_I is ≥ 45 nm. For the rest W_I values, a very significant increment in sensor performance is exhibited by the modified concave SR-SD system. With W_I = 30 nm, WS_{avg} and WS_{max} show 37.6% and 65.16% increment when it comes to concave SR-SD structure.

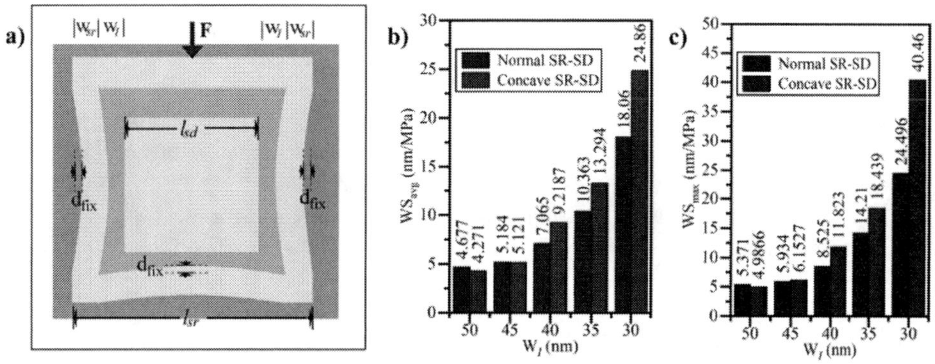

Figure 3. (a) Schematic representation of the Concave SR-SD structure with d_{fix}=25 nm. A comparison of (b) average wavelength sensitivity and (c) maximum wavelength sensitivity with a reduction in the width of insulator cavity W_I for normal and concave SR-SD structures is proposed.

4. Conclusion

A compact, sensitive, tunable, metal-insulator-metal type nanostructure based plasmonic sensor is theoretically proposed for pressure detection using the finite element method. The normal SR-SD structure exhibits maximum pressure sensitivity of 24.86 nm/MPa. Optimization was done on normal SR-SD by bending three sides of a square ring, transforming the structure to concave SR-SD. When the structure became concave SR-SD, the average and maximum sensitivity increased by 37.6% and 65.16%, respectively. Functional comparison of concave SR-SD design with normal SR-SD revealed a rise in sensitivity, reaching a maximum pressure sensitivity of 11.823 nm/MPa for a W_I value of 40 nm. Further, the detailed W_I-λ_{res} analysis revealed its inverse correlation with a maximum sensitivity reaching 24.496 nm/MPa (normal SR-SD) and 40.46 nm/MPa (concave SR-SD) under W_I = 30 nm condition. Also, a 286.14% and 482.06% increase in average sensitivity was observed for normal and concave SR-SD structures, respectively, when the insulator cavity width was reduced to 30 nm from 50 nm. From the simulation results, we suggest a concave SR-SD design with excellent pressure sensitivity for pressure monitoring applications.

5. Acknowledgements

The authors acknowledge the computational facility extended by the Central University of Kerala. The University Grants Commission, Government of India, funded the work with research grant number 2368-MRP/15-16/KLMG002/UGC-SWRO.

6. References

[1] Rajasekar R and Robinson S 2019 Nano-Pressure and Temperature Sensor Based on Hexagonal Photonic Crystal Ring Resonator *Plasmonics* **14** 3–15
[2] Yu X, Yuan Y, Xiao B, Li Z, Qu J and Song J 2018 Flexible plasmonic pressure sensor based on layered two-dimensional heterostructures *J. Light. Technol.* **36** 5678–84
[3] Dinodiya S and Bhargava A 2021 A Comparative Analysis of Pressure Sensing Parameters for

Two Dimensional Photonic Crystal Sensors Based on Si and GaAs *Silicon*
[4] Xu Y, Bai P, Zhou X, Akimov Y, Png C E, Ang L K, Knoll W and Wu L 2019 Optical Refractive Index Sensors with Plasmonic and Photonic Structures: Promising and Inconvenient Truth *Adv. Opt. Mater.* **7** 31–3
[5] Vijaya Shanthi K and Robinson S 2014 Two-dimensional photonic crystal based sensor for pressure sensing *Photonic Sensors* **4** 248–53
[6] Sasi S, Francis S M, Jacob J and Thomas V I 2021 A Tunable Plasmonic Refractive Index Sensor with Ultrabroad Sensing Range for Cancer Detection *Plasmonics*
[7] S S, Francis S M, Ramachandran A, Jacob J and Ipe Thomas V 2022 Dual channel plasmonic hybrid system as potential multi-analyte and multi-parameter sensor *Opt. Laser Technol.* **149** 107853
[8] Dehghan B, Sadeghi M and Adelpour Z 2019 The optical characteristics of the defected plasmonic waveguide under pressure *Optik (Stuttg).* **184** 44–9
[9] Jia P, Kong D and Ebendorff-Heidepriem H 2020 Flexible Plasmonic Tapes with Nanohole and Nanoparticle Arrays for Refractometric and Strain Sensing *ACS Appl. Nano Mater.* **3** 8242–6
[10] Tao S, Chen D, Wang J, Qiao J and Duan Y 2016 A high sensitivity pressure sensor based on two-dimensional photonic crystal *Photonic Sensors* **6** 137–42
[11] Lim S, Oh J M, Yoo B, Han C J, Lee B J, Oh M S and Kim J W 2021 Transparent and stretchable capacitive pressure sensor using selective plasmonic heating-based patterning of silver nanowires *Appl. Surf. Sci.* **561** 149989
[12] Yu X, Yuan Y, Xiao B, Li Z, Qu J and Song J 2018 Flexible plasmonic pressure sensor based on layered two-dimensional heterostructures *J. Light. Technol.* **36** 5678–84
[13] Lv B, Chen X and Liu C 2020 A highly sensitive piezoresistive pressure sensor based on graphene oxide/polypyrrole@polyurethane sponge *Sensors (Switzerland)* **20**
[14] Paliwal N and John J 2018 Design and modeling of highly sensitive lossy mode resonance-based fiber-optic pressure sensor *IEEE Sens. J.* **18** 209–15
[15] Mansouri M, Mir A, Farmani A and Izadi M 2021 Numerical Modeling of an Integrable and Tunable Plasmonic Pressure Sensor with Nanostructure Grating *Plasmonics* **16** 27–36
[16] Palizvan P, Olyaee S and Seifouri M 2018 An Optical MIM Pressure Sensor Based on a Double Square Ring Resonator *Photonic Sensors* **8** 242–7
[17] Chou Chao C-T, Chou Chau Y-F, Chen S-H, Ji Huang H, Ming Lim C, Raziq Rahimi Kooh M, Thotagamuge R, Chiang H-P, Chao C, Chau C, Maragò M and Runowski M 2021 Ultrahigh Sensitivity of a Plasmonic Pressure Sensor with a Compact Size Citation
[18] P. B. Johnson and R. W. Christy 1972 Optical Constant of the Nobel Metals *Phys. Rev. B* **6** 4370–9
[19] Bérenger J P 2007 *Perfectly Matched Layer (PML) for computational electromagnetics* vol 8

IOP Conf. Series: Materials Science and Engineering 1263 (2022) 012005 doi:10.1088/1757-899X/1263/1/012005

Numerical Study on the Effect of ZrS_2 on CZTSSe Photovoltaic Device Using SCAPS 1-D

Titu Thomas[1]

[1]Department of Physics, Nirmala College, Muvattupuzha -686661, Kerala, India

tt@nirmalacollege.ac.in

Abstract. CZTSSe based photovoltaic devices are gaining attention recently. They have many favorable properties like less costly and simple manufacturing processes, comparably nontoxic and easily available constituent components, and most importantly, excellent optoelectronic properties. Herein, we propose a CZTSSe based solar cell and aim to report for the first time a new material for the buffer layer: Zirconium Sulphide (ZrS_2). The suggested device here is Al-doped ZnO(AZO)/ZrS_2/CZTSSe/Mo. Here we use a numerical simulation package called Solar Cell Capacitance Simulator or SCAPS 1-D to analyze the output of the device with varying input parameters. To explore the impact of the ZrS_2 layer on the functioning of the suggested device,its donor density was changed from 10^{12} cm^{-3} to 10^{16} cm^{-3}. The simulations indicate that the donor density doesn't particularly affect the output parameters of the device within the tested range. Besides the influence of the ZrS_2 layer, a study was also carried out to find the role of operating temperature and the intrinsic layer on the proposed device. Most of the parameters declined rapidly with the increase in temperature while they remain constant with the change in ZnO thickness. Efficiency dropped to 9% at 500K from 23 % at 300K and the efficiency of the device remained 23% with the variation of intrinsic layer thickness. As per the simulation results, we can conclude that ZrS_2 is an appropriate material as buffer layer for photovoltaic devices with a CZTSSe absorber layer.

1. Introduction

Solar energy is the only alternative to the growing energy crisis. Solar cells can convert a considerable amount of solar energy into electrical energy and can produce high energy density with less cost as compared to other renewable energy sources which makes them ideal for various applications. Today various solar cell technologies are available and a major portion of the photovoltaic industry depends on thin film based devices.

Kesterite semiconductor solar cells have gained much attention during the last decade due to their favorable optoelectronic properties. Particularly CZTSSe which is a p-type semiconductor having earth-abundant constituent elements, tunable band gap of 0.9-1.5eV, absorption coefficient over 10^4 cm^{-1},[1],[2],[3] etc. Researchers were able to attain an efficiency of 12.6 % and 14% [4],[5]with CdS/In_2S_3 and CdS layers respectively but, the Shockley–Queisser limit for CZTSSe based solar cells is 32%.[6]

Efforts are also being carried out to replace the buffer layers based on Cd, In, Ga, etc which are rare, costlier, and toxic [7]. So the photovoltaic community was looking for a better buffer layer that can go with CZTSSe absorber layers to produce the same results. It is in this context we are introducing a new semiconductor compound Zirconium Sulfide (ZrS_2) as an efficient substitute for the buffer layer.

2. Simulation methodology

A numerical simulation package called the Solar Cell Capacitance Simulator or SCAPS 1-D[8] is used to analyse the proposed device numerically. This software was originally designed for heterojunction silicon solar cells by the electronics research group at University of Gent, Belgium.[9],[8],[10] There are many other softwares available in the market like MATLAB, Simulink, etc. But SCAPS is very user-friendly and has many advantages over any other similar programs. We can vary different influencing factors like thickness, band gap, doping concentration, defect density, and many other parameters, and the results are available in various formats like I-V, C-V graphs, band diagrams, etc. It can simulate any device with up to 7 layers and can also study the influence of interfacial layers which are crucial in carrier recombination within a thin film solar cell. SCAPS simulation uses the Poisson equation and the Charge Carrier equations in the semiconductor carrier mechanism[11],[12] as given from (1-5). Here, the electric potential is denoted by Ψ, n represents the elementary electronic charge, ε represents the dielectric constant, electron and hole concentration represented by e and h, the current density of both carriers represented by $\int_n$ and $\int_p$, rate of carrier production as C_G and rate of carrier recombination as C_R, N_d and P_d are electron and hole diffusion coefficients while the electron and hole mobilities are represented as m_n and m_p respectively.

In this work, we varied the carrier density of the ZrS_2 layer and the intrinsic Al-ZnO thickness. The effect on the device performance due to the variation in the ambient operating temperature was also investigated.

$$\frac{\partial^2\Psi}{\partial x^2} = \frac{n}{\varepsilon}(e-h) \quad (1)$$

$$\frac{\partial e}{\partial t} = \frac{1}{n}\frac{\partial \int_n}{\partial x} + (C_G - C_R) \quad (2)$$

$$\frac{\partial h}{\partial t} = -\frac{1}{n}\frac{\partial \int_p}{\partial x} + (C_G - C_R) \quad (3)$$

$$\int_n = nN_d\frac{\partial e}{\partial x} - nm_n e\frac{\partial \Psi}{\partial x} \quad (4)$$

$$\int_p = -nP_d\frac{\partial h}{\partial x} - nm_p h\frac{\partial \Psi}{\partial x} \quad (5)$$

The proposed device here is Al-doped ZnO(AZO)/ZrS_2/CZTSSe/Mo as shown in Figure 1. The incident radiation falls on the molybdenum top electrodes to the absorber layer which is the CZTSSe where then, electron hole pairs are generated. Then we have the buffer layer ZrS2 to facilitate the flow of charge carriers to the opposite electrodes. The buffer layer is capped by a window layer, which is the ZnO layer. This window layer corrects the band alignment and ensures the smooth flow of carriers to the respective electrodes. An AM1.5 spectrum was used for illuminating the device and light power of $1000 W/m^2$. The shunt and series resistances were kept fixed at 1000 Ω and 1.5Ω, respectively during the entire simulation. The values of various parameters of the devices are taken from already reported works[13],[14],[15],[16],[17] and a few by reasonable assumptions as listed in Table 1

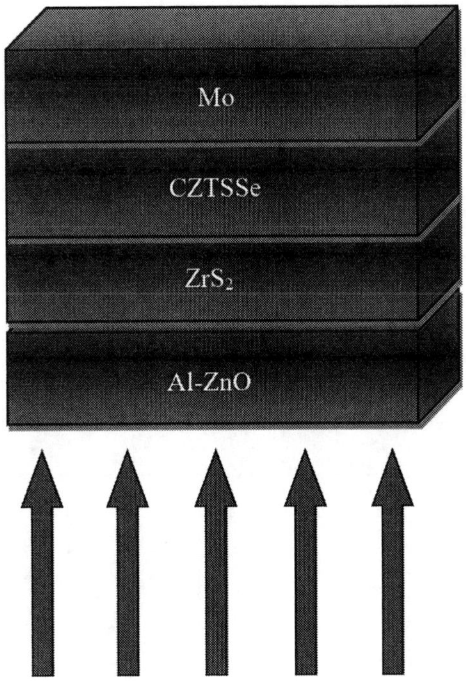

Figure 1. Device structure

Table 1. Simulation parameters of each material used

Parameters	CZTSSe	ZrS_2	Al-ZnO
Thickness(μm)[14]	0.2-2	0.1	0.03-0.07
ε_r[14]	13.6	16.4	9
μ_n(cm^2/Vs)[14]	300	2300	100
μ_h(cm^2/Vs)[14]	30	1300	25
N_A(cm^{-3})[14]	10^{12}-10^{18}	0	0
N_D(cm^{-3})[14]	0	10^{12}-10^{16}	10^{18}
E_g(eV)[14]	1.5	1.2	3.3
CB DOS(cm^{-3})	2.2×10^{19}	2.2×10^{18}	2.2×10^{18}
VB DOS(cm^{-3})	1.8×10^{19}	1.8×10^{19}	1.8×10^{19}
V_h(cm/s)[14]	1×10^7	1×10^7	1×10^7
V_n(cm/s[14])	1×10^7	1×10^7	1×10^7
χ(eV)[14]	4.5	4.7	4.6

IOP Conf. Series: Materials Science and Engineering 1263 (2022) 012005 doi:10.1088/1757-899X/1263/1/012005

3. Results and discussion

3.1. Change of ambient Temperature

A solar cell is strictly an outdoor functioning device and hence the ambient temperature has a critical role in their working. Here we have changed the operating temperature from 300K to 500K and evaluated the changes in various parameters. Figure 2 indicates that, with the increase in temperature all the optoelectrical parameters of the device declined steadily. Consider the efficiency of the device which drastically decreased from 23.4 % at 300K to only 9.8% at 500K. The increase in energy might disrupt the band gap and makes it narrow. This increases the internal recombination rate of charge carriers, preventing them from reaching the electrodes and thereby reducing the device efficiency.

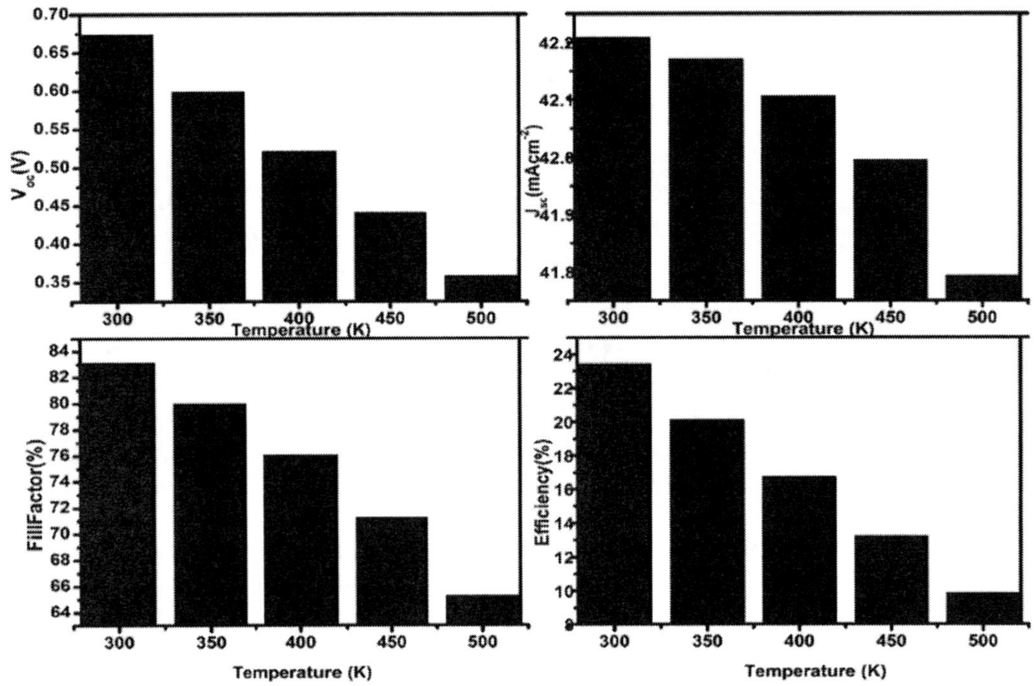

Figure 2. Variation of photovoltaic parameters with change in temperature

3.2 Variation of Carrier Density doping

The electrical properties of the device can be altered by doping the layers. In this study, We changed the ZrS_2 layer's carrier density from 10^{12} cm^{-3} to 10^{16} cm^{-3}.And as shown in Figure 3 most of the photovoltaic parameters had little effect on the change in carrier density of the ZrS_2 layer. The Voc, FillFactor and Efficiency remained fairly at 0.67 V, 83%, and 23% respectively. But the J_{SC} value slightly increased from 41 $mAcm^{-2}$ to 42 $mAcm^{-2}$.With the increase in buffer layer carrier density, the number of ionized free electrons increases, which favors the current density.

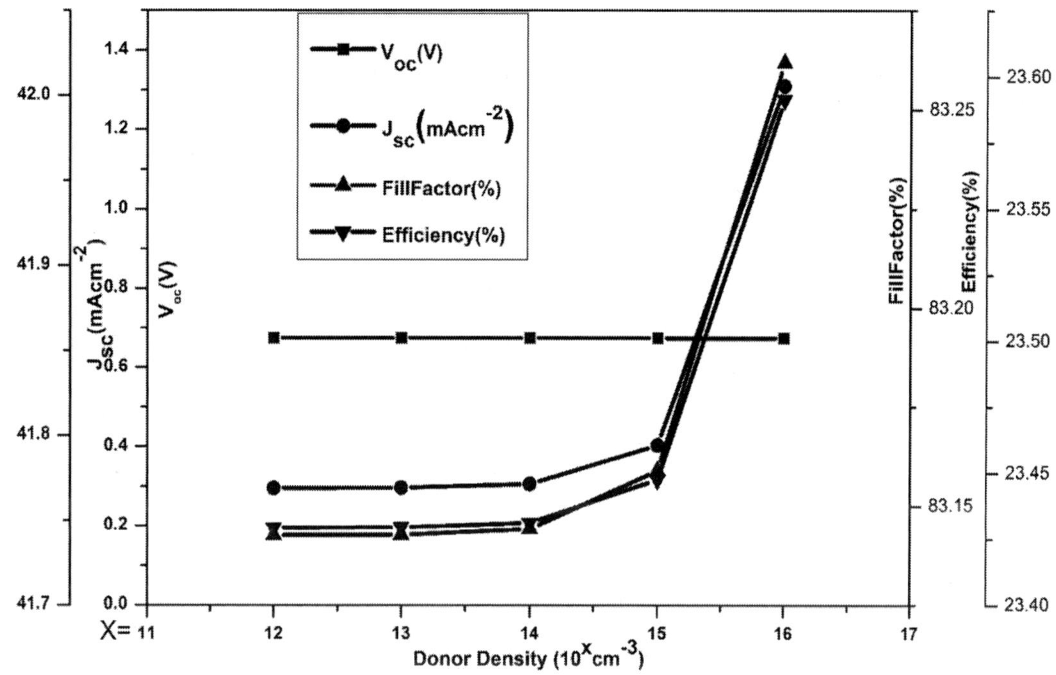

Figure 3. Variation of photovoltaic parameters with change in donor density of ZrS_2 layer

3.3 Variation of the Thickness of Intrinsic layer

The intrinsic ZnO layer channel the carriers to the electrodes. By altering the thickness from 30 nm to 70 nm, its effect on the parameters was studied. And as expected there was a reduction in current density from 41.81 $mAcm^{-2}$ to 41.77 $mAcm^{-2}$ along with the efficiency of the device as the thickness of the ZnO intrinsic layer increased. The carriers have to travel more distance to reach the electrodes when the thickness increases and it will undergo recombination in between, reducing the actual number of electrons reaching the active region. This cause the current density and efficiency to decrease, as clearly indicated in Figure 4.

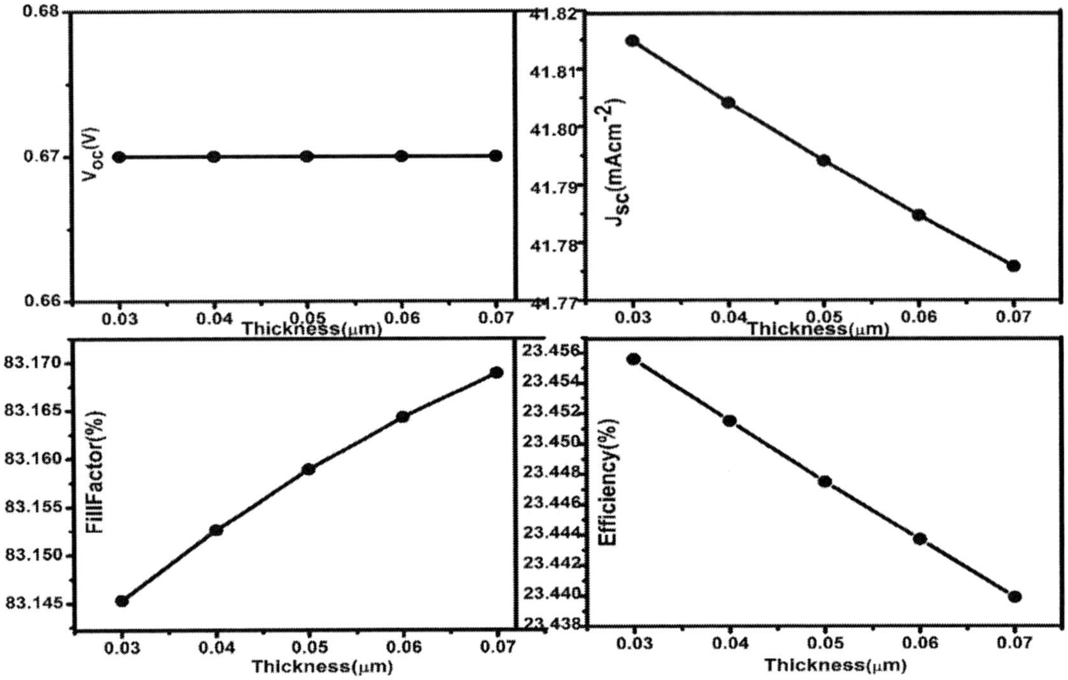

Figure 4. Effect of photovoltaic parameters with change in thickness of the intrinsic layer

4. Conclusions

In the present work, the simulation package, SCAPS- 1D was utilised to find out the feasibility of utilising a novel buffer layer, ZrS_2 for CZTSSe based photovoltaic devices and thereby aim to reduce the use of toxic materials for buffer layers. The numerical study was carried out on the device structure Al-ZnO/ZrS_2/CZTSSe/Mo and the various parameters were varied. From the results, it was concluded that the optimum carrier density of ZrS_2 was $10^{16}cm^{-3}$. The ZnO thickness of 30 nm was found best for the working of the proposed device and the ideal operating temperature for the device was 300K beyond which the output parameters declined rapidly. From the results obtained it can be safely conclude that ZrS_2 is undoubtedly an excellent substitute for the toxic Cd, In based buffer layers for solar cells with CZTSSe as the absorber layer.

References

[1] Ramasamy K, Malik M A and O'Brien P 2012 Routes to copper zinc tin sulfide Cu2ZnSnS4 a potential material for solar cells *Chem. Commun.* **48** 5703

[2] Hirai Y, Hidaka Y, Kurokawa Y and Yamada A 2012 Improvement of the Band Profile of Cu(In,Ga)Se2 Solar Cells with High-Ga Content Prepared Using a Five-Stage Method *Jpn. J. Appl. Phys.* **51** 10NC03

[3] Altamura G and Vidal J 2016 Impact of Minor Phases on the Performances of CZTSSe Thin-Film Solar Cells *Chem. Mater.* **28** 3540–63

[4] Wang W, Winkler M T, Gunawan O, Gokmen T, Todorov T K, Zhu Y and Mitzi D B 2014 Device Characteristics of CZTSSe Thin-Film Solar Cells with 12.6% Efficiency *Adv. Energy Mater.* **4** 1301465

[5] Winkler M T, Wang W, Gunawan O, Hovel H J, Todorov T K and Mitzi D B 2014 Optical designs that improve the efficiency of $Cu_2ZnSn(S,Se)_4$ solar cells *Energy Environ. Sci.* **7** 1029–36

[6] Shockley W and Queisser H J 1961 Detailed Balance Limit of Efficiency of p-n Junction Solar Cells *Journal of Applied Physics* **32** 510–9

[7] Anon Optoeletronic investigation of Cu2ZnSn(S,Se)4 thin-films & Cu2ZnSn(S,Se)4/CdS interface with scanning probe microscopy | SpringerLink

[8] Burgelman M, Nollet P and Degrave S 2000 Modelling polycrystalline semiconductor solar cells *Thin Solid Films* **361–362** 527–32

[9] Ouédraogo S, Zougmoré F and Ndjaka J M 2013 Numerical Analysis of Copper-Indium-Gallium-Diselenide-Based Solar Cells by SCAPS-1D *International Journal of Photoenergy* **2013** e421076

[10] Burgelman M, Verschraegen J, Degrave S and Nollet P 2004 Modeling thin-film PV devices *Prog. Photovolt: Res. Appl.* **12** 143–53

[11] Mostefaoui M, Mazari H, Khelifi S, Bouraiou A and Dabou R 2015 Simulation of High Efficiency CIGS Solar Cells with SCAPS-1D Software *Energy Procedia* **74** 736–44

[12] Anon SCAPS manual most recent.pdf

[13] Zhang W-C, Tang J-Y, Niu Y-H, Huang R, Chen L and Jiang M-Y 2021 Study the best ratio of S and Se in CZTSSe solar cells with nontoxic buffer layer *Journal of Renewable and Sustainable Energy* **13** 033701

[14] Moustafa M, Al Zoubi T and Yasin S 2022 Exploration of CZTS-based solar using the ZrS2 as a novel buffer layer by SCAPS simulation *Optical Materials* **124** 112001

[15] Benzetta A E, Abderrezek M and Djeghlal M E 2021 Numerical study of CZTS/CZTSSe tandem thin film solar cell using SCAPS-1D *Optik* **242** 167320

[16] Et-taya L, Benami A and Ouslimane T 2022 Study of CZTSSe-Based Solar Cells with Different ETMs by SCAPS *Sustainability* **14** 1916

[17] Minbashi M, Omrani M K, Memarian N and Kim D-H 2017 Comparison of theoretical and experimental results for band-gap-graded CZTSSe solar cell *Current Applied Physics* **17** 1238–43

IOP Conf. Series: Materials Science and Engineering 1263 (2022) 012006 doi:10.1088/1757-899X/1263/1/012006

Photoluminescence study of reddish orange emitting Eu^{3+} activated $LaPO_4$ Nanoparticles via hydrothermal method

Aswathy R Chandran[1]*, Linju Ann Jacob [2], Issac Paul [1], Gijo Jose[1]

[1] Department of Physics, SB College ,Changanacherry., Kottayam, 686101,India.
[2].Department of Physics, Baselius college, Kottayam,686001,India
*Corresponding author: Mobile : +917736139023;E-mail: asu.achu@gmail.com

Abstract : Lanthanum phosphate ($LaPO_4$) belongs to the family of rare earth phosphates characterized as a fluorescence material. Europium ion is known for its orange –red fluorescence. In order to include orange –red fluorescence for pure white light generation we are doping $LaPO_4$ with Eu^{3+}. The crystalline planes are identified from the XRD pattern show that the particles have monoclinic structure with pure $LaPO_4$. The addition of sodium ions to the $LaPO_4$: Eu^{3+} sample it is found that the luminescence property gets increased. It is also found that reversal of the emission spectrum intensity takes place for the sodium doped sample which indicates that Eu^{3+} ions are located in a highly symmetric environment.

1. Introduction

Rare earth activated phosphates have gained significant attention in the fields of application based glasses, laser application [1,2], fluorescent lamps[3,4], plasma display panels[4,5] as well as electrical conductivity application [6]. In recent years, solid state lighting, solar energy application and magnetic materials [7] have been identified as potential area for rare earth activated phosphates. Phosphate ceramics owing to their exceptional thermal and chemical stability are identified as excellent host for rare earth doping that are highly demanding in the field of solid state lighting application. Rare earth activated phosphates can meet the immediate demands in the current scenario of science and technology such as less power consumption, eco-friendly ,appreciable efficient with long life time energy sources .These material can act as potential phosphor converted white light-emitting diodes (pc-WLEDs) which are regarded as the next generation of green light sources. [8-10].

Researchers have special interest to broaden the frequency range as well as introducing new colours that emitted from LED due to their high demand in various challenging fields such as security and forensic application. Inorganic phosphors are employed as a supplementary material to broaden the emission spectrum because the light emitted from LEDs is limited to a fairly small range of nanometer scale [11]. Due to the high stability of energy level transitions and a wide variety of emission wavelengths, many phosphors are doped with rare earth (RE) ions.

Lanthanum phosphate acts as an potential host for lanthanide ions, mainly terbium, cerium, and europium due to their similarity in ionic radii and chemical valency [12-14] .Due to their simplicity in processing into products with great screen coverage, high resolution, powerful emission, and extended service lives and spherical particles are preferred in phosphors .The most efficient method for producing nanosized phosphors with excellent morphology and uniform composition is the hydrothermal reaction method is the reason for selecting this synthesis method for our work [15].

2. Experimental section

$LaN_3O_9.6H_2O$ and $Eu(NO_3)_3.6H_2O$ were obtained from Sigma Aldrich and $(NaPO_3)_6$,citric acid and NaOH Pellet were obtained from CDH ,and all chemicals are of analytical grade.

2.1 Preparation method for Sample A

$LaN_3O_9.6H_2O$ and $Eu(NO_3)_3.6H_2O$ solutions were mixed with $(NaPO_3)_6$ solution , it was stirred for 2 hours, and placed in an air-tight Teflon jar, and heated at 180 °C for 24 hours in an oven (hydrothermal treatment). The obtained white precipitate were dried at 60°C and annealed at 900 °C for 2 hours.

2.2 Preparation method for Sample B

The preparation method of Sample B is same as that of Sample A, but here the obtained precipitate is centrifuged with distilled water for 5 times followed by washing with ethanol. The precipitate were dried at 60°C and annealed at 900°C for 2 hours.
Both obtained samples were powdered using agate mortar for further characterisation .

2.3 Characterization Technique

In order to find the crystalline nature and particle size of the sample, X-ray diffraction study was performed using X-ray diffractometer (PANalytical X-ray Diffractometer) with $Cu\ K\alpha$ radiation ($\lambda = 1.54$ Å) for 2θ ranging from 10° to 60°.The thermogravimetric analysis of the sample is obtained by using Shimadzu thermal analyser DT 40. The fluorescence properties were measured using Horiba fluoromax 4 spectrometer. The chemical composition of the sample were determined by using Energy Dispersive X-ray Spectrometry on Carl Zeiss EVO 18 Secondary Electron Microscope with EDS.

3. Results and discussion

TGA analysis curve of $LaPO_4$: Eu^{3+} (3 mol %) particles after annealing at 900 °C depicted in Figure 1.It is clear that the prepared sample is thermally stable up to 700°C. The phase purity of the sample can be verified by analysing XRD pattern for samples annealed at 450°C, 600°C and 900°C and are shown in Figure 2.This confirms that the formation of pure monoclinic phase of $LaPO_4$ happens at 900°C and we have selected 900°C as the annealing temperature for the preparation of the sample.

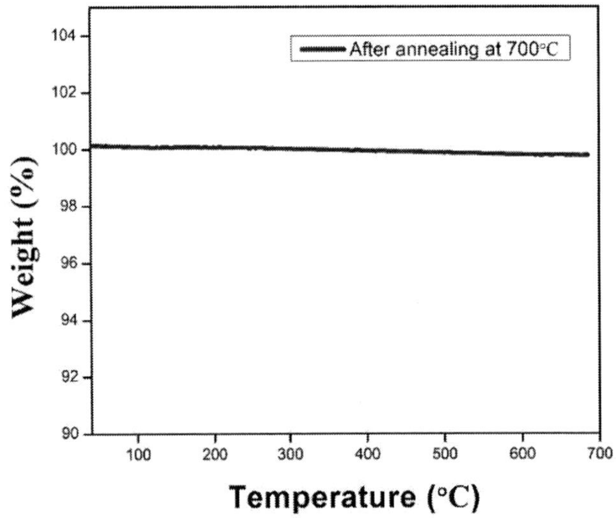

Figure :1 TGA Analysis of $LaPO_4$: Eu^{3+} (3 mol %) particles after annealing.

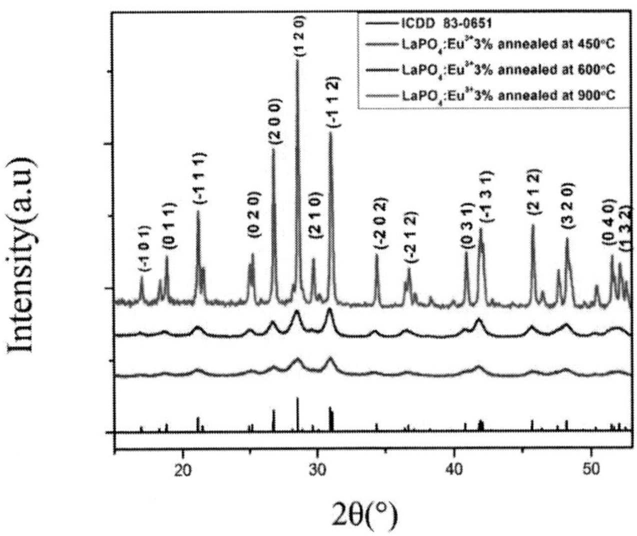

Figure :2 XRD pattern of $LaPO_4$: Eu^{3+} (3 mol %) at different temperatures

IOP Conf. Series: Materials Science and Engineering 1263 (2022) 012006 doi:10.1088/1757-899X/1263/1/012006

The XRD patterns of $LaPO_4$: Eu^{3+} (3 mol %)Sample A and $LaPO_4$: Eu^{3+} (3 mol %)Sample B along with the standard data for the monoclinic $LaPO_4$ are shown in Figure. 3.

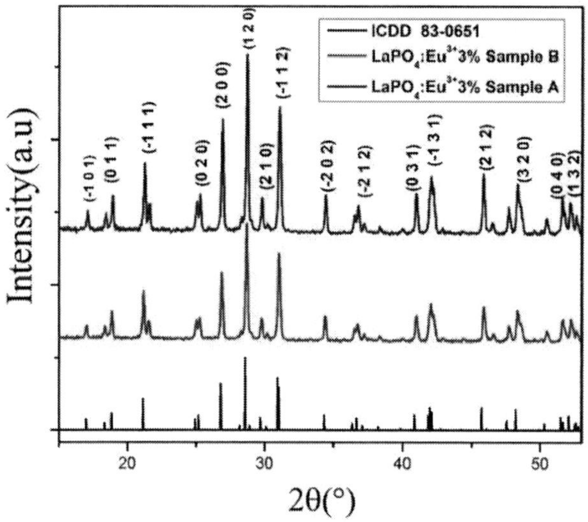

Figure :3 XRD pattern of $LaPO_4$: Eu^{3+} (3 mol %) Sample A and Sample B

In good accord with the literature, the diffraction patterns of the products can be matched with a pure monoclinic phase of $LaPO_4$ (ICDD card no. 83-0651). No considerable phase change is detected by the incorporation of Eu^{3+} ions into the host matrix .The results indicate that the hydrothermal method is a better alternative for the synthesis of $LaPO_4$ material .When comparing to those of pure $LaPO_4$,the diffraction peaks of $LaPO_4$: Eu^{3+} exhibit almost similar pattern , which may be caused by the negligible difference in ionic radii between Eu^{3+} and La^{3+} in the ninefold coordination of monoclinic structure [16]. The average crystallite size of the particle can be calculated using Debye-Scherrer formula

$$D=\frac{K\lambda}{\beta Cos\ \theta}$$

where K = 0.90, is a constant, λ is the wavelength of the X-ray, β and θ are the full width at half maxima (FWHM) and diffraction angle of the diffracted peaks, respectively [17].

The average crystallite size of the samples A and Sample B are 48.77nm and 23.04 nm respectively.

It is evident from the comparison of the intensity of diffraction patterns of samples A and Sample B in Figure 3. that the addition of Na^+ to $LaPO_4:Eu^{3+}$ enhance the crystallinity of sample A.

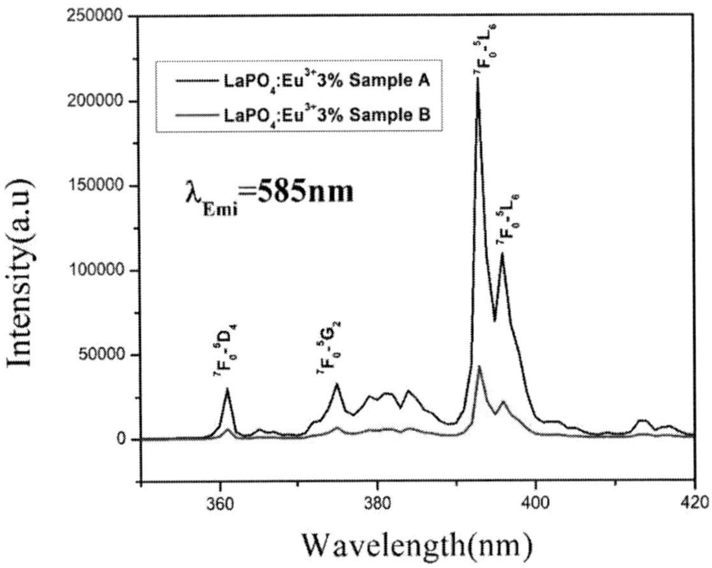

Figure 4: The excitation spectrum of $LaPO_4$: Eu^{3+} (3 mol %) particles

The photoluminescence excitation spectrum of 3 mol % Eu^{3+} doped $LaPO_4$ with and without Na^+ doped monitored at 585 nm is illustrated in the Figure 4. The spectrum consist of a set of sharp peaks ranging from 350 to 470 nm range .these peaks are attributed due to the direct f-f characteristics peaks of Eu^{3+} we have identifies peaks at 361 nm ,375 nm 393 nm and 396 nm due $^7F_0$-$^5D_4$, $^7F_0$-$^5G_2$, $^7F_0$-$^5L_6$,and $^7F_0$-$^5L_6$ respectively,among these 393 nm is the most prominent one .The photoluminescence emission spectrum of 3 mol % Eu^{3+} doped $LaPO_4$ monitored under 393 nm from 580 nm to 630 nm is depicted in the Figure 5. There are several sharp peaks at 586 nm, 591 nm and 593 nm corresponds to orange emission and 611 nm, 614 nm and 619 nm corresponding to red emission due to the characteristic emission of Eu^{3+}[18,19].Stark splitting of energy levels of Eu^{3+}under the strong crystal field accounts for the splitting of each emission peak in the emission spectra [20]. Among these emission peaks, the magnetic dipole transition $^5D_0$-$^7F_1$ (orange emission) is more intense comparing to the electric dipole transition $^5D_0$-$^7F_2$ (red emission) of the Eu^{3+} ions. Hence this matrix Eu^{3+} ions occupy inversion center sites, as $^5D_0$-$^7F_1$ transition should be relatively strong, while the $^5D_0$-$^7F_2$ transition should be relatively weak. The orange-red emission lines at around 586 nm-593 nm originating from the magnetic dipole transition $^5D_0$-$^7F_1$ are the dominant bands for the as-synthesized $LaPO_4$: Eu^{3+} nanocrystals. As stated by the Judd–Ofelt theory, electric dipole transition ($^5D_0$-$^7F_2$) is allowed only when rare earth occupied sites without an inversion centre [21].

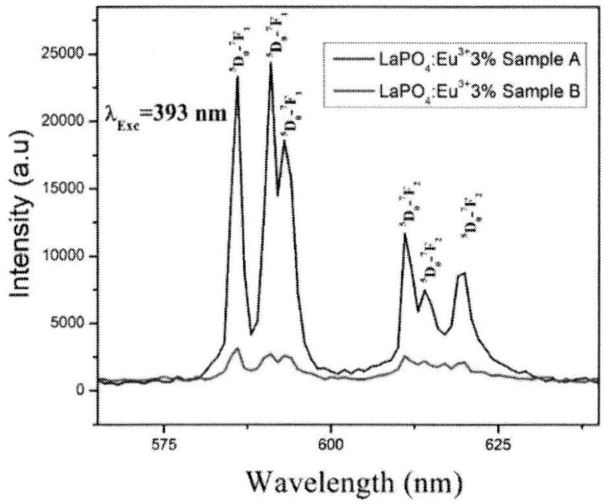

Figure 5: The Emission spectrum of $LaPO_4$: Eu^{3+} (3 mol %) particles

Figure 6 represents the energy level diagram of Eu^{3+} ion in $LaPO_4$ host matrix. The energy transfer mechanism can be studied with the help of this diagram .The molecule in the ground state of Eu^{3+} that is $^7F_0$ is excited to $^5L_6$ up on 393 nm excitation [22]. Then the molecule relax back to the excited state through non radiative emission, which is represented in the dotted lines in the diagram from which characteristic emission of Eu^{3+} triggered.

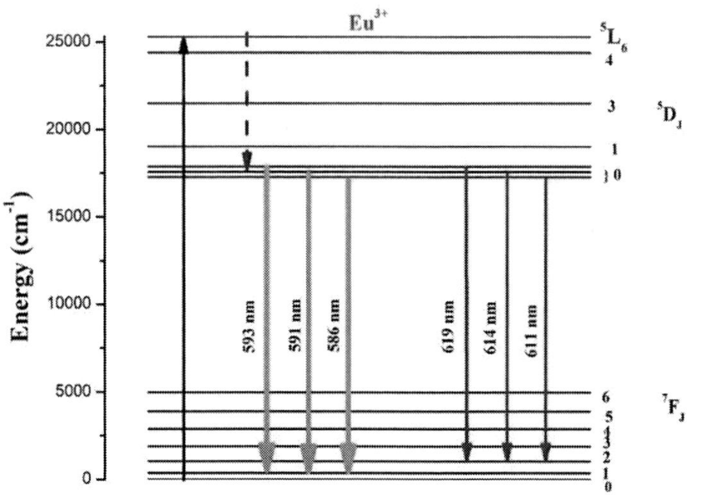

Figure 6: Schematic energy level diagram of $LaPO_4$: Eu^{3+} (3 mol %) particles

In this experiment characteristic peaks of $LaPO_4:Eu^{3+}$(3 mol %)Sample A is more intense than $LaPO_4:Eu^{3+}$ (3 mol %)Sample B because the presence of Na^+ in the $LaPO_4:Eu^{3+}$ (3 mol %) Sample A. The presence of Na^+ in Sample A was confirmed using EDS Spectrum as shown in Figure 7.

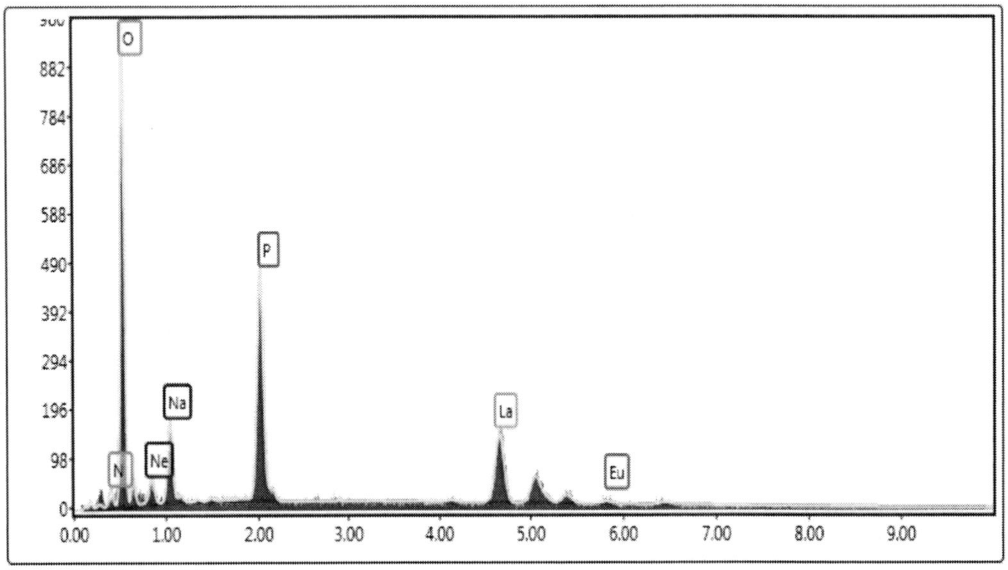

Figure 7: The EDS Spectrum of $LaPO_4$: Eu^{3+} (3 mol %) Sample A particles

The Commission Internationale de I'Eclairage (CIE) chromaticity coordinates of the emission colour of the phosphor using photoluminescence emission spectrum data of Sample A and Sample B under 393 nm excitation are calculated and indicated in the CIE diagram. Due to the presence of Na^+ in the sample A enhances the orange red emission compared with Sample B and this orange-red emission as shown in Figure 8.In the Figure 8, the photograh of sample excited under 393 nm is given in the inset. The CIE chromaticity coordinates for Sample A and Sample B are (0.5381,0.3874)and (0.4042,0.3706) respectively and the colour purity of the Sample A is increased from 32.5 %(colour purity of Sample B) to 77.8 % due to the presence of Na^+ ion in the Sample A.

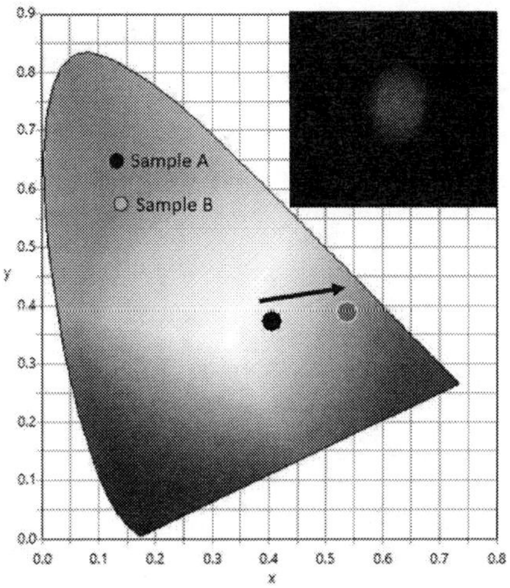

Figure 8.CIE of $LaPO_4$:Eu^{3+} (3 mol %) particles

4. Conclusion

The hydrothermal approach is found to be successful in preparing monoclinic $LaPO_4$:Eu^{3+}crystalline phosphors as inferred from X-Ray diffraction analysis. From thermogravimetic analysis of the prepared sample and the XRD pattern of the sample annealed at different temperature shows that the formation of monoclinic phase of $LaPO_4$ with purity occurs at 900°C. It is concluded that sample A (with Na^+) is more crystalline when comparing to that of Sample B (without Na^+). It is obvious that the addition of Na^+ to $LaPO_4$:Eu^{3+} enhances the crystallinity of the sample .The photoluminescence studies shows that Sample A nanophosphor emits the most intense reddish orange light comparing with that of Sample B .The excitation spectrum exhibits a narrow intense peak at 393 nm when monitored under 585 nm .The emission spectrum consist of sharp characteristics peaks of Eu^{3+} at orange and red region with splitting ,but orange emission is more intense compared to red emission unlike usually observed from that of other Eu^{3+} doped inorganic phosphors, since Eu^{3+} occupies the site with an inversion centre .The CIE chromaticity coordinates of the emission colour of Sample A and Sample B are computed and fall in the reddish orange region in the CIE diagram . The colour purity of the emission of the sample is found to be enhance due to the presence of Na^+ .This prepared sample is found to be an excellent candidate as phosphors for phosphor converted LED application as well as forensic and high security application.

References

[1] Stouwdam J W, Hebbink G A, Huskens J and Veggel F C J M van, Chem. Mater., 2003, 15: 4604.
[2] Albrand K R, Attig R, Fenner J, Jesser J P and Moot D. Res. Bull.,1974, 9: 129.
[3] Buissette V, Moreau M, Gacoin T, Boilot J P, Chane-Ching JY and Le Mercier T.Chem. Mater., 2004, 16: 3767.

[4] Kang Y C, Kim E J, Lee D Y and Park H D. 2002, 347: 266.
[5] Rao R P and Devine D J. 2000, 87-89: 1260.
[6] Kitamura N, Amezawa K, Tomii Y, and Yamamoto N. Solid State Ionics, 2003, 162-163: 161.
[7] Schüler D, Buchert M, Liu R, Dittrich S and Merz C. Report. Darmstadt: Öko-Institut eV; 2011. Deutsch
[8] G.B. Nair, H.C. Swart, S.J. Dhoble, and Prog. Mater. Sci. 109 (2020), 100622,
[9] B.A. Aswathy, P. Prabhakar Rao, and V.G. Suchithra, Mater. Lett. 229 (2018) 182–184.
[10] Y. Guo, B.K. Moon, B.C. Choi, J.H. Jeong, and J.H. Kim, Mater. Res. Bull. 88 (2017) 166–173
[11] Blasse, G. and Grabmaier, B. C. Luminescent Materials; Springer- Verlag: Berlin, 1994.
[12] Riwotzki, K.; Meyssamy, H.; Schnablegger, H.; Kornowski,A.; Haase and M. Angew. Chem., Int. Ed. 2001, 40, 573.
[13] D. Tu, W. Zheng and P. Huang, X. Chen, Chem. Rev. (2017) (in press),
[14]Vinitha Varkey, Aswathy R. Chandran, E. Tomlal Jose, Issac Paul and Gijo Jose, 2021, 47,921-926.
[15] Hiroaki Onoda and Takehiro Funamoto,2016,3,122-128
[16].L.A. Boatner, Rev. Mineral. Geochem. 48 (2002) 87–121
[17] A.L. Patterson, The scherrer formula for X-ray particle size determination, Phys. Rev. 56 (1939) 978–982. doi:10.1103/PhysRev.56.978.
[18] Jianzheng Li, Xuewen Xu, Ying Fan, Yangxian Li, Long Hu, and Chengchun Tang,2010,124, 1172-117
[19] Na Niu, Piaoping Yang, Yan Wang, Wenxin Wang, Fei He, Shili Gai and Dong Wang,2011,509, 3096-3102
[20]S. Sisira, Linju Ann Jacob, Kukku Thomas, Dinu Alexander, P.R. Biju, N.V. Unnikrishnan and Cyriac Joseph,2019,209,197-207
[21] YAN Ruo-xue, SUN Xiao-ming, WANG Xun, PENG Qing and LI Ya-dong. Chemistry A European Journal, 2005, 11(7): 2183-2195.
[22] W. T. Carnall, P. R. Fields, and K. Rajnak,1968,49

Photonic band gap analysis of 1D TiO_2/SiO_2 photonic crystals using plane wave method for thin film solar cell applications

Raghvendra Sarvjeet Dubey[1], M.V. Someswararao[2], and Sigamani Saravanan[3*]

[1,3*]Department of Nanotechnology, Swarnandhra College of Engineering & Technology, Narsapur-534 280, West Godavari (AP), India
[2]Department of Physics, SRKR Engineering College, Bhimavaram (A.P.), India

*Correspondsing Author: shasa86@gmail.com

Abstract. The properties of photonic crystals that allow or inhibit the propagation of electromagnetic (EM) waves in between photonic band gap (PBG) regimes have proved to be significant. In this work, we investigated the PBG analysis of one-dimensional TiO_2/SiO_2 photonic crystal using plane wave method (PWM). The PBG width depends of on the various optical parameters such as lattice constant (Λ), center wavelength (λc), thickness of the layers (d), dielectric constant (ε) and refractive indices (n). Among various parameters, the center wavelength (300-1100nm), the thickness of TiO_2 (28-103 nm) and SiO_2 (51-189 nm) layers were optimized for the tuned bandgap. The obtained results revealed that the PBG shifting towards the lower frequency region and reducing the size due to the increment of center wavelength and thicknesses. This result is useful for the understanding the way of photon propagation within artificial structure and it could be possible for the better back reflector in thin film solar cells.

1. Introduction

Photonic crystals (PCs) are being demanded in nanophotonics, optoelectronic devices etc [1-2]. The PC structure consists of two periodic refractive indices or dielectric constant materials can possess a photonic band gap (PBG). The PCs can be divided by one- (1D), two- (2D) and three-dimensional (3D) structures. It possesses PBGs in which no photon states can exist, so that the light propagation allowed even at the sharp bending with very low loss. Nowadays, various computational methods are developed for designing of these 1D, 2D and 3D photonic crystal structures [3]. The one-dimensional photonic crystals (1DPCs) also known as DBR layers. Among the various computational methods, the plane wave method is well-suited and refers to solving electromagnetic (EM) issues using Maxwell's equations. The plane wave method is an efficient approach for the calculation of transverse electric and transverse magnetic polarization (modes) of such periodic structures [4]. This method has successfully applied in a broad range of problems, such as scattering from metal objects and semiconductor devices, antennas, micro-strip circuits, EM absorption (%) in the human body exposed to radiation etc. The PCs are found suitable for the improvement of light absorption in thin film solar cells (TFSCs). The manipulations of the photons are well discussed in the literature [5]. Jalali demonstrated the impact of distributed Bragg's reflector (DBR) as a back-end reflector in thin film c-Si solar cells. The author reported an improved light scattering in the shorter wavelength due to DBR and nanograting which helped in the enhancement of light absorption in the longer spectral region [6]. Tavanbakhsh et al. proposed thin-film Si solar cells integrated with a DBR-in-grating back reflector. The explored the tuning of refractive index, which is important to achieve broad reflectance bands. They achieved 22.04% cell efficiency using a DBR-in-gratings as back side reflector integrated thin film Si solar cells [7]. Heidarzadeh et al. studied the optical performance of ultra-thin Si solar cells using a DBR and nanogratings. The light path length was enhanced within the absorber region by using the DBR. They reported 20% of cell efficiency from 3 μm thick Si solar cells [8]. Gevorkian et al. theoretically presented the light transport of 1D diluted photonic crystal. They investigated the straightening light effect in the visible spectral region and observed the highest absorption efficiency in solar cells. It depends of polarization conditions (s and p) and s-polarized light reflected for different incident angles of light [9]. Lu et al. theoretically and experimentally investigated an angle dependent omnidirectional PBG using 1DPCs of comprised hyperbolic metamaterials HfO_2 and Ag. The frequency range enhanced due to the incident angle materials and showed red-shifting. The experimental results were found in better agreement alongwith the simulated results and fabricated nanostructures were useful for photonic devices [10]. Saravanan and Dubey fabricated the TiO_2/SiO_2 multilayer structure using sol-gel spin-coater and suggested for TFSC applications. The broader obtained while red-shifting was noticed due to the increment of the number of alternative dielectric layers (5, 7, 9 and 11) [11]. Normani et al. Presented a design of 1D SiO_2/TiO_2 photonic crystals for the low-cost calorimetric and ratiometric refractive index (RI) sensing applications. They studied the sensitivity of distributed Bragg reflector (DBR) consisting of two- to five- alternative SiO_2/TiO_2 stacks. Finally, the two stacks based 1D photonic crystals exhibited the highest sensitivity and showed the ratio of reflectance intensity in between 1st and 3rd order reflectance for better ratiometric parameters. Finally, they suggested the potential application in fabricating a portable device for environmental detections [12]. Segovia-Chaves et al. theoretically calculated the PBG structure for DBR pillar made up of GaAs in the air medium by using guided mode expansion (GME) method. The optical performance of the designed structure was investigated by considering the dielectric constant (ε) of GaAs on the applied hydrostatic pressure. The PBG decrement was noticed by enhancing the hydrostatic pressure due to that band gap was found shifted towards higher frequency [13]. Deparis and Daif reported the optimization of 1D DBR (a-Si/TCO) structures using the transfer matrix method (TMM). They reported about 10% enhancement in current density, which was attributed to the integrated DBR [14].

In this work, our primary aim is to calculate the PBG of four SiO_2/TiO_2 multilayers by varying center wavelength and the thickness of the DBR layers using the plane wave method. The designing parameters and theoretical model are explained in section 2 and the obtained results are discussed in section 3. Finally, concluded the present work in section 4.

2. Designing approach

The plane wave method (PWM) is the best choice to analyze the band structures of 1D, 2D and 3D photonic crystals for TE and TM polarization conditions. The photonic crystals are well proven in their capability to tune the propagation of electromagnetic waves (EM). In plane waves, confinement of light can be done by choosing the highest refractive index contrast. The work of Yablonovitch and John on such structures claimed the existence of forbidden bands which prohibits the propagation of light [15-16]. This phenomenon yields the PBG (PBG). The PBG strongly dependents on various parameters, such as thickness (d), refractive index (n), period (Λ) etc. The schematic diagram of 1DPC (or DBR) structure is shown in Figure 1. The photonic band structures are designed to exhibit a high reflectance at assumed wavelengths. Here, 'n_1' and 'n_2' are the refractive index of the SiO_2 and TiO_2 materials. These materials have low- and high refractive index. The choice of these materials refractive indices of the selected materials are defined as,

$$n_i = \frac{\gamma\lambda}{4\pi} \qquad (1)$$

Where, 'λ' is the wavelength and 'γ' is the total exponential loss coefficient. The DBRs consists of SiO_2 layer with the refractive index of n_1=1.45 and another thin film layer of TiO_2 having its refractive index n_2=2.65. Here, the air was considered as the background materials with its refractive index of '1'. The periodic layers are arranged alternately.

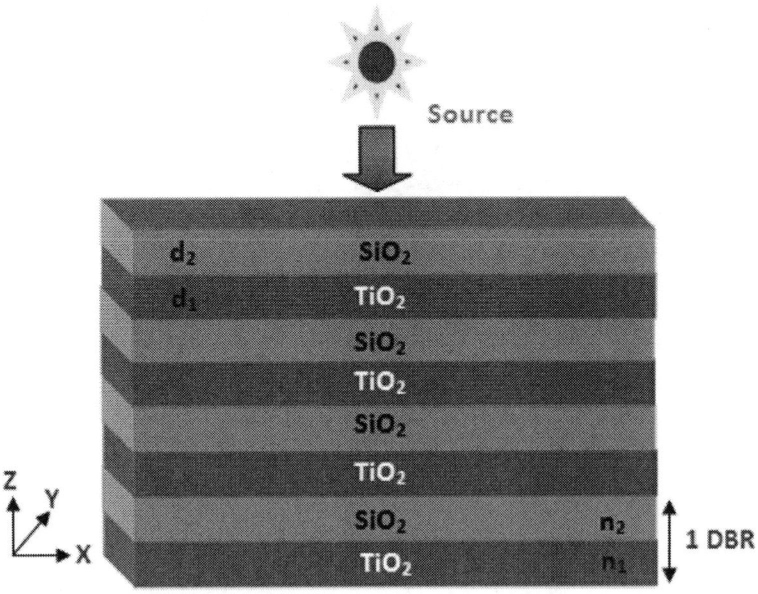

Fig.1 The illustration of 1D of TiO_2/SiO_2 photonic crystals.

Table 1. Optical and structural parameters of 1D TiO_2/SiO_2 photonic crystals

S.N.	Center Wavelength, λc (nm)	DBR Layers		Period, Λ (nm)
		TiO_2 d_1 (nm)	SiO_2 d_2 (nm)	
1	300	28	51	79
2	350	33	60	93
3	400	37	68	105
4	450	42	77	119
5	500	47	86	133
6	550	51	94	145
7	600	56	103	159
8	650	61	112	173
9	700	66	120	186
10	750	70	129	199
11	800	75	138	213
12	1050	99	181	280
13	1100	103	189	292

Further, the thickness of the selected layer calculated using quarter wavelength formula,

$$d_i = \frac{\lambda_c}{4n} \qquad (2)$$

Where, 'λc' is the center wavelength, 'n' is the refractive indices of the selected materials. The lattice constant is an important parameter to tune the PBG. The lattice constant can defined as the thickness of each dielectric layer as shown here.

$$\Lambda = d_1+d_2 \qquad (3)$$

Where, 'd_1'and 'd_2' are the thicknesses of the SiO_2 and TiO_2 materials. The calculated thicknesses of the layers and center wavelengths are as tabulated in Table-1.

3. Results and Discussion

In the proposed designed and periodically arranged 4DBR structures of TiO_2 and SiO_2 layers investigated by PWM. Figure 2 shows the four DBR structures of the SiO_2/TiO_2 materials with refractive indices including the dielectric constant.

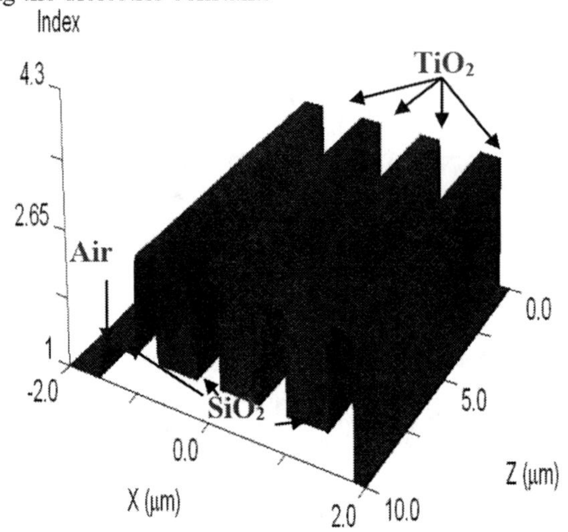

Fig. 2 The refractive index profile of the photonic crystals multilayers and air medium.

Figure 2 shows the four DBR structures of the TiO_2, SiO_2 materials with corresponding refractive indices. The four alternative layers periodically arranged in the X-direction, it shows the refractive index variation of the corresponding materials. Further, the bar diagram shows the refractive index of TiO_2 (n_{TiO2}=2.65), and SiO_2 (n_{SiO2}=1.45) along with the background air medium (n_{air}=1). Each layer, followed the same optical properties such as thickness, refractive index, and period, according to the equations (1)-(3). The one-dimensional photonic crystals also called as DBR layers have capable to propagate photons within the photonic crystals like electrons in the semiconductor materials.

Initially, the DBR layer thickness is considered as 28 (TiO_2) and 51 nm (SiO_2) with lattice constant of 79 nm under 300 nm center wavelength (λc). Finally designed 4DBR layers and calculated the width of PBG as 165 nm within the frequency range (f) of 300 to 465 nm as shown in Figure 3(a). This PBG is created in photonic crystals like the electronic band gap in semiconductor materials. Next, DBR thickness varied as 33 nm (TiO_2) and 60 nm (SiO_2) with the center wavelength of 350 nm (λc). The simulated results showed the PBG from the frequency range of 295 to 450 nm. The total PBG calculated as 155 nm, which was reduced and shifted to the lower frequency region as depicts in Figure 3(b) [18]. Consequently, the PBG is created within the 4DBR layers under various center wavelengths such as 400, 450, 500 and 550 nm as depicted in Figure 3(c) -(f). With the effect of incident wavelengths, the PBG size reduced (125, 120 & 100 nm) and shifted to the lower frequency region. The incident light energy is expected to be totally reflected and DBR layers act as a high reflectance for the incident wave. Similarly, Joannopoulos et al. reported that the PBG of the DBR layers is able to control (tune) light with the spontaneous emission [19]. Furthermore, we extended and studied the PBG of different center wavelengths such as 600, 650, 700, 750 and 800 nm as depicted in Figure 4(a) -(e). The calculated band gap varies (85, 65, 60, 45 and 35 nm) and is reduced gradually due to the thickness and incident wavelength as tabulated in Table 2.

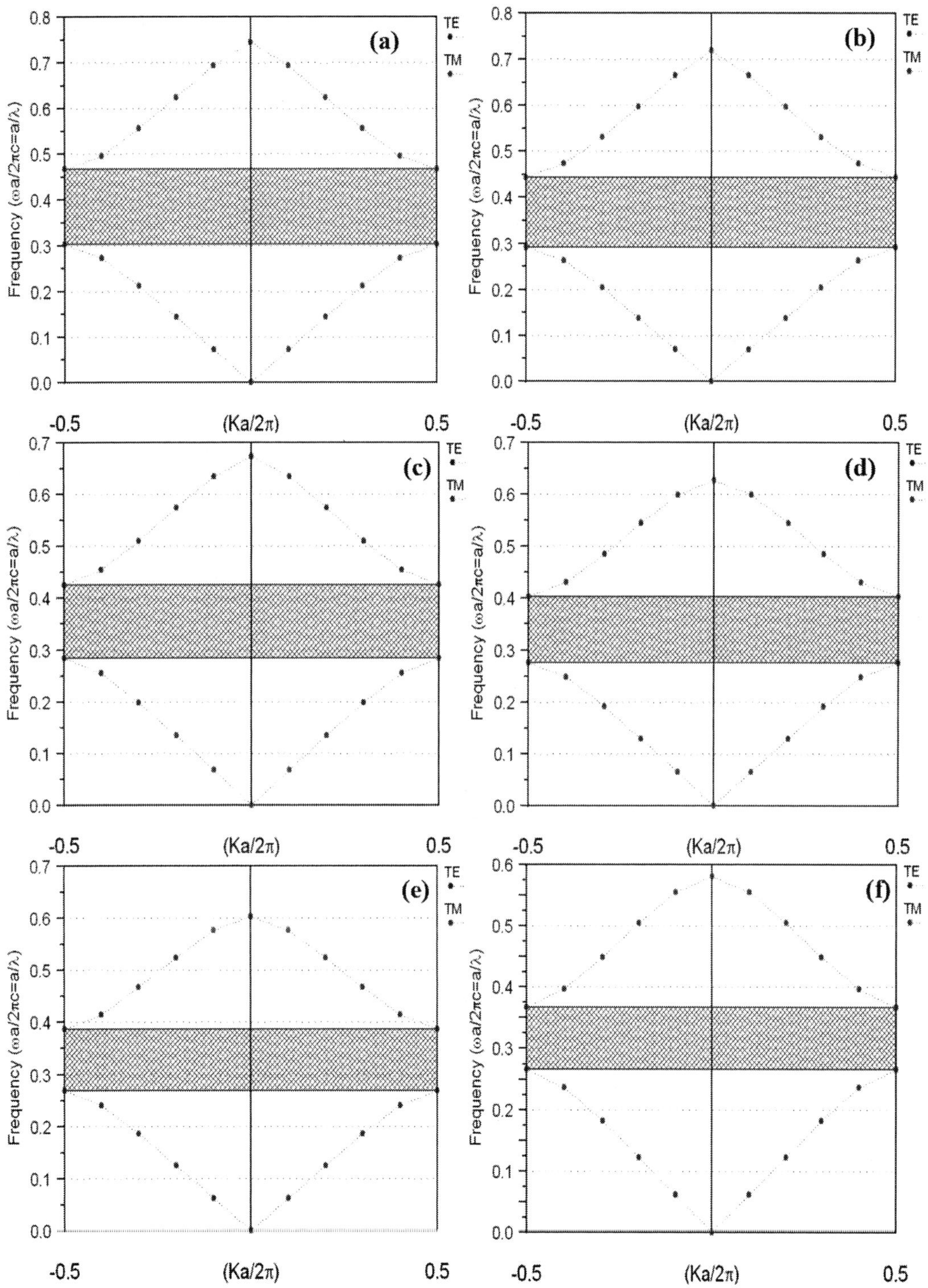

Fig. 3. The PBGs of TiO_2/SiO_2 1DPCs at various center wavelengths.

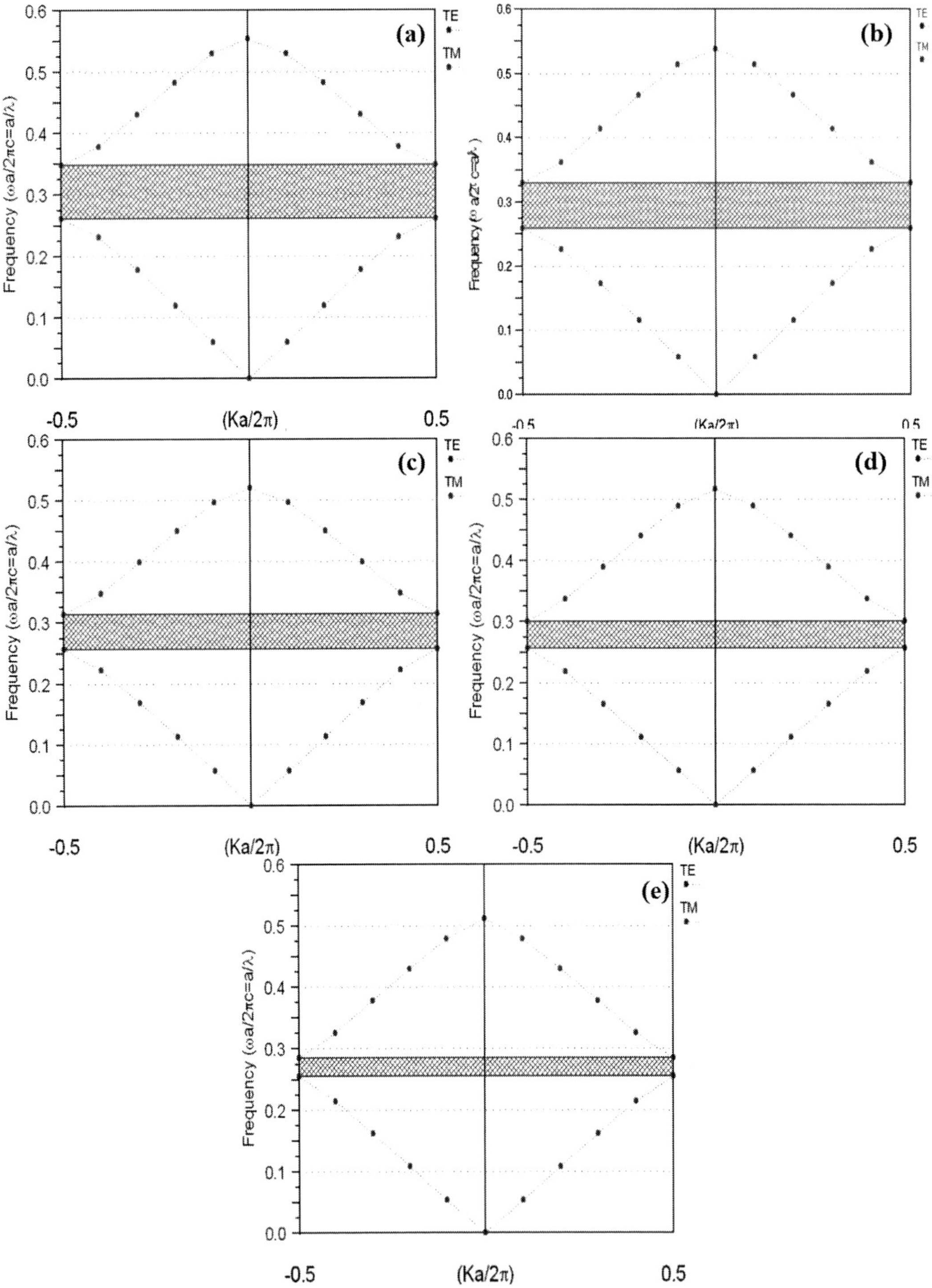

Fig. 4. The PBGs of TiO_2/SiO_2 1DPCs at various center wavelengths.

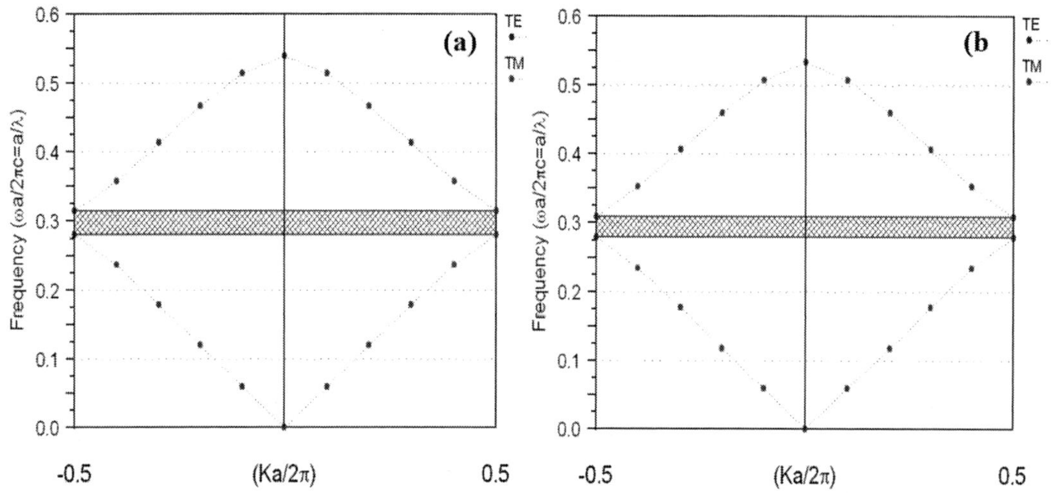

Fig. 5. The PBGs of TiO_2/SiO_2 1DPCs at center wavelengths (a) 1050 and (b) 1100 nm).

Zou et al. proposed 10DBR (a-Si/Si) layers and optimized the thickness. They found DBR layer thickness increases, the parasitic losses suppressed and short-circuit current increased up to 3.7 mA/cm^2 in thin film Si solar cells [20]. Similarly, Sheng et al. investigated the optical performance of 1DPCs (DBR, a-Si/SiO_2) integrated as back reflector thin film Si solar cells with the center wavelength of 800 nm (λc) and period (Λ=194 nm). They achieved 2.95 mA/cm^2 current density due to the influence of five DBR layers used as back reflector [21].

Table 2. Calculated the PBG values for various center wavelengths.

S.N.	λc (nm)	PBG f1 (nm)	PBG f2 (nm)	PBG (nm)
1	300	300	465	165
2	350	295	450	155
3	400	285	425	140
4	450	280	405	125
5	500	270	390	120
6	550	270	370	100
7	600	265	350	85
8	650	260	325	65
9	700	260	320	60
10	750	255	300	45
11	800	250	285	35
12	1050	280	315	35
13	1100	280	310	30

In the continuation of this band gap analysis, Figure 5(a) -(b) represents the infrared region of two different center wavelengths such as 1050 and 1100 nm considered and calculated the width of the total band gap as 35 and 30 nm (Table 2). These DBR layers helped to enhance reflectivity and overall enhanced optical performance in thin film Si solar cells as reported by Kuo-Hai Yang and Jaw-Yen Yang [22]. This theoretical investigation focused on the PBG of DBR layers. The practical realization of a DBR could be fabricated by diverse experimental techniques such as sol-gel spin-coating, dip-coating, sputtering, radio-frequency magnetron sputtering, plasma-enhanced chemical vapor deposition (PECVD), e-beam evaporation [23-27]. Although, the fact that the thin TiO_2/SiO_2 layers foreseen were really thin this ensures the highest collection of charge carriers for improved cell efficiency. But, the optical performance, decreased when the thickness of the layers beyond 100 nm due to the lower life time of the carriers [14].

4. Conclusion

In summary, the PBG of 1D TiO_2/SiO_2 photonic crystals investigated using plane wave method. The center wavelength (from 300 to 1200 nm) and thickness of the DBR layers were optimized. As the center wavelength at the ultraviolet region (300-400nm) and reduced thickness of DBR were shown the broader PBG (140-165nm). However, the visible (700-900 nm) and infrared (900-1100 nm) spectral region received reduced PBG thickness (30-125 nm) and shifting towards the lower frequency region. Moreover, the simulated results showed the optimal PBG structures which will be useful and integrated as a better back-end reflector in thin film solar cells.

References

[1] Basu Mallick S., Sergeant N.P., Agrawal M. Lee J.Y., Peumans P. Coherent light trapping in thin-film photovoltaics. *MRS Bull.*, 2011, **36**, 453-460.
[2] Hervé Rigneault, Jean-Michel Lourtioz, Claude Delalande, Nanophotonics, *Intech Open,* 2010, 1, 17-84.
[3] Dubey R.S., Gautam D.K. Development of simulation tools to study optical properties of one-dimensional photonic crystals. *J. Electromagnet. Waves Appl.*, 2008, **22** (5-6), 849-860.
[4] Liliana P., Mona M. Dimensional Analysis of the Photonic Crystals. *U.P.B Sci. Bull. Series A,* 2008, **70** (4), 15-20.
[5] Zeng L., Bermel P., Yi Y., Alamariu B., Broderick K., Liu J., Hong C., Duan X., Joannopoulos J., Kimerling L. Demonstration of enhanced absorption in thin film si solar cells with textured photonic crystal back reflector. *Appl. Phys. Lett.*, 2008, **93**, 221105.
[6] Jalali T. Impact of one-dimensional photonic crystal back reflector in thin-film c-si solar cells on efficiency. Appl. Phys. A, 2018, **124**, 370.
[7] Tavanbakhsh A., Bahrami A., Dehdast M., Amirkhan S. A novel optimized multilayer back reflector for solar applications.*Chin. J. Phys.*, 2015, **53** (5), 100502-1-8.
[8] Heidarzadeh H., Tavousi A. Performance enhancement methods of an ultra-thin Si solar cell using different shapes of back grating and angle of incident light.*Materials Science & Engineering B,* 2019, **240**, 1-6.
[9] Gevorkian Z., Gasparian V., Cuevas E. Straightening of light in a one dimensional dilute photonic crystal. *Sci. Rep.,* 2019, **9**, 14053-1-6.
[10] Lu G., Zhou X., Zhao Y., Zhang K., Zhou H., Li J., Diao C., Liu F., Wu A. Du G. Omnidirectional photonic bandgap in one-dimensional photonic crystals containing hyperbolic metamaterials. *Opt. Express,* 2021, **29** (20/27), 31915-31923.
[11] Saravanan S., Dubey R.S. Fabrication, characterization of TiO_2/SiO_2 multilayers using sol-gel spin coating method. *Nanosyst: Phys Chem Math.*, 2019, **10** (1), 63-69.
[12] Normani S., Vedova N.D., Lanzani G., Scotognella F., Paterno G.M. Design of 1D photonic crystals for colorimetric and ratiometric refractive index sensing. *Optical Materials: X,* 2020, **X8**, 100058.
[13] Segovia-Chaves F., Baron E.N., Vinck-Posada H. Photonic band structure in a one-dimensional distributed bragg reflector Pillar. *Mater. Res. Express,* 2020, **7**, 126201.
[14] Deparis O., Daif O.E. Optimization of slow light one-dimensional bragg structures for photocurrent enhancement in solar cells. *Opt. Lett.,* 2012, **37** (20), 1-3.
[15] Yablonovitch E. Inhibited spontaneous emission in solid-state physics and electronics. *Phys. Rev. Lett.,* 1987, **58**, 2059.
[16] John S. Strong localization of photons in certain disordered dielectric superlattices. *Phys. Rev. Lett.,* 1987, **58**, 2486.
[17] Saravanan S., Dubey R.S. One-dimensional photonic crystals (Si/SiO_2) for ultrathin film crystalline Si solar cells. *Nanosyst: Phys Chem Math.,* 2020, **11** (2), 189-194.

[18] Bipin K. S., Ashish B, Praveen C.P., Vipul R. Multi-channel photonic bandgap consequences in one-dimensional linear, exponential, and hyperbolic graded-index photonic crystals. *J. Opt. Soc. Am. B.,* 2020, **37**, 523-532.
[19] Joannopoulos J.D., Johnson S. G., Winn J.N., Meade R. D. *Photonic crystals: Molding the Flow of Light",* 2nd Edition, Princeton University Press, Princeton, 2008.
[20] Zou Y., Sheng X., Xia K., Fu H., Hu J. Parasitic loss suppression in photonic and plasmonic photovoltaic light trapping structure. *Opt. Express,* 2014, **22** (S4), A1197-A1203.
[21] Sheng X., Johnson S.G., Broderick L.Z., Michel J., Kimerling L.C. Integrated photonic structures for light trapping in thin-film si solar cells. *Appl. Phys. Lett.,* 2012, **100**, 111110-1-3.
[22] Kuo-Hui Y., Jaw-Yen Y. The analysis of light trapping and internal quantum efficiency of a solar cell with DBR back reflector. *Sol.Energy,* 2009, **83**, 2050.
[23] Saravanan S., Dubey R.S. Ultraviolet and visible reflective TiO_2/SiO_2 thin films on Si using sol-gel spin coater. *Nanosyst: Phys. Chem. Math.,* 2021, **12** (3), 311-316.
[24] Prontera C.T., Pugliese M., Giannuzzi R., Carallo S., Esposito M., Gigli G., Maiorano V. Flexible distributed Bragg reflectors as optical outcouplers for oleds based on a polymeric anode. *Journal of Information Display,* 2021, **22** (1), 39-47.
[25] Alias M.S., Alatawi A.A., Chong W.K., Tangi M., Stegenburgs E., Shakfa M.K., Ng T.K., Albadri A.M., Alyamani A.Y., Ooi B.S. *High reflectivity YDH/SiO_2 distributed Bragg reflector for uv-c wavelength regime. IEEE Photonics Journal,* 2018, **10** (2), 2200508-1-6.

Structural and photoluminescence properties of europium oxide doped fluoroborate optical glasses

Z Tirupal Naik and **B Hemalatha Rudramadevi**

Department of Physics, Sri Venkateswara University, Tirupati-517 502, India.

E-mail : drbhrd@gmail.com

Abstract. A sequence of zinc-magnesium-lithium-fluoroborate (ZMLB) optical glasses doped with different Eu^{3+} concentrations were synthesized through melt quenching technique. The non-crystalline characteristic of the synthesized glasses was proved by X-ray diffraction studies and the FT-IR transmittance spectra have been used to study the various vibrational bands in glass systems. The photoluminescence characteristics were studied under an excitation with 393 nm and it exhibits four emission peaks around at 590, 615, 654 and 700 nm assigned to $^5D_0 \rightarrow {}^7F_1$, $^5D_0 \rightarrow {}^7F_2$, $^5D_0 \rightarrow 7F_3$ and $^5D_0 \rightarrow {}^7F_4$ electronic transitions of Eu^{3+} ion, respectively. Color chromaticity values were estimated from luminescence spectra for all the synthesized samples and these parameters indicate the emission in red color region and cold light emission. All these results suggest that the Eu^{3+} ions doped ZMLB glasses are a potential candidate for red light generation at 615 nm to explore the new material for solid state light emitting diode applications.

Keywords: Borate glasses, structural properties, Photoluminescence, red emission.

1. Introduction

The applications of rare earth (RE) ions activated glass matrix are visible light emission, laser instruments, color display instruments and optoelectronic devices. The use of borate optical glasses in different professional and industrial fields has increased significantly in the last few years [1-4]. High ionic conduction, high transparency and relatively high stability are the main characteristics of the borate optical glass matrix. Additionally, borate is the best host for transition lanthanide and metal ions. The lanthanide ions are extensively utilized for their fascinating emission characteristics that generate from their f-f transitions having specific luminescence peaks, therefore, they are used in a wide variety of applications [5-7]. Various exercises have been conducted to advance the borate optical glasses with high efficiency by adding alkaline or alkali modifiers and/ or dopants. Borate glasses are modified by alkali ions to terminate the extended amorphous glass connections and generate oxygen molecules that do not bridge. Zinc in glass matrix influences as a network generator at high concentration and acts as an optical glass network changer at low content. By adding magnesium oxide and lithium fluoride as a second network modifier to increase the number of electrons released and decrease the hygroscopic property of borate glass materials [8]. Luminescence characteristics of europium ions (Eu^{3+}) have been extensively studied in different materials owing to precise peak strong red luminescence for the utilization of lighting, display and sensor gadgets [9].

2. Experimental method

Chemical content of the prepared optical glasses 10ZnO-10MgO-20LiF-(60-x)B_2O_3-xEu_2O_3 (where x= 0, 0.1 and 0.3 mol%) were appropriated for the glass synthesis through melt quench method. Analytical grade (10-gram batch) chemicals were getting into examination for the configuration of glass. This evaluation was done and the chemicals were ground softly in an agate mortar using a pestle. A blended chemical mixture was heated in a crucible. It was placed in a furnace with regulated temperature for melting at 1100 ^{0}C for 1 h to uniform melts. For acquiring the good quality optical glasses, the melts were poured in between two smooth surfaced brass plates. The XRD spectra of the synthesized glasses were registered on X-ray diffractometer (Seifert, model 3003 TT) with CuK_α radiation (λ = 1.5406 Å). FT-IR spectra of the prepared glass samples were measured by a Nicolet-5700 FT-IR spectrometer using the KBr pellet method (500 to 4000 cm^{-1}). The emission and excitation of Eu^{3+} activated ZMLB optical glasses were recorded through PERKIN-ELMER FL 6500 spectrophotometer constituted with pumping source as Xe-arc lamp (450 W).

3. Results and Discussions

3.1. X-ray diffraction analysis

Figure 1 denotes the general X-ray diffraction profiles of un doped and doped 10ZnO-10MgO-20LiF-(60-x)B_2O_3-xEu_2O_3 (where x= 0, 0.1 and 0.3 mol%) glass matrix. It was found that all glasses displayed flat diffraction profiles without any significant diffraction bands. In this way, it can be determined that the synthesized glass matrix possesses non-crystalline properties [10].

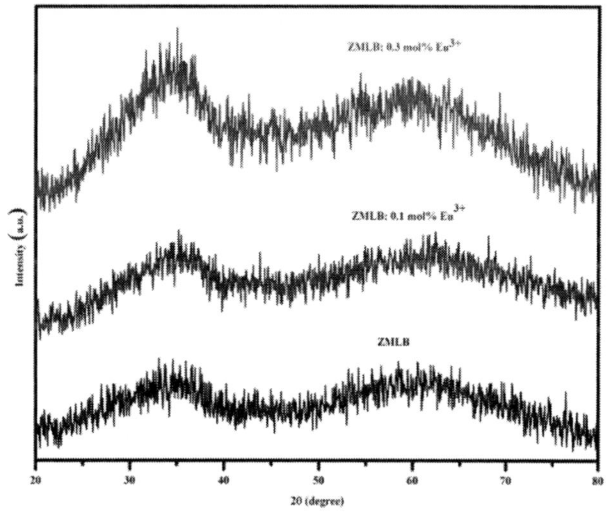

Figure 1. XRD spectra of host ZMLB and Eu^{3+} (0.1 and 0.3 mol%) doped glasses.

3.2. FT-IR spectral analysis

The FT-IR spectra of the un doped and Eu^{3+} doped glasses were registered to investigate vibrational modes and structural groups of molecules as shown in figure 2. The glass systems have narrow shoulders and peaks. These bands were occurring at wavenumber 693, 873, 1160, 1599, 2855 and 2923 cm^{-1}. The illustration of band at 693 cm^{-1} becomes oxygen bond among the two boron atoms with trigonal composing the BO_3–O–BO_3 bending vibration modes [11]. The broad band around 873 cm^{-1} was corresponding to the BO_4 symmetrical stretching vibration in a different structural group. The bands positioned at 1160 and 1599 cm^{-1} were owing to the asymmetric stretching vibrations of the borate triangles with non-bridging oxygen. The vibration modes at 2855 and 2923 cm^{-1} were owing to the hydrogen bonding of the glass surface. The broad shoulder around 3410 cm^{-1} was due to stretching vibration of the hydroxyl groups.

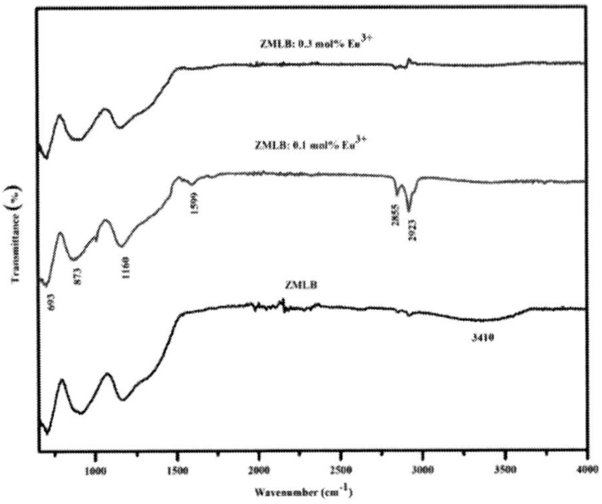

Figure 2. FTIR spectra of host ZMLB and Eu^{3+} (0.1 and 0.3 mol%) doped glasses.

3.3. Excitation and emission spectral analysis

Figure 3 illustrates the excitation spectrum, it consists of four bands at 380, 393, 413 and 464 nm analogous to the $^7F_1\rightarrow{}^5L_7$, $^7F_0\rightarrow{}^5L_6$, $^7F_1\rightarrow{}^5D_3$ and $^7F_0\rightarrow{}^5D_2$ transitions of Eu^{3+} ion, respectively. Among all the excitation transitions $^7F_0\rightarrow{}^5L_6$ was the prominent one and this wavelength was used to get the emission spectra of the glass samples[12-14]. Figure 4 exhibits the emission spectra of the Eu^{3+} activated ZMLB glass samples which were measured under an excitation wavelength of 393 nm. The synthesized samples' emission spectra peaks were positioned at 590 ($^5D_0\rightarrow{}^7F_1$), 615 ($^5D_0\rightarrow{}^7F_2$), 654 ($^5D_0\rightarrow{}^7F_3$) and 700 ($^5D_0\rightarrow{}^7F_4$) nm belonging to Eu^{3+} ion f-f electronic transitions. Luminescent band at 615 nm was the prominent peak while remaining three luminescent bands were relatively lower. From luminescence spectra, $^5D_0\rightarrow{}^7F_2$ transition was belong to electric dipole transition and delicate to the circumstances surrounding of Eu^{3+} ion than remaining transitions [15]. The magnetic dipole transition $^5D_0\rightarrow{}^7F_1$ was autonomous of the internal symmetry.

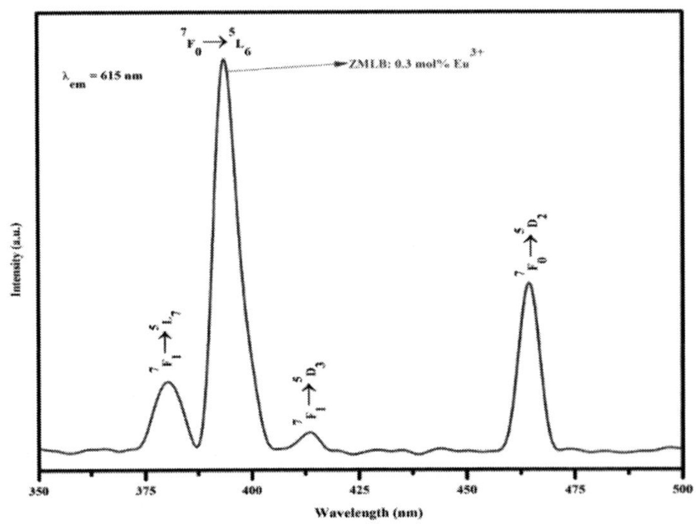

Figure 3. Excitation spectrum of ZMLB: 0.3 mol% Eu^{3+} glass.

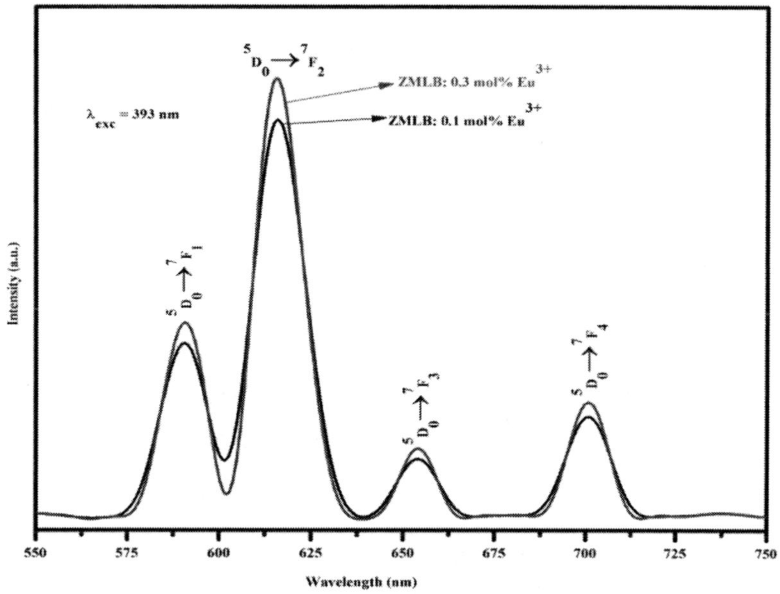

Figure 4. Emission spectra of ZMLB: xEu^{3+} (x= 0.1 and 0.3 mol%) glasses.

3.4. CIE chromaticity coordinates

In order to determine the CIE 1931 (Commission International d'Eclairage) values, the luminescence spectra were used as input for the coordinate formula. Based on the amalgamation of three elementary colors, the CIE chart shows all the available colors [16]. The chromaticity coordinates are determined from the tri-stimulus values using the following equations.

$$x = \frac{X}{X+Y+Z} \quad (1)$$

$$y = \frac{Y}{X+Y+Z} \quad (2)$$

$$z = \frac{Z}{X+Y+Z} = 1-x-y \quad (3)$$

In the CIE 1931 chromaticity picture, the standard (x, y) coordinates are (0.33, 0.33). This is analogous to the white color emission when it is cornered in the middle. The CIE coordinates (x, y) and CCT values were measured and tabulated in table 1 and the color chromaticity picture of the Eu^{3+}: ZMLB optical glasses are exhibited in figure 5. The current investigation of the CIE coordinates of synthesized glasses are occur in the red color area in the CIE 1931 color chromaticity picture and confirms that the synthesized Eu^{3+}: ZMLB optical glasses are applicable for red color emitted display and laser applications [17].

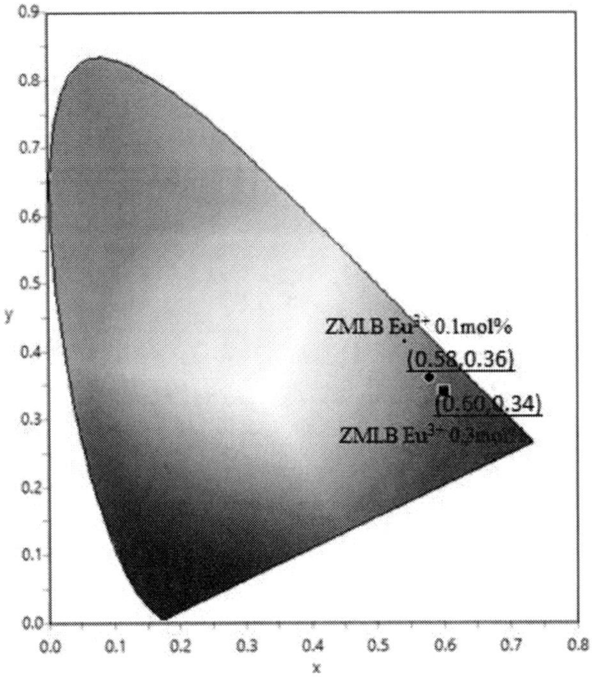

Figure 5. CIE co-ordinates of ZMLB: xEu^{3+} (x= 0.1 and 0.3 mol%) glasses.

Table 1. The CIE chromaticity coordinates and CCT values.

ZMLB: x Eu^{3+}	X	Y	CCT
0.1 mol%	0.58	0.36	1368
0.3 mol%	0.60	0.34	1184

4. Conclusion

The Eu^{3+} (x= 0, 0.1 and 0.3 mol %) ion doped zinc magnesium lithium fluoroborate optical glasses have been synthesized and characterized. The outcome of XRD confirms the non-crystalline property of the prepared glass samples. FTIR spectral investigation affirms the existence of BO_3 and BO_4 units. The photoluminescence characteristics were studied under excitation with 393 nm and it exhibits four emission peaks around 590, 615, 654 and 700 nm. The emission band at 615 nm is the prominent peak whereas remaining three emission bands are relatively smaller. The emission spectra of $^5D_0 \rightarrow ^7F_2$ transition represent the electric dipole transition and delicate to environment surrounding the Eu^{3+} ion than remaining transitions. The $^5D_0 \rightarrow ^7F_1$ is the magnetic dipole transition and is independent of the internal symmetry, CIE values were determined from emission spectra of all the prepared samples. All these results suggest that the Eu^{3+} ions doped ZMLB glasses are capable candidates for red light generation at 615 nm to explore the new material for solid state light emitting diode applications.

References

[1] W. H. Zachariasen, 1932 *J. Am.Chem. Soc.* **54** 3841.

[2] Y. S. M. Alajerami, S. Hashim 2012 *J.M. Struct.* **1026** 159.

[3] M. J. Weber,1990 *J. Non-Cryst. Solids* **123** 208.

[4] G. Blasse 1985 *J. less-common met.* **112** 1.

[5] G. D. Mahan,1967 *Phys. Rev. Lett.* **153** 882.

[6] S. Tang, C. Shao, 2010 *J. Phys. Chem. Solids.* **71** 273.

[7] F. Zaman, N. Srisittipokakun, 2021 *Opt. Mater.* **119** 111300.

[8] K. Annapurna, M and S. Buddhudu, 2005 *J.M. Struct.* **741** 53.

[9] J. S. Bae, and J.C. Park, 2003 *Appl. Phys. Lett.* **82** 3629.

[10] X. Zhao and X. Wang 2007 *J. Alloys Compd.* **433** 352.

[11] B. Sun, and H. Xia 2003 *Chemical Physics Letters.* **368** 412.

[12] K. Mariselvam and S. Karthik, 2019 *Chem. Phys. Lett.* **525** 110379,

[13] G. Wang and Z. Jiang,2005 *Phys. Lett. A.* **341** 285.

[14] J. Anjaiah and N. Veeraiah, 2014 *Physica B Condens. Mat.* **454** 156.

[15] G. V. J. Gowda and S. N. Nazrin, 2021 *J. Alloys Comp.* **871** 159585.

[16] R. T. Karunakaran and S. Arumugam,2009 *Physica B Condens. Mat.* **404** 3995.

[17] L. Zur, J and W. A. Pisarski, 2016 *Opt. Mater.* **6**

Structural and optical characteristics of nanoparticles of zinc oxide based ternary compounds generated by simple sol-gel technique.

T Mohan Kumar* and D Karuna Sagar.

Department of Physics, University College of Science, Osmania University, Hyderabad, 500007, Telangana State, India.

* Corresponding author, email id: mohan.phys@gmail.com.

Abstract. A simple sol-gel process was employed to synthesize $Zn_{1-x}Cd_xO$ (x = 0, 0.02, 0.04, 0.06) nanoparticles. The powders have a Hexagonal Wurtzite phase, according to X-ray diffraction investigations. The findings of Rietveld refinement fitting revealed a considerable shift in the lattice parameters of $Zn_{1-x}Cd_xO$ compounds with increasing cadmium content. The average crystallite size of undoped ZnO, $Zn_{0.98}Cd_{0.02}O$, $Zn_{0.96}Cd_{0.04}O$, and $Zn_{0.94}Cd_{0.06}O$ compounds was determined using Scherrer formula to be 41.58 nm, 38.05 nm, 37.92 nm, and 39.52 nm, respectively. SEM micrographs exhibit needle-like features in cadmium doped ZnO compounds, but not in undoped ZnO compounds. These micrographs also reveal that the nanostructures have a random size distribution and become more agglomerated as the cadmium concentration rises. The optical band gap, as determined by Ultraviolet-Visible Spectroscopy, decreased from 3.22 to 3.15 eV as cadmium content increased. The photoluminescence spectrum recorded at room temperature by 310 nm excitation wavelength. PL spectra exhibited three different emission bands around 410 nm, 460 nm and 510 nm. The broadness of strong green emission peak was observed to increase with cadmium concentration. All the luminescence peaks are explained as due to various defects like zinc vacancy, oxygen vacancy, zinc interstitial and their complexes.

Keywords: ZnO, Sol-gel method, Rietveld refinement, bandgap tuning, Photoluminescence.

1. Introduction

II–VI group semiconductor compounds have fascinated significant interest in latest years owing to their widespread usage in several domains of opto-electronic technology. Zinc oxide (ZnO) is a popular compound in the II–VI group. At ambient temperature, ZnO is, an *n - type* semi-conductor with hexagonal wurtzite crystal structure, having a direct bandgap value of 3.37 eV and large exciton binding energy about 60 meV [1–4]. Because of its superior electrical, optical, remarkable thermal characteristics, and chemical stability, ZnO has sparked the attention of many researchers [1,5]. Recently, ZnO nanoparticles have received much interest due to their extensive variety of technical applications in opto-electronic devices [1,6], gas sensors [7], solar cells [8–9], photo-detectors [10], laser diodes [11–12], and light emitting diodes (LEDs) [12–13].

In general, the properties of semiconductors can be improved further, doping was considered as one of the effective ways. Transition metal ions are good candidates for doping to change the optical properties of the material [2,4–5,13]. Incorporation of such impurities/dopants can improve the optical properties of semiconductors with or without changing the structure of the host [14–15]. In this context, elements like aluminum, barium, calcium, cadmium, cobalt, copper, iron, lithium, manganese, magnesium, sodium, nickel, etc are used as doping agents to tune the optical features of ZnO. Unlike the other elements, it is observed that the influence of cadmium on ZnO is less discussed in the literature. When zinc oxide is combined with cadmium ions (i.e. Cd^{2+}), they can either replace the Zn^{2+}

sites or move to the interstitial places of the host ZnO network. Furthermore, because of the difference in ionic radii, substitution can cause lattice deformation and expansion / contraction. In this situation, Cd^{2+} (0.74 Å) has a larger ionic radius over Zn^{2+} (0.60 Å) [16–17], it may therefore cause expansion in the dimensions of crystal lattice and may cause modifications in the optical characteristics of the material by altering their energy gap. To fabricate an optical device, tuning of energy gap is necessary and ZnCdO is considered as one of the suitable material among ZnO based materials [4–5]. Hence, Cd doped ZnO nano material have attracted much attention of many researchers. Consequently, electrical and optical studies have been made on Cd doped ZnO thin films [4–5, 17–22] but there is a limited literature on optical studies of Cd doped ZnO nanoparticles [23–26].

A A Jacob *et al.* [24] have synthesized "Cd alloyed ZnO nanoparticles by means of *Co-precipitation method* for the production of Photodetectors" and analyzed their structural, optical and photo active centre studies on $Zn_{1-x}Cd_xO$ nanoparticles. They observed a change in the absorption edge towards visible region with the increase in Cd content. R Zhao *et al.* [25] also have synthesized "Cd doped ZnO nanoparticles through a *surfactant-mediated method*" and studied the effect of Cd on gas sensing property of ZnO. The material showed high performance in sensing *n*-butanol out of the other gases studied. N Rana *et al.* examined "the influence of cadmium incorporation on the structure and optical characteristics of zinc oxide compound synthesized by *sol-gel derived polymeric precursor technique*," and discovered that the optical band gap for $Zn_{1-x}Cd_xO$ alloys shifted to the right [26]. R Santhi *et al.* [23] analyzed "the optical and structural characterization of cadmium incorporated zinc oxide nanoparticles produced by *precipitation technique*" and reported that the optical band-gap diminished to 3.17 eV from 3.44 eV and enhanced the photo-emission with cadmium content, particularly green emission till 4% of Cd content. But they have observed an additional XRD peak when Cd content reaches 5% and could not establish the formation of additional phase and the explanation was found inadequate. All these studies specify the results in their own way still, leave a scope to prepare the material by employing a different experimental technique and to study the photoluminescence properties of CdZnO compound in detail to understand the outcome of Cd content in ZnO. Based on the reasons mentioned above, the goal of this present study has been to prepare single phase compounds of undoped and Cd-doped ZnO nanoparticles using the sol-gel technique and to investigate their structure and optical characteristics by undertaking optical absorption and photoluminescence studies.

2. Experimental

2.1. *Materials*

Source material for the synthesis of $Zn_{1-x}Cd_xO$ (x=0, 0.02, 0.04, 0.06) nanoparticles were Zinc nitrate (hexa hydrate) [$Zn(NO_3)_2\ 6H_2O$, ~ 99.5% purity], Cadmium nitrate (tetra hydrate) [$Cd(NO_3)_2\ 4H_2O$, ~ 99.7% purity], Citric acid (mono hydrate) [$C_6H_8O_7\ H_2O$, ~ 99.6% purity], Ethylene glycol [$C_2H_6O_2$, ~ 99.5% purity], and Ammonia solution [NH_4OH, ~ 25%] taken from SD fine (Analytical reagent grade) chemicals and used without additional purification.

2.2. *Method*

Sol-gel method was used to synthesize all $Zn_{1-x}Cd_xO$ compounds as the method costs less and offers homogeneity, perfect material combination, atomic level mixing of metal ions and excellent control over materials. To prepare $Zn_{1-x}Cd_xO$ compounds, Cadmium nitrate tetra hydrate and Zinc nitrate hexa hydrate were employed as cadmium and zinc sources, respectively. For the preparation of each $Zn_{1-x}Cd_xO$ compound, stoichiometric (molar) ratios of both Zinc (0.01 M, in case of x = 0.02) and Cadmium (0.0002 M for x = 0.02) sources were suspended in 100 ml of double distilled water to get a homogeneous precursor solution. The solution was stirred vigorously (by using magnetic stirrer with hot plate) for 1 hour at 300 K i.e., room temperature. Citric acid (mono hydrate) was also added to the solution mixture to match with the metal ion (M) to citric acid (CA) mole ratio i.e., M:CA = 1:1.2.

After 1 hour of stirring, the pH value was measured to be in between 3 and 4. While stirring, the solution was adjusted to attain a pH of 7 by adding Ammonia solution drop by drop. Then the solution was heated at 80°C for an hour to form the gel. Then ethylene glycol was added to initiate the burning of the gel. Ash like powder was collected and grounded for 1 hour. The obtained powders were annealed in atmospheric air medium at 600°C for 4 hours as the compounds under the present study contain oxygen and are noncorrosive. Following this process all the compounds of $Zn_{1-x}Cd_xO$ with x = 0, 0.02, 0.04, 0.06 were prepared and used for characterization, optical absorption and photoluminescence studies. ZC00, ZC02, ZC04, and ZC06 were assigned to the prepared samples for x = 0 (ZnO), x = 0.02 ($Zn_{0.98}Cd_{0.02}O$), x = 0.04 ($Zn_{0.96}Cd_{0.04}O$) and x = 0.06 ($Zn_{0.94}Cd_{0.06}O$) respectively.

2.3. Characterization

All ZC00, ZC02, ZC04, ZC06 compounds' X-Ray Diffraction pattern was traced using a Panalytical - X'pert powder X-Ray diffractometer by means of CuKα radiation (=1.5406) at a scan speed of 0.02°/sec. To examine the microstructure and elemental properties of the particles, a ZEISS EVO – 18 modeled scanning electron microscope outfitted with an Energy Dispersive X-Ray spectro-meter was used. The optical characteristics of the compounds were investigated using a PG Instruments T90+ UV-Vis double beam spectro-photometer operating from 250 to 850 nm wavelength range. The Photoluminescence measurements were carried out using a Spectro Fluorimeter (Jobin - Yvon Fluorolog – 3 – 11) with a 450W Xenon lamp as the excitation source at room temperature in the wavelength region starting from 350 to 650 nm. PL measurements of all the compounds were traced at an excitation wavelength 310 nm.

3. Results and Discussion

3.1. Structure (XRD)

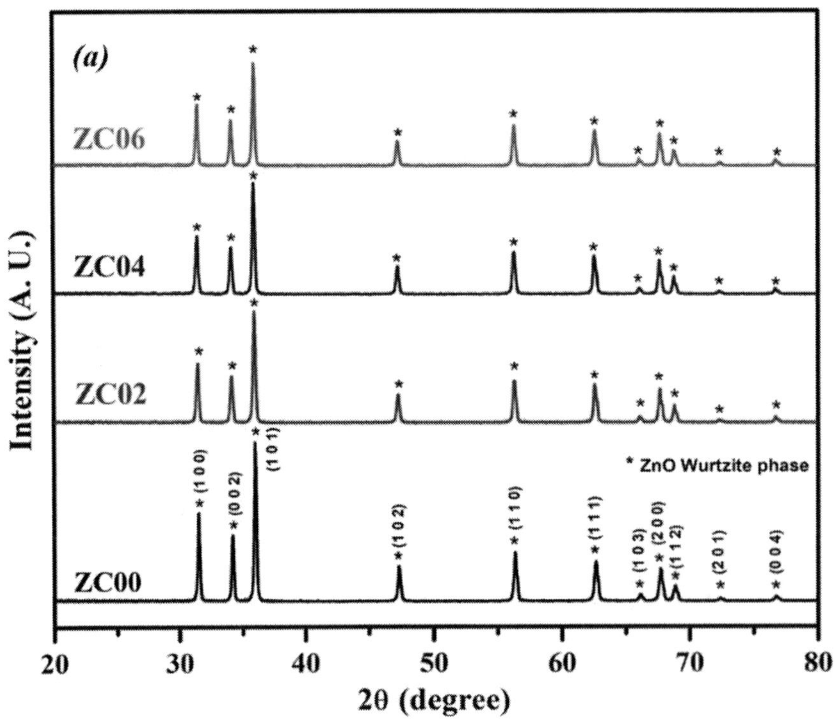

Fig. 1: (a) X-Ray diffractograms of prepared compounds.

X-Ray diffraction (XRD) patterns of ZC00, ZC02, ZC04, ZC06 nanopowders were presented in *Fig. 1(a)*. The recorded powder-XRD models were employed with Rietveld refinement method as it is a method for estimating an approximation structural model for the actual structure based on the profile intensities derived from step-scanning measurements of synthesized materials [27]. This was undertaken to characterize the structural characteristics of the material by using the FULLPROF suit software and the Pseudo-Voigt function to fit the various parameters to the data point. The typical refined pattern for ZC04 ($Zn_{0.96}Cd_{0.04}O$) compound is shown in *Fig.2*. The goodness of fit (GoF) value is close to '1', indicating an excellent fit and confirming that the improvements are excellent [28]. From the sharp and high intense XRD peaks of the compounds, it is evident that all of the particles are extremely crystalline nature. According to Joint committee on Powder Diffraction Standards (JCPDS) Card No. 36-1451 [23–26], the typical peaks possess hexagonal wurtzite structure. In the XRD results of all of the compounds, no extra or other impurity-related peaks are found, showing that the structure of ZnO wurtzite is not influenced by Cd^{2+} doping. Diffraction peaks of undoped ZnO compound are observed at an angle 2θ = 31.52°, 34.20°, 36.02°, 47.33°, 56.37°, 62.66°, 66.17°, 67.75°, 68.89°, 72.40°and 76.76° which correspond to the Miller Indices (1 0 0), (0 0 2), (1 0 1), (1 0 2), (1 1 0), (1 1 1), (1 0 3), (2 0 0), (1 1 2), (2 0 1) and (0 0 4) respectively. All of these peaks and Miller Indices are associated with ZnO's typical Hexagonal wurtzite crystal structure [23–26]. However, a slight change in the positioning of the diffraction peaks onto lower diffraction angle was noticed in all Cd incorporated ZnO compounds (See *Fig. 1(b)*). N Rana *et al.* [26] noticed a similar shift in a CdZnO compound produced by precursor method. This change might be attributed to the substitution of cadmium ion (bigger radius of Cd^{2+} ion is about 0.74 Å) replacing host Zn^{2+} ion (lesser ionic radius, 0.60 Å) in all $Zn_{1-x}Cd_xO$ compounds. This evidences the very nature of Cd^{2+} ion substitution in place of Zn^{2+}ion in ZnO lattice.

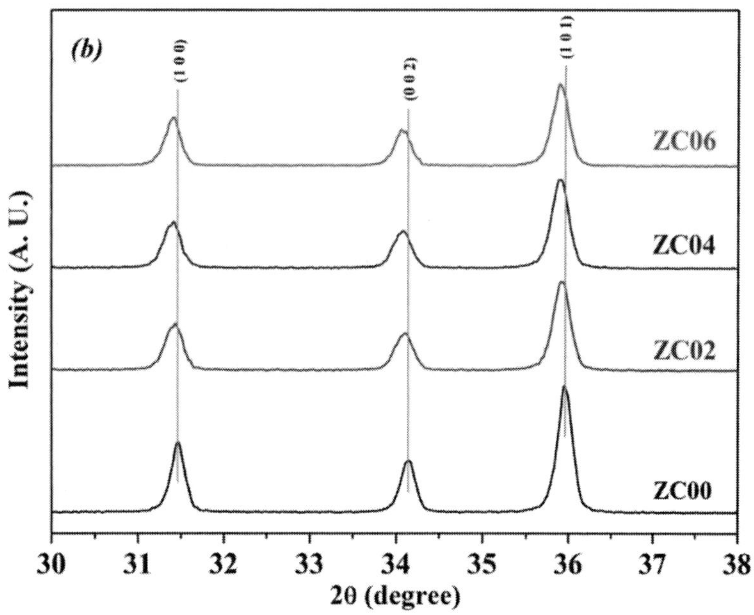

Fig. 1(b): Angular shift in the characteristic XRD peaks of ZC02, ZC04 and ZC06 compounds compared to ZC00 (undoped ZnO).

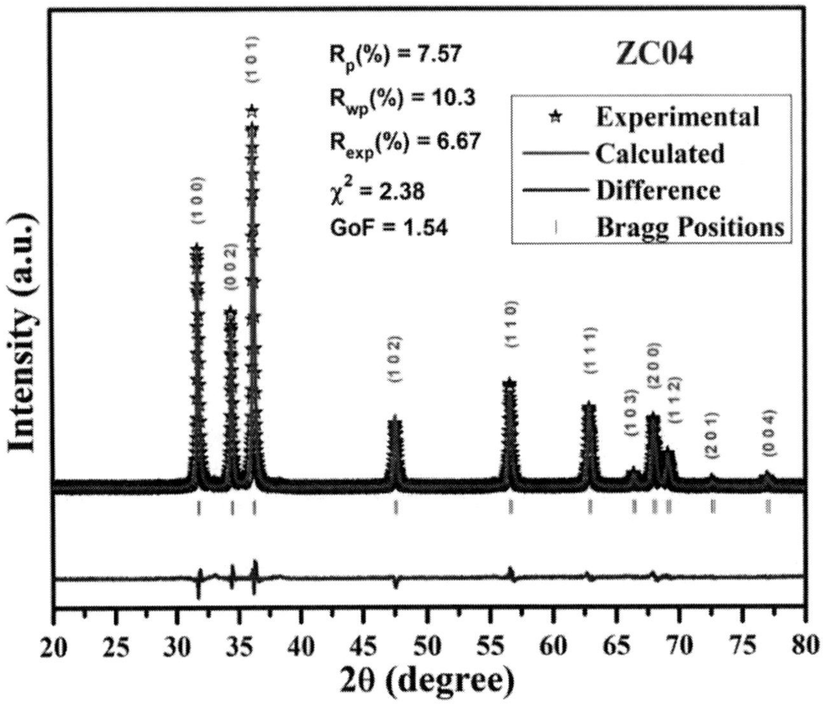

Fig. 2: Rietveld refinement fit for ZC04 ($Zn_{0.96}Cd_{0.04}O$) sample. Observed (dot lines) data and calculated (red lines) data overlap, with the expected peak positions (marked as |) and the difference in the patterns (blue line) is shown at the bottom.

The Scherrer Formula was employed to compute the average crystallite-size of compounds [29]:

$$D = \frac{K\,\lambda}{\beta_{hkl}\ Cos\ \theta}$$

where, D is the average crystallite size, K is a parameter linked to crystallite geometry (K = 0.9 for spherical crystallites), λ is the wavelength of CuKα radiation (λ = 1.5406 Å), β is the diffraction peak's full-width at half-maximum (FWHM, in radians), and θ is the diffracted angle.

For hexagonal structure, the lattice parameters *a, c* are given by [30]:

$$\frac{1}{d_{hkl}^2} = \frac{4}{3}\left[\frac{h^2 + hk + k^2}{a^2}\right] + \frac{l^2}{c^2}$$

where, the inter-planar distance is denoted by *d*, and the Miller indices are *h*, *k*, and *l*, while the lattice parameters are *'a'* and *'c'*.

The lattice constants/parameters '*a*' and '*c*' were calculated from (1 0 0) and (0 0 2) positions by using [29]:

$$a = \frac{\lambda}{\sqrt{3}\ Sin\,\theta_{(100)}}$$

and

$$c = \frac{\lambda}{Sin\,\theta_{(002)}}.$$

The volume of the hexagonal system's unit cell was determined by [30];

$$V = \left(\frac{\sqrt{3}}{2}\right)a^2 c$$

where, 'a' and 'c' are lattice parameters.

For hexagonal structure of zinc oxide (ZnO), the Zn–O bond length is estimated by [30]:

$$L = \sqrt{\frac{a^2}{3} + \left(\frac{1}{2} - u\right)^2 c^2}$$

where, u is the atomic position/internal parameter of hexagonal structure given by

$$u = \frac{a^2}{3c^2} + 0.25$$

Strain (ε) present in the lattice was estimated by the following equation [29].

$$\varepsilon = \frac{\beta_{hkl}}{4\tan\theta}$$

The required data of β_{hkl} and θ were taken from the observed XRD patterns of all the compounds.

In the case of adsorption as well as reactions on the surface of nano-particles, specific surface area (SSA) is very important [30]. A large specific surface area value is a common indicator of a high aspect ratio for nanostructured materials [30].The Specific surface area of nanoparticles of each compound was determined using the relation [30]:

$$SSA = \frac{6000}{\rho D}$$

where, ρ is the density of the nanoparticles prepared (is calculated from XRD, Rietveld refinement) and D is the crystallite size of the corresponding compound.

A dislocation is commonly known as a crystallographic imperfection or irregularity inside a crystal [30]. In general, a topological imperfection is dislocation. Hardness increases with increasing dislocation density. As a result, the dislocation density (δ) was taken into account in the following equation [29–30]:

$$\delta = \frac{1}{D^2}$$

where, D is the crystallite size of the compounds.

The calculated parameters of lattice parameters/constants (a and c), volume of the unit cell (V), bond length (L), strain (ε), average crystallite size (D), density (ρ), dislocation density (δ), and specific surface area (SSA) of ZC00, ZC02, ZC04 and ZC06 compounds are given in following table (Table 1). The table shows that the average crystallite sizes estimated for the ZC00, ZC02, ZC04 and ZC06 compounds are 41.58 nm, 38.05 nm, 37.92 nm, and 39.52 nm respectively. As the particle size of all the compounds fall under the range of nano-scale, one can infer that the Sol-gel method of preparation of $Zn_{1-x}Cd_xO$ compounds yields nanoparticles. It also indicates that when cadmium doped ZnO compounds are compared to undoped ZnO compounds, the average crystallite size declines. The influence of size effect on other properties can be observed prominently if the crystallite size is less than 10 nm. In the present study the crystallite sizes vary in the nano scale range 38 nm to 41 nm and therefore, we assume that the crystallite size do not have significant effect on the properties [31].

Table 1: The fit parameters, lattice parameters, volume of cell, density, Zn–O bond length, strain, average crystallite size, dislocation density and specific surface area of undoped ZC00, ZC02, ZC04 and ZC06 nanoparticles.

Parameters	*ZC00*	*ZC02*	*ZC04*	*ZC06*
R_p (%)	8.41	7.57	7.57	7.36
R_{wp} (%)	10.7	11.1	10.3	10.3
R_{exp} (%)	6.08	6.72	6.67	6.68
χ^2	3.12	2.73	2.38	2.37
R_{Bragg} (%)	3.20	2.74	3.18	2.47
R_F(%)	3.98	2.90	3.59	2.46
GoF	1.76	1.64	1.54	1.54
a (Å)	3.2745	3.2766	3.2791	3.2811
c (Å)	5.2396	5.2432	5.2466	5.2496
c/a	1.600	1.600	1.600	1. 599
V(Å^3)	48.65	48.75	48. 84	48.94
L (Å)	1.8905	1.8917	1.8932	1.8944
ε	0.1252	0.1377	0.1382	0.1319
D (nm)	41.58	38.05	37.92	39.52
ρ(g/cm^3)	5.671	5.673	5.667	5.676
δ [x10^{10}](lines/m^2)	633.601	699.751	700.911	654.701
SSA (m^2/g)	26.221	27.931	27.981	26.981

The calculated lattice constants/parameters '*a*' and '*c*' of all Cd doped compounds differed with that of ZnO. This might be because the radius of the Cd^{2+} ion is larger than that of the Zn^{2+}. Further, it causes lattice distortion and subsequently increases strain in doped ZnO compounds. As a result the lattice constants of cadmium doped ZnO compounds increased when compared to undoped ZnO. Though lattice constants varied slightly with cadmium doping, the *c/a* ratio remained same and remained equal to that of the standard Wurtzite ZnO (*c/a* standard = 1.601). The cell volume of each compound was also increased with cadmium concentration but was close to that of ideal wutzite ZnO structure. A similar observation was also published by M Kahouli *et al.* [29] and R Shanthi *et al.* [23]. Cadmium addition has no discernible impact on sample density. Cadmium incorporation lengthens the Zn-O bond. When compared to an undoped zinc oxide molecule, cadmium addition increases lattice strain. Despite increasing the lattice strain, cadmium doped zinc oxide materials exhibit nonlinear increment behavior of the lattice strain. The lattice strain of ZC06 is smaller than that of ZC04 due to the full with half maximum discrepancies that exist between them, demonstrating the present difference, but both are larger than the undoped compounds. The increased specific surface area (see Table 1) of cadmium doped compounds indicates that the compounds are more suitable for optoelectronic device applications [30].

3.2. Elemental and Micro-structure study (EDX and SEM)

Although Electron Dispersive X-Ray (EDX) Spectrum is a semi-quantitative method with limitations as compared to EELS (in cooperation with TEM) for identifying elemental information on the nano scale particles, it does provide information on the fundamental and component elements present in the substance. Therefore, we employed the EDX in this present work to investigate the elemental chemistry (composition) of the synthesised substances. The EDX spectrum of ZC00, ZC02, ZC04 and ZC06 compounds is shown in *Fig.3*. The Spectrum confirmed the presence of Cd^{2+}dopant in compounds except undoped ZnO. The observed weight percentages match well, within the experimental limitations, with the compositions selected while preparing the solution mixture (Table 2).

The morphology and microstructure of the synthesized compounds were examined by using SEM and the images of all the compounds are shown in *Fig.4.* SEM micrographs show needle like structures in cadmium doped ZnO compounds whereas, such needles are not found in undoped ZnO compound. The change in morphology may be attributed to cadmium incorporation. These micrographs also indicate that the nanostructures have random size distribution and they tend to get more agglomerated with increase of cadmium content. From SEM the grain size of the compounds observed is about 40 to 60 nm in all the compounds which is in accordance with crystallite size from XRD.

Table 2: Weight percentages of Zn, Cd and O from EDX

Element	***Weight percentage***			
	ZC00	***ZC02***	***ZC04***	***ZC06***
Zinc	80.34	78.00	75.55	73.16
Cadmium	0.00	2.20	4.96	7.70
Oxygen	19.66	19.80	19.49	19.14
Total	100.00	100.00	100.00	100.00

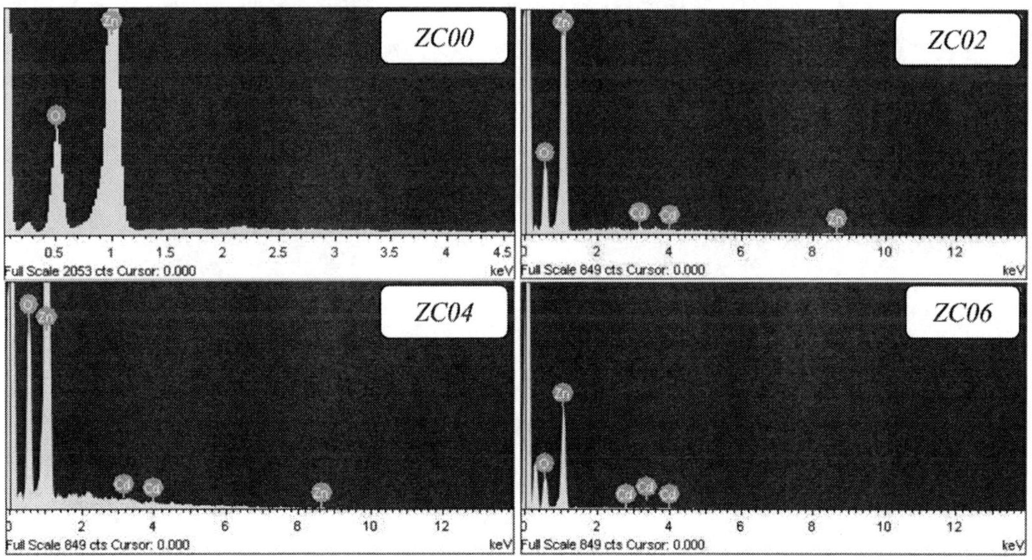

Fig. 3: Electron Dispersion X-Ray (EDX) Spectrum of CZ00, CZ02, CZ04 and CZ06 compounds.

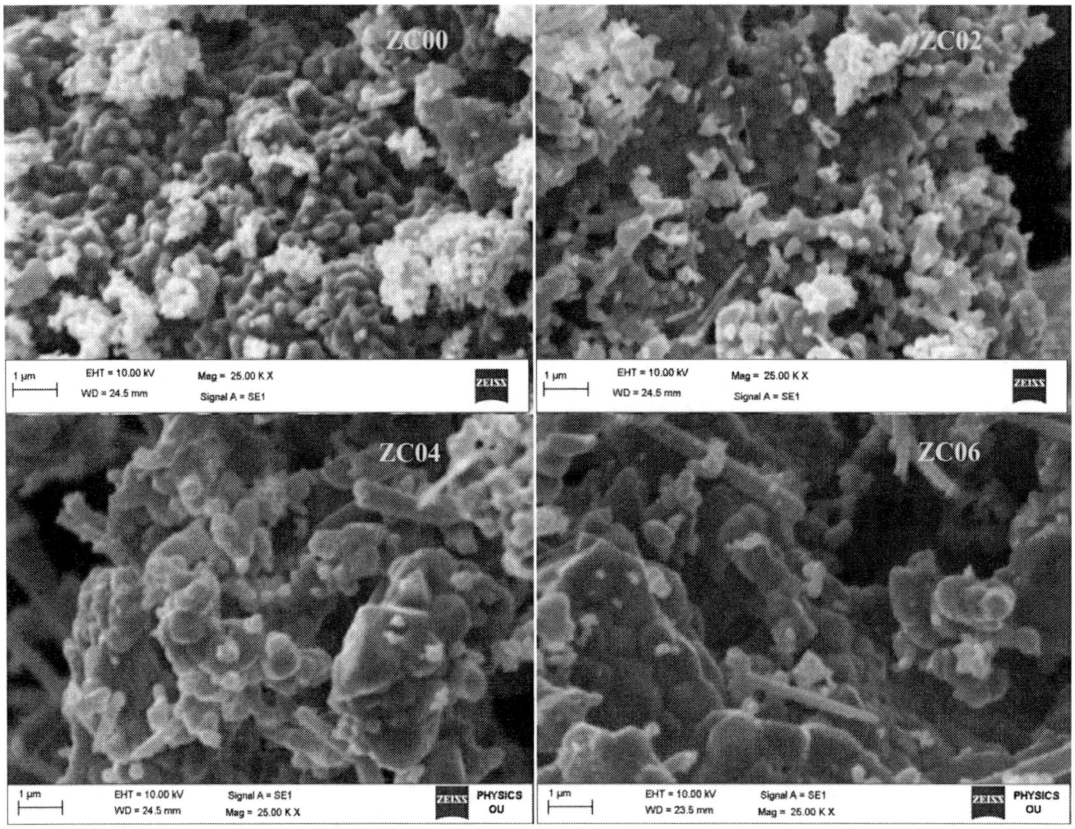

Fig. 4: Scanning Electron Microscope (SEM) images of undoped ZnO and cadmium doped ZnO nanostructures at 10 K magnification.

3.3. *Bandgap and Emission Studies*

3.3.1. *UV-Visible Spectroscopy*

The optical properties of nanopowders of all compounds were studied using UV–Visible spectrophotometer in 250 – 850 nm wavelength region. The variations of optical transmittance as well as the first derivative of transmittance of each compound are revealed in *Fig. 5(a)* and *Fig. 5(b)* respectively. The characteristic band for pure ZnO's Wurtzite hexagonal phase is a sharp band at 375 nm, as shown in *Fig. 5(a)*. Because the exciton binding energy of ZnO (60 meV) is greater than the thermal energy at room temperature, this sharp band can be attributed to exciton absorption at room temperature (26 meV). As seen in *Fig. 5(a)*, the optical transmittances of ZC00, ZC02, ZC04 and ZC06 are 93%, 92%, 89% and 88% respectively. It shows clearly that the transmittance decreases with the increment of Cd content. This suggests that Cd ions are causing the formation of defect centres in host lattice (zinc oxide) proportionate to Cd content.

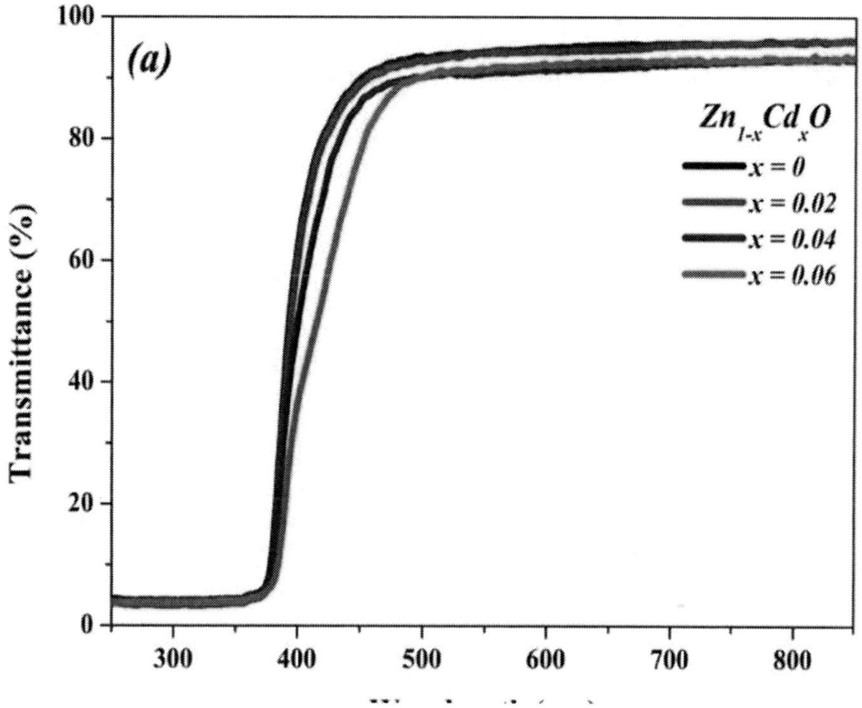

Fig. 5 (a): Variation of optical transmittance with wavelength for undoped ZC00, ZC02, ZC04 and ZC06 compounds.

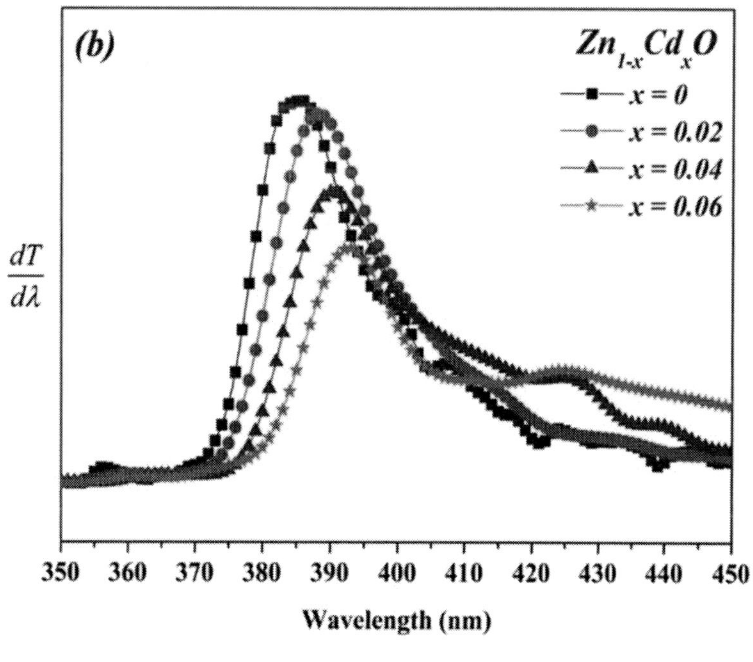

Fig. 5(b): the first derivative of transmittance of undoped ZC00, ZC02, ZC04 and ZC06 compounds.

The first derivative of transmittance with respect to wavelength determines the optical band-gap of the synthesised **ZC00,** ZC02, ZC04 and ZC06 compounds [32].The direct band gaps of the nanopowders are found to be 3.22, 3.19, 3.17 and 3.15 eV respectively. Doping Cadmium into Zinc oxide lattice results in the decrease of band gap and further, it decreases with the increase in Cadmium concentration. A similar result was observed with others [24, 26, 33–34]. Cd-alloyed ZnO compounds exhibit a bandgap in the blue region, according to A A Jacob *et al.* [24]. Cadmium's 5s orbital state dominates over zinc oxide's higher 4s state directly below the conduction band when it is incorporated into the zinc oxide lattice, potentially lowering the bandgap. According to A A Ziabari *et al.* [16], the decrease in band gap with increasing cadmium concentration was due to the contributions of hybridization of 4s (of zinc) and 5s (of cadmium) electronic states, as well as the cadmium-induced intensification of p-d repulsion and tensile strain. The increased strain observed in the present study (from XRD data) in Cd-doped ZnO compounds when compared to undoped ZnO also supports the observation (reduction in energy gap) made in all $Zn_{1-x}Cd_xO$ compounds.

3.3.2. Photoluminescence (PL) Study. The room-temperature photo-luminescence (RTPL) spectra of **ZC00,** ZC02, ZC04 and ZC06 powdered compounds were recorded in the wavelength range of 350–650 nm at 310 nm excitation wavelength and all the spectra are shown in *Fig. 6.* All the graphs in the figure show three PL peaks out of which two are dominantly appearing and the other one is subtle. Figure also shows that the intensity of all the peaks decreases indicating decrease of luminescent centres with the increment in Cd content. To understand the wavelength at which individual peak appears, full-width at half-maximum and the peak intensity; PL emission spectra of all compounds are normalized and de-convoluted. Spectra of all the compounds after de-convolution are shown in *Fig.7.* The wavelength of each de-convoluted peak, area under the peak, intensity of corresponding peak and FWHM values for all spectra are given in Table 3. One can distinguish from Table 3 that,

(i) the first peak in undoped and Cd introduced ZnO compounds appear nearly at the same wavelength (~ 410 nm),
(ii) the second peak, which appears at 457 nm for ZC00 (undoped ZnO), appears at higher wavelengths i.e. 463 nm, 466 nm and 467 nm for ZC02 ($Zn_{0.98}Cd_{0.02}O$), ZC04 ($Zn_{0.96}Cd_{0.04}O$) and ZC06 ($Zn_{0.94}Cd_{0.06}O$) compounds respectively,
(iii) the third peak, which appears at 510 nm for undoped ZnO, appears at lower wavelengths i.e. 499 nm, 484 nm and 483 nm for ZC02 ($Zn_{0.98}Cd_{0.02}O$), ZC04 ($Zn_{0.96}Cd_{0.04}O$) and ZC06 ($Zn_{0.94}Cd_{0.06}O$) compounds respectively.

If we compare FWHM of all PL peaks of ZC00 (undoped ZnO) with their corresponding peaks of ZC02 ($Zn_{0.98}Cd_{0.02}O$), ZC04 ($Zn_{0.96}Cd_{0.04}O$) and ZC06 ($Zn_{0.94}Cd_{0.06}O$) compounds it can be seen (from the data given in Table 3) that the value of FWHM of first and third peak increases whereas, for second peak it decreases with the enhancement of Cd content.

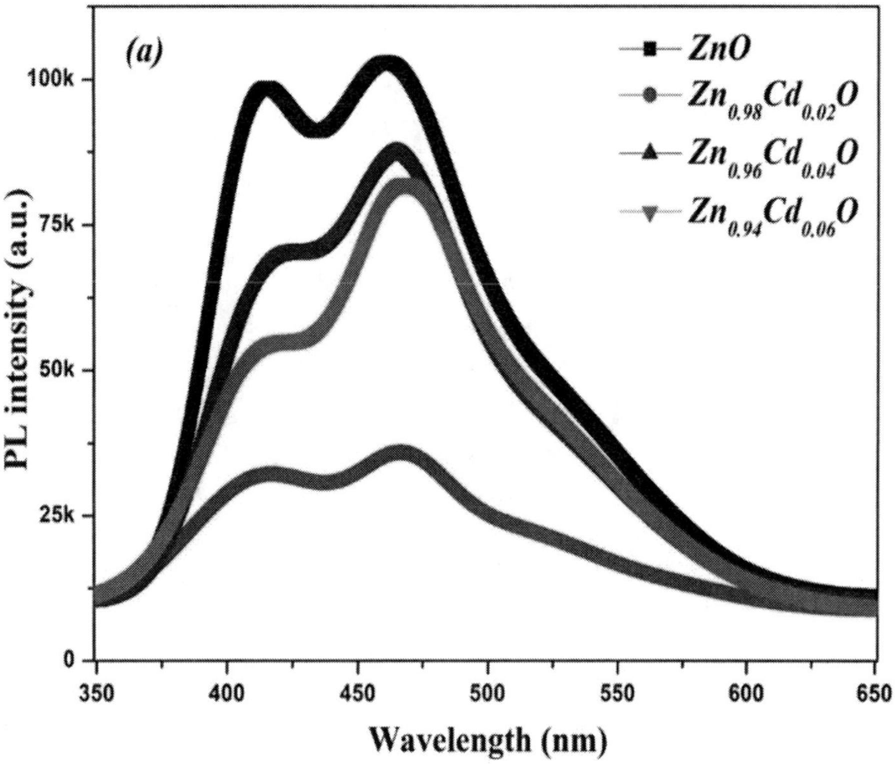

*Fig. 6: The photoluminescence emission spectra for **ZC00,** ZC02, ZC04 and ZC06 compounds with wavelength at room temperature.*

Ismail Polat *et al.* [15] investigated the PL distinguishability of Cu doped ZnO at ambient temperature and discovered that localised defect levels in the energy band gap increased PL. One of the two observed peaks, centred at 379 nm, was attributed to free excitons recombination in the UV range with both no-phonon replica contributions [15, 35]. The second peak was ascribed to intrinsic defects in the ZnO host lattice such as zinc vacancy (V_{Zn}), interstitial zinc (Zn_i), oxygen vacancy (V_O), oxygen interstitials (O_i), and copper impurities [1, 15]. It was located in the wavelength range 400 to 720 nm, matching to the green luminescence range. M Silambarasan et al. [11] investigated the PL emission spectra of undoped and Fe doped ZnO nanoparticles and discovered a high PL emission (blue emission) at 400–416 nm in pure ZnO nanoparticles. This intense blue emission was attributed to exciton recombination at the near band edge (NBE) of ZnO nanoparticles [11]. On the wide PL spectrum, the shoulder peak of blue (about 450 and 467 nm) and blue-green (494 nm) were also seen [11]. Normally, visible emissions were related to a variety of intrinsic ZnO defects, including V_O, O_i, V_{Zn}, Zn_i, O_{Zn} (oxygen antisite), and a compound of oxygen vacancy and zinc interstitial (V_O+Zn_i) [11, 36–39]. The blue emission at the shoulder peak was ascribed to a transition between V_{Zn} and Zn_i defects, whereas the green emission was attributed to a transition between Zni and Oi defects. The RTPL spectrum of ZnO nanowires produced on ZnO:Ga/glass substrates was studied by Cheng-Liang Hsu et al. [10]. They noticed that PL spectra showed a substantial peak at around 377 nm, with a long extremity in the longer wavelength range. The high PL peak was attributed to exciton-exciton collision-induced free excitation recombination [40]. Deep level emissions (green and yellow bands) were also formed as long tails and were connected to the singly ionised oxygen vacancy in zinc oxide [41]. They found the presence of significant UV emission at 377 nm and a very weak green band in ZnO nanowires with good crystalline quality [10].

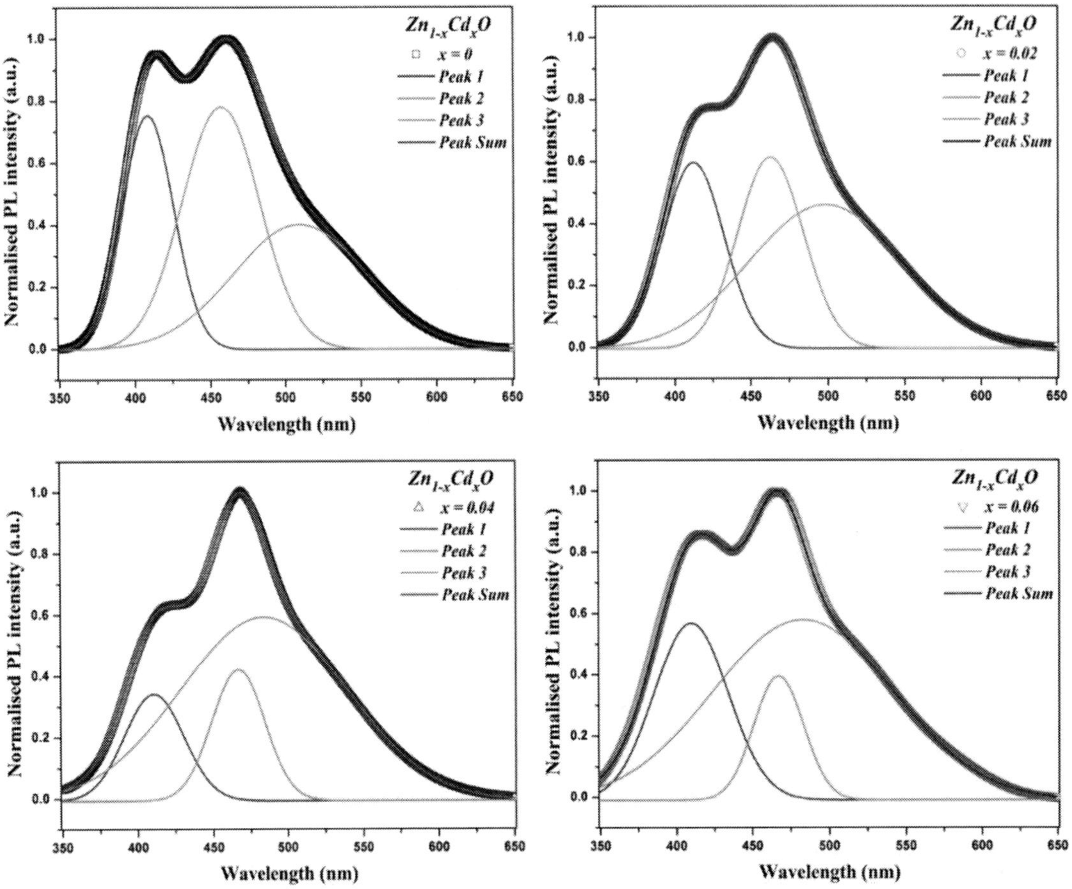

*Fig. 7: The de-convoluted Gaussian peak fits for **ZC00**, ZC02, ZC04 and ZC06 compounds.*

T Tatsumi *et al.* [42] used annealing in O_2 and N_2 atmospheres to study the intrinsic imperfections present in zinc oxide films formed with molecular beam epitaxy technique. According to their annealing experiments, PL emission at 3.358 eV is created by excitons bonded to V_O. Interstitial Zn deficiencies were shown to be responsible for the green-yellow fluorescence detected at 2.3 eV in as-grown ZnO epitaxial films. When compared to other nano-structures [43], the PL emission spectra of a nanorod and nanowall junction had the highest intensity proportion of ultraviolet to green-yellow emission and the shortest FWHM of the UV peak [42]. Based on density functional theory, Anderson Janotti et al. [44] proposed that V_{Zn} are deep acceptors and are associated with the often seen green luminescence in various studies [45-46]. According to Kohan *et al.* [47] as well as R Vidya *et al.* [48], the green, yellow, and red photoluminescence peaks of undoped ZnO compounds generated under varied circumstances can be attributed to defect complexes such as Zn-vacancy clusters and (V_O + Zn_i). They [47–48] also hypothesized that the red/orange luminosity seen in Zn-rich samples may be caused by ZnO antisite defects. In Zn-rich and O-rich materials, (V_O + Zn_i) complexes may induce yellow luminescence. The green luminescence peak that is frequently observed in ZnO might be generated by (V_O + Zn_i) complexes.

In summary, the PL spectrum of ZnO is divided into two regions: UV (near band edge emission, NBE) emission and Visible (deep level emission, DLE) emission. The NBE emission occurs at 3.3 eV, with an FWHM of 160 meV. UV emission has been attributed to free-exciton recombination [2,3,5,6,10,15]. Although green is the most common visible emission, other colors such as yellow and orange can be seen in rare situations. The green emission is caused by inherent ZnO imperfections such as oxygen vacancies and zinc vacancies [5–6,10,12,15,44,48]. All of the compounds in our investigation had three significant peaks: a violet band peak at ~ 410 nm, a high intensity blue band peak at ~ 460 nm, and a broad green band peak at ~ 510 nm. The dominant violet, blue and green emission (all in the visible region) peaks observed in the compounds may correspond to intrinsic defects present in ZnO [5–6,42,44,48–51]. The violet emission band is created by an electron transfer from the shallow donor level to the valance band (VB) and indicates a radiative recombination transition. The incorporation of Cd^{+2} in to ZnO lattice may cause reduction in the intensity of violet and blue emissions and broaden the green emission band. The reduction in intensity could be due to reduction in V_{Zn}, Zn_i and Zn_O defects proportionate to Cd^{+2} ion incorporation and even due to less particle size. In general, quantum confinement effects can only be detected in extremely tiny nanostructures [1, 6], which are smaller than the size of the exciton Bohr radius (2.34 nm) in ZnO [1, 6, 31]. However, no such effect would be expected in our compounds as the particle size of each ZnCdO compound is much above the exciton Bohr radius in spite they (41.58, 38.05, 37.92, and 39.52 nm) being in nano range. We, therefore, can understand that the observed changes in photoluminescence emission as well as optical band gap are due to Cd incorporation but not due to size effect [31]. Strong violet emission observed in all the compounds suggests that the compounds have high defect density and was also supported by dislocation densities calculated from XRD. High-quality nanostructures with less strain and a large surface area may have a larger density of radiative or non-radiative imperfections (or both) [1, 10]. The blue emission band in our compounds may be owing to radiative transition of an electron jumping from zinc interstitial (Zn_i) to oxygen interstitial (O_i) [6, 48–51]. The drop in the blue band suggests that Cd^{+2} doping reduces the concentration of Zn_i, which causes deep donor levels in the energy gap. The green band broadening is caused mostly by an electron transfer from doubly ionized zinc vacancy (V_O^{2+}) to oxygen vacancy and zinc interstitial complex (V_O+Zn_i) [11, 15, 44, 48]. The red shift of all bands in all $Zn_{1-x}Cd_xO$ nanopowders indicates that the doping of Cd has prominent effect on the band gap of compounds. Similar bandgap contraction of ZnCdO compounds was discovered in the findings of Y.R. Sui *et al.* [52]. However, they have only researched UV emission (350 to 500 nm) and have not studied about green emission (350 to 650 nm) in their work. That is the significance of the present work over past efforts.

4. Conclusions

ZnO, $Zn_{0.98}Cd_{0.02}O$, $Zn_{0.96}Cd_{0.04}O$ and $Zn_{0.94}Cd_{0.06}O$ compounds were successfully prepared using sol-gel technique. XRD, SEM, EDX, UV transmittance, and Photoluminescence techniques are used to investigate the structure and optical characteristics of the prepared compounds. The XRD analysis confirmed no impurity phases, and the refinement fits show that all of the compounds have a wurtzite structure. From XRD data the average crystallite size of undoped ZnO, $Zn_{0.98}Cd_{0.02}O$, $Zn_{0.96}Cd_{0.04}O$ and $Zn_{0.94}Cd_{0.06}O$ compounds was observed as 41.58 nm, 38.05 nm, 37.92 nm, and 39.52 nm respectively. The lattice parameters are affected by the incorporation of larger Cd^{2+} ion in place of smaller Zn^{2+} ion in ZnO lattice. The optical band gap was found to show red shift; show a discrepancy from 3.22 eV to 3.15 eV with the increase in cadmium content. Visible photoluminescence (PL) was observed with the increase in cadmium concentration. By producing a strong green emission in the visible luminescence range, Cd inclusion has systematically and considerably affected the band gap. The blue emission band in all compounds was due to radiative transition of an electron jumping from zinc interstitial (Zn_i) to oxygen interstitial (O_i). The decrease in blue band indicated that the concentration of Zn_i which cause deep donor levels in the energy gap decreased by Cd^{+2} doping. The broadening of green band was mainly due to an electron transition from doubly ionized zinc vacancy (V_{Zn}^{2+}) to the complex of oxygen vacancy and zinc interstitial (V_O+Zn_i).

Acknowledgement

The corresponding author wishes to thank the Head of the Department of Physics for his ongoing encouragement and assistance in carrying out the study at the Department, as well as for facilitating

XRD, SEM, and UV facilities. Furthermore, the authors express gratitude to the Head, SAIF, IIT-Madras for his assistance in performing Photoluminescence Studies. Additionally, the authors express gratitude to the University Grants Commission (UGC) of India for providing financial support for the current study.

References

[1] Ü Özgür, Ya I Alivov, C Liu, A Teke, M A Reshchikov, S Doğan, V Avrutin, S J Cho, and H Morkoç, *A comprehensive review of ZnO materials and devices*, Journal of Applied Physics, 98, 041301 (2005), http://dx.doi.org/10.1063/1.1992666.

[2] T. Mohan Kumar, T. Shekharam, M Nagabhushanam, *"Effect of Cadmium on Structure and Optical Properties of ZnO Nanopowders by Sol-Gel Method"*, Materials Today: Proceedings 3 (2016) 3621–3625. https://doi.org/10.1016/j.matpr.2016.11.004.

[3] M.H. Huang, S Mao, H. Feick, H. Yan, Y. Wu, H Kind, E. Weber, R. Russo, P.Yang, *Room-temperature ultraviolet nanowire nanolasers*, Science 292 (2001) 1897–1899, DOI: 10.1126/science.1060367.

[4] D.W. Ma, Z.Z. Ye, J.Y. Huang, L.P. Zhu, B.H. Zhao, J.H. He, *Effect of post-annealing treatments on the properties of $Zn_{1-x}Cd_xO$ films on glass substrates*, Materials Science and Engineering B 111 (2004) 9–13, https://doi.org/10.1016/j.mseb.2003.12.007.

[5] R. Vettumperumal, S. Kalyanaraman, R. Thangavel, *Photoconductive UV detectors based heterostructures of Cd and Mg doped ZnO sol gel thin films*, Materials Chemistry and Physics 145 (2014) 237–242, http://dx.doi.org/10.1016/j.matchemphys.2014.02.008.

[6] A.B. Djurisic, A.M.C.Ng, X.Y.Chen, *ZnO nanostructures for optoelectronics: Material properties and device applications*, Progress in Quantum Electronics 34 (2010) 191–259, https://doi.org/10.1016/j.pquantelec.2010.04.001.

[7] Wei Yang, Xiao Xiao, Baijun Fang, Hexia Deng, "*Nanorods-assembled ZnO microflower as a powerful channel for n-butanol sensing*", Journal of Alloys and Compounds, 860 (2021) 158410, https://doi.org/10.1016/j.jallcom.2020.158410.

[8] M. Krunks, A. Katerski, T. Dedova, I. Oja Acik, A. Mere, *Nanostructured solar cell based on spray pyrolysis deposited ZnO nanorod array*, Solar Energy Materials & Solar Cells 92 (2008) 1016– 1019, https://doi.org/10.1016/j.solmat.2008.03.002.

[9] Xiaobin Xu, Min Wu, Michael Asoro, P. J. Ferreira, D. L. Fan, *One-Step Hydrothermal Synthesis of Comb-Like ZnO Nanostructures*, Crystal Growth & Design 12 (2012) 4829–4833, https://doi.org/10.1021/cg3005773.

[10] C.L. Hsu, S.J. Chang, Y.R. Lin, P.C. Li, T.S. Lin, S.Y. Tsai, T.H. Lu, I.C. Chen, *Ultraviolet photodetectors with low temperature synthesized vertical ZnO nanowires*, Chemical Physics Letters 416 (2005) 75–78, https://doi.org/10.1016/j.cplett.2005.09.066.

[11] D. C. Agarwal, U.B. Singh, Srashti Gupta, Rahul Singhal, P. K. Kulriya, Fouran Singh, A. Tripathi, Jitendra Singh, U.S. Joshi, D.K. Avasthi, "*Enhanced room temperature ferromagnetism and green photoluminescence in Cu doped ZnO thin film synthesised by neutral beam sputtering*", Scientific Reports 9 (2019) 6675, doi: https://doi.org/10.1038/s41598-019-43184-9.

[12] Chao Ping Liu, Kingsley O. Egbo, Chun Yuen Ho, Ying Wang, Cong Kang Xu, Kin Man Yu, Wide-Gap Zn1−xNixO Alloy: A Transparent p-Type Oxide, Physical Review Applied, 12 (2020) 024049, https://link.aps.org/doi/10.1103/PhysRevApplied.13.024049.

[13] M. Silambarasan, S. Saravanan, T. Soga, *Effect of Fe-doping on the structural, morphological and optical properties of ZnO nanoparticles synthesized by solution combustion process*, Physics E 71 (2015) 109–116, doi: http://dx.doi.org/10.1016/j.physe.2015.04.002.

[14] Z. Ben Ayadi, L. El Mir, K. Djessas, S. Alaya, *Electrical and optical properties of aluminum-doped zinc oxide sputtered from an aerogel nanopowder target*, Nanotechnology 18 (2007) 445702–445707, doi: https://doi.org/10.1088/0957-4484/18/44/445702.

[15] Ismail Polat, Salih Yılmaz, Ilknur Altın, Emin Bacaksız, Münevver Sokmen, *The influence of Cu-doping on structural, optical and photocatalytic properties of ZnO nanorods*, Materials Chemistry and Physics 148 (2014) 528–532, https://doi.org/10.1016/j.matchemphys.2014.07.011.

[16] A.A. Ziabari, F.E. Ghodsi, *Optoelectronic studies of sol–gel derived nanostructured CdO–ZnO composite films*, Journal of Alloys and Compounds 509 (2011) 8748–8755, https://doi.org/10.1016/j.jallcom.2011.06.050.

[17] T. Makino, Y. Segawa, M. Kawasaki, A. Ohtomo, R. Shiroki, K. Tamura, T. Yasuda, and H. Koinuma, *Band gap engineering based on* $Mg_xZn_{1-x}O$ *and* $Cd_xZn_{1-x}O$ *ternary alloy films*, Applied Physics Letters 78 (2001) 1237–1239, https://doi.org/10.1063/1.1350632.

[18] Shuai Chen, Qingxuan Li, Ian Ferguson, Tao Lin, Lingyu Wan, Zhe Chuan Feng, Liping Zhu, Zhizhen Ye, "*Spectroscopic ellipsometry studies on ZnCdO thin films with different Cd concentrations grown by pulsed laser deposition*", Applied Surface Science, 421 B (2017) 383–388, dio: https://doi.org/10.1016/j.apsusc.2017.02.264.

[19] Kazutoshi Takahashi, Masaki Imamura, Jang Hyo Chang, TooruTanaka, Katsuhiko Saito, QixinGuo, Kin ManYu, WladekWalukiewicz, "*Three-dimensional band structure and surface electron accumulation of rs-*$Cd_xZn_{1-x}O$ *studied by angle-resolved photoemission spectroscopy*", Scientific Reports, 9 (2019) 8026, doi: https://doi.org/10.1038/s41598-019-44423-9.

[20] Nishant Kumar, Anchal Srivastava, "*Faster photoresponse, enhanced photosensitivity and photoluminescence in nanocrystalline ZnO films suitably doped by Cd*", Journal of Alloys and Compounds, 706 (2017) 438–446, dio: https://dploi.org/10.1016/j.jallcom.2017.02.244.

[21] Luis M.B. Vargas, Suelen de Castro, Marcelos L. Peres, Marcio P.F. de Godoy, Demétrio A.W. Soares, "*Tuning positive and negative photoconductivity in* $Zn_{1-x}Cd_xO$ *films*", Journal of Alloys and Compounds, 749 (2018) 734–740, doi: https://doi.org/10.1016/j.jallcom.2018.03.327.

[22] Jesús Zúñiga-Pérez, "*ZnCdO: Status after 20 years of research*", Materials Science in Semiconductor Processing, 69 (2017) 36–43, doi: https://doi.org/10.1016/j.mssp.2016.12.002.

[23] R. Santhi, C. Shanthi, M. Sathya, K. Pushpanathan, *Self-assembled flower-like microstructure in* $Zn_{1-x}Cd_xO$ *nanoparticles*, Trans. Nonferrous Met. Soc. China 27 (2017) 2031–2042, https://doi.org/10.1016/S1003-6326(17)60228-0.

[24] A.A. Jacob, L. Balakrishnan, S. R. Meher, K. Shambavi, Z.C. Alex, *Synthesis of* $Zn_{1-x}Cd_xO$ *Nanoparticles by Co-Precipitation: Structural, Optical and Photodetection Analysis*, International Journal of Nanoscience, Vol. 16, No. 3 (2017) 1760015, https://doi.org/10.1142/S0219581X17600158.

[25] R. Zhao, K. Li, Z. Wang, X. Xing, Y. Wang, *Gas-sensing performances of Cd doped ZnO nanoparticles synthesized by a surfactant-mediated method for n-butanol gas,* Journal of Physics and Chemistry of Solids (2017), https://doi.org/10.1016/j.jpcs.2017.08.039.

[26] N. Rana, Subhash Chand, Arvind K.Gathania, *Tailoring the structural and optical properties of ZnO by doping with Cd*, Ceramics International Volume 41, Issue 9, Part B, (2015), Pages 12032–12037, https://doi.org/10.1016/j.ceramint.2015.06.017.

[27] H. M. Rietveld, *Line profiles of neutron powder-diffraction peaks for structure refinement*, Acta Cryst. 22 (1967) 151, doi: https://doi.org/10.1107/S0365110X67000234.

[28] R.A. Young, D.B. Wiles, *Profile shape functions in Rietveld refinements*, J. Appl. Cryst. 15 (1982) 430–438, https://doi.org/10.1107/S002188988201231X.

[29] M. Kaholi, A. Barhoumi, Anis Bouzid, A. Al-Hajry, S. Guemazi, *Structural and optical properties of ZnO nanoparticles prepared by direct precipitation method*, Superlattices and Microstructure 85 (2015) 7–23, https://doi.org/10.1016/j.spmi.2015.05.007.

[30] Anshuman Sahai, Navendu Goswami, *Structural and vibrational properties of ZnO nanoparticles synthesized by the chemical precipitation method*, Physica E 58 (2014) 130 – 137, http://dx.doi.org/10.1016/j.physe.2013.12.009.

[31] Luke D. Geoffrion, Gregory Guisbiers, *Quantum confinement: Size on the grill!*, Journal of Physics and Chemistry of Solids 140 (2020) 109320, https://doi.org/10.1016/j.jpcs.2019.109320.

[32] M. Yousefi, M. Amiri, R. Azimirad, A.Z. Moshfegh, *Enhanced photoelectrochemical activity of Ce doped ZnO nanocomposite thin films under visible light*, Journal of Electroanalytical Chemistry 661 (2011) 106–112, https://doi.org/10.1016/j.jelechem.2011.07.022.

[33] F Wang, Z Ye, D Ma, L Zhu, F Zhuge, *Formation of quasi-aligned ZnCdO nanorods and nanoneedles*, Journal of Crystal Growth 283, (2005) 373–377, https://doi.org/10.1016/j.jcrysgro.2005.05.063.

[34] L. M. Kukreja, S. Barik and P. Mishra, *Variable band gap of ZnO nanostructures grown by pulsed laser deposition*, Journal of Crystal Growth 268 (2004) 531–535, https://doi.org/10.1016/j.jcrysgro.2004.04.086.

[35] D. C. Reynolds, D. C. Look, B. Jogai, C. W. Litton, T. C. Collins, W. Harsch, and G. Cantwell, *Neutral-donor–bound-exciton complexes in ZnO crystals*, Phys. Rev. B 57, 12151 (1998), https://doi.org/10.1103/PhysRevB.57.12151.

[36] A.K. Singh, V. Viswanath, V.C. Janu, *Synthesis, effect of capping agents, structural, optical and photoluminescence properties of ZnO nanoparticles*, Journal of Luminescence 129 (2009) 874–878, https://doi.org/10.1016/j.jlumin.2009.03.027.

[37] P.S. Xu, Y.M. Sun, C.S. Shi, F.Q. Xu, H.B. Pan, *The electronic structure and spectral properties of ZnO and its defects*, Nuclear Instruments and Methods in Physics Research B 199 (2003) 286–290, https://doi.org/10.1016/S0168-583X(02)01425-8.

[38] Z.G. Wang, X.T. Zu, S. Zhu, L.M. Wang, *Green luminescence originates from surface defects in ZnO nanoparticles*, Physica E 35 (2006) 199–202, https://doi.org/10.1016/j.physe.2006.07.022.

[39] Haibo Zeng, Guotao Duan, Yue Li, Shikuan Yang, Xiaoxia Xu, and Weiping Cai, *Blue Luminescence of ZnO Nanoparticles Based on Non-Equilibrium Processes: Defect Origins and Emission Controls*, Advanced Functional Materials 20 (2010) 561–572, https://doi.org/10.1002/adfm.200901884.

[40] Seung Chul Lyu, Ye Zhang, Hyun Ruh, Hwack-Joo Lee, Hyun-Wook Shim, Eun-Kyung Suh, Cheol Jin Lee, *Low temperature growth and photoluminescence of well-aligned zinc oxide nanowires*, Chemical Physics Letters 363 (2002) 134–138, https://doi.org/10.1016/S0009-2614(02)01145-4.

[41] B.J. Jin, S.H. Bae, S.Y. Lee, S. Im, *Effects of native defects on optical and electrical properties of ZnO prepared by pulsed laser deposition*, Materials Science and Engineering B 71 (2000) 301–305, https://doi.org/10.1016/S0921-5107(99)00395-5.

[42] T. Tatsumi, M. Fujita, N. Kavamoto, M. Sasajima, Y. Horikoshi, *Intrinsic Defects in ZnO Films Grown by Molecular Beam Epitaxy*, J. Appl. Phys. 43 (2004) 2602–2606, https://doi.org/10.1143/JJAP.43.2602.

[43] Eun-Cheol Lee, Y.-S. Kim, Y.G. Jin, and K. J. Chang, *Compensation mechanism for N acceptors in ZnO*, Phys. Rev. B 64 (2001) 085120, https://doi.org/10.1103/PhysRevB.64.085120.

[44] Anderson Janotti and Chris G. Van de Walle, *Native point defects in ZnO*, Physical Review B 76 (2007) 165202, https://doi.org/10.1103/PhysRevB.76.165202.

[45] D. C. Reynolds, D. C. Look, B. Jogai, and H. Morkoç, *Similarities in the band edge and deep-centre photoluminescence mechanisms of ZnO and GaN*, Solid State Commun. 101 (1997) 643–646, https://doi.org/10.1016/S0038-1098(96)00697-7.

[46] D. C. Reynolds, D. C. Look, B. Jogai, J. E. Van Nostrand, R. Jones, and J. Jenny, *Source of the yellow luminescence band in GaN grown by gas-source molecular beam epitaxy and the green luminescence band in single crystal ZnO*, Solid State Commun. 106 (1998) 701–704, https://doi.org/10.1016/S0038-1098(98)00048-9.

[47] A. F. Kohan, G. Ceder, D. Morgan, and Chris G. Van de Walle, *First-principles study of native point defects in ZnO*, Phys. Rev. B 61, (2000) 15019–15027, https://doi.org/10.1103/PhysRevB.61.15019.

[48] R. Vidya, P. Ravindran, H. Fjellvag, B. G. Svensson, E. Monakhov, M. Ganchenkova,and R. M. Nieminen, *Energetics of intrinsic defects and their complexes in ZnO investigated by density functional calculations*, Physical Review B 83, (2011) 045206, https://doi.org/10.1103/PhysRevB.83.045206.

[49] Andrew Bah, Kim Yong Lim, Fuhua Wei, Anjam Khursheed, Chorng Haur Sow, "*Fluorescence Invigoration in Carbon-Incorporated Zinc Oxide Nanowires from Passage of Field Emission Electrons*", Scientific Reports 9 (2019) 9671, doi: https://doi.org/10.1038/s41598-019-46177-w.

[50] C. Ton-That, L. Weston, and M. R. Phillips, *Characteristics of point defects in the green luminescence from Zn- and O-rich ZnO*, Physical Review B 86, (2012) 115205, https://doi.org/10.1103/PhysRevB.86.115205.

[51] C. Li, G. Fang, Q. Fu, F. Su, G. Li, X.Z. Wu, X. Zhao, *Effect of substrate temperature on the growth and photoluminescence properties of vertically aligned ZnO nanostructures*, Journal of Crystal Growth 292 (2006) 19–25, https://doi.org/10.1016/j.jcrysgro.2006.03.061.

[52] Y.R. Sui, Y. Cao, X.F. Li, Y.G. Yue, B. Yao, J.H. Lang, X.Y. Li, J.H. Yang, *Effects of Cd concentration on structure and optical properties of the ternary* $Zn_{1-x}Cd_xO$ *nanopowder prepared by sol–gel method*, Physica E: Low-dimensional Systems and Nanostructures, Volume 70, 2015, Pages 46-51, https://doi.org/10.1016/j.physe.2015.02.021.

IOP Conf. Series: Materials Science and Engineering 1263 (2022) 012010 doi:10.1088/1757-899X/1263/1/012010

Photocatalytic dye degradation efficiency of Co doped ZnO nanostructure

Nithya S George[1], Lolly M Jose[1] and Arun Aravind[1]

[1]Center for Advanced Functional Materials (CAFM), Department of Physics, Bishop Moore College Mavelikara, Alappuzha District, Kerala, India

E-mail: arun@bishopmoorecollege.org

Abstract. The influence of transition metal doping on the dye degradation efficiency of ZnO nanostructures are investigated by pristine and 3% Co doped ZnO nanostructures (Co: ZnO) grown by simple hydrothermal method. Phase purity and crystal structure of synthesized samples are revealed by X-ray diffraction (XRD) and the spectra confirms the phase pure material with hexagonal wurtzite structure. The crystalline size is found to decrease with Co doping. Optical characterization was done by UV-Visible absorption spectroscopy. Optical study confirms that the band gap energy of the samples during doping with Co decreases as compared to pure ZnO. The photocatalytic activity of the synthesized samples under sunlight over the Crystal Violet (CV)dye was investigated for pure and doped samples. The result showed that the pure ZnO samples act as an efficient material for photocatalysis as compared to 3% Co doped sample.

1. Introduction

Mankind is driving himself towards sustainable development. Wastewater treatment is an essential component for this. Transition Metal Oxides (TMOs) are explored for various application studies including wastewater treatment due to their unique characteristics. Among various metal oxides, ZnO has been studied a lot due to its flexible, notable features among different fields. ZnO having a wide energy gap of 3.3 eV, large exciton binding energy (60meV), long term stability, n type conductivity and good transparency reported as an efficient photocatalyst. The rapid recombination of photogenerated electrons and holes decreases the photocatalytic efficiency of ZnO nanostructure [1,2]. Therefore, it is needed to suppress the recombination of charge carriers to achieve higher efficiency since the photocatalytic efficiency depends on the transfer of these charge carriers. This can be achieved by modifying the surface or by doping with proper transition metals. Transition metals act as the center for capturing the photogenerated electrons and holes from ZnO and thus blocking the recombination. It can tune the band gap energy of the ZnO nanostructure [3,4].

Our main aim is to investigate how cobalt doping affects the photocatalytic dye degradation efficiency of the ZnO nanostructure. The reason for carrying out this work is based on the wide band gap of pure ZnO nanostructure, where photocatalytic dye degradation is mainly attributed due to absorption around the UV region. In a practical case since the solar spectrum consists of around 7% UV radiation and almost 47% visible light and infrared radiation. Therefore, the study focuses on transition metal doping on ZnO nanostructure for decreasing its band gap and thereby increasing its efficiency. To use natural sunlight for dye degradation application, the band gap of ZnO has to be reduced and thus cut into narrow gaps. Among other transition metals, cobalt (Co) possesses similar ionic radii (around 0.08nm) to that of ZnO (0.074nm). The size of nanocrystals varied and bandgap of the materials get modified by the influence of Co on the ZnO crystal [5]. Co can able to modulate the optical bandgap energy of the pristine sample due to the presence of abundant electron states. Photocatalytic dye degradation studies of ZnO and transition metal doped ZnO nanostructures were already reported. People are exploring the future aspects for device fabrication. Studies on Methylene Blue, Methyl Orange dye degradation by ZnO nanostructures were well explored already [6,7]. Crystal violet is highly flammable in its solution state, harmful to both mankind and environment and can cause cancerous cell generation within body [5]. Few studies are done for photocatalytic dye degradation of Crystal Violet dye by hydrothermally prepared Co doped ZnO nanostructures. Thus, we have chosen this material to explore its possibilities in device fabrication for future studies. Another notable point paved light onto is the minimized reaction time taken for the synthesis of Co doped ZnO nanostructures. In this work, the photocatalytic activity of ZnO and Co: ZnO (3%) were examined using Crystal Violet (CV) as model dye along with sample characterization using Xray Diffraction (XRD), UV Visible spectroscopy.

2. Experimental details

2.1. Synthesis of ZnO and Co: ZnO nanostructures

Pure ZnO nanostructure was synthesized by taking a required quantity of Zinc Nitrate as the metal precursor. pH of the solution was adjusted using NaOH and after stirring the solution to make a homogenous dispersion for half an hour. It is placed in hydrothermal oven for 150°C with 3h time duration. After the prescribed reaction time, it is properly filtered out, washed using DI water and dried in oven. For the preparation of Co doped ZnO nanoparticle synthesis, 3% Cobalt nitrate is mixed with the Zinc Nitrate solution as mentioned above. After that, the procedure followed the same as that in case of synthesis of pure ZnO samples.

2.2. Photocatalytic application study of prepared samples

Photocatalytic dye degradation performance of ZnO and Co: ZnO samples carried out under natural sunlight using Crystal Violet (CV) dye. 200mL of CV solution with an initial concentration of 10 ppm taken. 10 mg of prepared nanoparticles were added to the uniform solution of dye and kept in dark with stirring to attain the adsorption desorption equilibrium. It is then placed under sunlight for irradiation. After regular time duration, UV Visible spectra were taken by using the spectrometer and recorded. Photocatalytic dye degradation efficiency of the samples was calculated using the expression (equation (1)):

$$\text{Degradation rate } \eta\ (\%) = \frac{C_0 - C}{C_0} \times 100\% = \frac{A_0 - A}{A_0} \times 100\% \quad (1)$$

Where C_0 refers to the concentration of dye solution at time t=0 minute and C, the final concentration of the solution [4].

2.3. Effect of pH on CV dye degradation

Effect of pH on dye degradation were investigated by varying the pH from 3 to 7 (3,5 and 7) using HCl and NaOH. 20ml of 10ppm dye solution were separated and pH is adjusted. Adding 10mg photocatalyst into the stock solution and after attaining adsorption desorption equilibrium, placed under solar irradiation. UV Vis spectra measurement taken at regular interval of time.

2.4. Characterization of ZnO and Co: ZnO samples

X-ray diffraction analysis (XRD) of prepared samples was done using the Xray diffractometer (D8 Advanced Bruker instrument) using Cu- Kα radiation (λ= 1.5417 Å), scanning angle 2θ between 20° -80°. By using Jasco V 570 UV-Vis NIR spectrophotometer, UV Visible absorption spectra recorded in the range of 200 to 800 nm for optical and photocatalytic measurements.

3. Results and discussion

3.1. X-ray Diffraction analysis

The purity of the prepared samples and the crystal structure were known from X-ray diffraction analysis (XRD). Here the spectra (figure 1) show peaks corresponding to (100), (002) and (101) planes which are best indexed to the standard datasheet (JCPDS 0.36-1451) of hexagonal wurtzite ZnO nanostructure with P63mc space group [2]. No other secondary peaks or impurities were noticed which confirms the proper doping of Co over ZnO crystal lattice. Also, it proved that the original crystal structure of ZnO nanostructure was not affected by doping with Co. By the Debye Scherrer formula, the crystalline size can be calculated. Average crystalline size can be found by using the following expression (equation (2)):

$$D = \frac{0.9\lambda}{\beta\cos\theta} \quad (2)$$

Where D, the average crystalline size in nm, λ refers to the Xray wavelength (1.5141Å), θ corresponds to the Braggs angle in degrees and β full width half maximum (FWHM) in radians. The average crystalline size of as-prepared samples calculated for ZnO, the size is 21.02nm and for Co: ZnO, it is 19.552 nm. The size of the sample was found to be decreased on doping by 3% Co. Decrease in size of the doped sample may be due to transition metal doping which suppresses the nucleation and growth rate [6]. It is best explained by D Bryan et al in terms of classical nucleation model. Even though the ionic radii are similar, doping of Co^{2+} creates lattice strain which corresponds to the dependency with lattice parameters [Vegard's law]. The lattice strain induced due to Co^{2+} addition results in much difficulty for Co: ZnO sample nucleation than pure ZnO, thus reducing the growth rate [9,11]. Micro strain presence on the sample was evaluated by Williamson Hall (W-H) method. By plotting 4sinθ against βcosθ (figure 2), the average crystalline size can be calculated and the values were tabulated in table 1. From the slope of the graph, strain can be found and from the y-intercept, crystalline size can be calculated.

IOP Conf. Series: Materials Science and Engineering 1263 (2022) 012010 doi:10.1088/1757-899X/1263/1/012010

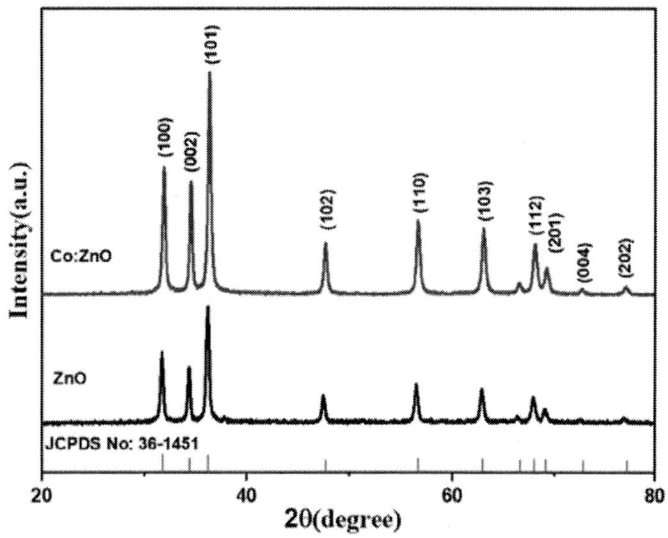

Figure 1. XRD spectra of ZnO and 3% Co: ZnO nanostructure

Table 1. Crystalline size and micro-strain calculation from Debye Scherrer and W-H plot method.

Sample ID	By Debye- Scherrer formula		By W-H method	
	Average D(nm)	Average strain	Average D(nm)	Average strain
ZnO	21.023	0.0041223	39.98	0.00172
Co: ZnO	19.552	0.0041223	36.41	0.00139

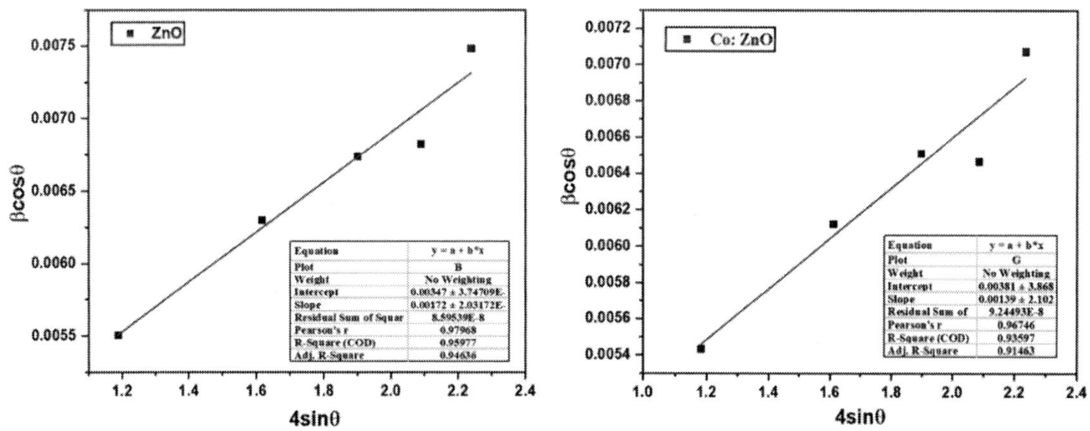

Figure 2. W-H plot of hydrothermally synthesized ZnO and Co: ZnO Nanostructures

3.2. UV Visible spectra analysis

Optical absorption spectra were recorded to study the nature of electronic transition in the material. From the spectra (figure 3), it is seen that a strong absorption band around 370 to 395 nm. Absorbance spectra of the ZnO sample seem to be decreased around 380 nm. Also, the band edge of Co: ZnO nanostructure shifted towards a longer wavelength region compared to ZnO band spectra. The observed redshift in the doped sample as being due to the sp-d exchange interactions between the band electrons and localized d electrons of doped Co^{2+} ions over the ZnO lattice [1]. By Tauc plot relation (equation (3)), value of optical band gap energy of the material was calculated using the expression,

$$\alpha h\vartheta = A\left(h\vartheta - E_g\right)^n \tag{3}$$

Where A is the proportionality constant, h is the planck's constant, ϑ refers to the incident photon frequency (Hz), E_g is the bandgap energy(eV) and n is the power factor which has values ½ for direct allowed transitions, 3/2 for direct forbidden and 2 or 3 for indirect allowed or indirect forbidden transitions. n=1/2 is taken here because ZnO is a direct band gap material [3].

Extrapolating the linear portion of the graph connecting (hϑ) and $(\alpha h\vartheta)^2$, energy band gap of the samples can be found, 3.2 eV for ZnO and 3.14 eV for Co: ZnO sample. Reduction in band gap with Co doping resulted due to the reason of s-d and p-d interaction which causes negative and positive correlation to the conduction band and valence band separately.

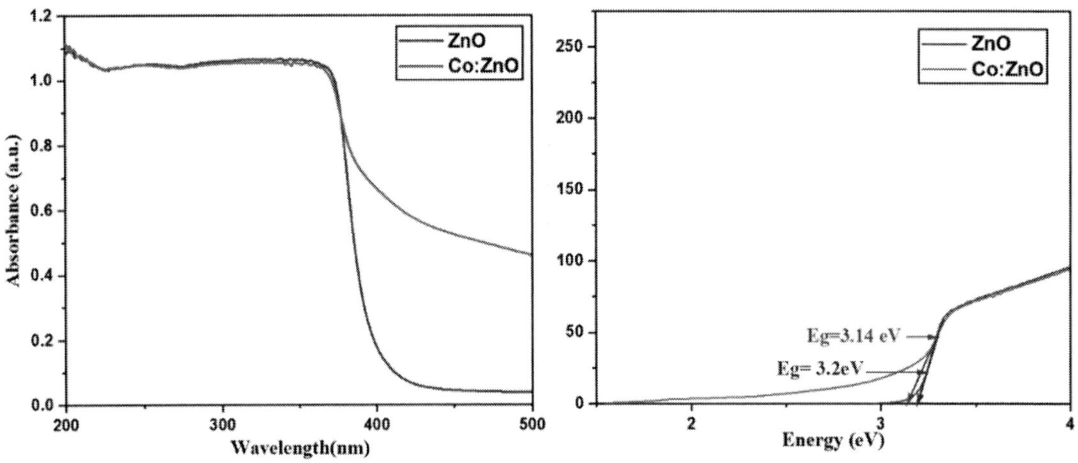

Figure 3. UV Visible absorption study – Absorption spectra and tauc plot corresponding to ZnO and Co: ZnO nanorods.

Band gap energy of the material was also found by using the Boltzmann fitting method to get a more accurate value (figure 4). It is expressed as the following empirical relation (equation (4)):

$$E_{gap}^{Boltz} = E_0^{Boltz} - n_{dir-ind}^{Boltz} \times \delta E \tag{4}$$

Where n_{dir}^{Boltz} is 0.3 and n_{ind}^{Boltz} is 4.3 as calculated experimentally for direct and indirect optical bandgaps [8].

By Boltzmann fitting, the band gap energy values for ZnO and Co: ZnO samples were found as 3.2 and 2.9 eV respectively.

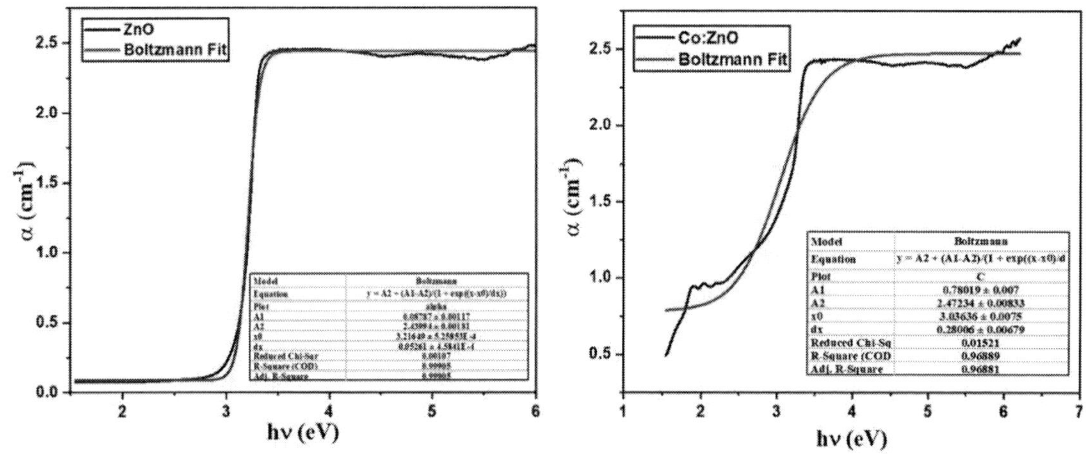

Figure 4. Boltzmann fit curves for band gap energy calculation of ZnO and Co: ZnO nanostructure.

3.3. Photocatalytic dye degradation

Photocatalytic degradation of polluting dyes can be studied over two steps. The primary stage includes the adsorption of dye over the ZnO nanocrystal surface. The second step involves the irradiation of these adsorbed dyes with natural sunlight which resulted in the generation of exciton pairs. The photogenerated negative charge carriers in the conduction band of ZnO react with oxygen species adsorbed on the surface of ZnO forming superoxide radicals(O_2^-). On the other hand, the holes at the valence band interact with the hydroxy groups to develop highly active hydroxyl radicals (OH). It also resulted in the production of OH radicals in water molecules. These highly reactive radicals react with organic dye which results in the degradation and decoloration of dye solution [4].

Percentage degradation of CV dye by ZnO and Co: ZnO samples were calculated using equation (1) and found as 44.4% and 34.96% respectively (figure 5). While we studied this particular compound, although we expected the properties to get enhanced, what happened was the other. But our study was helpful in finding these particular characteristics of ZnO nanostructure so that it has its own characteristic features. Photocatalytic dye degradation activity of ZnO nanoparticle is due to the presence of defect states which creates as a result of donor and acceptor states, including oxygen vacancies, interstitial Zn atoms and Zinc vacancy, interstitial oxygen respectively. This resulted in the electron transfer between the donor states and the dye. Cationic CV dye absorbs these donor state electrons and results in the decomposition of dye. The decrease in the photocatalytic dye degradation rate of Co: ZnO sample may be due to the lack of generation of active OH radicals to sustain the photocatalytic activity [7]. As we can observe in reported works, one of the factors that enhances the photocatalytic efficiency of a nano catalyst is the reduction in the bandgap along with other properties such as surface area, fast charge transfer rate, thermal stability, etc. But in this case, we could observe a decrease in photocatalytic efficiency of ZnO nanostructures. Similar observation was marked by Lima et al and Turkyilmaz et al [10,11]. The decrease in photocatalytic efficiency upon Fe, Co, Ni and Mn doping on ZnO lattice were also reported in a detailed review paper [12]. A table comparing the photocatalytic degradation of different transition metal doped ZnO nanostructures were tabulated in Table 2. The reduction in photocatalytic activity of the Co doped ZnO nanostructures might be due to the generation of various defects or vacancies along with this the deepening of bandgap levels between the valence band and conduction band also lead to the increased recombination rate for the photoinduced charge carriers. Thus, reducing the amount of active OH and O^{2-} radicals for the effective photodegradation of CV dye. It can also be explained using the band tailing parameter.

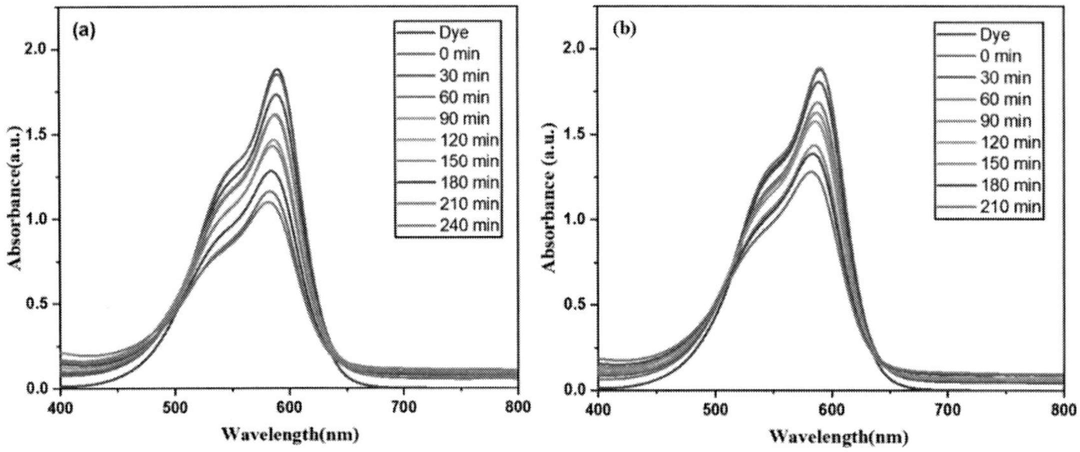

Figure 5. Absorbance spectra of CV dye using (a) ZnO nanostructure (b) degradation of CV with Co: ZnO nanostructure

The variability observed in CV concentration with sunlight exposure time for ZnO and Co: ZnO as photocatalyst were graphically plotted and fitted data were represented in figure 6. It follows pseudo first-order kinetics as follows:

$$\ln\left(\frac{C}{C_0}\right) = Kt \quad (5)$$

Where C corresponds to the concentration of reactant at time t, C_0 refers to the concentration at t=0 minute, K represents the rate constant and t, the time [5]. The graph connecting ln C/C_0 vs exposure time is shown in figure 6. From the pseudo first order kinetic relation (equation (5)), there seems a linear relationship between $\ln(C/C_0)$ and sunlight irradiation time. The photoreaction rate was found to be highest for ZnO. High-rate constant implies better photocatalytic activity. Thus, from the present study, it can be concluded that ZnO pure sample chosen to be a better candidate for photocatalytic study compared to doped ZnO sample. It is expected to have a higher degradation rate, by tuning the dopant in the ZnO crystal structure.

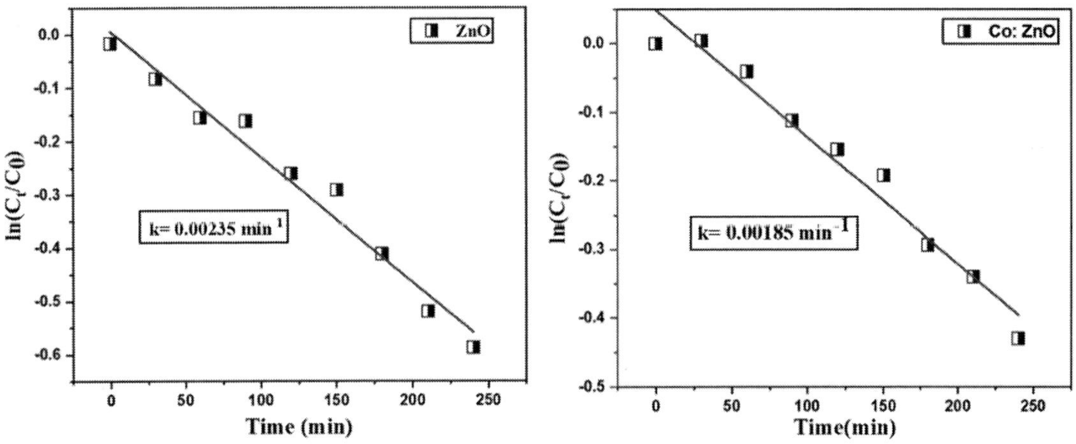

Figure 6. ln (C_t/C_0) vs Time curve of ZnO and Co: ZnO nanostructures hydrothermally prepared at 150^0C for 3h

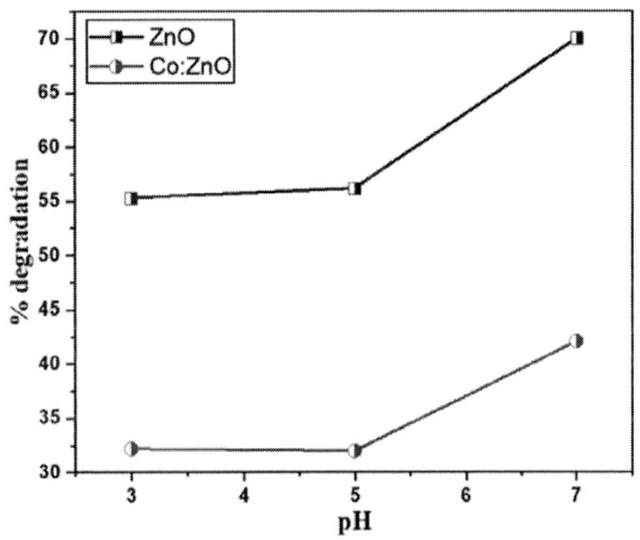

Figure 7. Percentage degradation of CV dye by ZnO and Co doped ZnO nanostructures with various solution pH after at time t=60min

For analysing the effect of pH in order to confirm the photocatalytic efficiency of ZnO nanostructure, solution pH is varied and observed the results (figure 7). On investigating the effect of pH on dye degradation of CV dye, notable reduction in the photocatalytic degradation was observed. As pH value increased from 3 to 7, the degradation increased up to 42% within 60min for Co doped ZnO sample. For ZnO nanostructure, the efficiency increased to 70% within one hour. The solution pH has significant effect in the degradation of dye which can be optimised in order to get better efficiency [7]. The efficiency of ZnO further confirmed by this study.

Table 2. Comparison study on photocatalytic activity of various transition metal doped ZnO nanostructures.

Coupled photocatalyst	Pollutant dye	Light source used	Degradation / Time (%/ min)		Reference
			ZnO	TM[a] doped ZnO	
In/ ZnO	Crystal Violet	UV	86/ 210	85/210	5
Fe/ ZnO	Tartrazine	427nm	93.7/ 60	43/60	11
Co/ ZnO	Methylene Blue	UV	high	low	2
Mn/ ZnO	Tartrazine	427nm	93.7/ 60	27.6/60	11
Mn/ ZnO	Methylene Blue	Sunlight	high	low	13
Co/ ZnO	Methyl Orange	Sunlight	70/60	42/60	This work

[a] TM corresponds to Transition Metal

4. Conclusion

By the low-cost hydrothermal method, pure and Co: ZnO nanostructures were prepared successfully. XRD analysis reveals the hexagonal wurtzite structure of the ZnO nanoparticle. Crystalline size was found to decrease with Co doping and is expected to be effective for catalytic application. UV Visible spectra analysis showed a redshift in the band gap energy on doping. Photocatalytic dye degradation of CV dye over ZnO and Co: ZnO photocatalyst were investigated and it is evident that ZnO shows better catalytic performance. A better combination of transition metal doping was planned to be done for future application studies.

References

[1] Chao Xu, Lixin Cao, Ge Su, Wei Liu, Xiaofei Qu and Yaqin Yu 2010 Preparation, characterization and photocatalytic activity of Co-doped ZnO powders *J.Alloys Compd.* **497** 373–376

[2] Manjula G N, Nirmala M, Rekha K and Anukaliani A 2011 Structural, optical, photo catalytic and antibacterial activity of ZnO and Co doped ZnO nanoparticles *Mater. Lett.* **65** 1797–1800

[3] Raghavendra B, Parutagouda S P, Shivaraj R M, Vijeth H, Murari M. S.d and Udaya B K 2019 The role of cobalt doping in tuning the band gap, surface morphology and third-order optical nonlinearities of ZnO nanostructures for NLO device applications *RSC Adv.* **9** 22302

[4] Sini K, Biswarup S and Satyabrata M 2014 Enhanced photocatalytic activity of Co doped ZnO nanodisks and nanorods prepared by a facile wet chemical method *Phys. Chem. Chem. Phys.* **16** 12741

[5] Ben A S, BelHadjltaief H, Duponchel B, Leroy G, Amlouk M, Guermazi H, Guermazi S 2019 Enhanced photocatalytic activity against crystal violet dye of Co and In doped ZnO thin films grown on PEI flexible substrate under UV and sunlight irradiations *Heliyon.* **5** e01912Another reference

[6] Muthukumaran S and Gopalakrishnan R 2012 Structural, FTIR and photoluminescence studies of Cu doped ZnO nanopowders by co-precipitation method *Opt. Mater. (Amst).* **34** no. 11 pp. 1946–1953

[7] Manish M, Manoj S and Pandey O P 2014 UV–Visible light induced photocatalytic studies of Cu

doped ZnO nanoparticles prepared by co-precipitation method *Sol. Energy.* **110** 386–397

[8] Zanatta A R 2019 Revisiting the optical bandgap of semiconductors and the proposal of a unified methodology to its determination *nature.* **9** 11225

[9] Bryan, J. Daniel Schwartz, Dana A and Gamelin, Daniel R 2005 Critical Nucleus Size, Composition, and Energetics in the Synthesis of Doped ZnO Quantum Dots (arXiv preprint cond-mat/0502079)

[10] M K Lima et al 2014 Co- doped ZnO nanoparticles synthesized by an adapted sol- gel method: effects on the structural, optical, photocatalytic and antibacterial properties *J Sol-Gel Sci Technol* **72** 301–309

[11] Türkyılmaz Ş Ş, Güy N, and Özacar, M 2017 Photocatalytic efficiencies of Ni, Mn, Fe and Ag doped ZnO nanostructures synthesized by hydrothermal method: The synergistic/antagonistic effect between ZnO and metals *Journal of Photochemistry and Photobiology A: Chemistry*, **341** 39–50

[12] Samadi M, Zirak M, Naseri A, Khorashadizade E and Moshfegh A Z 2016 Recent progress on doped ZnO nanostructures for visible-light photocatalysis *Thin Solid Films* **605** 2–19.

[13] Rekha K, Nirmala M, Nair M G and Anukaliani A 2010 Structural, optical, photocatalytic and antibacterial activity of zinc oxide and manganese doped zinc oxide nanoparticles *Physica B: Condensed Matter* **405**(15) 3180–3185.

Cadmium sulphide nanoparticles from Cadmium (II) complex of (Cyclododecylidineamino)thiourea

Jisha George[1], V S Lekha[1], G RathikaNath[2] and K.Rajesh[1,*]

[1]Department of Chemistry, University College (Research Centre, University of Kerala) Trivandrum-695034, (Kerala) India

[2]Department of Chemistry, KSM DB College (Research Centre, University of Kerala) Sasthamcotta-690521, (Kerala) India

*rajesh_k_k@yahoo.com

ABSTRACT Novel ligand (Cyclododecylidineamino)thiourea (CDDATU) and its Cadmium (II) complex were synthesized and characterized by IR, CHNS and Thermo gravimetric analysis.The complex was found to give highly crystalline, good quality, mono-dispersed Cadmium sulphide nanoparticles through polyol synthesis method using Glycerol as high boiling solvent. Characterization of Cadmium sulphide nanoparticles were done using SEM, EDX, TEM, UV, PL and PXRD studies.

1. INTRODUCTION

Cadmium chalcogenide semiconductor nanoparticles show size dependent optical, electric and magnetic properties[1]. These nanocrystals could be prepared by a number of different synthetic techniques[2]. One of them is the Single Source Molecular Precursor (SSMP) method. It is an effective way for manufacturing defect free, high-quality nano materials with large surface areas and superior stoichiometric constitution[3]. The technique started with the work of Brennan et al in 1989[4].To synthesize semiconductor nanoparticles with uniform metal ion distribution at the molecular level, various researchers developed this method to a special approach of nano-synthesis to be known as the Single Source Molecular Precursor approach[5].

Direct band gaps for wurtzite structure CdS, and bulk cubic zinc blend are 2.4 EV and 3.53 EV respectively[6]. Also it shows high phosphorescence in the visible region[7]. It finds many applications in various fields like photochemical degradation, photodetector, solar, etc among others.

This workdeals with the application of Cadmium complex of freshly prepared (Cyclododecylidineamino)thiourea, CDDATU as SSMP in preparation of Cadmium sulphide nanoparticles. The common name of the ligand having the IUPAC name

(Cyclododecylidineamino)thiourea is Cyclododecanonethiosemicarbazone as it is derived from the reaction between Cyclododecanone and thiosemicarbazide.

2. EXPERIMENTAL

2.1. Synthesis of (Cyclododecylidineamino)thiourea(CDDATU) Ligand

Thiosemicarbazide (0.18226 g, 2mM), and Cyclododecanone (0.3085 g, 2mM) were mixed in methanol and refluxed for three hours. A white crystalline precipitate was got. The yield percentage was 82%. Elemental analysis report : Calculated (Found) for CDDTSC ($C_{13}H_{25}N_3S$) : C, 61.2 (61.1) ; H, 9.8 (9.9) ; N, 16.4 (16.4) ; S, 12.4 (12.3). Significant **IR** bands: 3403, 3218 (sym&asym NH_2), 3142 (N-H) , 1591 (C=N) , 1073 (N-N), 1371, 861 ν/δ(C=S). IR was taken using KBr pellet method.

H^1NMR (500MHz, $CDCl_3$, ppm) : 8.64 (1H s N-H), 7.20(1H b s NH_2), 6.18(1H b s NH_2), 2.3525, 2.264 (2H t, J=2.25Hz , 6.5 Hz C(3, 13)H_2), 1.71 (2H s C(12)H_2), 1.64 (2H t J=7.1 Hz C(11)H_2), 1.335-1.25 (14H m C(4-10)H_2. **MS (EI**, amu) : 278.17 $[C_{13}H_{25}N_3S+Na]^+$, 256.17 $[C_{13}H_{25}N_3S+H]^+$, 239.16 $[C_{13}H_{23}N_2S]^+$, $[C_{12}H_{22}N]^+$.

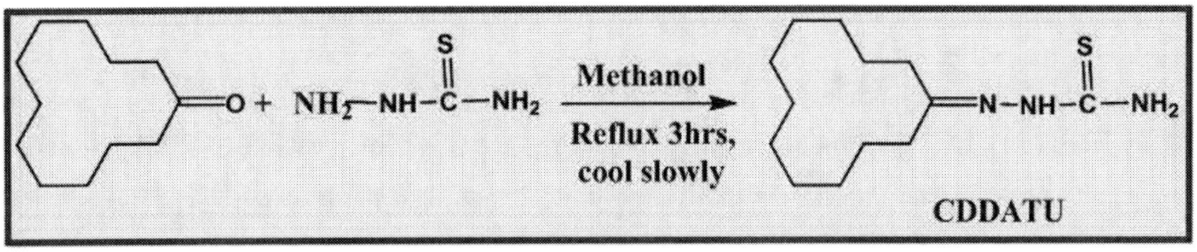

Scheme 1. Synthesis of (Cyclododecylideneamino)thiourea

2.2. Synthesis of Cd(II) complex of CDDATU Ligand

The ligand (CDDATU) and $Cd(OOCCH_3)_2.2H_2O$, both as 0.1 M solutions in methanol were mixed in 2:1 ratio by continuous stirring with a glass rod. Formation of Cd(II) complex was indicated by the appearance of yellow coloration. By refluxing for three hours, the reaction was brought to a close. Percentage Yield was 74%. Anal. Cal. For Cd(II) Complex, ($C_{30}H_{56}N_6S_2O_4Cd$) : C, 57.32 ; H, 8.92 ; N, 13.38 ; S, 10.19. Found : C, 57.14 ; H, 8.73 ; N, 13.40 ; S, 10.15.

IR (KBr, ν =cm^{-1}) :3401, 3285 (NH_2sym. and assym.), 3169 (N-H), 1597 (C=N) , 1107 (N-N), 1313,836 ν/δ(C=S), 563,507 (M-N), 457 (M-S).

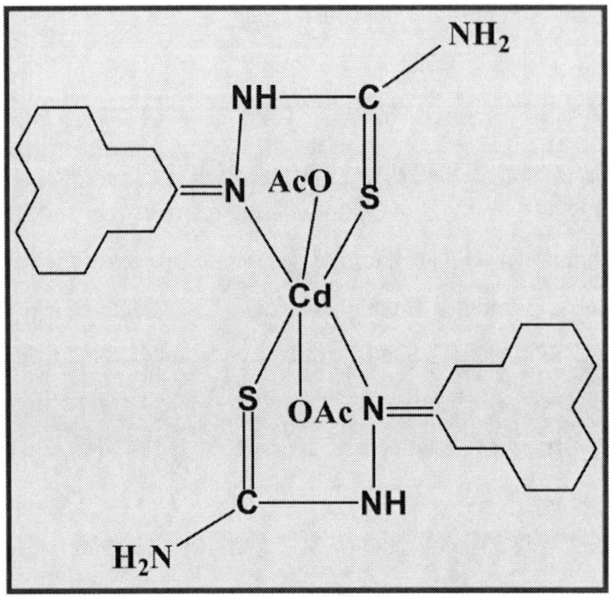

Scheme 2: Structure proposed for Cd(II) complex of CDDATU

2.3. Synthesis of nanoparticles

An amount of 15 ml of glycerol was heated to boiling (297 °C). A known volume of SSMP (the above-prepared metal complex), dispersed in glycerol itself, is added to the boiling solvent using a glass syringe and a long needle after sonication at 75 °C for 15 minutes. The boiling solution's temperature abruptly dropped by about 70°C. Annealed for 20 minutes by briefly boiling and then added to a beaker containing about 20 mL methanol to cause CdS nano regime precipitation. The precipitated CdS was then dried after filtration and washing with methanol.

3. RESULTS AND DISCUSSION

Though IUPAC name denotes the ligand as a derivative of thiourea, it is actually a thiosemicarbazone synthesized by a simpler procedure. Cd(II) complex, which was the precursor for synthesis of cadmium sulphide nanoparticles, was prepared from the ligand (Cyclododecylidineamino)thiourea (CDDATU). Thermal decomposition of this precursor Cd(II)complex in high boiling solvent glycerol (boiling point 297°C) yield CdS nanoparticles. The ligand, complex and synthesized CdS nanoparticles were characterized by various studies.

3.1. Characterisation of CDDATU and its Cd(II) Complex

3.1.1. IR:

The NH2 and NHCS vibrations are attributed to the broad medium intensity bands detected at (3401-3201) &(3180-3140) cm^{-1}, respectively[8,9]. They were only marginally impacted by the coordination, which suggests that these groups do not coordinate during complex creation. As expected, aliphatic ring vibrations are detected between 2850 and 2950 cm-1. The absence of any band between 2500 and 2800 cm^{-1}, which corresponds to S-H, is evidence of the ligand's thione tautomer existence[10–14]. On complexation, the 1592 cm^{-1} band caused by (C=N) of ligand was blue shifted due to the bond's increased strength, which strengthened N-H bond in the amide group[13–17]. The coordination of nitrogen by azomethine is confirmed by a strong band (1075 cm^{-1}) of N-N stretching vibrations. A blue shift of this band in the spectrum of the cadmium complex is caused by bond strength increase[13–16,18]. The spectrum is quite complicated as a result of the several bands that the general C=S group connected to N produces absorption at 1560 - 700 cm^{-1}. But ν/(C=S) stretching and bending vibrations of C=S group can be mapped to strong absorptions at 1357–1380 cm^{-1} and medium intensity vibrations at 838–892 cm^{-1}, regions respectively. Drop in both vibrational frequency and intensity in the spectrum of cadmium complex indicates weakening of C=S bond due to coordination of Sulphur with Cadmium[19]. Additional absorption bands in 575–500 & 455-500 cm^{-1} regions are respectively caused by M-N and M-S bond vibrations, in the cadmium complex. As a result, the ligand CDDATU undergoes coordination in neutral mode through azomethine N and thione S in its Cadmium complex, where it is bidentate. Figure 1 is the IR spectra of CDDATU and its Cd(II) complex..

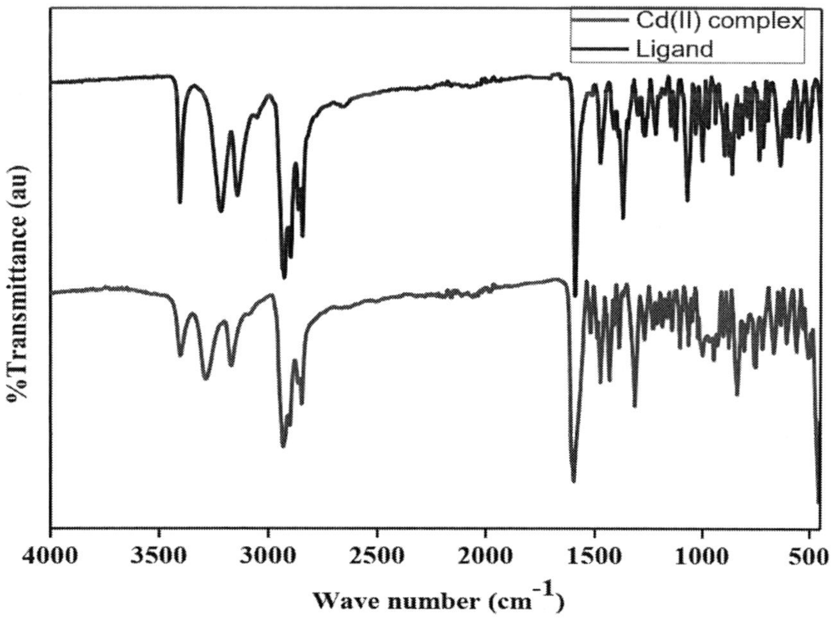

Figure 1. CDDATU and complex with Cd(II)- IR spectra

3.1.2. H[1]NMR spectrum of CDDATU

H[1]NMR spectrum of CDDATU (Figure 2) was taken in $CDCl_3$. The peak for the solvent is found at 7.264 ppm, and the peak for water in $CDCl_3$ is found at 1.596 ppm. The molecule exists as its thione tautomer because there are no peaks that can be assigned to the secondary N-H proton at 8.647 ppm and there is a broad 1H singlet at that location. The two NH_2 protons are in two separate chemical environments because they integrate into two, one at 7.220 ppm (chemical shifts in δ) and the other at 6.179 ppm (broad singlets). C(3)H_2 and C(13)H_2 are represented by two 2H triplets, at 2.3525 (J=6.25 Hz) and 2.264 ppm (J=6.5 Hz) respectively. C(12)H_2 protons are represented by a 2H singlet at 1.709 ppm, and C(11)H_2 protons are represented by a 2H triplet (J=7 Hz) centred at 1.642 ppm. A multiplet at (1.335-1.255) integrates as a 14H peak in the spectrum and can be attributed to C(4-10)H_2 protons that are strongly coupled to their neighboring protons[13,14].

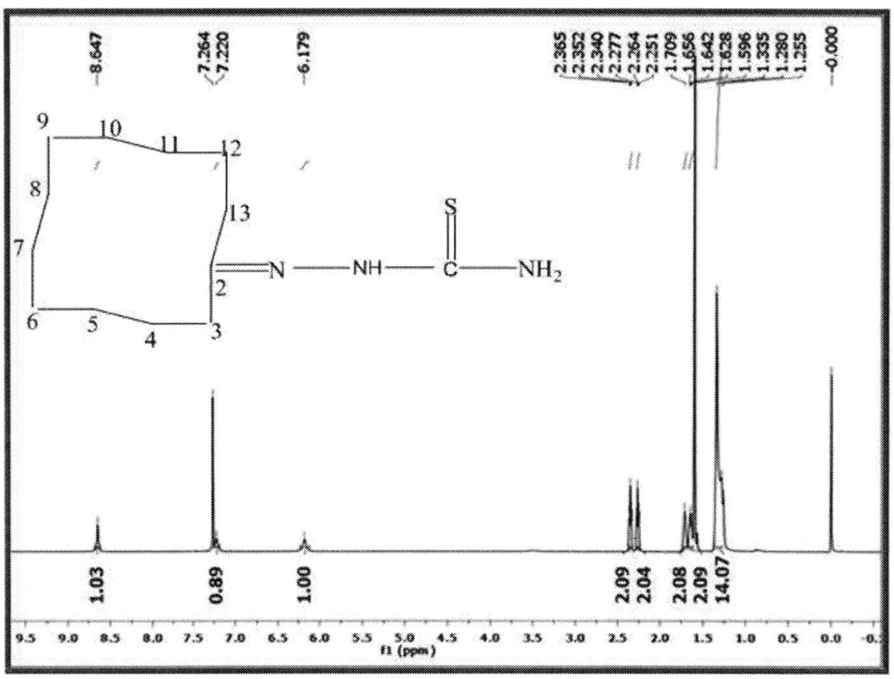

Figure.2. H[1]NMR spectrum of CDDATU

3.1.3. EI-MS spectrum of CDDATU

In EI-MS spectrum for the compound CDDATU, [$C_{13}H_{25}N_3S$] (Figure 3),the M^+ or parent ion peak should have been at m/z 255 amu. But in the obtained spectrum, there is an adduct peak correspond to the species [$C_{13}H_{25}N_3S$+Na] at m/z 278.17 amu. A peak at m/z 256.18 amu correspond to the species [$C_{13}H_{25}N_3S$+H], [M+H] was also found. Also there are two fragment peaks at m/z values 239.15 amu and 180.17 amu, correspond to the species [$C_{13}H_{23}N_2S$] and [$C_{12}H_{22}N$] respectively. They might have developed as a result of the ligand molecule losing its NH2 and NHCSNH2 atoms, respectively.

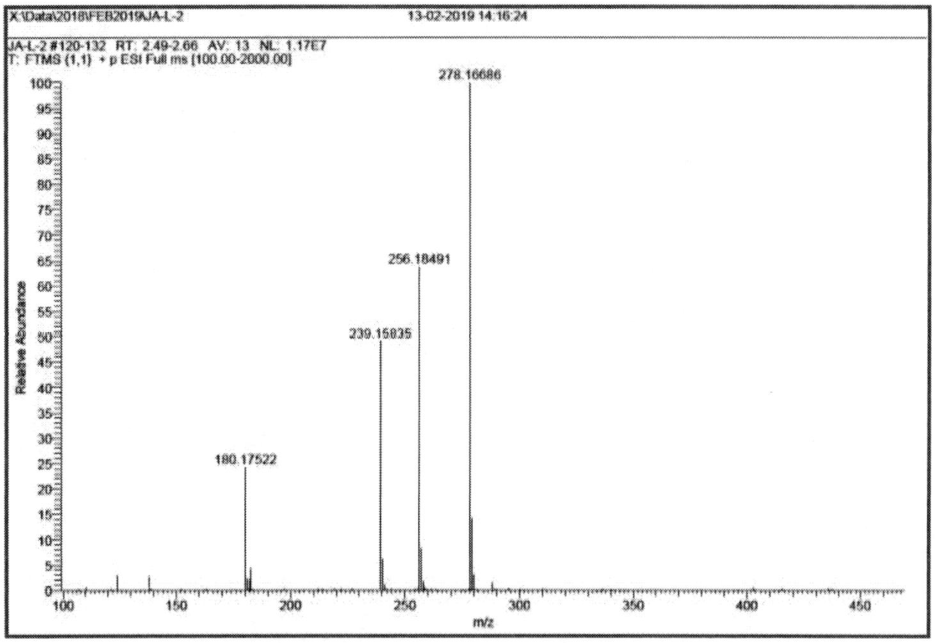

Fig. 3. EI-MS Spectrum of CDDATU

3.1.4. Thermal studies of Cd(II) complex

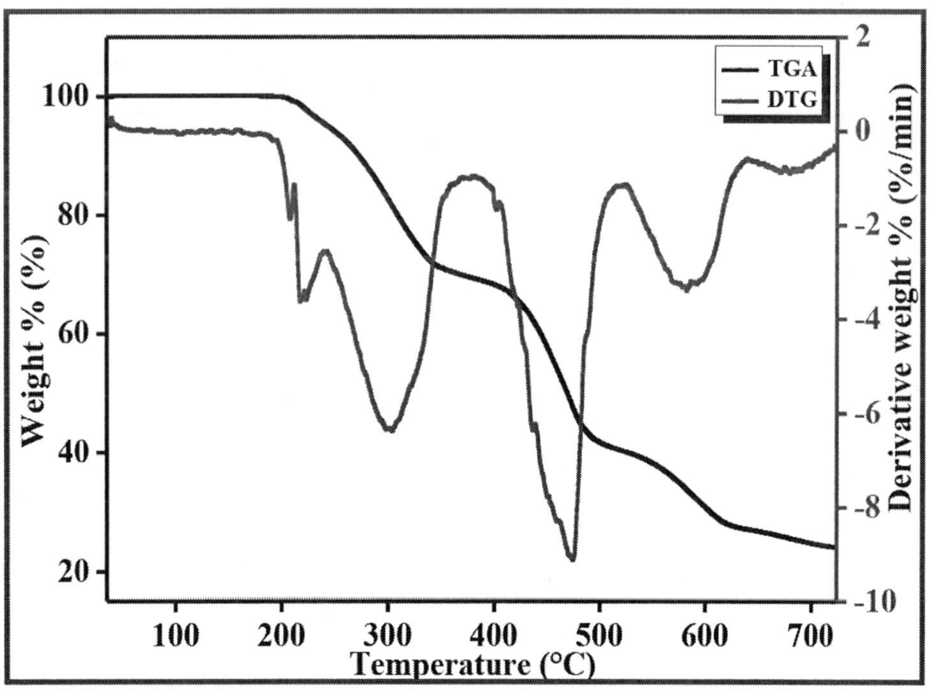

Figure. 4. Thermo Gravimetric Analysis curves for the Cadmium complex

TG was taken from 20°C to 700°C in N_2 and is given in figure 4.The Cd(II) complex undergoes decomposition in 4 stages. The 1st stage is between 200 – 240°C. The second stage occurs between

250 – 340°C. The first two stages of decomposition occurs rapidly in a consecutive manner. Third stage of decomposition occurs between 420 – 490°C. The inflection point was detected at 473.26°C. Fourth stage of decomposition starts at 530°C and proceeds very slowly till a constant weight of approximately ~23% (CdS residue), of the cadmium complex taken and which is close to the percentage of CdS expected from the precursor complex[13,14].

3.2. Characterization of synthesized CdS Nanoparticles.

3.2.1. SEM, EDX and TEM

SEM of CdS nanoparticles (Figure 5(a)) shows that they have a varied form and size distribution. But individual existence of particles without any agglomeration can clearly be seen from SEM image and also the fact that there is better distribution leading to increase in surface area at nano regime.

EDX spectrum (Figure 5(b)) shows that synthesized CdS nanoparticles are pure, consisting solely the elements cadmium and sulphur close to the nominal ratio as 50.93:49.07 for Cd :

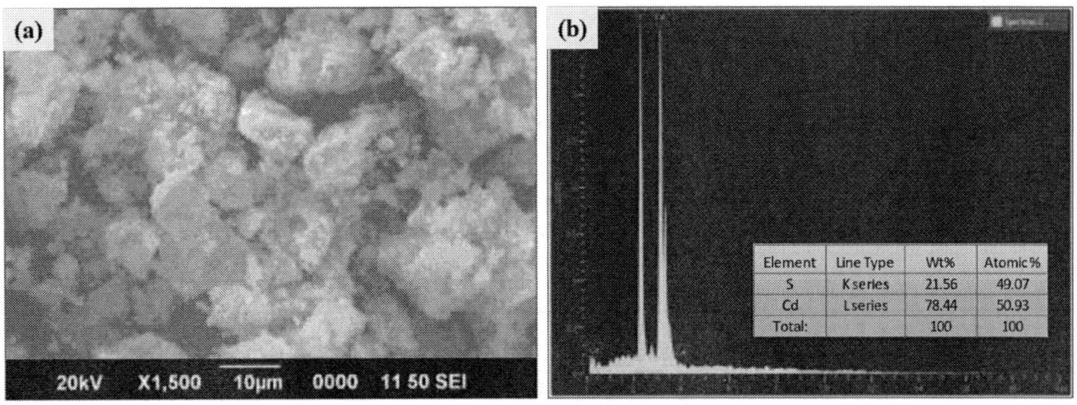

Figure.5. (a) SEM image and (b) EDX spectrum for synthesized CdS

Figure 6(a), is the TEM picture of CdS nanoparticles and displays largely mono-dispersed, clearly defined, rod-shaped particles.

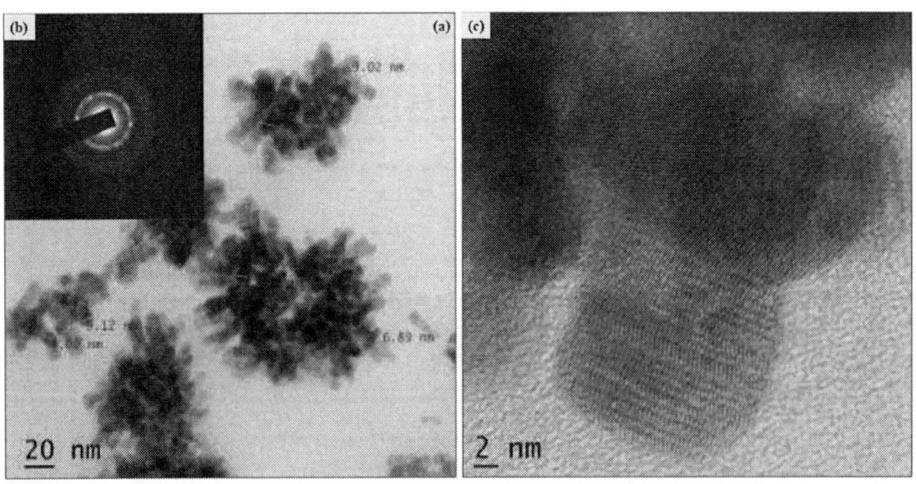

Figure.6. (a)TEM, (b) SAED pattern and (c) HRTEM images of CdS

Particle sizes range from 6.74 nanometers to 10.96 nanometers, with an average of 8.49 nanometers. The SAED pattern (6b) exhibits well-spaced, symmetrical arcs of increasing intensity in the diffraction rings, indicating hexagonal crystalline structure. Additionally, tiny, strong patchy patterns that point to the existence of CdS nanocrystals can be noticed. The HRTEM (Figure 6(c)) reveals that the crystal development is occurring along the (102) plane with a lattice spacing of 0.26 nm.

3.2.2. UV- Visible spectra

A clear idea about the size distribution of synthesized semiconductor nanoparticles could be obtained by UV-Vis spectra[20] and it is given in Figure7(a). In UV spectrum of CdS nanoparticles absorption peak is at 370 nm, indicating a blue shift towards lower wavelength when compared with the value of bulk CdS (515 nm).

Band gap (Eg) of synthesized CdS nanoparticles can be calculated using Tauc relation, in which $(\alpha hv)^2$ was plotted versus (hv) in the Tauc figure,where α is the absorption coefficient of produced nanoparticles, v is the frequency and h is Planck's constant,. Linear region of the plot, when extrapolated towards the energy axis yields the optical energy (band gap). Tauc plot for synthesized CdS is shown in Figure 7(b).

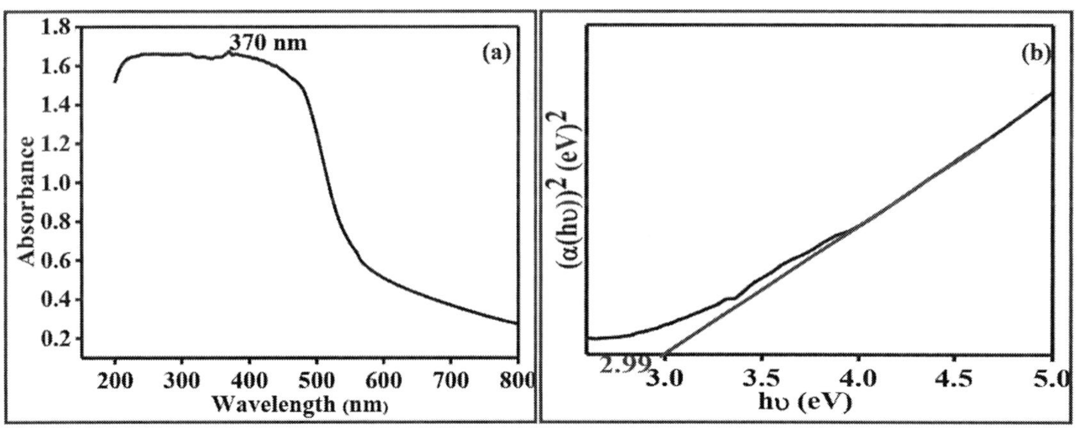

Figure.7(a) and (b) UVandTauc plots

For synthesized CdS nanoparticles, the band gap is changed to 2.99 from 2.91 for bulk CdS. Thus from these results, blue shift in absorbance and expansion of band gap are indications of the presence of synthesized CdS in nano regime [20].

3.2.3. Photo Luminescence studies

The room temperature photoluminescence spectra of synthesized nano CdS was recorded using Jasco FP 750 spectrometer and is given inFigure 8 (at an excitation wavelength of 360nm). Generally PL properties of semiconductor nanocrystals depend on particle size, crystallinity or defect[21]. Two emission peaks are usually observed for semiconductor nanocrystals. One of these results from trapped surface state emission, and the other from interstitial emission[22]. Typically, the first one is sharp, and the second one is broad.[23]. In our case, as in the case of any nano semiconductor, broad and asymmetric multi emission peaks are observed and this may be because of the absence of capping agent and also size heterogeneity[24].

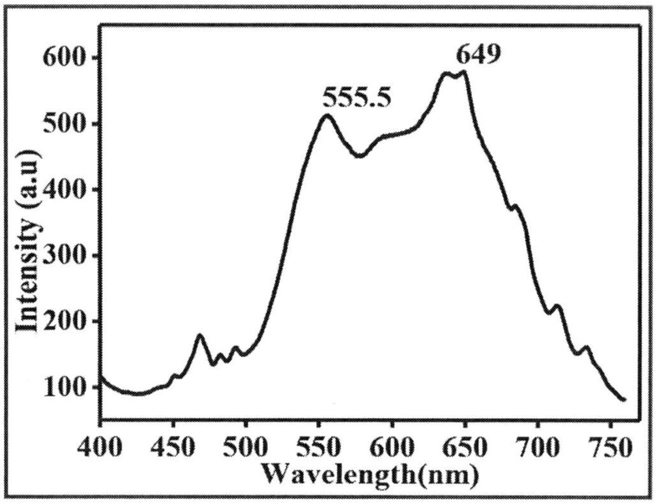

Fig.8. PL spectra of CdS

PL spectrum was taken in 450 – 750 nm region. There was a maximum at 649 nm. Splitting of the PL peaks may have resulted from the presence of CdS nanoparticles of various sizes [25] and also due to the presence of polygonal particles[26]. The small intensity peaks with maximum at 468 nm constitutes blue shift region. The region above 500 nm constitute orange – red region. These emissions are due to the fact that in the PL phenomenon, different vacancy and defects related surface states and deep level states could play major role and that subsequently change the nature of the emission spectra[27]. Constant change in local fields and surface charge density may have resulted in broadening of the peaks[28].

3.2.4. X-ray diffraction (XRD) measurements

For synthesized CdS nanoparticles the XRD patterns (Fig.9) show main diffraction peaks indexed at (100), (002), (101), (110) and (112) planes matched to different planes of hexagonal CdS[29]. The obtained patterns matches with JCPDS data card No.(00-041-1049). The peaks were broader indicating that the presence of nano particles. CdS dimension was calculated to be 7.20 nm by using Debye Scherer equation[30]. Calculated lattice parameters were a=b=4.134A° and c=6.722A° and this matches well with the values a = b= 4.141A° and c = 6.720A° in the JCPDS file No. (00-041-1049). Also the percentage crystallinity from the obtained diffraction patterns of CdS is calculated as 78.58.

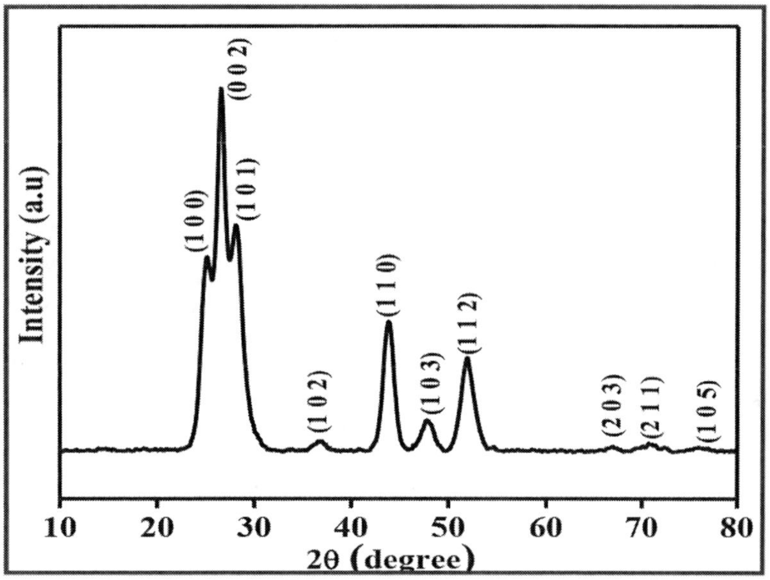

Fig.9. PXRD patterns of CdS

Conclusion

The results of the study demonstrate that the synthetically produced Cadmium metal complex of the ligand CDDATU is an excellent SSMP for good quality CdS nanoparticles.

Acknowledgement

This work was done as a part of PhD thesis at University College, Trivandrum, Kerala. The authors thankfully acknowledge University of Kerala for research fellowship and also the technical supports of NIIST Trivandrum and SAIF (CUSAT).

References

[1] Li Z, Zhang J, Du J, Mu T, Liu Z, Chen J and Han B 2004 Preparation of cadmium sulfide/poly(methyl methacrylate) composites by precipitation with compressed CO2 *Journal of Applied Polymer Science***94** 1643–8

[2] Ma R M, Wei X L, Dai L, Huo H B and Qin G G 2007 Synthesis of CdS nanowire networks and their optical and electrical properties *Nanotechnology***18** 5

[3] Ahamad T and Alshehri S M 2012 Synthesis of CdS Nanocrystals Using Polymer Metal Complex as a Single Source Precursor and their Physicochemical Properties *Nano Hybrids***1** 45–56

[4] Brennan J G, Siegrist T, Carroll P J, Stuczynski S M, Brus L E and Steigerwald M L 1989 The Preparation of Large Semiconductor Clusters via the Pyrolysis of a Molecular Precursor *Journal of the American Chemical Society***111** 4141–3

[5] Rees W, Research G K-J of materials and 1996 U 1996 Preparation and characterization of several group 12 element (Zn, Cd)-bis (thiolate) complexes and evaluation of their potential as precursors for 12–16 *cambridge.org***11** 3005–16
[6] Zeiri L, Patla I, Acharya S, Golan Y and Efrima S 2007 Raman spectroscopy of ultranarrow CdS nanostructures *Journal of Physical Chemistry C***111** 11843–8
[7] Sun Z, Li F, Xu L, Liu S, Zhao M and Xu B 2012 Effects of Dawson-type tungstophosphate on photoelectrochemical responses of cadmium sulfide composite film *Journal of Physical Chemistry C***116** 6420–6
[8] Agarwal R K, Singh L and Sharma D K 2006 Synthesis, spectral, and biological properties of copper(II) complexes of thiosemicarbazones of Schiff bases derived from 4-aminoantipyrine and aromatic aldehydes *Bioinorganic Chemistry and Applications***2006** 1–10
[9] Rapheal P and Manoj E 2007 Syntheses and EPR spectral studies of manganese (II) complexes derived from pyridine-2-carbaldehyde based N (4)-substituted thiosemicarbazones: Crystal *Polyhedron***26** 5088–94
[10] Reddy A S, Krishna L S, Rashmi H K, Devi P U M, Sarala Y and Reddy A V 2016 Synthesis, spectroscopic characterization and biological applications of Cu(II) and Ni(II) complexes with 2-butyl-4-chloro-5-formylimidazole thiosemicarbazone *Journal of Applied Pharmaceutical Science***6** 107–12
[11] Suni V, Kurup M R P and Nethaji M 2005 Unusual isolation of a hemiaminal product from 4-cyclohexyl-3- thiosemicarbazide and di-2-pyridyl ketone: Structural and spectral investigations *Journal of Molecular Structure***749** 177–82
[12] Tian Y P, Yu W T, Zhao C Y, Jiang M H, Cai Z G and Kun Fun H 2002 Structural characterization and second-orderTian, Yu Peng, et al. "Structural Characterization and Second-Order Nonlinear Optical Properties of Zinc Halide Thiosemicarbazone Complexes." Polyhedron, vol. 21, no. 12–13, Pergamon, June 2002, pp. 1217–22, doi *Polyhedron***21** 1217–22
[13] George J, Nath G R, Lekha V S and Rajesh K 2022 Zinc Complex of Cyclododecanone Thiosemicarbazone as Single Source Precursor for ZnS Nanoparticles by Polyol Method *Asian Journal of Chemistry***34** 2055–60
[14] George J, Lekha V S, G R N, Mary Y S, Al-Otaibi J S and K R 2022 Synthesis, crystal structure and anti-tumour activity studies of 4- Tertiarybutylcyclohexanonethiosemicarbazone *Journal of Molecular Structure***1265**
[15] Campbell M J M, Grzeskowiak R, Thomas R and Goldstein M 1976 Infrared spectral study of pentaco-ordinated cobalt (II) complexes of thiosemicarbazones *Spectrochimica Acta Part A: Molecular Spectroscopy***32** 553–7
[16] Chandra S and Kumar Y 1983 Manganese (II) complexes of some nitrogen-oxygen and nitrogen-sulphur donor ligands *Proceedings of the Indian Academy of Sciences - Chemical Sciences***92** 249–55
[17] Chandra S and Tyagi M 2008 Ni(II), Pd(II) and Pt(II) complexes with ligand containing thiosemicarbazone and semicarbazone moiety: Synthesis, characterization and biological investigation *Journal of the Serbian Chemical Society***73** 727–34
[18] Joseph M, Suni V, Prathapachandra Kurup M R, Nethaji M, Kishore A and Bhat S G 2004 Structural, spectral and antimicrobial studies of copper(II) complexes of 2-benzoylpyridine N(4)-cyclohexyl thiosemicarbazone *Polyhedron***23** 3069–80

[19] Rana V B, Jain P C, Swami M P and Srivastava A K 1975 Thiosemicabazones as ligands-I. Spectrochemical studies on trivalent metal complexes of 1-phenyl-orthohydroxy-4-benzamido thiosemicarbazone *Journal of Inorganic and Nuclear Chemistry***37** 1826–8

[20] Shukla S N, Gaur P and Rai N 2015 Complexes of tetraethylthiuram disulphide with group 12 metals: single-source precursor in metal sulphide nanoparticles' synthesis *Applied Nanoscience (Switzerland)***5** 583–93

[21] Onwudiwe D C, Krüger T P J and Strydom C A 2014 Laser assisted solid state reaction for the synthesis of ZnS and CdS nanoparticles from metal xanthate *Materials Letters***116** 154–9

[22] Geng B, Ma J and Zhan F 2009 A solution phase thermal decomposition molecule precursors route to ZnS:Cu2+ nanorods and their optical properties *Materials Chemistry and Physics***113** 534–8

[23] Goudarzi A, Aval G M, Park S S, Choi M C, Sahraei R, Ullah M H, Avane A and Ha C S 2009 Low-Temperature Growth of Nanocrystalline Mn-Doped ZnS Thin Films Prepared by Chemical Bath Deposition and Optical Properties *Chemistry of Materials***21** 2375–85

[24] Murugadoss G 2012 ZnO/CdS nanocomposites: Synthesis, structure and morphology *Particuology***10** 722–8

[25] Nisha K D, Navaneethan M, Dhanalakshmi B, Hayakawa Y, Ponnusamy S and Muthamizhchelvan C 2013 Formation and morphological investigation of petal-like cadmium sulphide nanostructures *Optical Materials***35** 1652–8

[26] Pradhan N, Katz B and Efrima S 2003 Synthesis of High-Quality Metal Sulfide Nanoparticles from Alkyl Xanthate Single Precursors in Alkylamine Solvents *Journal of Physical Chemistry B***107** 13843–54

[27] Prasad K S, Amin T, Katuva S, Kumari M and Selvaraj K 2017 Synthesis of water soluble CdS nanoparticles and study of their DNA damage activity *Arabian Journal of Chemistry***10** S3929–35

[28] Kar S, Panda S and Satpati, B, Satyam, PV Chaudhuri S 2006 Morphology and size dependent optical properties of CdS nanostructures *Nanoscience Nanotechnology***6** 771–6

[29] Nair P S, Radhakrishnan T, Revaprasadu N, Kolawole G and O'Brien P 2002 Cadmium ethylxanthate: A novel single-source precursor for the preparation of CdS nanoparticles *Journal of Materials Chemistry***12** 2722–5

[30] Cullity, BD. Stock S 2001 *Elements of X-ray Diffraction* (Prentice-Hall)

IOP Conf. Series: Materials Science and Engineering 1263 (2022) 012012 doi:10.1088/1757-899X/1263/1/012012

Optical Studies of doped Nd_2O_3 Nanoparticles for LED applications

M M Antoinette

Post graduate Department of Physics, St. Joseph's College for Women, Alappuzha, Kerala, India

marieli.fdcc@gmail.com

Abstract. Rare earth sesquioxide nanoparticles have been immensely used in wide range of diverse photoluminescent applications. In the present investigation, we report a simple and less expensive technique of synthesizing pure and doped Nd_2O_3 nanocrystalline powders using combustion method. Powder X-ray diffraction analysis was done to study the structural characterization of the prepared samples. The surface morphology of the prepared samples was studied with the help of SEM analysis. The surface micrographs showed small amount of agglomeration. The UV-Vis data analysis and photoluminescence studies were carried out to understand the optical properties of the samples. On doping the optical properties of the synthesized samples were enhanced, and these properties revealed that they can be promising materials for LED applications.

1. Introduction

Rare-earth oxides have electronic configurations which make them uniquely stable and possess distinctive optical, electronic, magnetic and chemical properties. The synthesis of first-class rare earth (RE) doped nanoparticles with uniform shape and size is of immense significance both for the exploration of their various properties and for their potential applications. This has sparked considerable scientific interest because these rare-earth oxide nanoparticles show improved electronic, magnetic, optical and structural properties due to its nanoscale dimensions [1].

Neodymium sesquioxide nanoparticles are used for various optical applications. Among the rare-earth sesquioxides, Nd_2O_3, a semiconductor with wide band gap, has captivated the focus of several researchers due to its widespread potential applications [2]. Spherical and rod like structures of Nd_2O_3 nanocrystals were synthesized for light emitting diodes (LEDs) [3]. Michel et al., prepared Nd_2O_3 nanostructured microspheres which were able to sense gases like CO_2, CO and ethanol vapour by solution co-precipitation process [4]. Jian-Hua et al. carried out studies on the photoluminescence property of synthesized Nd_2O_3 using sodium bis (2-ethylhexyl) sulfosuccinate/toluene and propanol by microemulsion method [5]. Nd^{3+} ion is one among the RE ions which is efficiently used in solid state lasers. It is also used for upconversion fluorescence. [6,7].

Various methods have been used to control the shape and properties of the nanomaterials. Rare-earth (RE) oxides are prepared by different methods namely solgel [8], hydrothermal [9], microwave-assisted [10], solvothermal [11], solution combustion [12], molten salt method [13], co-precipitation [14]. Among the different methods of preparing nanopowders, combustion synthesis is one of the best suitable methods for producing nanopowders with improved powder characteristics at a lower reaction time and calcination temperature. The synthesized products of combustion method have lesser impurities and are chemically homogeneous. When RE^{3+} ions are doped in a host material, a novel material with enhanced luminescence properties can be obtained. So here we have selected Nd_2O_3 as the host material and doped it with Tb^{3+} ion to discover the influence of Tb^{3+} ions on the luminescence of Nd_2O_3.

2. Experimental

Pure and Tb^{3+} doped Nd_2O_3 nanopowders were synthesized using the combustion method. Neodymium (III) nitrate hexahydrate was taken and distilled water was subsequently added to it. Then the fuel, urea (2.5 gm) required for combustion synthesis, was added to it and stirred till a homogeneous precursor solution was obtained. It was then dried at around 200° C and the resulting powder was calcined at 900°C for 3 hours to remove the impurities present in it. Nd_2O_3 nanocrystalline powders were obtained. The required amount of $Tb(NO_3)_3.6H_2O$ was added to $Nd(NO_3)_3.6H_2O$ and the same procedure was followed to prepare the doped sample, $(Nd_{0.97}Tb_{0.03})_2O_3$.

The structural, morphological and optical studies of the synthesized samples were carried out with the help of Bruker Eco D8 Advance X-ray diffractometer, scanning electron microscope (ZEISS EVO 18 SEM), transmission electron microscope (TEM, JEOL JEM-2100), Perkin Elmer, Lambda 365 UV-Vis-NIR Spectrophotometer and Perkin Elmer, Lambda Model 45 spectrometer. All these measurements were taken at room temperature.

3. Results and discussion

3.1 Powder X-Ray diffraction Analysis

The structure of the synthesized $Nd_2O_3$and Tb^{3+} doped Nd_2O_3 nanoparticles and its phase purity were investigated with the help of powder X-ray diffraction (PXRD) analysis. The X-ray diffraction patterns of undoped and Tb^{3+} doped Nd_2O_3 nanoparticles shown in figure 1 are exactly indexed as cubic structure having space group $Ia\overline{3}$ whose lattice constants are a=b=c=11.08Å (JCPDS No. 21-0579). No characteristic peaks of impurities are observed. These results indicate that the prepared samples are highly pure free from all contaminations and that the doped Tb^{3+} ions completely occupy the Nd^{3+} sites in these nanophosphors.

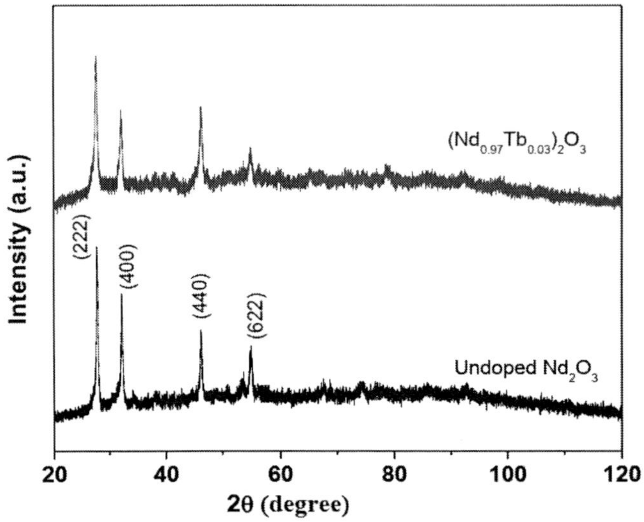

Figure 1. Indexed PXRD pattern of undoped and Tb^{3+} doped Nd_2O_3 nanoparticles.

3.2 SEM Analysis

Scanning Electron Microscopic (SEM) analysis was done for investigating the surface morphology of the synthesized material. The obtained morphology of the synthesized sample is shown in figure 2. The SEM image of Tb^{3+} doped Nd_2O_3 shows a small amount of agglomeration of tubular structures. This may be because of the strong interactions among nanoparticles due to their high surface energy during calcination. To get better information of the morphology and the size of the particles, Transmission Electron Microscopy (TEM) analysis was carried.

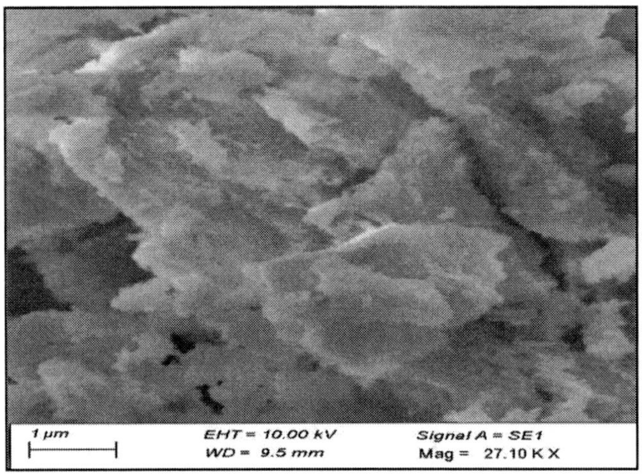

Figure 2. SEM image of Tb^{3+} doped Nd_2O_3 nanoparticles.

3.3 TEM Analysis

The TEM image gives better clarity of the size of the particles of the prepared sample. The TEM image of the prepared sample is showed in figure 3. It shows that they synthesized particles are nanosized and in tubular form.

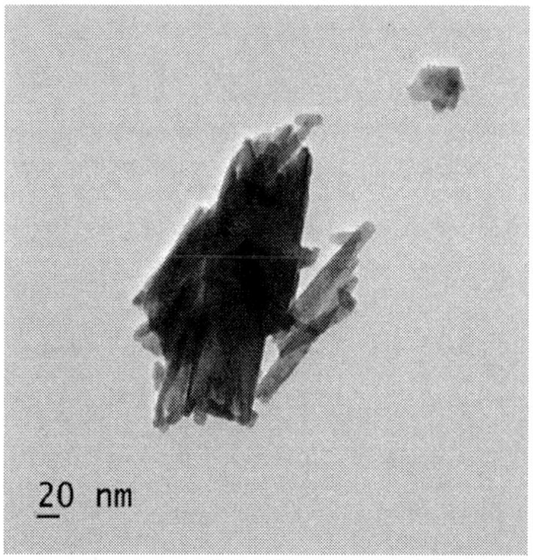

Figure 3. TEM image of Tb^{3+} doped Nd_2O_3 nanoparticles.

3.4 UV-Vis Spectral Analysis

The Ultraviolet-Visible absorption spectrum of the synthesized Tb^{3+} doped Nd_2O_3 nanoparticles is shown in figure 4. A broad peak at around 248 nm and a slightly sharp peak with low intensity at around 360 nm is obtained. The absorbance generally depends on factors like surface roughness, impurity centres, band gap and oxygen deficiency.

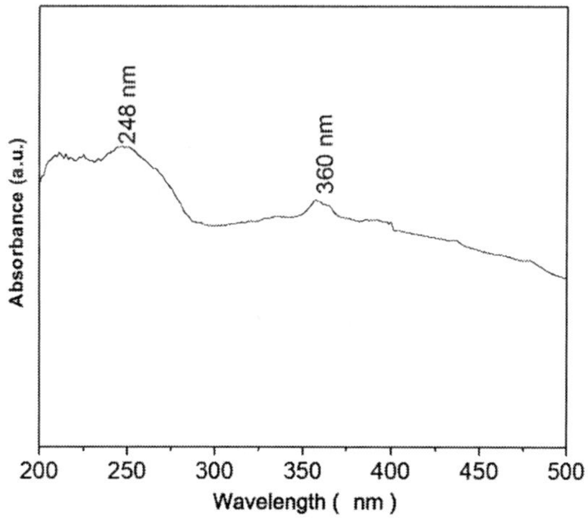

Figure 4. Absorption spectra of Tb^{3+} doped Nd_2O_3 nanoparticles.

3.5 *Photoluminescence Studies*

The photoluminescence (PL) spectrum of the prepared Nd_2O_3 and Tb^{3+} doped Nd_2O_3 nanoparticles excited at 360 nm is shown in figure 5. It is seen that on doping Tb^{3+} ions, there was no change in the peak position but an enhancement in the relative intensity of the peak at 545nm when the concentration of the dopant was 3 mol%. It is because on doping Tb^{3+} ion, some surface defects which were formed in the lattice produced enhancement in the intensity of emission. The emission spectra showed that the peaks of the prepared materials are very sharp, thereby they can be attractive candidates for efficient optical applications especially LEDs. As the near-UV excitation range is from 345 to 420 nm, these synthesized nanoparticles can be well used in manufacturing UV LEDs.

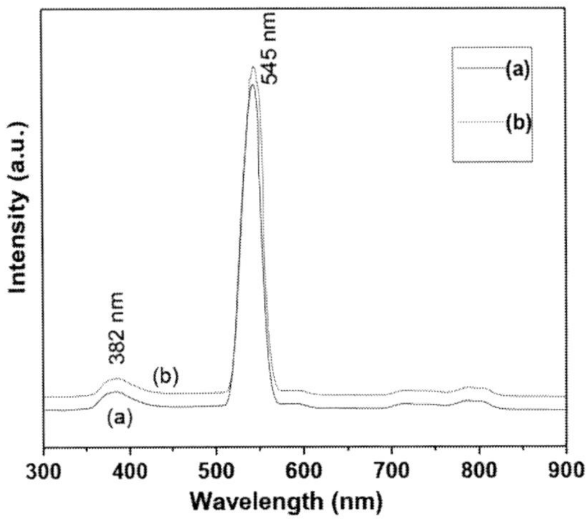

Figure 5. PL Spectra of (a) undoped and (b) Tb^{3+} doped Nd_2O_3 nanoparticles.

4. Conclusion

Pure Nd_2O_3 and Tb^{3+} doped Nd_2O_3 nanophosphors were successfully prepared using combustion synthesis. Powder X-ray diffraction analysis showed Nd_2O_3 and Tb^{3+} doped Nd_2O_3 nanoparticles having cubic structure with space group $Ia\bar{3}$ were prepared. SEM and TEM analysis were done to study the surface morphology. The SEM image of the synthesized sample showed small amount of agglomeration. The TEM image showed that tubular nanoparticles were formed. The absorbance peaks were observed at 248 and 258nm from UV-visible spectra. The photoluminescence studies showed that the emission intensity of Nd_2O_3 nanophosphors can be enhanced by the doping of Tb^{3+} ions and hence the synthesized material proved to be promising candidate in fabricating LEDs.

5. References

[1] Mortazavi-Derazkola S, Zinatloo-Ajabshir S and Salavati-Niasari M 2015 *J Mater Sci Mater Electron* **26** 5658
[2] Mendez M, Carvajal J J, Cesteros Y, Aguio M, Diaz F, Giguere A, Drouin D, Martinez-Ferrero E, Salagre P, Formentin P, Pallares J, Marsal L F 2010 *Opt Mater.* **32** 1686
[3] Umesh B, Eraiah B, Nagabhushana H, Nagabhushana B M, Nagaraja G, Shivakumara C, Chakradhar R P S 2011 *J Alloys Compd.* **509** 1146
[4] Michel C R, Martinez-Preciado A H, Contreras N L L, 2013 *Sensors and Actuators B*, **184** 8
[5] Jian -Hua R, Tong-Gang Z, Jian-Hua L, Juan K, Jia-Xin H, Lin G, 2008 *Chinese Physics B*, **17** 4669
[6] Lupei V, Lupei A, Ikesue A, 2005 *Appl Phys Lett.* **86** 111118
[7] Que W, Kam C H, Zhou Y, Lam Y L, Chan Y C, 2001 *J Appl Phys.* **90** 4865

[8] Liu L, Jiang H, Chen Y, Zhang X, Zhang Z, Wang Y, 2013 *J. Lumin.* **143** 423
[9] Liu G, Hong G, Wang J, Dong X 2007 *J Alloys Compd.* **432** 200
[10] Zawadaki M, 2008 *J Alloys Compd.* **451** 297
[11] Zawadaki M and Kepinski L 2004 *J Alloys Compd.* **380** 255
[12] Fu Y P, Wen S B, Hsu C S 2008 *J Alloys Compd.* **458** 318
[13] Liu T, Meng Q Y, Sun W J, 2015 *J Rare-earths* **33** 915
[14] Chandrasekhar M, Nagabhushana H, Sudheerkumar K H, Dhananjaya N, Sharma S C, Kavyashree D, Shivakumara C, Nagabhushana B M 2014 *Mater Res Bull.* **55** 237

IOP Conf. Series: Materials Science and Engineering 1263 (2022) 012013 doi:10.1088/1757-899X/1263/1/012013

Synthesis of Co^{2+} doped Cadmium borate nanopowder for luminescent applications

Lakshmiprasad Maddi*, Thirumala Rao Gurugubelli

Department of BSH, GMRIT, Rajam, Andhra Pradesh, India 532127
*Corresponding author: lakshmiprasad.m@gmrit.edu.in, Phone: (+91) 9121055670

Abstract. Nanoparticles embedded in host materials exhibit a wide variation in properties, viz., photocatalytic activity, luminescence to name a few. In the present study, Cadmium borate was taken as a host in which addition of Cobalt (Co^{2+}) was done through precipitation method. X ray diffraction (XRD) studies revealed only Cadmium borate peaks (indicating the replacement of Co^{2+} ions at Cd^{2+} sites, forming a substitutional solid solution), while morphology was found to be agglomerated irregular particles. Photoluminescent studies indicated their possible application for yellowish green coloured emission.

1. Introduction

Semiconductor nanoparticles exhibit different properties when compared to their bulk forms. Dilute Magnetic Semiconductors (DMS) are the ones in which cations in the host are substituted by transition metal ions that act as spin – polarized carrier sources, hence, making them suitable for spintronic applications [1-4]. To develop multi-function devices that provide such as magnetic, photonic and electronic responses, many efforts have been made. Properties of borate make them suitable for electronic, biological and catalysis applications [5-10]. Co, being a magnetic material, doping of Co reportedly added magnetic property to the transparent conducting oxide (CdO) [11-12]. While pure CdO displayed diamagnetic behaviour, paramagnetic behaviour was noted for Co^{2+} doped CdO. Formation of Co/ Ga doped CdO nanocomposites also led to significant growth in saturation magnetization M_s. Ligand field theory explains the color of transition metal complexes. The d – orbital degeneracy gets apart in the company of a ligand [13]. For instance, in the company of an octahedral ligand, three of the d – orbitals decrease their energy and form t2g orbitals, while the remaining two increase their energy to form eg orbitals. The current work describes the effect of Co^{2+} doping on the structural changes in cadmium borate nanopowder and their effect on the luminescent properties.

2. Materials and Methods

Cadmium nitrate, borax and cobalt oxide were procured from Merck Chemicals, India. Initially, 0.1 M borax (1.9068 g of $Na_2B_4O_7.10H_2O$) and cadmium nitrate (1.54 g of $Cd(NO_3)_2.2H_20$) were distinctly liquefied in 50 ml of deionised water. Then, obtained solutions were mixed and stirred magnetically. 30 minutes later, 0.001M of cobalt oxide solution (0.0037g of CoO dissolved in 50ml of dilute HNO_3) was added drop-by-drop to the mixer solution while it was being stirred [14-15]. Better atomic diffusion was achieved by using uniform magnetic stirring. The mixture was then transformed into an autoclave held at 180 °C for 3 h. The obtained product was then washed with ethanol and deionised water, following which the precipitate was separated. The resultant precipitate was then dried at 350 °C for 2 h inside an oven. Finally, the precipitate was then crushed with a pestle and mortar to get the fine product. The synthesis of the test substance is depicted in Fig. 1.

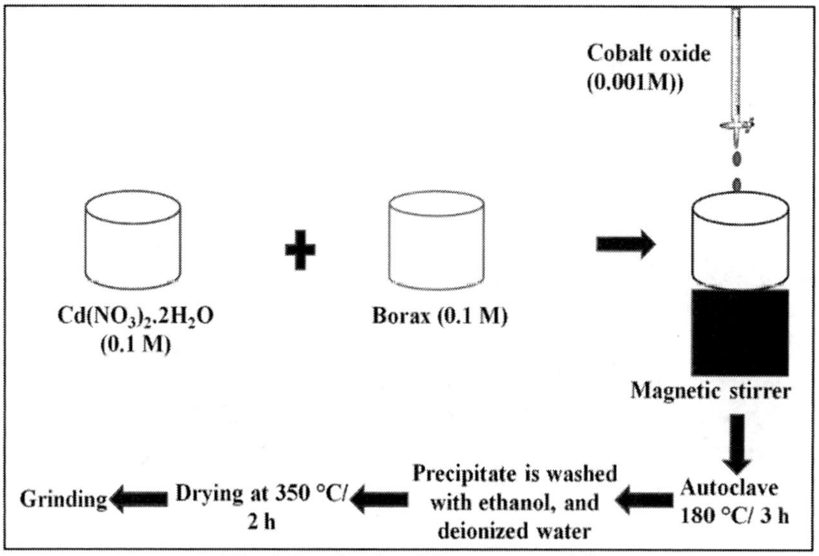

Fig. 1 Synthesis of the test material

PANalytical XPert make diffractometer was used with CuKα radiation for recording the XRD pattern (wavelength of 1.5406 Å). ZEISS EVO18 make Scanning Electron Microscope was used for morphological studies. Oxford EDS analyzer was employed for identifying the chemical composition. Jobin Yvon make fluorometer was used for Photoluminescence studies.

3. Results and Discussion

3.1. XRD analysis

Fig. 2 reveals the sharp and high intense peaks indicating the crystalline nature of Co^{2+} doped cadmium borate nanopowder [16, 17]. Diffraction peaks at 2θ = 29.06, 31.61, 38.58, 42.65, 47.18 were attributed to (2 0 0), (1 1 2), (1 1 3), (1 2 1), (1 1 4) diffraction planes of the orthorhombic crystal structure of cadmium borate (JCPDS: 39-1126). The lattice parameters of the test material were calculated to be a = 0.596, b = 0.475, c = 0.904 nm.

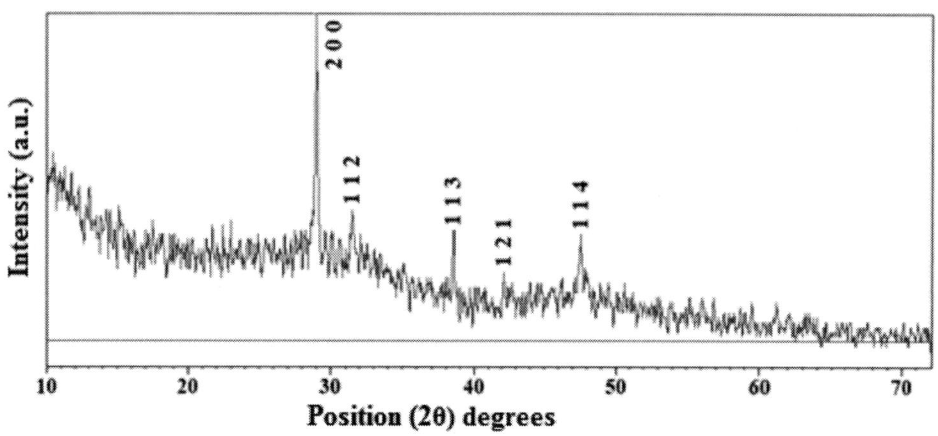

Fig. 2 XRD of Cobalt doped Cadmium borate nanopowder

The mean grain size was measured using Scherrer equation, $D = 0.9\ \lambda/\ \beta\cos\theta$, where β is the FWHM of the most intense peak (2 0 0) and θ is diffracting angle. Average crystal size was measured as 43 nm. Microstrain was measured using the formula, $\varepsilon = \beta\cos\theta/4$ as 8.058×10^{-4}.

3.2. Scanning electron microscopy (SEM)

Fig. 3 depicts the SEM micrographs of Co^{2+} doped cadmium borate exhibited irregular particle like morphology, while heat treatment resulted in some agglomeration [18].

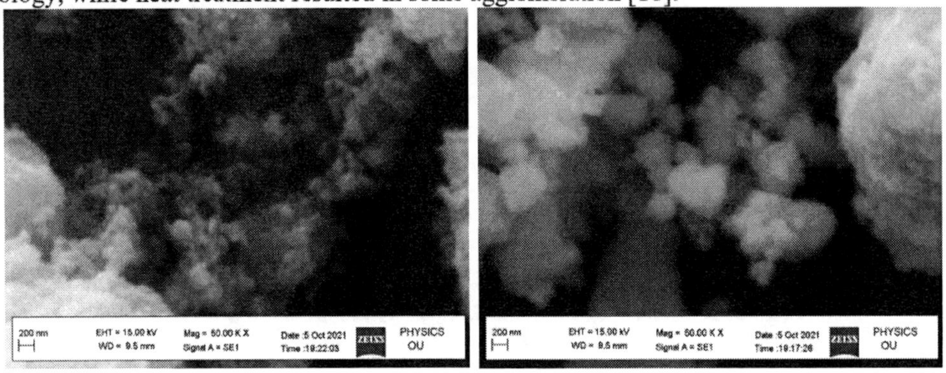

Fig. 3 SEM images of Co^{2+} doped Cadmium borate nanopowder

Elemental composition was examined using EDX. Fig. 4 confirms the presence of elements viz., Cd, Co and oxygen in the sample.

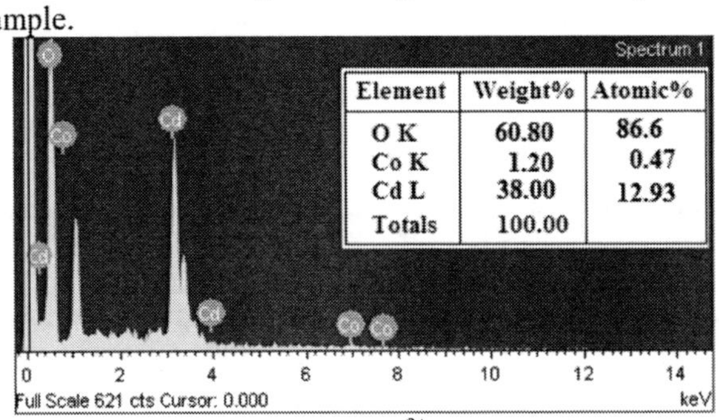

Element	Weight%	Atomic%
O K	60.80	86.6
Co K	1.20	0.47
Cd L	38.00	12.93
Totals	100.00	

Fig. 4 Energy dispersive studies (EDS) of Co^{2+} doped Cadmium borate nanopowder

3.3. Photoluminescence studies

Materials at nanoscale contain electrons and holes on the surface. These charge carriers readily excite under the influence of photon [19], implying photoluminescence of nanoscale materials are higher as compared to bulk materials. Fig. 5 represents the emission spectrum of Cobalt doped cadmium borate nanopowder under the photon excitation at 350 nm.

Luminescent properties of nanomaterials are greatly influenced by O-vacancies and Cd-vacancies or interstitials. Less number of defects, oxygen-vacancies and Cd-interstitials could be the possible reasons [20-22]. In the present investigations, the PL spectrum of Co^{2+} doped Cadmium borate nanopowder exhibited four characteristic emission bands at 440, 499, 546, 657 nm and one shoulder peak at 467 nm in the visible region. The emission peaks at 440 and 467 nm may arise due to the oxygen vacancies [23]. The observed peaks at 499 and 546 nm are ascribed to the cadmium vacancies or interstitial defects [24]. The emission peak at 657 nm is attributed to the electronic dipole transition of ${}^4A_{2g}(F) \rightarrow {}^4T_{1g}(F)$ of Co^{2+} ions [25]. Fig. 6 depicts the chromaticity diagram of the test material. From the photoluminescence data, the International Commission on Illumination (CIE) coordinates were calculated as (x, y) = (0.3349, 0.3830), which represents emission of yellowish green color.

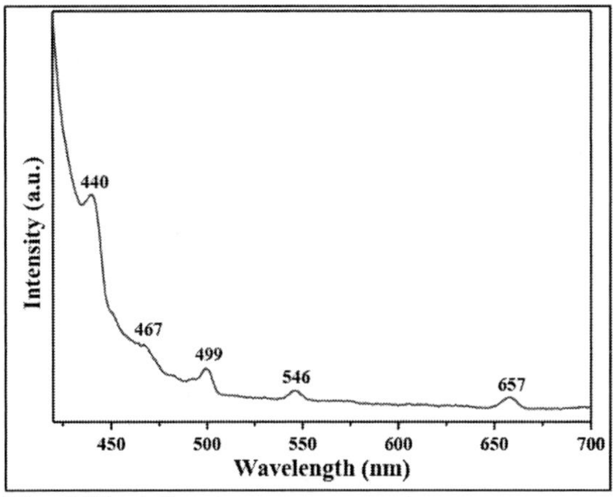

Fig. 5 Photoluminescence spectrum of Cobalt doped cadmium borate nanopowder

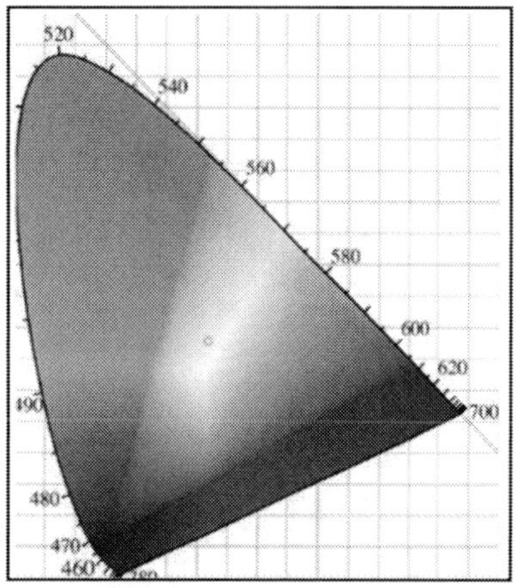

Fig.6 Chromaticity diagram of the test material

Conclusion

Co^{2+} doped Cadmium borate nanopowder was prepared by co-precipitation route. XRD reveals orthorhombic crystal structure of the material with size of 43 nm. SEM analysis reveals irregular shaped spheres and EDS confirms the presence of Co, Cd, and oxygen. PL bands were observed at 440, 467, 499 and 546 nm. The obtained material can be used for yellowish green light emission applications.

References

[1] Shim JH, Hwang T, Lee S, Park JH and Han SJ 2005 *Appl. Phys. Lett.* ***86*** 082503

[2] Wolf SA, Awschalom DD, Buhrman RA, Daughton JM, Molnar SV, Roukes ML, Chichelkanova AY and Treger DM 2001 *Science* **294** 1488

[3] Ghosh S and Mandal K 2010 *J. Magn. Magn. Mater.* **322** 1979

[4] Ohno H, 1998 *Science* **281** 951

[5] Prinz GA 1998 *Science* **282** 1660

[6] Schmidt G, Ferrand D, Molenkamp LW, Filip AT and Wees BJV 2002 *Phys. Rev. B* **62** 4790

[7] Fragoso WD, de Mello Donega C and Longo RK 2003 *J. Lumin.* **105** 97

[8] Muehlberg M, Burianek M and Edongue H 2002 *J. Cryst. Growth* **237** 740

[9] Stier O, Grundmann M and Bimberg D 1999 *Phys. Rev. B* **59** 5688

[10] Hosino A, Fujioka K, Oku T, Nakamura S, Suga M, Yamaguchi Y, Suzuki K, Yasukara M and Yamamoto K 2004 *Microbiol. Immunol.* **48** 985

[11] Mori T, Martin J and Nolas G 2007 *J. Appl. Phys.* **102** 073510

[12] Dakhel AA 2021 *J. Supercond. Nov. Magn.* **34** 889

[13] Arkaprava D, Parasmani R, Anumeet K, Balasubramanian C, Kanjilal D, Jha SN 2021 *Thin Solid Films* **736** 138908

[14] Gurugubelli TR, Ravikumar RVSSN, Koutavarapu R 2022 *J. Electron. Mater.* **51** 1876

[15] Gurugubelli TR, Ravikumar RVSSN, Reddy NB, Zyryanov V 2019 *AIP Conf. Proc.* **2063** 040045

[16] Chandiramouli R, Jeyaprakash BG 2013 *Solid State Sci.* **16** 102

[17] Huazhao Y and Li M 2007 *Acta Crystallograp. E* **63** 50

[18] Jakovljevic JK, Radoicic M, Radetic T, Konstantinovic Z, Saponjic ZV and Nedeljkovic J 2009 *J. Phys. Chem. C* **113** 21029

[19] Geoffroy A and Bringuiel E 1992 *Appl. Phys. Lett.* **61** 3172

[20] Wang Y and Herron N 1991 *J. Phys. Chem.* **95** 525

[21] Wahab R, Ansari SG, Kim YS, Seo HK and Shin HS 2007 *Appl. Surf. Sci.* **253** 7622

[22] Annalakshmi O, Jose MT, Venaktraman B and Amarendra G 2014 *Mater. Res. Bull.* **50** 494
[23] Thirumala Rao G, Babu B, Joyce Stella R, Pushpa Manjari V, Venkata Reddy Ch, Shim J, Ravikumar RVSSN 2015 *J. Mol. Struct.* **1081** 254
[24] Thirumala Rao G, Joyce Stella R, Babu B, Ravindranadh K, Venkata Reddy Ch, Shim J, Ravikumar RVSSN 2015 *Mater. Sci. Eng.* B **201** 72
[25] Ravindranadh K, Babu B, Rao MC, Shim J, Venkata Reddy Ch, Ravikumar RVSSN, 2015 *J. Mater. Sci. – Mater. El.* **26** 6667

Structural and optical studies of doped potassium-sodium niobate ceramics

V T Thrivikraman and K Sudheendran

Research Department of Physics, Sree Kerala Varma College, Thrissur, 680011, Mob No. +919946372517, thrivikraman.vt@gmail.com

Abstract. In the fields of sensors, actuators and ultrasonic gadgets, piezoelectric ceramics based on lead free KNN[1-8] had been brought due to the development in overall performance. The KNN based substances have the gain of low dielectric constants, excessive coupling coefficient and excessive mechanical electricity than lead containing ceramics that cause them to appropriate for excessive frequency transducers. The traits of KNN may be changed through appropriate dopants. [11].Here we use Bi^{3+} to dop with KNN to change the properties. Structural determinations of all studied solid solutions are completed through XRD and photoluminescence research had been achieved through the usage of spectrophotometer. Optical spectroscopy evaluation has been accomplished for every solid solution. Doping KNN with Bi^{3+} at concentrations of 0.5 wt%, 1 wt % and 1.5wt%, respectively, improves the optical properties

1. Introduction

A piezoelectric ceramics are materials that can produce electric energy by the application of mechanical stress. Piezoelectric ceramics are utilized in numerous packages which include sensors, transducers and actuators [1,2,4]. The most piezoelectric ceramics contain lead zirconium titanate (PZT). The PZT consists of approximately 60 wt % of lead. Since lead is a poisonous material that influences human fitness and the surroundings. It increases ecological hassle as well. Thus through the begin of early 2000s there was developing interest with inside to improve and commercialize piezoelectric ceramics which might be lead-free because of environmental and public fitness concerns. Lead-free piezoelectric ceramics (LFPEC) have applications in electronics and optoelectronics, transportation, power, industrial, instrumentation, life science, defence, security and consumer products . In 2008 the European Union legislated to update all present PZT additives through lead free ceramics. This has accelerated a extensive unfold studies at the improvement of novel lead free piezoelectric ceramics. Many alternate sources are being investigated through many scientists all around the world, a number of them are, barium titanate bismuth-alkaline metal titanates and niobates mainly the $K_{0.5}Na_{0.5}NbO_3$ solid solution abbreviated KNN. The groups of potassium sodium niobate, bismuth sodium titanate have the benefits of low dielectric constants, excessive coupling coefficient and better mechanical electricity in well-known than lead containing ceramics that cause them to appropriate for excessive frequency transducers. The most important problems of KNN processing are, the compounds, in particular that K_2O and Na_2O are notably unstable. However many of the lead free piezo substances, KNN- based substances had been taken into consideration as one of the maximum promising applicants because of a large piezoelectric constant (d_{33}) and excessive Curie temperature. Consequently, KNN based lead free piezoelectric ceramics had been studied from the angle of optimizing their overall performance for multilayer actuators, doubtlessly for power scavenging packages. KNN suitable for the fabrication of PbO free piezoelectrics because it follows a series of ferroelectric phase transitions (12). At excessive temperature, KNN (50:50) is cubic however under 410 °C, it transforms to a ferroelectric tetragonal shape with next transitions to orthorhombic (2100 °C) and rhombohedral (-123 °C) on in addition cooling.The properties of KNN may be changed through appropriate dopants.

Sintering affects the phase structure and microstructure. Sintering effect can decorate piezoelectricity, inclusive of two step sintering, spark-plasma sintering, hot press sintering etc.

2. Materials and strategies

The method used to obtain the polycrystalline pattern of KNN is the solid- state reaction. The raw substances taken are K_2CO_3, Na_2CO_3, and Nb_2O_5. Since alkali factors are unstable, on the way to compensate the loss, an additional 5 wt % of Na_2CO_3 was added. The raw substances had been taken in keeping with a composition of $K_{0.5}Na_{0.5}NbO_3$ + x wt % Bi_2O_3 (x = zero, 1, 1.5, and 2 wt %) and had been blended the usage of a tumbling ball mill with agate media and acetone for 3hours.

The blended powder dehydrated and calcined at 700 °C for 5 hrs. The phase purity of the ceramic Powders had been characterized through X-ray diffraction (XRD) analysis (model). The PL emission Spectra had been tested the usage of a spectro flurophotometer RF-5301 pc. 350 nm and 300 nm had been used as the excitation wavelengths. A Jasco UV-Vis-NIR spectrophotometer geared up with 150 mm integrating sphere is used for diffuse reflectance measurements of powder samples. Spectra had been measured with inside the wavelength variety 200-2500 nm. The reflectance R. extinction coefficient k and refractive index n variant of natural KNN and Bismuth doped KNN are noted. . The reflectance R(λ) found to be increased when wavelength increased, more steeply among 300-600 nm. The doping concentration variation effect on extinction coefficient and refractive index had been studied.

3. Results and Discussion

Figure 1describes the X-ray diffraction (XRD) of pure and doped KNN ceramic powders.The shape is tetragonal (space group P4mm) for all of the compositions.

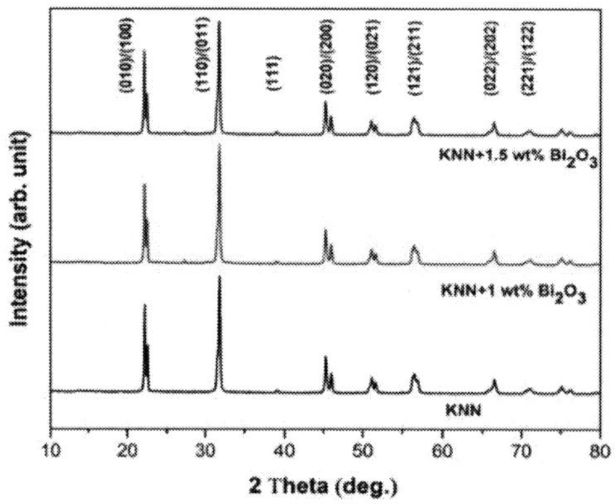

Figure (1) X-ray diffractogram of the natural and doped KNN ceramic powders

X-ray diffraction (XRD) is used for the characterization of materials like crystal shape, crystallite size and strain. XRD is used for phase identification of a crystalline material and can provide information on unit cell dimensions. The analyzed materialis finely ground, united and common volume composition is determined. X-ray diffraction (XRD) enables to locate the geometry using X-rays.

3.1. Optical analysis of pure and doped KNN

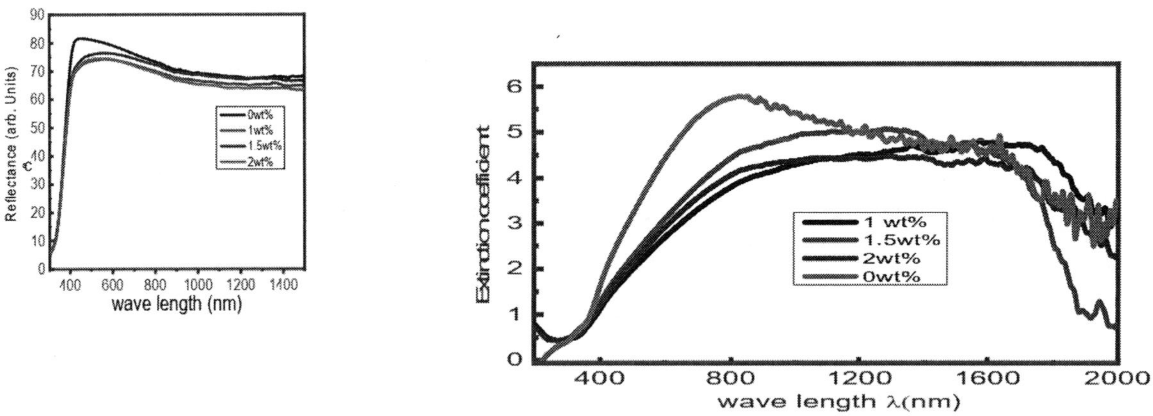

Figure [2 a, b] reflectance and extinction coefficient k spectra for the natural and Bismuth doped KNN powders

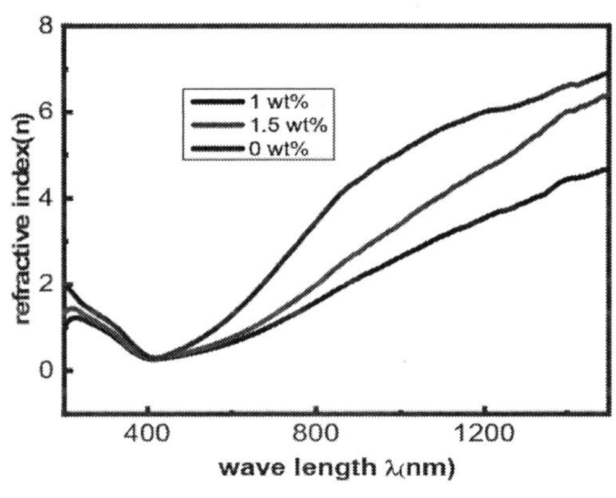

Fig.2c.Refractive index plot for natural and Bismuth doped KNN powders

The optical characteristics of the organized ceramic powders had been investigated via calculating the optical diffused reflectance spectra (DRS). The DRS measurements had been executed within side the variety from 200 nm to 2000 nm, and they're shown in figure 2. The reflectance R (λ) increases while wavelength increases, extra steeply among 300-600 nm. A huge hump took place in ~500nm variety, similar to pink and darkish pink mild there after it stay nearly a steady level. Figure 2 (b) and a 2(c) indicates the real and imaginary section of the optical constants[13,14] of the doped and undoped ceramic powders prepared. By increasing the doping content for the ceramic powders, each the refractive and extinction indices are found reducing. The essential band-gap absorption caused reducing the refractive index and extinction coefficient .The increase of dopant concentration may enhance the order of the material, this accompanied by the increasing of optical gap. There is an inverse proportional between optical gap and refractive index, so the increase of optical gap may accompanied by the decrease of refractive index

The refractive index (n) is expressed by specular reflectance spectrum (R) and phase change (Φ) .The Kramers-Kronig (K-K) equation is applied to specular reflectance spectrum (R) and phase change (Φ), phase change (Φ) was calculated by K-K conversion of specular reflectance spectrum (R) and then, the refractive index (n) was calculated as follows using the software provided by Jasco.

$$n = \frac{1-R}{1+R-2\sqrt{R}\cos\emptyset} \qquad \emptyset(\omega) = \frac{2\omega}{\pi}P\int_0^\infty \frac{ln\sqrt{R(\omega')}}{\omega'^2-\omega^2}d\omega'$$

3.2. Photoluminescence study of natural KNN and Bi^{3+} doped KNN

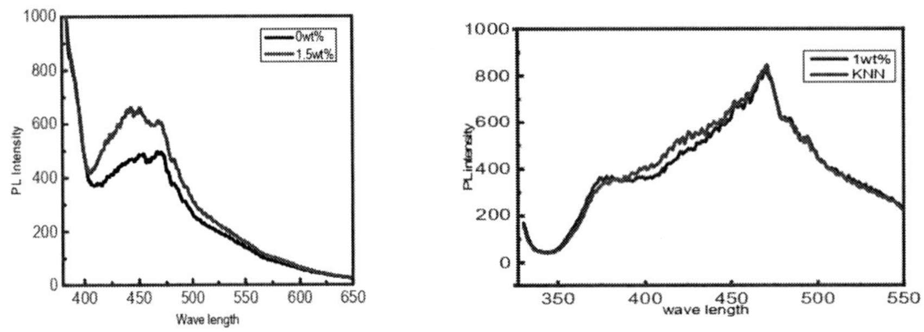

Figure.3 (a) PL spectra for the natural and Bismuth doped KNN for the excitation wave duration of 350 nm and 300 nm

Characterization of the optical and electronic properties of semiconductors and molecules are done by Photoluminescence spectroscopy. The method itself is fast, contactless, and non destructive. Figures indicate PL spectra of natural KNN and Bismuth doped KNN samples with inside the wavelength variety of 300–600 nm at room temperature.To obtain PL spectra of powder samples the excitation wave length used is 300nm. The photoluminescence emission spectrum is obtained in ultraviolet/visible region. Both KNN and doped KNN have awesome emission bands at room temperature. The discovered PL spectrum peaks in among 375 nm and 400 nm can be ascribed to near band emission (NBE) within side the UV visible which indicates the band to band transition. The peaks round 475 nm may be attributed to blue or green emission band within side the visible region that are related to defects with inside the pattern. The emission in green region indicates oxygen vacancies, the height depth of NBE-decreased and of disorder peaks stays unchanged with Bismuth doping. This means the bismuth doping will increase crystal imperfections. Defect states emissions bands had been discovered because of formations of intermediate power degrees due to formation of oxygen vacancies and crystal defects which provide upward thrust to blue/green emission bands. The sharp UV and visible emissions had been happening which reveal that KNN ceramics can be used for ultraviolet or visible laser production. This photoluminescence study of Potassium Sodium Niobate results in their packages in light emitting diodes, optical storage and in telecommunication devices.

4. Conclusion

Both natural and Bismuth doped KNN ceramics and Bismuth doped KNN ceramics powders had been synthesized efficiently through solid state route and their structure, optical and photoluminescence properties had been scrutinized. XRD evaluation discovered perovskite orthorhombic crystal shape at room temperature. Optical examine discovered a lower in optical band gap energy with accelerated doping attention. Photoluminescence spectra have an emission band with inside the ultraviolet or Visible region, which discover their utility in the fields of electro-optics

Acknowledgements
The authors acknowledge the facilities provided by the UGC, DST, FIST, SERB and KSCSTE in setting up facilities at Sree Keralavarma College, Thrissur. We also acknowledge the help received from department of Physics, Vimala College, Thrissur for taking PL spectra and department of Physics St. Thomas College, Thrissur for taking XRD of the samples.

References

1) David, R.W., *Modern Ceramic Engineering: Properties, Processing and Use in Design*, ed. r. Edition. 2006.
2) University of Cambridge. *Dielectric Materials from: http://www.doitpoms.ac.uk/tlplib/dielectrics/index.php*. 2008 -2009.
3) Wu, J., D. Xiao, and J. Zhu, *Potassium-sodium niobate lead-free piezoelectric materials: past, present, and future of phase boundaries. . .*
4) Rödel, J.J., Wook Seifert, Klaus T. P. Anton, Eva-Maria Granzow, Torsten Damjanovic, Dragan, *Perspective on the Development of Lead-free Piezoceramics.* Journal of the American Ceramic Society, 2009.
5) Bell, A.J., *Ferroelectrics: The role of ceramic science and engineering.* Journal of the European Ceramic Society.
6) Takenaka, T.N., H. Hiruma, Y. Yoshii, Y. Matumoto, K., *Lead-free piezoelectric ceramics based on perovskite structures.* Journal of Electroceramics, 2007. .
7) Panda, P.K., *Review: environmental friendly lead-free piezoelectric materials.* Journal of Materials Science, 2009.
8) Aksel, E. and J.L. Jones, *Advances in Lead-Free Piezoelectric Materials for Sensors and Actuators.* Sensors, 2010.
9) Wood, E.A., *Polymorphism in Potassium Niobate, Sodium Niobate and Other ABO3 Compounds.* Acta Crystallographica.
10) Birol, H., D. Damjanovic, and N. Setter, *Preparation and characterization of (K0.5Na0.5)NbO3 ceramics.* Journal of the European Ceramic Society, 2006.
11) Fluckiger, U., and Arend, H,, *On The Preparation Of Pure, Doped And Reduced KNbO3 Single Crystals.* Journal of Crystal Growth, 1978..
12) Guo, Y., K.-i. Kakimoto, and H. Ohsato, *Phase transitional behavior and piezoelectric properties of (Na0.5K0.5)NbO3–LiNbO3 ceramics.* Applied Physics Letters, 2004.
13) Kepinska M, Starczewska A, Duka P. Method of determining dispersion dependence of refractive index of nanospheres building opals. Opt Mater.
14) Shannon RC, Lafuente B, Shannon RD, et al. Refractive indices of minerals and synthetic compounds. Am Mineral. 2017.

IOP Conf. Series: Materials Science and Engineering 1263 (2022) 012015 doi:10.1088/1757-899X/1263/1/012015

Novel Intense Red Emitting Eu^{3+} Doped $CePO_4$ Nanocrystals for Solid State Lighting Applications

S Sisira [1]*, K P Mani[2], P Punathil[3], L A Jacob[4], B Baby[5], P R Biju[5], N V Unnikrishnan[5], C Joseph[5]*
[1]Department of Physics, Sree Narayana College, Alathur, Palakkad, Kerala India, Pin: 678 682
[2]Inter National School of Photonics, CUSAT, Ernakulam- 682022, Kerala, India,
[3]University of Verona, Italy
[4]Department of Physics, Baselius College, Kottayam, Kerala, India. Pin: 686 001
[5]School of Pure and Applied Physics, Mahatma Gandhi University, Kottayam-686560, India

*Corresponding author: cyriacmgu@gmail.com, sisirasivan0@gmail.com

Abstract. Novel red emitting europium doped Cerium phosphate nanocrystals were synthesized by microwave assisted sol gel method. X-ray powder diffraction analysis identified the monoclinic structure of synthesized samples. The morphology of the samples were found to beconstructed from elongated spheres and is explained with the help of TEM analysis. Intense orange red emission on excitation with Ce^{4+} - O^{2-}charge transfer band is established by photoluminescence analysis. The effect of annealing on the efficiency of excitation with Ce^{4+} - O^{2-}charge transfer band is demonstrated and is explained in association with the concentration of surface Ce^{4+}. Chromaticity coordinates indicate good colour purity of the sample. All the results indicated that microwave assisted method is suitable for synthesizing red emitting $CePO_4$:Eu phosphors and become a potential candidate for optoelectronic and biological applications.
Key words: Cerium phosphate; microwave synthesis; Rietveld refinement; Europium;

1 Introduction

Rare earth based luminescent materials have attracted much attention by many researchers over the last few years in terms of lighting applications owing to their energy saving properties [1-2]. Nowadays, in the field of lighting mainly in the fabrication of white LEDs, blue LED chip with a yellow-emitting YAG: Ce^{3+} phosphor strategy is extensively used even though its color rendering properties are poor due to the lack of red component [3-4]. In order to compensate the scarcity of red component the only solution is the incorporation of suitablered phosphor in LEDs in combination with YAG:Ce^{3+} phosphor. Hence in recent years the search for novel red emitting phosphors became the focus of many researchers which are beneficial for white LEDs [5].

In the field of phosphors, trivalent rare earth ions are widely used as activators owing to the intense narrow emission and their independent nature of peak positions with crystal field environment [6]. Among the different rare earth ions one of the important activator is Eu^{3+}, which gives out intense bright red emission ranging from580 - 720 nm due to $^5D_0 \rightarrow {}^7F_J$intra configurational transitions [7-8]. Moreover, Eu^{3+} is considered as a potential candidate to probe the environment around the europium ion in a matrix via its hypersensitive transitions [9].

The selection of host is an important factor while considering the luminescence characteristics of a phosphor [8]. Rare earth orthophosphates have attracted more interest in recent years since they exhibit unique luminescence properties and showed high chemical stability and thermal stability [9]. Cerium Phosphate with chemical formula $CePO_4$ among various monazite type rare earth phosphates ($RePO_4$) is extensively investigated owing to the presence of Ce^{3+}- an excellent sensitizer for rare earth ions [10]. From many literatures it is well understood that unwanted non-radiative energy loss via multiphonon transition must be reduced to have an efficient phosphor. Hence it can be ascertained that cerium phosphate with low phonon energy ~ 1100 cm^{-1} is an appropriate and efficient host for phosphor materials [11]. A number of literatures are available on investigating the luminescent properties of pure and certain rare earth doped cerium phosphate. Among these most of them are based on Terbium (III) and Dysprosium (III) doped $CePO_4$ nanocrystals and which are widely used in optoelectronic applications. [12-13]. Intense red emitting samarium (Sm^{3+}) doped $CePO_4$ nanocrystals is also reported in which variation of Sm^{3+} luminescence with doping concentration and annealing is investigated [14]. However, to the best of our knowledge photoluminescence investigations on Eu^{3+}:$CePO_4$ nanocrystals are not reported yet. Since Eu^{3+} activated luminescent nanomaterials are promising candidates for various applications owing to their intense red emission with better color purity, activating Eu^{3+} in $CePO_4$ is the well-defined goal of present work for the development of efficient red emitting phosphor.

2. Synthesis and characterization

2.1. Synthesis

A detailed synthesis method is presented in our previous work for the synthesis of Eu^{3+} doped $CePO_4$ [14].The sample synthesized at 600°C and 900°C were chosen for the detailed study and were labeled as S1and S2 respectively.

2.2. Characterization

The X-ray powder diffraction patterns were recorded using a Rigaku Ultima IV diffractometer. Rietveld refinement were done using General Structure Analysis System (GSAS) program. SHIMADZU IR Prestige 20 spectrometer used for recording Fourier Transform Infrared spectra. Transmission Electron Microscopic observations were performed on JEOL JEM 2100 transmission electron microscope. Perkin Elmer Lambda 25 UV–Vis spectrometer was used to record the absorption spectra of the samples. Photoluminescence analyses were carried out by Horiba Jobin-YvonFlouromax-4 spectrofluorometer.

3. Results and discussions

3.1. X-ray powder diffraction analysis

X-ray powder diffraction patterns of samples are shown in figure 3.1. The diffraction patterns are identical and matches well with monoclinic cerium phosphate ($CePO_4$) on comparing with standard data as per ICDD no. 89-2431.The average crystallite size calculated using Debye-Scherrer equation was found to be 40.7 and 148.8 nm respectively for the samples S1 and S2[12].

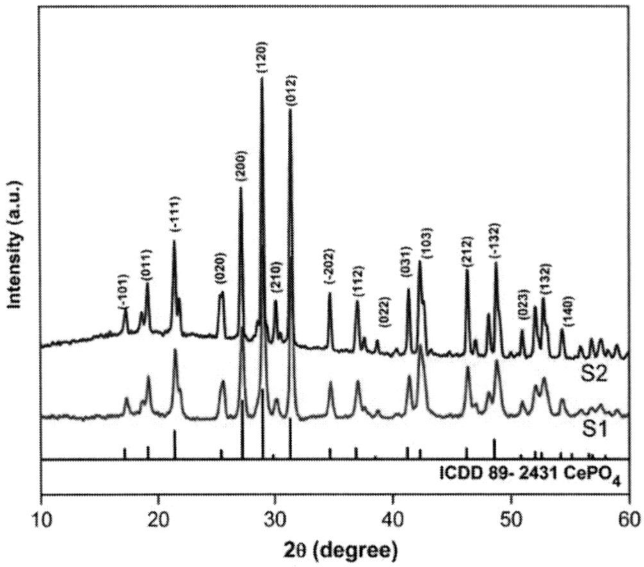

Figure 3.1: X-ray powder diffractograms of $Ce_{1-x}PO_4$: Eu_x^{3+} nanocrystals

The Rietveld refinement of $Ce_{1-x}PO_4$: Eu_x^{3+} nanocrystals were carried out using General Structure Analysis System (GSAS) package and the corresponding GIXRD data and the refinement results are presented in figure 3.2a-b. The structural parameters from the literature were taken for refinement [15]. The Goodness of fit (χ2) obtained is 1.49 and 1.57 respectively for the samples S1 and S2. Refined lattice parameters for $Ce_{1-x}PO_4$: Eu_x^{3+} are given in table 3.1 shows good agreement with the standard data of pure $CePO_4$ [16], which further confirms the substitution of Ce^{3+} ions by Eu^{3+} ions in $CePO_4$ nanocrystals.

Table 3.1: Rietveld refinement data

Parameter	600°C	900°C
χ^2	1.49	1.57
a(Å)	6.8027	6.7922
b(Å)	7.0264	7.0149
c(Å)	6.4741	6.4657
α (degree)	90.00	90.00
β(degree)	103.51	103.49
γ(degree)	90.00	90.00
Micro strain	6.52×10^{-4}	3.62×10^{-4}
Crystallite size (t) (nm)	45.3	154.9

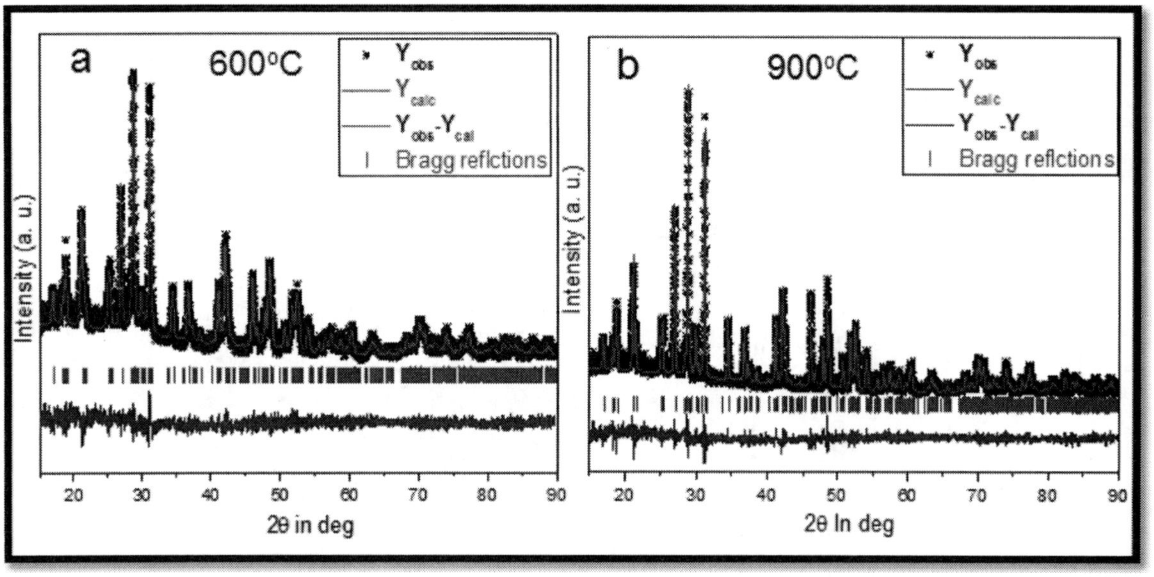

Figure 3.2: Rietveld refinement result of $Ce_{1-x}PO_4$: Eu_x^{3+} nanocrystals synthesized at a) 600°C an b) 900°C, Original data: black curve, Rietveld fit: red curve, phase reflection: Vertical magentalines and the difference between observed and calculated intensities: blue curve

3.2 Fourier transform infrared spectroscopy

The FTIR spectra of $C_{1-x}PO_4$: Eu_x^{3+} nanocrystals annealed at 600 and 900°C are shown in figure 3.3. The phosphate vibrational `modes are observed in the range 400–1200 cm^{-1} and the different nature of splitting (shown in the inset) that detected for the samples S1 and S2 are explained in detail in our previous work [10].

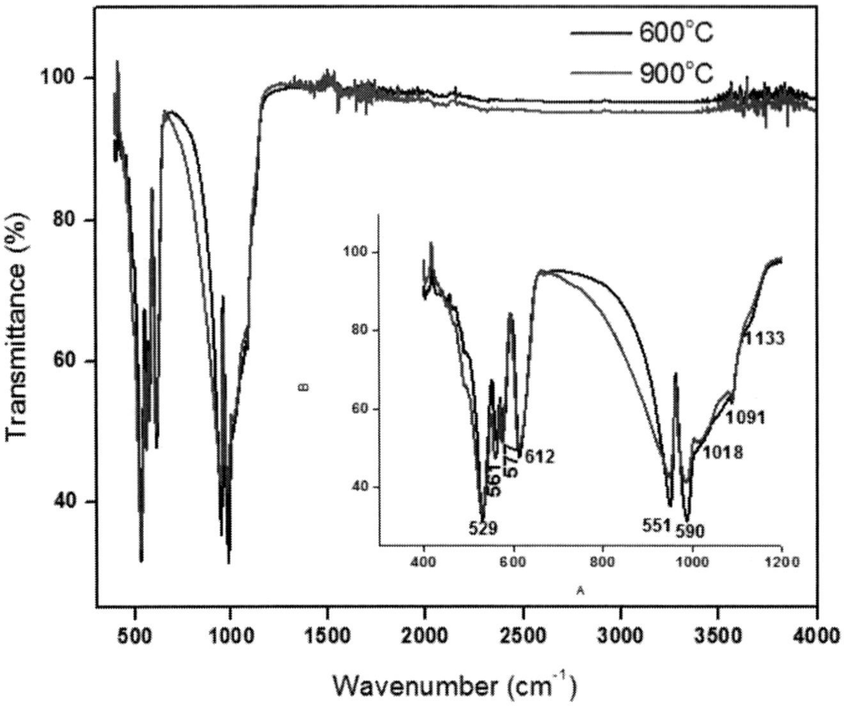

Figure 3.3: FTIR spectra of $Ce_{1-x}PO_4$: Eu_x^{3+} nanocrystals

3.3 Transmission Electron Microscopy

TEM analysis was carried out to reveal the morphology of the samples S1 and S2 and the TEM images recorded are given in figures 3.4a-c and 3.4d respectively. TEM image shown in figure 3a-b clearly demonstrate that the obtained $Ce_{1-x}PO_4$:Eu_x^{3+} nanocrystals were about 100-300 nm diameter aggregates which were further constructed of elongated spherical particles of 20-25 nm in diameter. Even though $Ce_{1-x}PO_4$:Eu_x^{3+} aggregates are observed to be irregular in shape the close examination of the encircled portion in figure 3.4a and 3.4c reveal that they showed a tendency to form nanorod stacks. The nanorod formation can be explained in relation with the coalescence induced by oriented random attachment processes that may happen under microwave irradiation [18].The TEM image of the sample synthesized at 900ºC in figure 3.4d indicated that the particles are large in size approximately equal to 300-600 nm range [18].

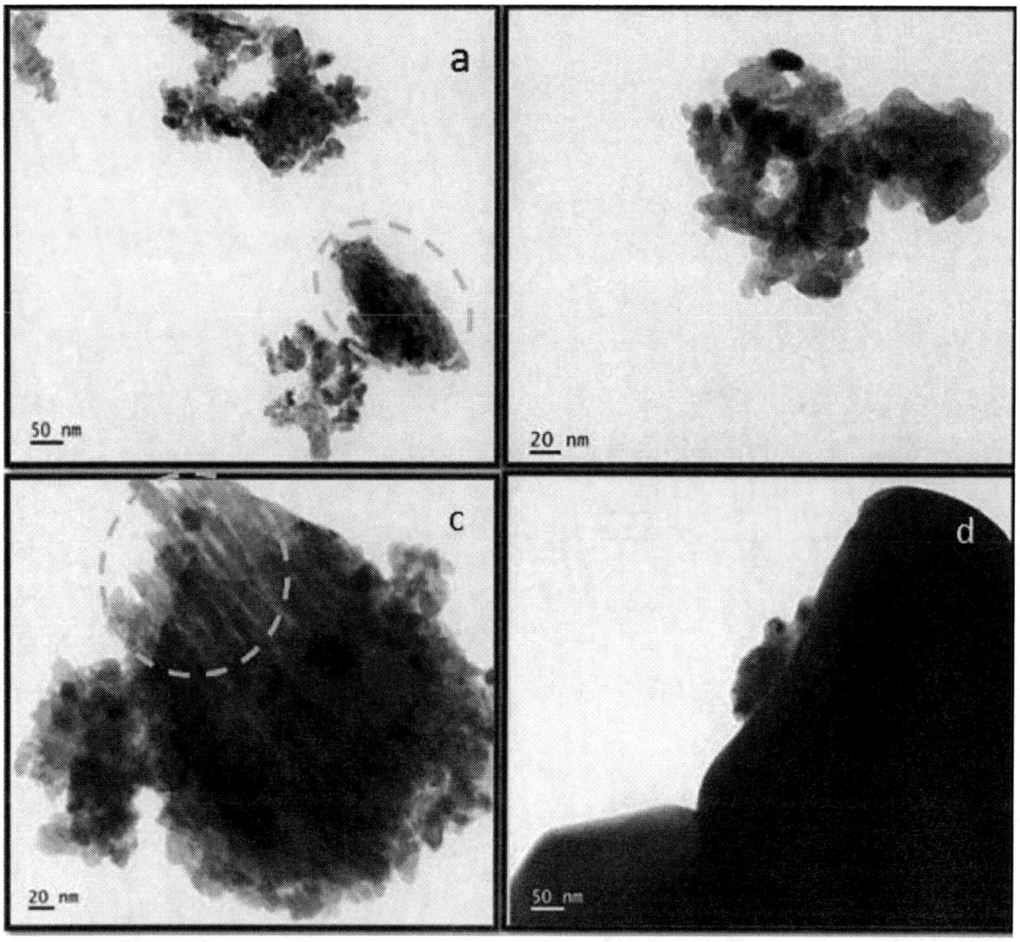

Figure 3.4: TEM images of $Ce_{1-x}PO_4:Eu_x^{3+}$ nanocrystals synthesized at (a-c) 600°C and (d) 900°C

The high resolution TEM images of $Ce_{1-x}PO_4:Eu_x^{3+}$ nanocrystals annealed at 600°C and 900°C are depicted in figure 3.5a and 3.5c. Well defined lattice fringes in tune with (012) crystal planes with inter-planar distance 2.85Å are observed for both samples. The lattice planes (200), (120) and (012) with d spacing 3.28 Å, 3.08Å and 2.85Å respectively could be indexed in the SAED pattern of 600°C annealed sample and is shown in figure 3.5b. Similarly for 900°C annealed sample the planes (200) and (210) corresponding to 2.85 Å and 2.97 Å are marked in figure 3.5d.

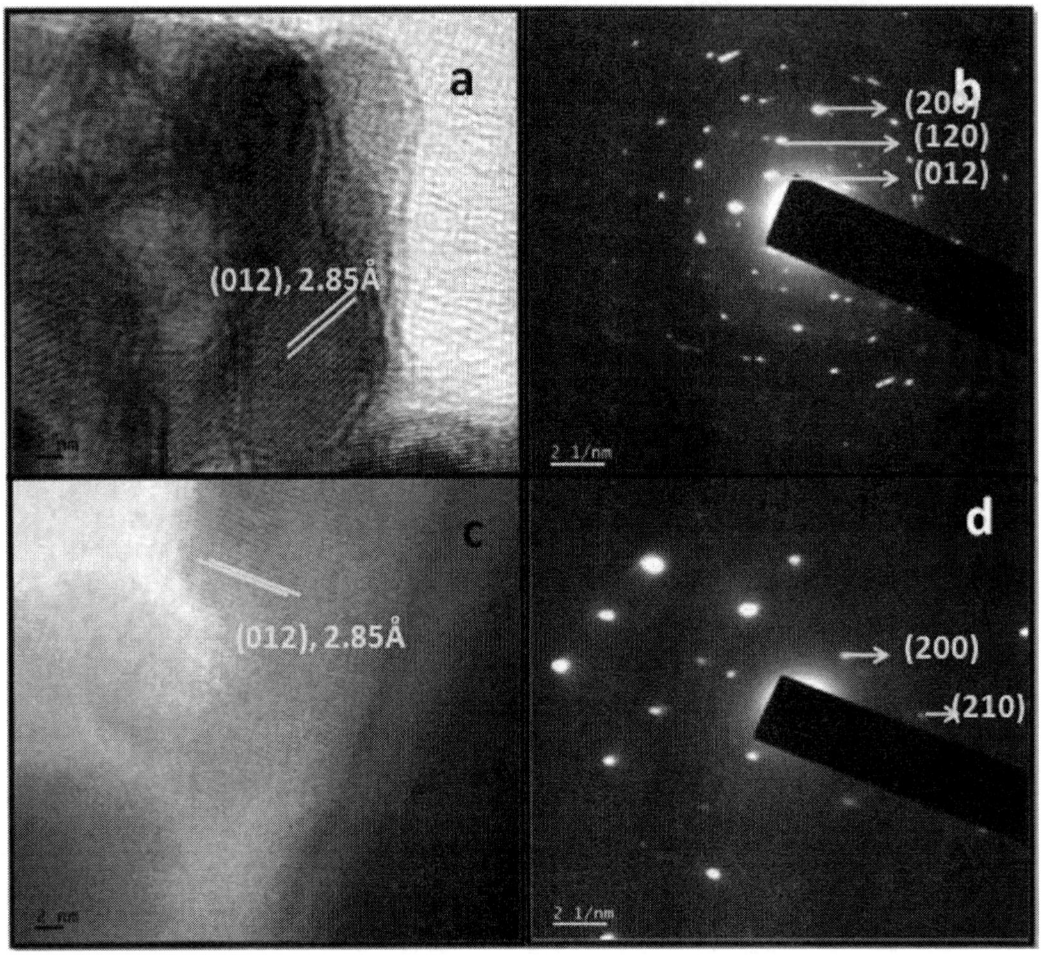

Figure 3.5: a & c HRTEM and b & d SAED pattern of $Ce_{1-x}PO_4:Eu_x^{3+}$ nanocrystals synthesized at 600 and 900°C respectively

3.4 UV-Visible Absorption studies

The UV-Visible absorption spectra of $Ce_{1-x}PO_4:Eu_x^{3+}$ nanocrystals annealed at 600 and 900°C are shown in figure 3.6. An absorption band assigned to the 4f-5d transition of Ce^{3+} with crystal field splitted peaks are observed [19]. The effect of Ce^{4+}-O^{2-} charge transfer transition is also there behind the broad peak at 333 nm [14]. According to our previous work, the presence of Ce^{4+} that observed in the absorption spectra is arised only from incomplete bonding structure that observed near the crystal surface of $CePO_4$ nanocrystals and is not from the bulk. Annealing caused the reduction of concentration of surface Ce^{4+} such that the intensity of peak at 333 nm is found to be decreased considerably on annealing of sample from 600 to 900°C [14].

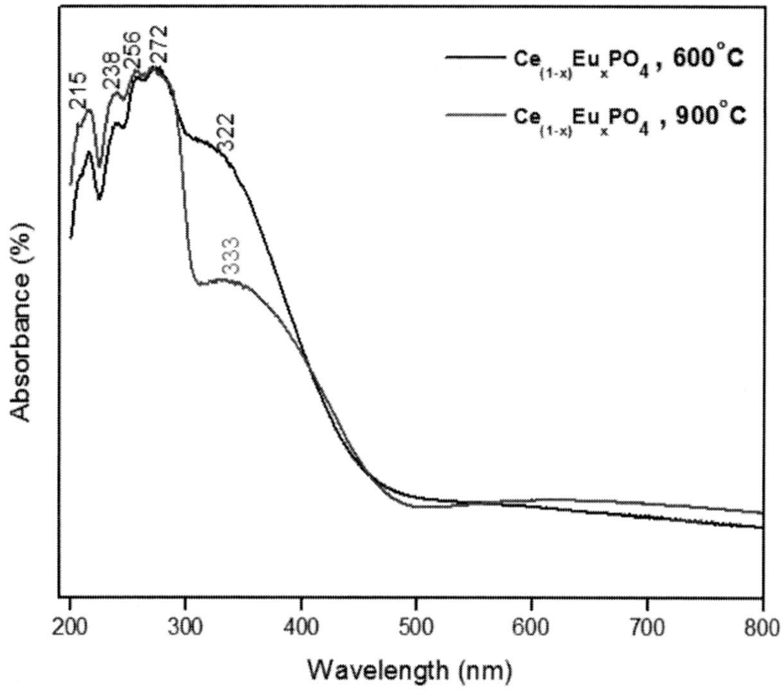

Figure 3.6: UV-Vis absorption spectrum of $Ce_{1-x}PO_4:Eu_x^{3+}$ nanocrystals.

3.5 Photoluminescence analysis

The photoluminescence excitation spectra of $CePO_4$: Eu^{3+} samples annealed at 600 and 900°Care recorded by monitoring the highest emission of Eu^{3+} at 589 nm in the wavelength range 200-500 nm and are depicted in figures3.7 and 3.8 respectively. Excitation spectrum of the sample at 600°C consists of a strong broad band in the range 225-300 with peak maximum at 333 nm and is attributed to the Ce^{4+}-O^{2-} charge transfer transition [20]. The excitation spectra of 900°C annealed sample shows a weak band at 333nm attributed to the Ce^{4+}-O^{2-} charge transfer transition showing a close agreement with the observation from absorptions spectra depicted in figure. Along with the Ce^{4+} charge transfer band, f-f transition peaks of Eu^{3+} are also observed. The f-f transition peaks observed at 399 and 419 were assigned to, $^7F_0 \rightarrow {}^5L_6$ and$^7F_0 \rightarrow {}^5D_3$ transitions respectively [21-22]. The charge transfer band associated with Ce^{4+} at 333 nm shows that they can be utilized for sensitization of Eu^{3+} emission. Besides, the excitation band at 333 nm is found to be more intense than the f-f transition peaks such that the band at 333 nm is chosen for further studying the emission characteristics of $Ce_{1-x}PO_4:Eu_x^{3+}$ nanocrystals.

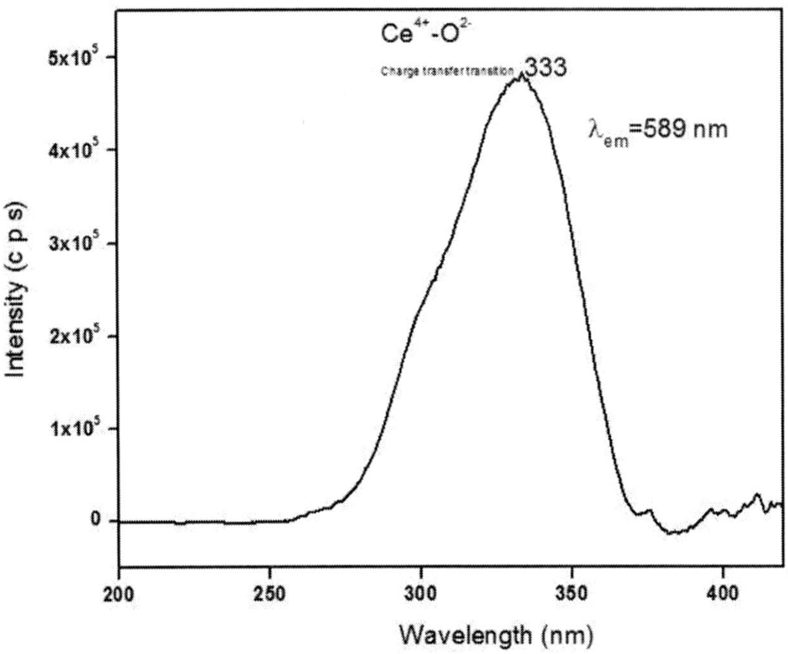

Figure 3.7: Excitation spectrum of $Ce_{1-x}PO_4:Eu_x^{3+}$ nanocrystals synthesized at 600°C

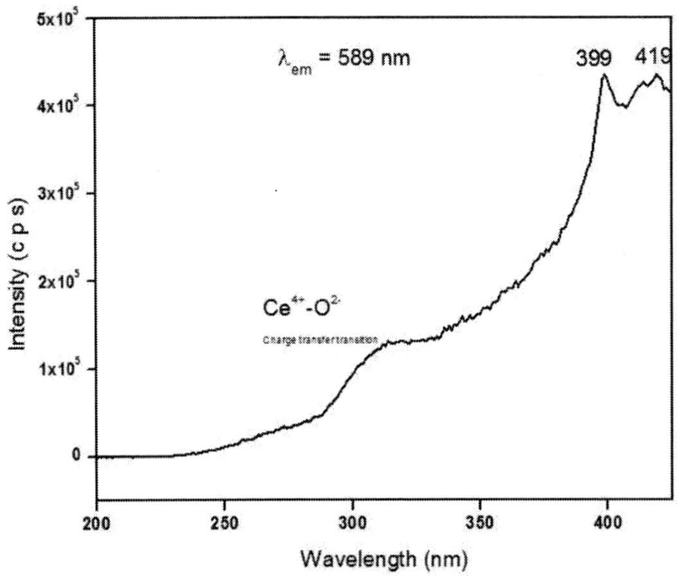

Figure 3.8: Excitation spectrum of $Ce_{1-x}PO_4:Eu_x^{3+}$ nanocrystals synthesized at 900°C

The photoluminescence emission spectra of $Ce_{1-x}PO_4:Eu_x^{3+}$ nanocrystals synthesized at 600°C is recorded on excitation with charge transfer band at 333nm in the wavelength range 550 to 750 nm and is shown in figure 3.9. The emission spectra exhibit emission peaks in the orange red region corresponding to $^5D_0 \rightarrow {}^7F_{J=1,2,3,4}$ transitions of Eu^{3+} [23]. Among emission peaks the peak at 589 nm is found to be sharp and intense and others are found to be splitted under strong crystal field effect.

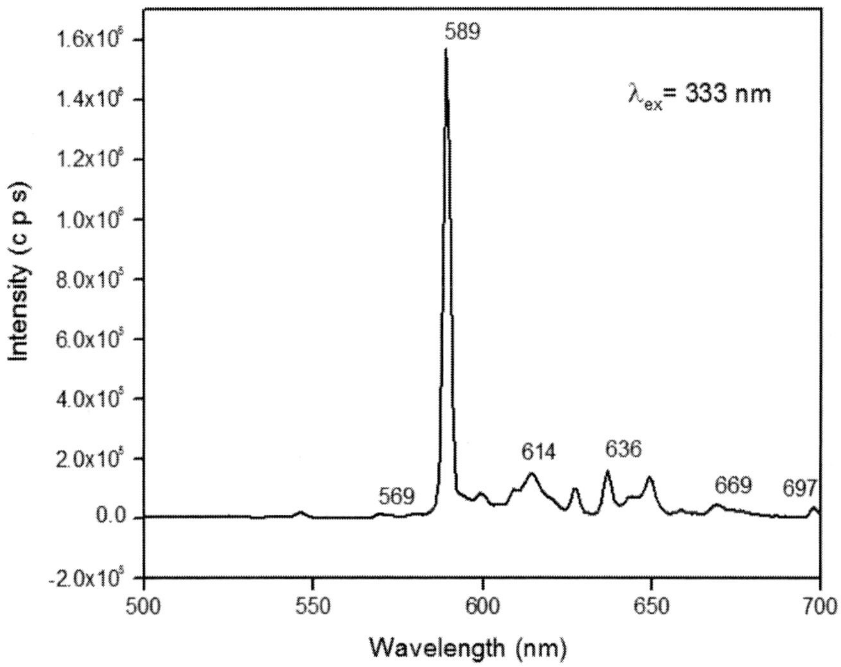

Figure 3.9: Photoluminescence emission spectrum of $Ce_{1-x}PO_4:Eu_x^{3+}$ nanocrystals synthesized at 600°C

The mechanism involved in the intense emission of Eu^{3+} observed in the emission spectra via charge transfer band excitation is explained as follows. On charge band excitation Eu^{3+} ion is raised to charge transfer state from the ground state when the sample is excited by 245 nm wavelengths. The sequential non radiative decay of Eu^{3+} ion from charge transfer state feeds $^5D_0$ level and is followed by radiative emission to $^7F_{J(J = 1, 2, 3, 4)}$ levels in the orange and red regions [21]. CIE coordinates are calculated and are found to be (0.58, 0.41) which is labelled in the CIE diagram given in figure 3.10.From the CIE diagram it is obvious that synthesized samples are capable of giving red emission which finds its candidature for in fabricating WLEDs.

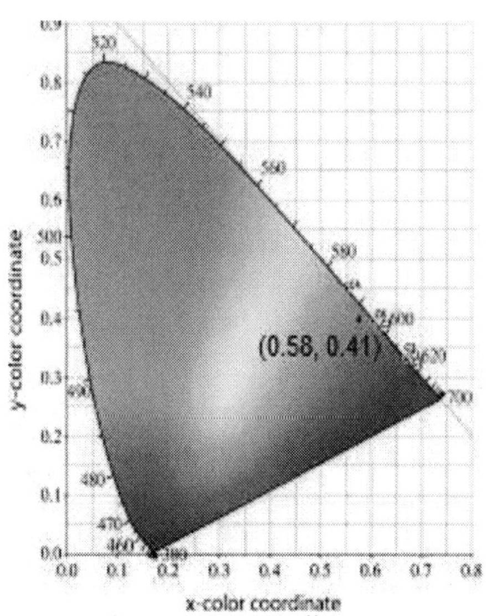

Figure 3.10: CIE diagram

4 Conclusions

Red luminescent novel $CePO_4:Eu^{3+}$ nanocrystals were prepared by microwave assisted method. The recorded X-ray diffractograms confirmed the monoclinic structure of all the samples. The phosphate vibrational modes of the monoclinic $CePO_4$were analyzed usingFourier transform spectroscopy.The morphology of the samples is revealed to be 100-300 nm diameter aggregates by TEM analysis. UV-Visible absorption spectrum shows a charge transfer band Ce^{4+}-O^{2-}suggests the possibility of sensitization of Eu^{3+} by Ce^{4+}. Intense red emission observed in the photoluminescence emission spectra and CIE analysis ascertained that the synthesized samples are appropriate for the fabrication of red emitting phosphors for WLEDs.

Acknowledgments
The author Kamal P Mani acknowledges the University of Grant Comission Govt. of India, New Delhi towards Dr D S Kothari Postdoctoral fellowship.

References

[1] Shimomura Y, Tetsuo H, Motoyuki S, Toshio A, Kaoru O, Naoto K, 2007 *J. Electrochem. Soc*,.**154** J35
[2] Mingyun G, Jianhua S, Tongming S, Quanfa Z, Jianting H, Aiqin J, 2010 *J. Mater. Sci. Technol.*, , **26(1)**, 45
[3] Qu X, Wong S C, Chi K T,**2010 IEEE Xplore, DOI: 10.1109/IECON.2007.4459976**
[4] Junrong L, Youfu Z, Wentao X, He L, Shuai L, Bin W, Kun W, 2020 *J. Adv. Ceram.* 9 45
[5] Haitao Z, Xuhai L, Renli F, Yahui S, He W, Qinjiang H, Xiufeng S, 2019 *J. of Lumin.* **211**1
[6] Zheng R Martín-R, Fernando A, María D A, Rafael V, Ana C P, 2019 *ACS Appl. Mater. Interfaces* **11** 7559
[7] Yuuki K, Jumpei U, Kotaro F, Masatomo Y, Shiro F, Takayuki N, Takashi T, Naoto H, Kenta H, Ryo M, Setsuhisa T, 2021 *Chem. Mater.* 22 8873
[8] Guzik M, Tomaszewicz E, Guyot Y, Legendziewicza J, Boulon G, 2015 *J. Mater. Chem. C*, **3** 8582
[9] Asiri S N, Hansnath T, 2021 *AIP Conference Proceedings* **2369** 020167
[10] Sisira S, Dinu A, Kukku T, Vimal G, Kamal P M P, Biju P R, Unnikrishnan N V, Cyriac J, 2017*Mater. Res. Express***4**025010
[11] Errandonea D , Gomis O, Rodríguez-Hernández P, Muñoz A, Ruiz-Fuertes J, Gupta M, Achary S N, Hirsch A, Manjon F J, PetersL, Roth G, Tyagi A K, Bettinelli M, 2018 *J. Phys.: Condens. Matter* **30** 065401
[12] Fen Z , Stanislaus S W, 2010*ACS Nano.*,**4** 99
[13] Gulnar K, Sudarsan V, Vatsa K, Hubli C, Gautam K, Vinu A, Tyagi K, *Cryst. Growth Des.*,2009**9(5)** 2451
[14] Sisira S, Linju Ann Jacob, Kukku T, Dinu A, Biju P R, Unnikrishnan N V, Cyriac Joseph, 2019 *J Lumin.***209** 197-297
[15] Toby B H, Von D, 2013 *J. Appl. Crystallography*, **46** 544
[16] Prabeesh P, Selvam I P, Potty S N, 2018 *Appl. Phys. A*,**124** 225
[17] Raeen O, Singh N R, 2013*Progress in Nanotechnol. Nanomat.***2** 26
[18] Leilane R. M, Mario L. M, Juan A, Elson L, 2010 *CrstEngComm*,doi:0.1039/c004034g
[19] Li Q and Yam V W W , 2007 *Angew. Chem.,Int. Ed. Engl.* **119** 3556
[20] Verma S, Bamzai K K, 2014 *J. of Nanopart.***2014** 125360

[21]Daibo Pi, FengW, Xianping F, Minquan W, Yong Z, 2005 *Spectrochim Act Part A: Molec. Biomolec.Spectr.* **61** 2455
[22]Boukerika A, Guerbous L, 2018 *J Lumin.* **145** 148
[23]YingchaoH, Xinyu W, Honglian D, Shipu L, 2013 *J Lumin.* **135** 281

Polarization-insensitive broadband perfect metamaterial absorber in the optical region

Raj Kumar[1], Bipin K Singh[2], Praveen C Pandey[1*]

[1] Department of Physics, Indian Institute of Technology (BHU), Varanasi 221005, India
[2]Department of Physics, University of Mumbai, Mumbai 400098, India

[*] Corresponding author: pcpandey.app@iitbhu.ac.in

Abstract. Metamaterials (MTMs) have various applications like plasmonic sensors, light trapping, light detector, color imaging, real invisible clock, magnetic resonance imaging, thermal imaging, solar cells, etc. We have used CST software to simulate four nano-rings-based broadband MTM absorbers in this paper. The simulated structure consists of three layers in the form of a metal-dielectric-metal that exhibit a good impedance near unity with plasmonic resonance characteristics. Tungsten (W) is chosen as the metal and silicon dioxide (SiO_2)as the dielectric. The designed structure exhibits an average absorption of 98.19% at the applied wavelength and also exhibits broadband absorption with almost perfect absorption. The physical dimensions, as well as the design of the proposed absorber, have been studied parametrically. Absorber performance has been investigated for transverse electric (TE) and transverse magnetic (TM) modes at wide angles up to 50°, which may be helpful for solar thermo-photovoltaic (STPV) and solar power harvesting device applications. For solar cell applications, we have calculated numerical values of short circuit current density (Jsc) and efficiency (η).

Keywords: Plasmonic metamaterial, perfect absorption, Polarization insensitive absorption.

1. Introduction

Power comes from various sources of energy. Non-renewable and renewable are two groups of energy. In the category of solar energy, the sun is the major source of energy. There are several methods for capturing solar energy, but photovoltaic (PV) cells are one of the most common. The external circuit collected the charge carriers generated by PV cells and generated electric current. For high efficiency, solar thermophotovoltaics (STPVs) systems need high absorbance of solar spectra because absorb photons' energies create a temperature difference between the layers. Synthetic metamaterials (MTMs) have double negative properties of permeability and permittivity [1]. Metamaterial (MTM) properties depend on the physical design structure that enables them to use for different applications [2]. In 2008, Landey *et al.* suggested the first theoretical and functional metamaterial absorber (MMA) in the GHz region [3]. Future THz applications were made possible thanks to a presentation by Tao *et al.* [4]. Since then there has been a lot of research based on MMA in the visual field. MTM absorbers have been composed of two-layers [5], three-layers [6], four-layers [7], and several layers [8] but most commonly used a three-layer structure. In the three-layer structure, capacitance is generated by the aid of a dielectric layer between the metal and resonator layers, and the metal is impedimented to the electromagnetic (EM) wave transmission [9].

Inspired by the previously reported work various applications of MMA in the visible region have been proposed here. The metal tungsten (W), which has a higher melting point (3422 °C)than other metals (Gold, Silver, Copper, and Chromium), is a primary driving force behind the research. Tungsten absorbers withstand high temperatures due to the high melting point of tungsten. The dielectric layer of silicon dioxide (SiO_2) is chosen because it has low relative permittivity and provides a high melting point (1710 °C). A new MMA is proposed in this work, which is composed of three-layer from 400 nm to 800 nm wavelengths and exhibits an average of 98.19% absorption with the whole optical spectrum. It had a wideband of absorption up to 99% between 548 nm to 712 nm. The main causes of high absorption are imaginary sections of impedance that are close to zero and real parts that meet at unity. To find the best MMA absorber, we have modified the geometry of the designed unit cells by adjusting the parameters. Short circuit current density (J_{sc} = 25.50 mA/cm2), fill factor (FF = 81.85%), open-circuit voltage (V_{oc} = 0.562 V), and conversion efficiency (η = 11.73%) have also been determined. This absorber is better-suitable for solar energy collecting and thermal photovoltaics applications because of its high refractory, polarization independence, broad incident angle insensitivity, and high efficiency.

2. Materials and method

The proposed MTM unit cell consists of three layers which were composed of a metallic layer of tungsten (W) and a lossless dielectric layer of silicon dioxide (SiO_2). The top (resonator) and bottom layer are considered to be tungsten metal while the intermediate layer is made of silicon dioxide material. The physical dimension of the proposed design is presented as a periodic form of the unit cell, front-view, and side-view, respectively in Figure 1. The most common metal-dielectric-metal (MIM) based three-layer design symmetrical structure used in this work. First, design the bottom plane and the dielectric layer with a total length and width of p = 400 nm. Here, bottom plane, dielectric, and resonator thickness are h = 100 nm, t_1 = 31 nm, and t_2 = 75 nm, respectively. Other, all the parameters of the unit cell include in Table 1, which easy to understand of metasurface of MTM. The primary factor in choosing this metal despite its substantial intrinsic losses is the tungsten resonator layer's excellent impedance matching with open space. The ohmic loss of W is low so it's demonstrated as an excellent absorber in the optical region. With the help of the intermediate layer, SiO_2 creates a suitable coupling with the resonator and bottom plane. With the aid of lossless resonance properties, the dielectric layer can match the impedance of free space with a good impedance. Note that the proposed unit cell is ultrathin (206 nm) which can be easily rolled off any STPV cell.

We have used the Computer Simulation Technology Microwave Studio (CST MW) software to simulate the design of the metamaterial absorber which is based on the finite integration technique (FIT). The components required to form periodic structures are called unit cell metamaterials. Figure 1 (b) shows the unit cell structure of the proposed MTM. The boundary condition is defined for a unit cell. Unit cell boundary conditions always extend the model to the x-y-plane of the global coordinate system. The incident electromagnetic radiations are polarized in such a way that the wave vector (k) is perpendicular to the geometric plane of the unit cell structure and the electric and magnetic fields propagate parallel to the structure plane. So, we have used the periodic boundary conditions on the x and y-axis. The z-axis, an open space with a perfectly matched layer (PML), represents a planar wave with linear polarization on the structure. To reduce reflections, PML limits are essentially implemented in the form of an absorbing material in which the impedance matches that of the material around it.

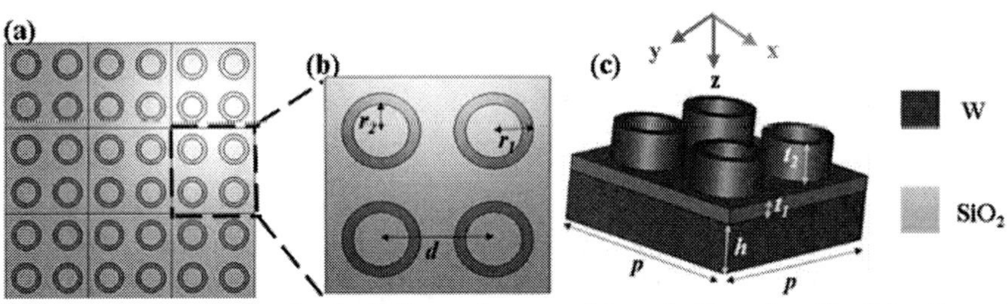

Figure 1. The proposed design's physical dimensions are (a) periodic unit cells, (b) a front view, and (c) a schematic representation.

Table 1. Parameters value in nm of a proposed unit cell.

Parameters	*p*	*h*	t_1	t_2	r_1	r_2	*d*
Values (nm)	400	100	31	75	70	50	200

3. Results and discussion

The top view of the proposed absorber corresponds to a Fabry-Perot cavity. The principle of absorption is based on interference reduction and enhancement at the interface. The EM field is transmitted and reflected many times on the interface in the MTM. Finally, the EM field is superimposed many times in the top-view plane. The bottom layer of tungsten plays a crucial role because the transmission approximately being near zero due to the skin's depth. So the EM field is completely absorbed which explains the principle of absorption of MTMs. Consequently, changing the structural and geometric characteristics of the suggested unit cell can affect the absorption efficiency and resonance frequency. From the S-parameters, the effective impedance has been extracted by using Eq. (1) and plotted in figure 2. The imaginary and real components of the impedance are approximately equal and zero. Using Eq. 2, the absorption A (ω) response could be calculated by the absorber [6].

$$Z_{eff} = \sqrt{\frac{(1+S_{11})^2 - S_{21}^2}{(1-S_{11})^2 - S_{21}^2}} \tag{1}$$

$$A(\omega) = 1 - T(\omega) - R(\omega) = 1 - |S_{21}(\omega)|^2 - |S_{11}(\omega)|^2 \tag{2}$$

Here, Transmission, $T(\omega) = |S_{21}(\omega)|^2$, and Reflection, $R(\omega) = |S_{11}(\omega)|^2$. When the impedance of the suggested structure $Z(\omega)$ is equal to the free space impedance Z_o with the formation of the top view resonators and structure periodicity, the condition of absorption reaches close to unity. Also, the reflectance is inversely proportional to absorption. Due to dispersive properties, these values are frequency-dependent. However, the maximum transmittance blocks by the bottom plane, so $T(\omega)$ is very lower, and obtain the perfect absorption which is relevant to the reflectance. So $A(\omega)$ equation can be expressed as,

$$A(\omega) = 1 - R(\omega) = 1 - |S_{11}(\omega)|^2 \tag{3}$$

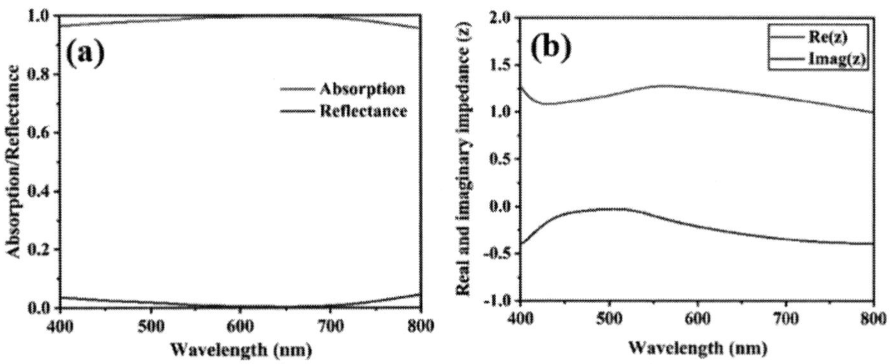

Figure 2. (a) Absorption and reflectance spectra of the proposed absorber (b) Imaginary and real components make up normalized impedance.

Figure 2(a) shows the absorption and reflectance spectra and Figure 2(b) indicates the impedance matching conditions of the design structure. If the normalized impedance of the imaginary part is closed to zero and the real part is closed to unity, it will show a good absorption near unity. The proposed design had 99.60% absorption at 649 nm and from 548 nm to 712 nm (164 nm wide bandwidth) demonstrating above 99% absorption. In the whole optical region, the absorber had an average of 98.19 % absorption.

Once S-parameters are known, other parameters of the device can be evaluated helps as magnetic susceptibility (χ_{ms}) and electric susceptibility (χ_{es}) mentioned below in equation [10]. These parameters are effective permeability and permittivity. Here, k_o (= $2\pi/\lambda$) is the free space wavenumber and d is dielectric thickness. In this method, scattering parameter S_{21} is not considered because transmission is nearly zero.

$$\chi_{es} = \frac{2j}{k_0}\frac{1-S_{11}}{1+S_{11}};\ \chi_{ms} = \frac{2j}{k_0}\frac{1+S_{11}}{1-S_{11}};\ \varepsilon_{eff} = 1+\frac{\chi_{es}}{d};\ \mu_{eff} = 1+\frac{\chi_{ms}}{d} \quad (4)$$

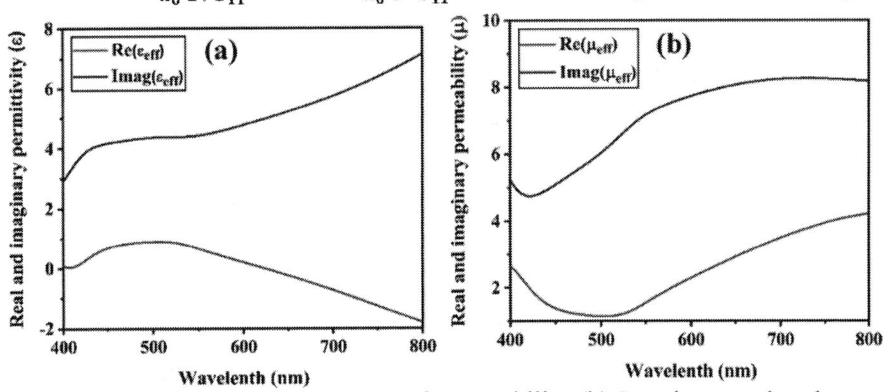

Figure 3. (a) Imaginary and real components of permeability (b) Imaginary and real components of permittivity.

3.1. Independency of polarisation and incidence angle

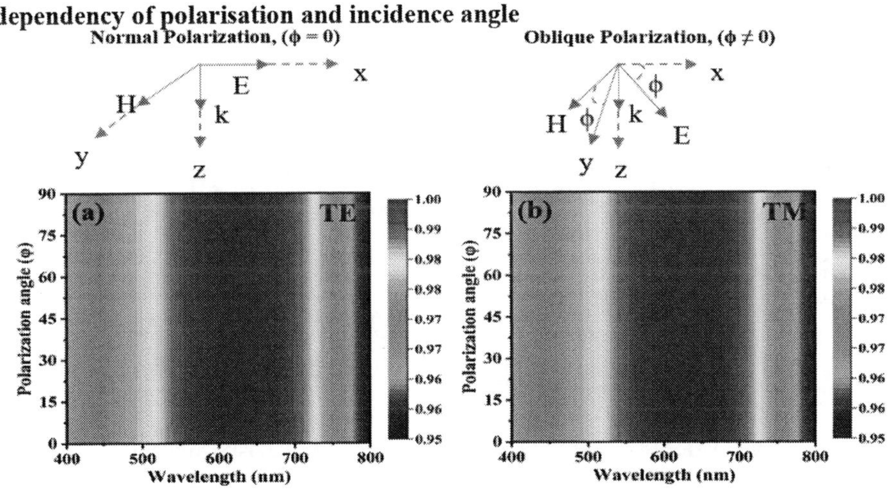

Figure 4. (a) TE (b) TM modes absorption for various polarisation angles (φ) from 0° to 90°.

We have investigated the performance of various polarization directions on solar spectra at normal incidence. The polarization angle (φ) equal to zero and 90° represents the direction of polarization along the x-direction and y-direction that's also called TE and TM polarization, respectively. Due to the geometric symmetry of the W ring array, which is shown in figures 4(a) and 4(b), the proposed absorber's absorption spectra are unaffected by changes in polarisation direction. The unit cell's stable absorbance is indicated by the independence of polarisation. As a result, polarisation independence-based MMA is employed for sensors, solar energy harvesting, solar cells, and other future applications. Besides, figures 5(a) and 4(b) show the absorption of absorbers with a different oblique incident angle for both modes. The absorber showed 95.90% average absorption for TE mode and 98.20% average absorption for TM mode from 0° to 50° incident angles. The two characteristics are very important for solar-related applications. When the theta (θ) angle is zero, gives a better absorption effect but when sweeps the theta angles as per interval angle, the absorption rate decrease due to an increase in the light reflection. The absorption rate of TM mode is more than the TE mode because it has a larger electric field intensity, excellent coupling, and gives better stability while with a weaker magnetic field, the lower coupling is the main reason for lower absorptivity in TE mode [11].

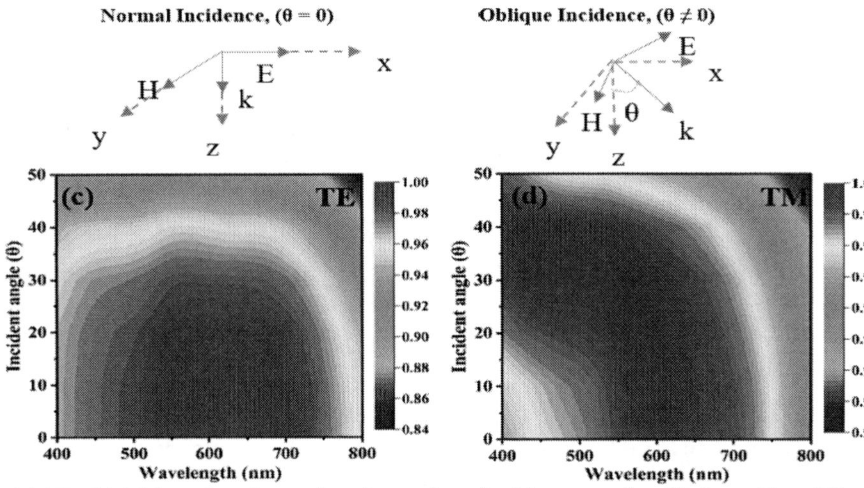

Figure 5. (a) TE (b) TM modes absorption for various incidence angles (θ) from 0° to 50°.

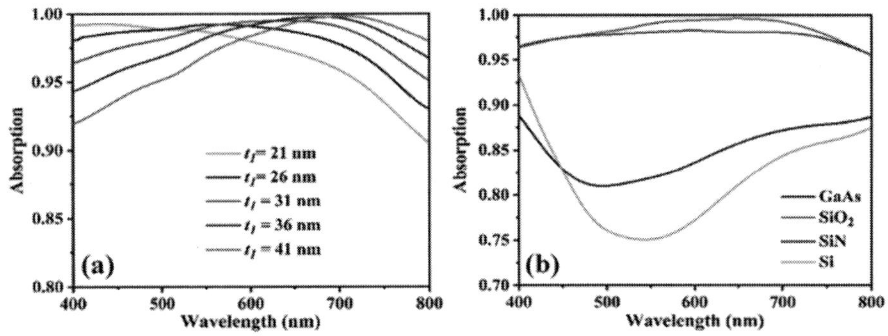

Figure 6. The absorption response of (a) various dielectric layer thicknesses and (b) various dielectric layers.

3.2. Absorption with a different dielectric thickness (t1) and different dielectric materials

The absorption was dependent on the geometric parameters of the proposed design. We investigated the mechanism of absorption with the changed dielectric thickness (t1) keeping the other parameters fixed. In Fig. 5(a), absorption magnitude is demonstrated with various thicknesses of the dielectric layer, where red curves show the desired result. The absorption effect was illustrated when changed the dielectric thickness from 21 nm to 41 nm. When the dielectric thickness increases or decreases, resonance wavelength shifts to lower or higher wavelengths which is mean overall capacitance changes in the resonator. The left shift resonance wavelength can be used for the application of an optical pressure sensor (28). Moreover, absorption characteristics of the absorber with different dielectric substrates are also investigated. Figure 5(b) shows the different absorption spectrums with different dielectric substrates such as gallium arsenide (GaAs), silicon nitride (SiN), silicon dioxide (SiO2), and silicon (Si). Comparing the results, the dielectric substrate of SiO2 has the maximum absorption rate in the whole optical region. The absorption spectrum of SiN is near the absorption rate of SiO2 but other substrates have a lower absorption. Therefore, SiO2 is one of the most remarkable dielectric substrates for different applications such as light detection sensors, real invisibility, and solar cell technologies.

3.3. Numerical investigation of short circuit current density (J_{sc}) and open-circuit voltage (V_{oc})

In this section, we have attempted the short-circuit current densities (J_{sc}) at various incident angles for both TE and TM modes in figure 7(a). J_{sc} is not the same for both modes at varying incidence angles. J_{sc} changes mostly depend on how many resonant modes are produced in the wavelength range used. Under AM1.5 sun illumination, J_{sc} can be determined using the following equation,

$$J_{sc} = \int_{\lambda_{min}}^{\lambda_{max}} \frac{e\lambda}{hc} . \Phi_{AM1.5}(\lambda). A(\lambda) d\lambda \quad (5)$$

Where, e is an electron's charge, h is the Planck's constant, c is the light speed, λ is the incident light wavelength, $\phi_{AM1.5}(\lambda)$ is the sun radiance AM 1.5, and A(λ) is this absorber's absorption, assuming the internal quantum efficiency is 100%. Table 2 shows the different values of J_{sc} from different angles.

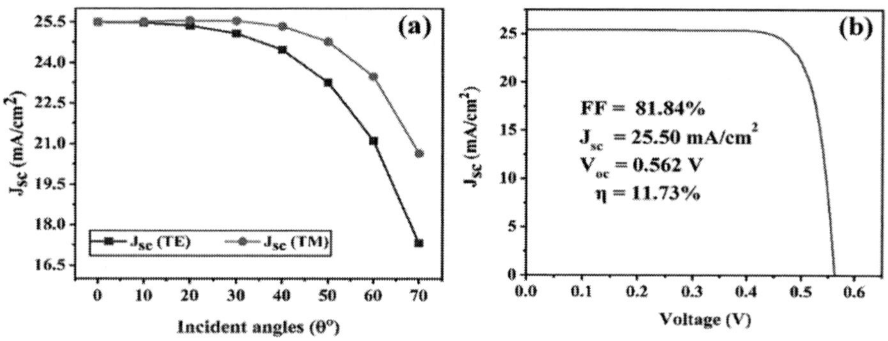

Figure 7. (a) The short circuit current density for both modes at various incidence angles (θ), and (b) The suggested MTM absorber's *J-V* graph for solar cells.

Table 2. For the TE and TM modes, J_{sc} with varied incidence angles.

Incident angles (θ)	0°	10°	20°	30°	40°	50°	60°	70°
J_{sc} (TE)	25.50	25.46	25.36	25.07	24.47	23.25	21.10	17.32
J_{sc} (TM)	25.50	25.51	25.55	25.53	25.33	24.77	23.48	20.64

Theoretically, we have also determined the open-circuit voltage (V_{OC}), fill factor (*FF*), and power conversion efficiency (η) which is displayed in figure 7(b). V_{OC} is the maximum voltage at zero current in the solar cell circuit. A solar cell's V_{OC} is computed using this formula [12]

$$V_{OC} = \frac{K_B T}{e} \ln\left(\frac{J_{sc}}{J_O} + 1\right) \quad (6)$$

Where, K_B is the Boltzmann constant, T = 300K, J_{sc} and J_o are the short circuit current density and saturation current, respectively.

The following equation can be used to compute the fill factor (FF) and the efficiency (η) for a metamaterial solar cell.

$$FF = \frac{\left(\frac{e \times V_{OC}}{K_B T}\right) - \ln\left(\frac{e \times V_{OC}}{K_B T} + 0.72\right)}{\left(\frac{e \times V_{OC}}{K_B T}\right) + 1} ; \eta = \frac{FF \times V_{OC} \times J_{SC}}{P_{in}} \quad (7)$$

Where P_{in} is the solar spectrum's incident flux A.M 1.5 is 1000 W/m².

4. Conclusion

We have demonstrated a broadband perfect absorber that is highly efficient, and wide-angle for the optical region from 400 nm to 800 nm. A metal-dielectric-metal structure is used to make the proposed absorber. The average absorption is 98.19% and also showed a broad bandwidth in the whole region. Better broadband absorption was achieved with the design structure because it has good impedance in nearly the free space and also silicon dioxide has lossless characteristics. We also studied the incident angle for both modes and the comparison of the absorption spectrum with other dielectric substrates. In addition, we have examined the short circuit current density at different angles for both modes. For the solar cells application, we have demonstrated the *J-V* graph and formed it to calculate the open-circuit voltage (V_{oc} = 0.562V), FF (81.84%), and efficiency (η =11.73%), respectively. Although the overall light-trapping structure has achieved broadband absorption enhancement at optical wavelengths, obtaining whole spectrum absorption enhancement remains a problem, and this will be the focus of our future study.

Acknowledgments

The University Grants Commission (UGC), India has provided the financial support in the form of the senior research scholarship to Raj Kumar and Dr. D. S. Kothari's Postdoctoral Fellowship to Dr. Bipin K. Singh. The authors are grateful for the financial support.

References

[1] Smith D R, Padilla W J, Vier D C, Nemat-Nasser S C and Schultz S 2000 Composite Medium with Simultaneously Negative Permeability and Permittivity *Phys. Rev. Lett.* **84** 4184–7

[2] Kumar R, Kumar M, Chohan J S and Kumar S 2022 Overview on metamaterial: History, types and applications *Mater. Today Proc.* **56** 3016–24

[3] Landy N I, Sajuyigbe S, Mock J J, Smith D R and Padilla W J 2008 Perfect Metamaterial Absorber **207402** 1–4

[4] Tao H, Landy N I, Bingham C M, Zhang X, Averitt R D and Padilla W J 2008 A metamaterial absorber for the terahertz regime: design, fabrication and characterization *Opt. Express* **16** 7181

[5] Kumar R, Singh B K and Pandey P C 2020 Study of Gallium Arsenide Based Perfect Metamaterial Absorber in the Broadband Region *2020 IEEE 17th India Counc. Int. Conf. INDICON 2020* 23–6

[6] Kumar R, Singh B K, Tiwari R K and Pandey P C 2022 Perfect selective metamaterial absorber with thin-film of GaAs layer in the visible region for solar cell applications *Opt. Quantum Electron.* **54** 416

[7] Tamilarasi Mani G and Mudachathi R 2022 Design and Analyses of Broadband Perfect Light Absorber for Visible and Near IR Frequencies using Plasmonic Metamaterials *IOP Conf. Ser. Mater. Sci. Eng.* **1219** 012011

[8] Su Z, Yin J and Zhao X 2015 Terahertz dual-band metamaterial absorber based on graphene/MgF_2 multilayer structures *Opt. Express* **23** 1679

[9] Wang J, Chen Y, Hao J, Yan M and Qiu M 2011 Shape-dependent absorption characteristics of three-layered metamaterial absorbers at near-infrared *J. Appl. Phys.* **109** 074510

[10] Yadav V S, Ghosh S K, Das S and Bhattacharyya S 2019 Wideband tunable mid-infrared cross-polarisation converter using monolayered graphene-based metasurface over a wide angle of incidence *IET Microwaves, Antennas Propag.* **13** 82–7

[11] Mahmud S, Islam S S, Mat K, Chowdhury M E H, Rmili H and Islam M T 2020 Design and parametric analysis of a wide-angle polarization-insensitive metamaterial absorber with a star shape resonator for optical wavelength applications *Results Phys.* **18** 103259

[12] Kumar R, Singh B K and Pandey P C 2022 Broadband metamaterial absorber in the visible region using a petal-shaped resonator for solar cell applications *Phys. E Low-dimensional Syst. Nanostructures* **142** 115327

Effect of temperature on structural, optical, and morphological properties of ED-CdTe thin film

Lekha verma and Ayush khare

Department of Physics, National Institute of Technology, Raipur, 492010, India

*Corresponding author's e-mail address: lekhaverma.85@gmail.com

Abstract. On fluorine-doped tin oxide (FTO) coated glass substrates, CdTe thin films were electrodeposited (ED) using an aqueous electrolyte bath solution. The temperature value of the electrolyte solution is one of the most important deposition parameters that should be adjusted to produce good quality photoconductive material. In our study, the films have been deposited at a different temperatures ranging from 50 to 70°C. Structural properties of the CdTe thin films were characterized using X-ray diffraction (XRD), and using UV–Visible (UV-Vis) spectroscopy, scanning electron microscopy (SEM), and energy dispersive X-ray analysis (EDX) techniques, and the optical and morphological properties were studied. The cubic crystalline structure of the ED-CdTe films is confirmed by the XRD analysis, and as the temperature is changed, the diffraction peak intensity significantly increased. In optical absorption spectra, the direct energy band-gap (E_g=1.48eV) is obtained. By adjusting the temperatures, the SEM analysis proves very good morphological growth, and the EDX study confirmed the atomic composition of the CdTe layers.

1. Introduction

The electrochemical production of thin CdTe films from sulphate [1], sulfate–tartrate [2], propylene carbonate [3], and ammonium chloride [4] electrolytes under different electrolysis conditions has received a lot of interest in recent years. As reported earlier that the type of electrolyte and electrolysis parameters such as temperature, deposition time, and pH significantly affect the different properties of CdTe thin film. [5]. Over the past ten years, the efficiency of the CdTe thin films has increased significantly, rising from 16.7% to 22.1 percent [6]. CdTe thin films have been prepared by spray pyrolysis, sputtering, close-spaced sublimation (CSS), chemical vapour deposition (CVD), thermal evaporation, electrodeposition (ED), and pulsed laser deposition (PVD) etc. The two electrode setup-ED technique is the most extensively utilised of these technologies due to its ease of use, large-area deposition, low chemical waste, high growth rate, and high throughput [7]. Research reports on the ED of thin film semiconductors using a two-electrode setup indicate the stability and sustainability of this method for the fabrication of high thin-film solar cells as compared to using a traditional three-electrode setup. [8]. The effect of temperature on the performance parameters of a CdTe thin films at 333 and 353 K is studied in this work. This research will aid in the design and implementation of the detailed analysis of the performance of single junction and tandem solar cell with respect to temperature.

IOP Conf. Series: Materials Science and Engineering 1263 (2022) 012017 doi:10.1088/1757-899X/1263/1/012017

2. Materials and methods

The initial electrolyte solution was prepared by 1.0M $CdSO_4$ of 99.0% purity in 500 ml of deionized (DI) water. After that, for about 50 hours, the prepared solution was electro-purified by using a cathodic potential that was just below the necessary voltage for Cd2+ ion reduction. The initial tellurium dioxide (TeO_2) was prepared by adding 1 gram of TeO_2 powder into diluted sulfuric acid (H_2SO_4), and 1000ppm of $CdCl_2$ in DI water. The concentrations of Te are kept low (~1.0–5.0mM) while Cd concentrations are kept high (~0.5–2.0mM). Using a magnetic stirrer, rotating at 300rpm, the pH of the electrolyte solution was set to 2.00 ± 0.02 and then heated for 12 minutes at 60°C and 80°C. The substrates used for ED were glass/FTO with a sheet resistance of ~7 Ω. Before the ED, the glass/FTO substrates were cut into small pieces with dimensions of 75mm × 25 mm × 1 mm and washed for 10 minutes in an ultrasonicator. The samples were washed with methanol and cleaned three times with DI water, then cleaned with acetone and DI water. Samples were lastly air-dried at room temperature. A graphite electrode is used as a working anode and a glass/FTO substrate is used as a working cathode immersed in the electrolyte solution.

We have prepared three samples with different temperatures of the electrolyte 60°C, 70°C, and 80°C. The source of electric power used for electrolytes is a small battery having a milliwatt range of 1.2 V and 1.6V. After the deposition, CdTe thin films were washed carefully with DI water and allowed to air dry at room temperature. Samples were then annealed for 10 minutes at 150°C in a preheated oven. Different properties of the resulting samples were investigated according to the different temperature values. Using PANalytical X'pert Multifunctional Powder x-ray diffractometer, the structural properties were analyzed. Optical and morphological studies of ED-CdTe samples were characterized using a UV-Vis spectrophotometer (Simadzu make), and a scanning electron microscope (Zeiss EVO 18) respectively.

3. Results and Discussions

3.1 Structural study

To determine the cathodic potential in which stoichiometric or non stiochiometric CdTe can be formed is the main aim of this study. With the help of XRD peak intensity, the amount of crystallinity was determined. Figure 1 demonstrates XRD intensity plotted with a 2θ angle for layers formed between 1340 and 1400 mV at temperatures 60°C,70°C, and 80°C of CdTe layers, and the cubic crystalline CdTe phases were observed (JCPDS card no. 98-018-1732). The dominant XRD peak and desirable orientation of the electrodeposited CdTe under all growth voltages and circumstances is the diffraction peak of CdTe (111) C, which corresponds to 2θ = 23.8°. Assigned peaks to CdTe, (002) C, (022) C, and (113) C associated to 2θ= 26.3, 37.9, and 46.0 along with the diffraction peaks of FTO were also found. Diffraction peak intensities increased with increasing the temperature, indicating that the films formed at 80°C temperature had better crystallinity than the other two. The fact that the (111) reflection dominates the XRD pattern of films deposited at higher temperatures is likely due to increased atom diffusivity in the substrate, this makes it easier for deposition to occur on the (111) plane during the formation of nanocrystalline CdTe films because it has lower surface energy than the (002), (022) and (113) planes. [9, 10]. We determined the grain sizes (D) (Eq.1), dislocation density (δ) (Eq.2) and strain (ε) (Eq.3) of the films using the Debye–Scherrer rule

$$D = 0.9\ k/\beta\ \cos\theta, \qquad (1)$$

$$\delta = \frac{1}{D^2}, \qquad (2)$$

$$\varepsilon = \frac{\beta\cos\theta}{4} \qquad (3)$$

Where,
k = wavelength of the X-ray radiation,
β = FWHM of the peak,

θ= Bragg angle,

Table 1 shows the estimated results of CdTe films at different temperatures.

Table 1. XRD results of CdTe thin film

	Temperature	hkl	2θ (°)	D(nm)	δ (lin/m^2)	ε (lin^{-2}m^{-2})
CdTe	80°C	(111)	23.8	43.78	48.3	0.12
CdTe	70°C	(111)	23.8	41.23	58.8	0.14
CdTe	60°C	(111)	23.8	40.56	60.7	0.15

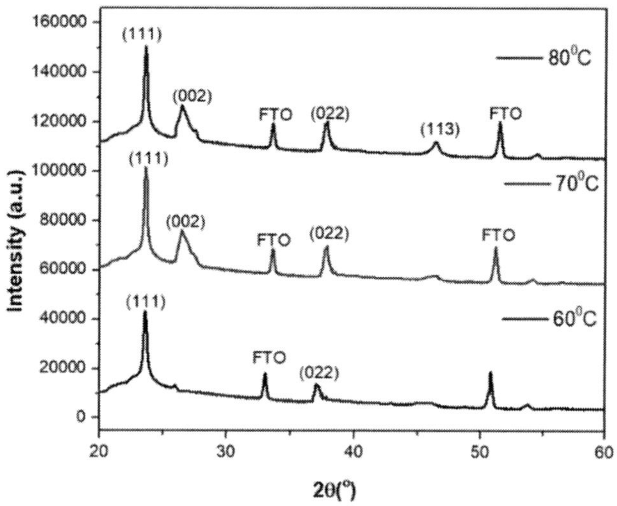

Figure.1 XRD pattern of CdTe thin films at different temperatures

3.2 Optical study

Optical properties of CdTe thin films can be done using UV-Vis Spectroscopy (UV-Vis). Using the data from UV–Vis, three different temperatures (60°C, 70°C and 80°C respectively), the square of the energy absorbance $(\alpha h\upsilon)^2$ was plotted with the photon energy ($h\upsilon$) as shown in Figure.2 (a), (b), and (c). Where υ=hc/λ and α is absorption coefficient, λ is the wavelength, and h is the plank's constant. From the intercepts on the hυ axis, according to the calculation of band gap, CdTe films deposited at 60°C, 70°C and 80°C were found to be 1.52 eV, 1.47 eV, and 1.45 eV, respectively. From this graph, the bandgap decrease as the value of temperature increases. It was observed that at temperature of 80°C produces the best results when compared to the other two. In the literature, this enhancement in qualities has been thoroughly reported [11]. The number of photogenerated charge carriers in the CdTe layer tends to grow with an increase in absorption, which improves the efficiency of the solar cell. E_g=1.45eV is found to be the average band gap value, which is evident in the literature [12].

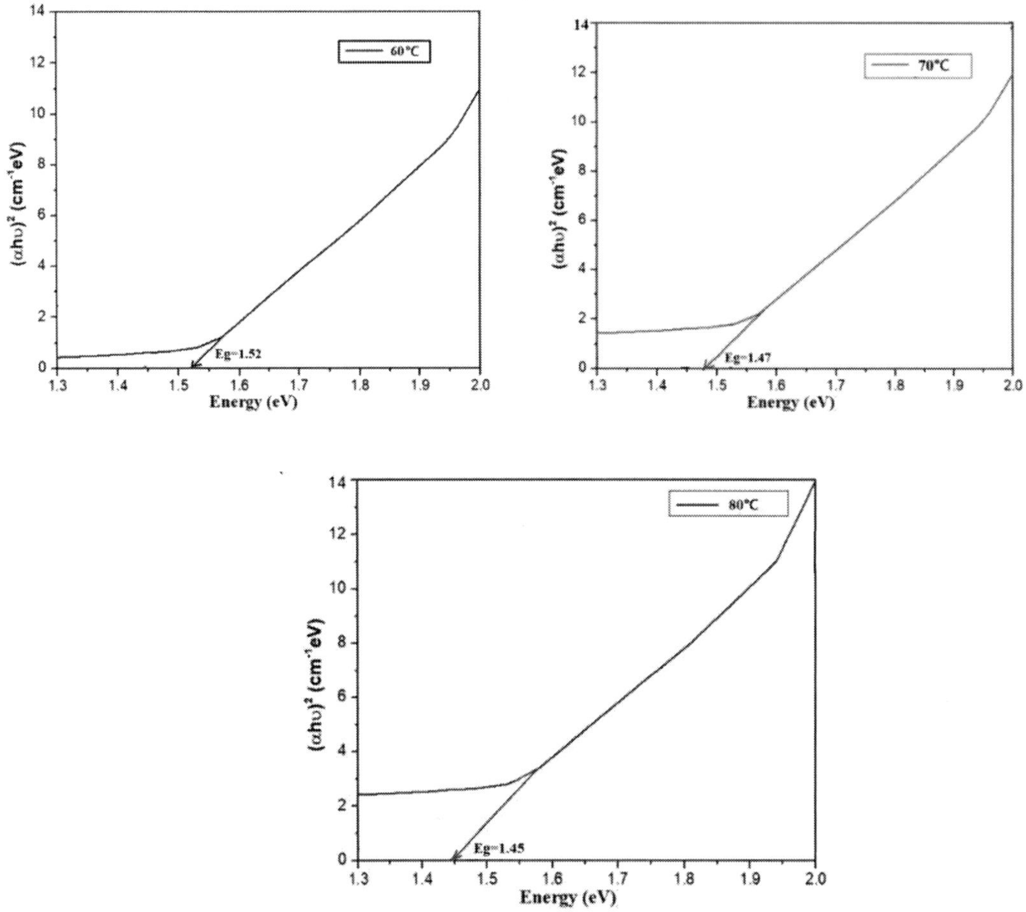

Figure.2 Tauc's plot of CdTe thin films at temperatures (a) 60°C (b) 70°C (a) 80°C

3.3 Morphological study

Morphology study can be done using Scanning Electron Microscopy (SEM). SEM results of CdTe thin films deposited at 60°C, 70°C and 80°C are exhibit in figure 3 (a) (b) (c) respectively. As previously reported the surface morphology and the average grain size of the films were strongly depends on deposition temperature. The films had uniform and homogeneous deposition, with similar grains and no cracks or pinholes, as seen in the figures. The size of the grains increases at temperature 80°C. However at the temperature of 60°C and 70°C particle shape changed from sphere to irregular geometric object. The particle size increased along with the temperature. The particles kept growing as the temperature increases to 80°C. As the temperature rises, grains grow in one direction, as shown by the XRD data. The SEM findings are in accordance with the research by Rosly et al. [13].

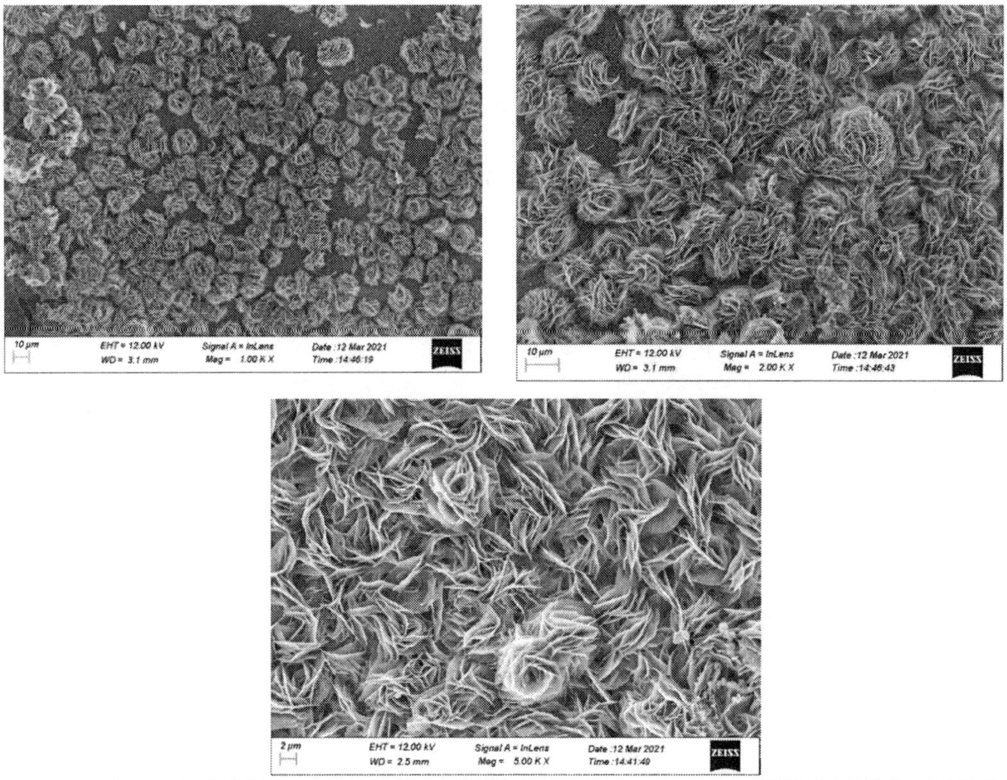

Figure.3 SEM images of CdTe thin films at temperatures (a) 60°C (b) 70°C (c) 80°C

3.4 Compositional Analysis

EDX is a great and reliable tool for investigating a chemical composition of material. Figure *4* shows the compositional analysis of CdTe layers using EDX results. The analysis shows that there are no significant differences in the chemical composition of cadmium and telluride in CdTe films formed on different temperatures. The EDX spectra also contain a few additional peaks that correspond to sulpher and oxygen in addition to Cd and Te (because of FTO substrate). Table.2 shows the EDS data of CdTe thin films. Undesired surface states can affect the vibrational and electronic characteristics of CdTe films, which can change the optoelectrical behaviour. These characteristics are important for applications in optoelectronic devices.

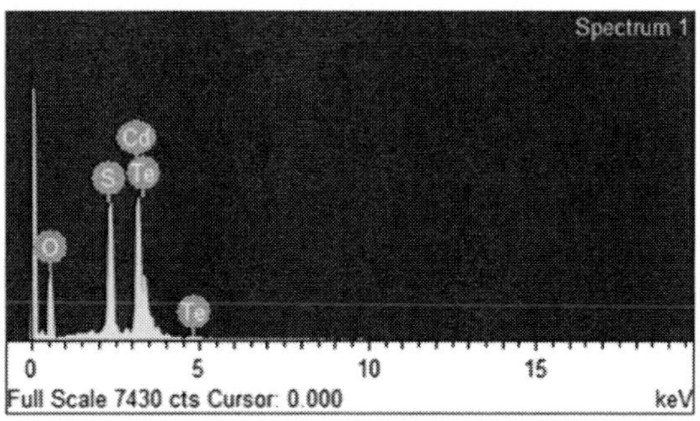

Figure.4 EDS spectra of CdTe thin films

Table.2 EDS data of CdTe thin films

Element	Weight%	Atomic%
O	44.47	78.16
S	12.70	11.14
Cd	42.34	10.59
Te	0.49	0.11
Total	100.00	

4. Conclusion

The impact of deposition temperature on the optical, structural, and morphological study of CdTe thin films has been comprehensively explored in order to improve the application of solar cell. The XRD analysis revealed that all of the deposited films had a polycrystalline character with their preferred orientation. The CdTe film deposited at 80°C had the largest grain size, ensuring greater crystallinity than the other two films. The elemental composition of the CdTe films does not vary substantially. According to previous research, the grain size was found to be between 24 and 45 nm. In the near-infrared region, all of the samples show good transparency, and the energy band gap achieved in our work was between 1.45 eV. Overall, this analysis looks at the sustainability of CdTe as a window layer, but more research and analysis are required before it can be used in CdTe solar cells to boost efficiency.

Acknowledgments

The Department of Metallurgical Engineering, NIT Raipur, India, helped the authors by performing XRD and SEM analyses at their laboratory.

References

[1] Panicker MPR, Knaster M, and Kroger FA 1978 *J. Electro-chem. Soc.* **4** 566
[2] Mamedov MN and Aliev AS 2008 *Inorganic Mat.* **8** 804-806
[3] Darkowski A and Cocivera M 1985 *J. Electro-chem. Soc.* **11** 2768
[4] Dergacheva MB, Statsyuk VN and Fogel LA 2004 *Rus. J. Appl. Chem.* **2** 26-30
[5] Werta SZ, Echendu OK and Dejene FB 2019 *J. Mat. Sci: Mater. Electron* **6** 01-11
[6] Lai H, Ren A, Wu L, Hao X, Zhang J, Wang W, Wei Q, Ni Z, and Feng L 2020 *Renewable Energy* **145** 133-140
[7] Ukarande A, Chaure S, and Chaure NB 2022 *Mater. Today: Proceedings*
[8] Echendu OK, Fauzi F, Weerasinghe AR and Dharmadasa IM 2014 *Thin So.l Films* **556** 529-534
[9] Ghorannevis Z, Akbarnejad E, and Ghoranneviss M 2016 *Journal of Theoretical and Applied Physics* **3** 225-231
[10] Klug H P and Alexander LE 1954 Diffraction Procedures, Chap. 9.
[11] Echendu OK, Okeoma KB, Oriaku CI and Dharmadasa IM 2016 *Adv. Mater. Sci.* **146** 4477-4484
[12] Sinha T, Lilhare D, and Khare A 2019 *Rare Metals* 1-7.
[13] Rosly HN, Rahman KS, Abdullah SF, Harif M N, Doroody C, Chelvanathan P, Misran H, Sopian K and Amin N 2021 *Crystals* **11** 73

Fabrication of TiO_2 based Dye-Sensitized Solar Cell using Nerium oleander as a sensitizer

J V Jayachithra[1,*], K Elampari[2], M Meena[3]

[1]*Research scholar, Department of Physics, S.T. Hindu college, Nagercoil, Tamilnadu, 629 002, India, affiliated to Manonmaniam Sundaranar University, Abishekapatti, Tirunelveli, Tamilnadu, 627 012, India.*
[2]*Associate Professor, Department of Physics, S.T. Hindu college, Nagercoil, Tamilnadu, 629 002, India.*
[3]*Assistant Professor, Department of Physics, S.T. Hindu college, Nagercoil, Tamilnadu, 629 002, India.*

*Corresponding author. E-mail: jvjayachithra@gmail.com

Abstract. The globe has already started using renewable energy sources, mainly solar energy, to meet the rising need for energy. The Dye-Sensitized Solar Cell (DSSC), one of many varieties of solar cells, is now popular because of its low manufacturing cost and ability to function in low light. In this work, TiO_2 and erbium-doped TiO_2 are chosen as photoanode and Nerium oleander as a sensitizer. The photoanode materials are prepared by one-step microwave assisted hydrothermal method. These nanomaterials and sensitizer are characterized by various characterization techniques that show significant results. The designed DSSC is evaluated by the current-voltage properties study. The efficiency of the fabricated TiO_2 and Er-doped TiO_2 based DSSCs is found to be 0.95 % and 2.95 % respectively.

1. INTRODUCTION

Among different forms of renewable energy, solar energy plays a dynamic role in the production of electricity because it is clean and it has an unlimited energy source. The photovoltaic effect is employed by solar cells to convert solar energy into electrical energy. A solar cell with less than 1% efficiency was created by Charles Fritts in 1883 using selenium and gold. [1]. Depending on the material composition, there are various varieties of solar cells on the market today. A third generation solar cell is the dye-sensitized solar cell (DSSC), invented by Grätzel and Regan (1991) with an efficiency of 7% using photoanode made of TiO_2 [2]. Investigation towards DSSC is increasing due to the ease and cheap cost of manufacturing and able to work in low-light conditions [3]. Even though DSSC is a promising one, still it have some difficulties like liquid electrolyte instability and dye degradation [4]. Currently, the most efficient DSSC with porphyrin dye achieved an efficiency of 13% [5].

DSSC comprises a transparent conducting oxide (TCO) regularly used are Indium doped tin oxide and Fluorine doped tin oxide, a nanoporous semiconducting material as a photoanode, sensitizer/dye, the electrolyte as a medium to exchange the electrons and platinum (Pt) or carbon as a counter electrode [4, 6]. For a photoanode material in DSSC, the metal oxide semiconductors like TiO_2, ZnO, SnO_2, NiO and Nb_2O_5 were used due to their large bandgap [4]. Because of its high dye loading capacity, good chemical stability and non-toxicity, TiO_2 was picked as a photoanode material [7, 8]. According to studies, the doping of TiO_2 with rare-earth elements enhanced its characteristics. Erbium (Er), one of the rare earth elements, has promising features like stability and improved photovoltaic activity when doped with TiO_2, making erbium a dopant for this work [9]. For the first time, we attempted to prepare bare and Er-doped TiO_2 via one-step microwave assisted hydrothermal method.

Another major area is the sensitizer/dye that absorbs the light and takes the excited electrons and moves them into the TiO_2 conduction band. Mostly, ruthenium complexes like N719, N3, N7 and N749 were used because of their stability and good electron transportability [4, 10]. However, the cost and toxicity of these dyes restricts its usage in DSSC. Researchers were aimed at eco-friendly and easily available sensitizer materials, particularly plant-based products [11]. Sensitizers are more abundant in the flowers, fruits, and leaves than in the bark and roots. [12]. Particularly, quinones, flavonoids and anthocyanin were available in natural dyes that enhance the properties of photoanode material [13]. The red Nerium oleander flower were chosen as a sensitizer due to effortlessly available nature. This work describes the effect of ethanolic extract of red Nerium oleander flower as a dye material, TiO_2 and Er-doped TiO_2 as photoanode materials for DSSC.

2. METHODOLOGY

2.1 Base materials

AR grade chemicals Titanium trichloride ($TiCl_3$), Erbium chloride hexahydrate ($ErCl_3.6H_2O$), Urea (CH_4N_2O), acetone, ethanol, ethylene glycol, potassium iodide, iodine and distilled water were used in this work.

2.2 Preparation of bare and Er-doped TiO_2

For the preparation of bare TiO_2, a homogeneous solution of $TiCl_3$ and urea (1:3 ratio) using distilled water were made at room temperature. For Er-doped TiO_2, 1 mol% of $ErCl_3.6H_2O$ was added to the solution containing $TiCl_3$ and urea (1:3 ratio) at room temperature. Both the solutions were separately irradiated using a domestic microwave oven. After the complete evaporation of the solvent, the collected precipitates were washed with distilled water and then allowed to dry naturally. Once the samples were dried, they were again washed with acetone, the final yield was collected and preserved for future use.

2.3 Characterization techniques

With a Cukα radiation of wavelength 1.5406 Å and an increment of 0.02° from 20° to 80°, the Powder X-Ray Diffraction (PXRD) was captured on a Rigaku Ultima IV X-Ray Diffractometer. The Field Emission Scanning Electron Microscopic (FESEM) analysis was done by Gemini 300, Field Emission Scanning Microscope, Carl Zeiss Company. The absorbance was examined by JASCO UV-Vis Spectrometer model: V-750 with the resolution of 0.1 nm.

2.4 Fabrication of DSSC

2.4.1 Preparation of photoanode. The ITO (Indium doped Tin Oxide) glass plates were cleaned with ethanol and the conductive side was found using a multimeter. In the conductive side of one glass plate, cover approximately 1/8'' of the surface using scotch tape. The doctor-blade technique was used to apply the TiO_2 paste made using ethanol on the uncovered portion of the glass plate and allowed to dry which was shown in figure 1. Once the glass plate was dried, transfer the glass plate to a hot plate so that the surfactant and solvent will evaporate from the coated TiO_2 nanomaterials.

2.4.2 Preparation of counter electrode. On the conductive side of another ITO glass plate, a thin layer of carbon was coated using candle flame which was shown in figure 1.

2.4.3 Extraction of dye from Nerium oleander. The fresh red Nerium oleander flower were bought from a neighbourhood market in Nagercoil, Tamil Nadu. With distilled water, the harvested flowers were cleaned, then allowed to air dry. Using a mortar and pestle, the dried flowers were pulverised. The powdered flowers were soaked in ethanol for 24 hours at room temperature in a glass beaker to create the natural colours. Whatman filter paper was used to filter it after that, and it was then put away for later use. The absorbance range of ethanolic extract of Nerium oleander was studied using UV-visible spectroscopic studies.

2.4.4 Preparation of electrolyte solution. In order to create the electrolyte solution, 10 ml of ethylene glycol was mixed with 0.127 g of iodine and 0.83 g of KI [14]. A sealed container was used to hold the solution after it had been thoroughly mixed to dissolve all of the I_2 and KI grains.

2.4.5 DSSC Assembly. For sensitizing the photoanode, TiO_2 coated glass plate was immersed in dye solution for 30 minutes. This plate was washed with ethanol and then allowed to dry at room temperature as displayed in figure 1. The coated surfaces of the two glass plates were facing inwards as they were put together. The two sides of the plates were clipped together using crocodile clips. A few drops of iodide/triiodide (I_3 / I_3^-) electrolyte solution were added between the glass plates and allowed to spread over the entire glass plate. In the same way, the 1 mol% Er-doped TiO_2 nanomaterial was used to fabricate DSSC. Under AM 1.5 sunlight, the I-V properties of the proposed DSSCs were assessed.

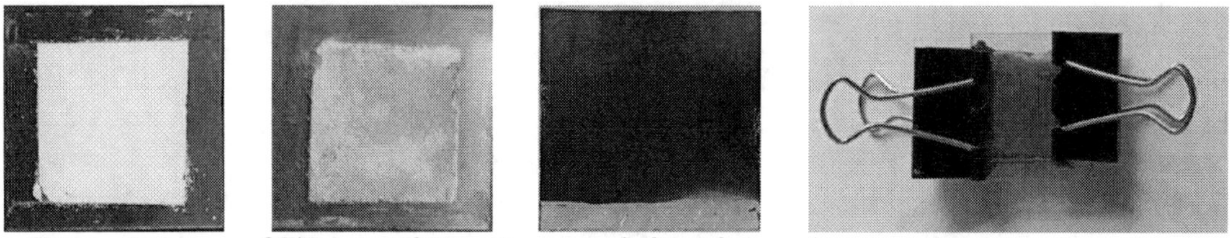

Figure 1. Images of TiO_2 coated ITO, Dye coated glass plate, carbon coated counter electrode and fabricated DSSC respectively.

3. INFERENCES

3.1 Powder X-Ray Diffraction (PXRD) analysis

PXRD technique was used to analyze crystal structure, crystal phase, and unit cell parameters. The PXRD graph of bare TiO_2 and 1 mol% Er-doped TiO_2 show that the samples are in anatase phase with tetragonal body-centered structure and belongs to $I4_1/amd$ space group. In addition, all the peaks are well matched with JCPDS file no: 21-1272 as shown in figure 2. For the photoanode material in DSSC, the anatase phase is highly recommended because of its greater charge transport capacity and low electron-hole recombination rate [15, 16]. Present method yielded a pure anatase phase TiO_2 that favours the goal of fabrication of DSSC. With the help of the Debye-Scherrer equation, the average crystallite size (D) was estimated [17]. Equation (1) was used to compute the dislocation density (δ) [18],

$$\delta = \frac{1}{D^2} \tag{1}$$

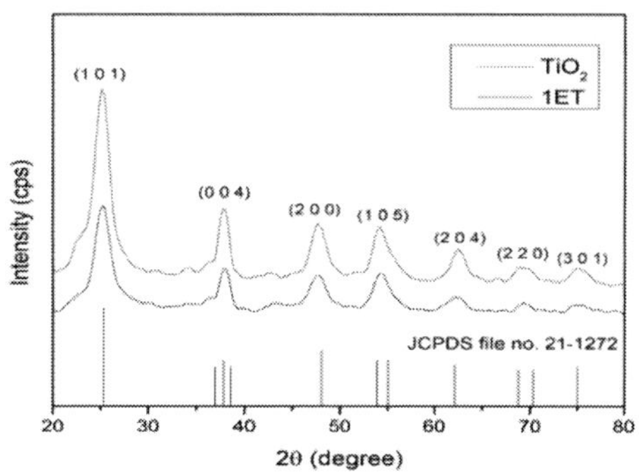

Figure 2. PXRD graph of bare and Er-doped TiO_2 in which 1ET represents 1 mol% Er-doped TiO_2.

On comparison with bare TiO_2, the 1 mol% Er-doped TiO_2 has less peak intensity and high dislocation density that confirms the incorporation of Er^{3+} ion into TiO_2 lattice. From table 1, it is noticed that after the addition of 1 mol% of Er, there is decrease in volume of unit cell and crystallite size but there is increase in dislocation density that may be due to the variation in the ionic radii of Ti^{4+} (0.605 Å) and Er^{3+} (0.89 Å) [19, 20].

Table 1. Calculated lattice parameters, crystallite size and dislocation density of bare and Er-doped TiO_2.

Sample	a=b (Å)	c (Å)	Volume of unit cell ($Å^3$)	Average D from Scherrer's equation (nm)	δ (10^{18} lines/m^2)
TiO_2	3.8158	9.4967	138.272	5.4094	0.0342
1ET	3.8165	9.4525	137.679	5.1894	0.0371

3.2 Field Emission Scanning Electron Microscopic (FESEM) analysis

The surface shape, particle size, and elemental composition were investigated by FESEM analysis. From figure 3, it is visible that there are no additional elements in the EDX image of bare and Er-doped TiO_2. This demonstrates the great degree of purity of the processed samples. In figure 3(b), there is a peak at 2.1 keV, which is due to gold coating on the sample during EDX analysis. The SEM micrographs of bare and Er-doped TiO_2 in the magnification of 10.00 KX show an irregular morphology with voids and pores as shown in figure 4. The inset graph in figure 4 shows the particle size histogram calculated using Origin software. The average particle size of bare TiO_2 and 1ET were found to be 7.88 nm and 12.52 nm respectively. The increase in particle size may be due to the agglomeration of nanoparticles after the incorporation of Er^{3+} ions.

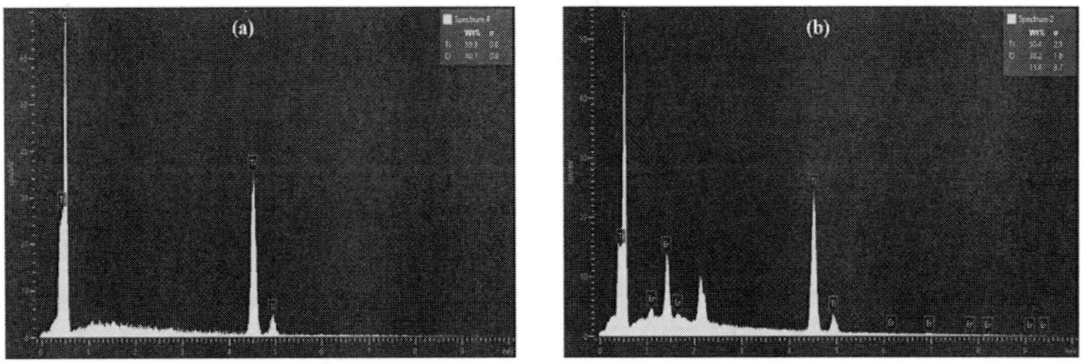

Figure 3. EDX spectrum of (a) bare TiO_2, (b) 1 mol% Er-doped TiO_2.

Figure 4. SEM micrograph of (a) bare TiO_2, (b) 1 mol% Er-doped TiO_2.

3.3 UV-Visible Spectroscopic analysis

The optical band gap and absorbance spectra were analyzed by Ultraviolet-Visible (UV-Vis) spectroscopic studies. From figure 5(a), it is noticed that the absorbance of TiO_2 ranges from 220 nm to 320 nm and there are two sharp peaks at 235 nm and 280 nm that show the maximum absorbance value. In 1 mol% Er-doped TiO_2, there is continuous absorption and the maximum absorption peak occurred at 320 nm. This demonstrates how the absorption changes after the addition of an Er dopant to longer wavelengths.

The optical band gap is calculated using Tauc equation [21]. The Tauc plot is drawn for Energy on x-axis and $(\alpha h\nu)^{1/n}$ on y-axis. The extrapolating line from the linear unit intersects on the x-axis that gives the optical band gap. The band gap of TiO_2 and 1 mol% Er-doped TiO_2 are indirect allowed which is 3.45 eV and 2.75 eV respectively as seen in figure 5(b). The as-prepared anatase TiO_2 show a wide band gap that may find application in photovoltaic devices, anti-reflective (AR) coatings for solar cells and optoelectronic devices especially as a gate in metal-oxide-semiconductor (MOS) transistor [4, 22, 23]. The Er^{3+} ion may have replaced the Ti^{4+} ion in 1 mol% Er-doped TiO_2, resulting in a narrower band gap that can be utilized for photocatalytic activity [24, 25].

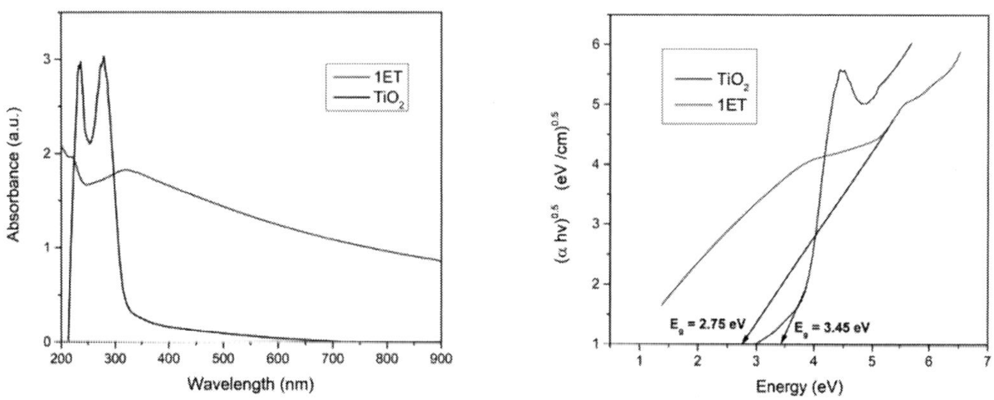

Figure 5. (a) Absorbance spectra (b) Tauc plot of bare and Er-doped TiO_2.

The absorbance of ethanolic extract of red Nerium oleander ranges from 200 nm to 400 nm and figure 6 displays three absorption peaks, located at wavelengths of 240 nm, 297 nm, and 332 nm.

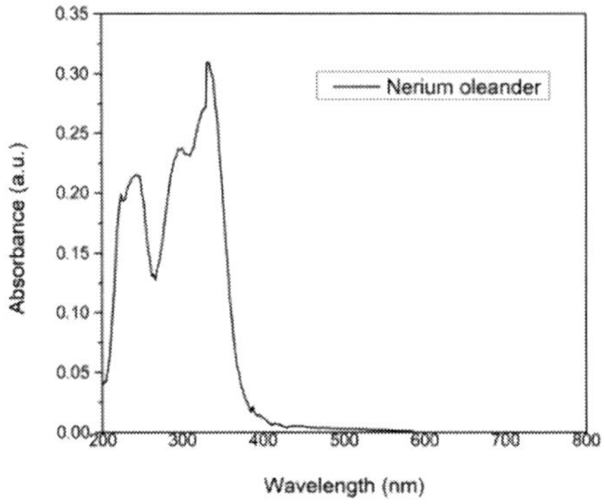

Figure 6. Absorbance spectra of ethanolic extract of red Nerium oleander.

3.4 I-V characteristics studies

The current-voltage (I-V) characteristics were studied under the condition (AM 1.5, temperature = 30°C, Irradiance level = 1000 W/m^2). The readings were recorded at geographical location of 77^{0}43' East longitude and 8^{0}17' North latitude (S.T. Hindu College, Nagercoil, Tamil Nadu, India). Figure 7 show the connections made for measuring the voltage. Under the direct sunlight, the voltages were recorded for resistance values ranging from 200 Ω to 5 kΩ and the corresponding current values were also calculated.

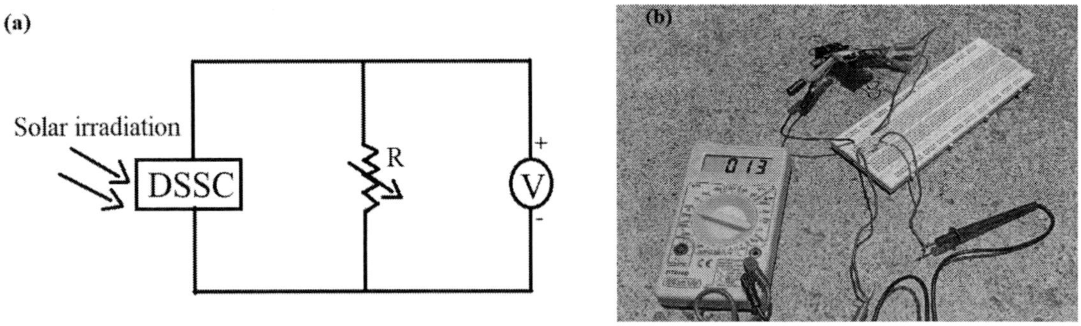

Figure 7. (a) Basic Circuit, (b) connection of fabricated DSSC.

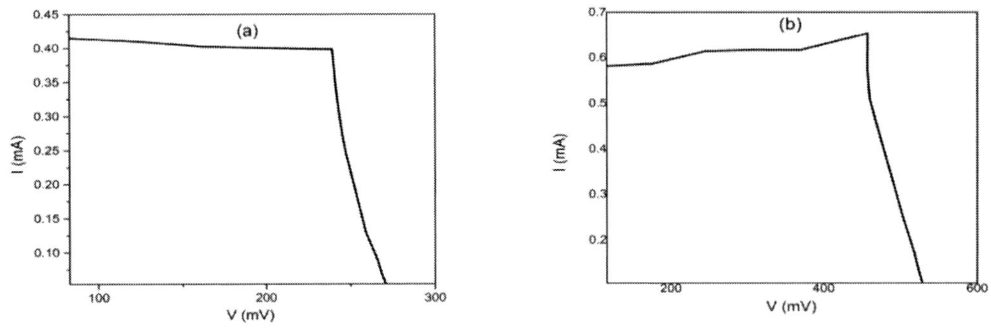

Figure 8. I-V characteristics curve of (a) TiO_2-based DSSC, (b) 1 mol% Er-doped TiO_2 based DSSC.

Figure 8 shows that the current steadily declines as the voltage rises until abruptly ceasing at open-circuit voltage (V_{oc}). A rapid decline in current occurs at maximum voltage (V_{max}). This can be the result of the cell's abrupt increase in resistance. The fill factor (FF) was calculated by using [26],

$$FF = \frac{V_{max} \times I_{max}}{V_{oc} \times I_{sc}} \quad (2)$$

The efficiency of power conversion (η) of DSSC was calculated by [26],

$$\eta\ (\%) = \frac{Isc \times Voc \times FF}{Light\ intensity} \times 100 \quad (3)$$

The formula used for calculating the Incident photon to current efficiency was given in equation (4) [27],

$$IPCE\ (\%) = \frac{1240 \times 10^{-9} \times I_{sc}}{\lambda \times P_{in}} \times 100 \quad (4)$$

where I_{sc} is the short-circuit current (mA), I_{max} is the maximum current (mA), λ is the wavelength (nm) and P_{in} is the incident power (W/m^2). Under sunlight, the calculated IPCE values for TiO_2-based and 1ET-based DSSCs were 0.94% and 1.32% respectively. Table 2 show the TiO_2-based DSSC has an efficiency of 0.95% with FF of 0.85, V_{oc} of 271 mV and I_{sc} of 0.415 mA. The 1ET-based DSSC has an efficiency of 2.95 % with FF of 0.88, V_{oc} of 582.65 mV and I_{sc} of 0.581 mA. The TiO_2 based DSSC with Nerium oleander dye show an efficiency which is 15.6 times greater than the reported work [28]. Additionally, when compared to DSSCs built entirely of bare TiO_2, 1ET-based DSSC exhibit enhanced conversion efficiency. This increase in efficiency may be due to the increased dye absorption, low electron-hole recombination and charge transfer resistance. One of the causes of the proposed DSSCs poor conversion efficiency may be due to the lower absorption of Nerium oleander sensitizer in the visible region as compared to the UV region.

Table 2. I-V parameters of fabricated DSSCs.

Parameters	Initial measurement		After 48 hrs	
	TiO_2	1ET	TiO_2	1ET
V_{max} (mV)	238.98	456.99	235.01	454.61
I_{max} (mA)	0.398	0.653	0.327	0.581
V_{oc} (mV)	271	582.65	291.28	586.52
I_{sc} (mA)	0.415	0.581	0.371	0.519
FF	0.85	0.88	0.71	0.87
η (%)	0.95	2.95	0.76	2.62

After 48 hrs, the I-V characteristics of the fabricated DSSCs were studied again under the same condition and the results were tabulated in table 2. It was observed that there was a decrease in I_{sc} and efficiency. Thus, the current carriers generated by the cell and time determines the efficiency of the fabricated DSSCs.

4. Conclusion

The bare TiO_2 and 1 mol% Er-doped TiO_2 nanomaterials were successfully prepared by one-step microwave assisted hydrothermal method. The results of the X-Ray diffraction technique show that the prepared nanomaterials exhibit pure anatase phase. Particle agglomeration is the cause of the increase in particle size between bare and Er-doped TiO_2, which were found to have particle sizes of 7.88 nm and 12.52 nm respectively. The bare TiO_2 and TiO_2 that had been doped with Er had optical bandgaps that were discovered to be 3.45 eV and 2.75 eV respectively. Both the bare TiO_2 and 1 mol% Er-doped TiO_2 were used as photoanode materials for fabricating DSSCs using Nerium oleander as sensitizer. The TiO_2-based DSSC show a conversion efficiency of 0.95 % whereas 1ET-based DSSC show 2.95 %. Based on the comparison with the reported work, the TiO_2 based DSSC show 15.6 times higher efficiency with Nerium oleander as sensitizer. The stability of the fabricated DSSCs were analysed after 48 hrs, which showed a decreased cell efficiency over time. By enhancing the assembling processes, the power conversion efficiency may increase. Further, the fabricated cells will be analyzed by studying the I-V characteristics using a solar simulator and source meter.

References

[1] Szabo L 2017 *The history of using solar energy*

[2] O'Regan B and Grätzel M 1991 A low-cost, high-efficiency solar cell based on dye-sensitized colloidal TiO2 films *Nature* **353** 737-40

[3] Manickam K, Venkatachalam M, Manickam D, Gowthaman P and Shanmugam S 2017 DYE SENSITIZED SOLAR CELLS-A REVIEW *JOURNAL FOR ADVANCED RESEARCH IN APPLIED SCIENCES* **4** 26-38

[4] Sharma K, Sharma V and Sharma S S 2018 Dye-Sensitized Solar Cells: Fundamentals and Current Status *Nanoscale Research Letters* **13** 381

[5] Mathew S, Yella A, Gao P, Humphry-Baker R, Curchod B F E, Ashari-Astani N, Tavernelli I, Rothlisberger U, Nazeeruddin M K and Grätzel M 2014 Dye-sensitized solar cells with 13% efficiency achieved through the molecular engineering of porphyrin sensitizers *Nature Chemistry* **6** 242-7

[6] S.N K, Hemalatha K, Balasingam S k, Clinton F, Akshaya S and Kim H J 2019 pp 1-16

[7] Awsha A, Alazoumi S and Elhub B 2021 A Review on the development of TiO2 photoanode for Solar Applications 1-9

[8] Madurai Ramakrishnan V, Natarajan M, Pitchaiya S, Santhanam A, Velauthapillai D and Pugazhendhi A 2021 Microwave assisted solvothermal synthesis of quasi cubic F doped TiO2 nanostructures and its performance as dye sensitized solar cell photoanode *International Journal of Energy Research* **45** 17259-68

[9] Venkatachalam P, Kalaivani T and Krishnakumar N 2019 Erbium doped anatase TiO2 nanoparticles for photovoltaic applications *Optical and Quantum Electronics* **51** 1-16

[10] Karmakar A S and Ruparelia J P A critical review on dye sensitized solar cells.

[11] Kavitha S, Praveena K and Lakshmi M 2017 A new method to evaluate the feasibility of a dye in DSSC application *International Journal of Energy Research* **41** 2173-83

[12] abdel-latif M, Abuiriban M, El-Agez T M and Taya S 2015 Dye-sensitized solar cells using dyes extracted from flowers, leaves, parks, and roots of three trees *International Journal of Renewable Energy Research* **5** 294-8

[13] Rout S K, Padhi P, Biswal M and Debata S 2018 A comparative study of a novel technique for the fabrication of dye sensitized solar cells using nano TiO2 and different dyes *Research & Reviews: Journal of Material Sciences* **6** 1-9

[14] Nuran A, Kento T, Daiki M and Fujiki A 2015 The Basic Research on the Dye-Sensitized Solar Cells (DSSC) *Journal of Clean Energy Technologies* **3** 382-7

[15] Carp O, Huisman C L and Reller A 2004 Photoinduced reactivity of titanium dioxide *Progress in Solid State Chemistry* **32** 33-177

[16] Roose B, Pathak S and Steiner U 2015 Doping of TiO 2 for sensitized solar cells *Chemical Society Reviews* **44** 8326-49

[17] Patterson A L 1939 The Scherrer Formula for X-Ray Particle Size Determination *Physical Review* **56** 978-82

[18] Ravikumar P, Ravichandran K and Sakthivel B 2012 Effect of Thickness of SnO2:F over Layer on Certain Physical Properties of ZnO:Al Thin Films for Opto-electronic Applications *Journal of Materials Science & Technology* **28** 999-1003

[19] Perez-Casero R, Perrière J, Gutierrez-Llorente A, Defourneau D, Millon E, Seiler W and Soriano L 2007 Thin films of oxygen-deficient perovskite phases by pulsed-laser ablation of strontium titanate *Physical Review B* **75** 165317

[20] Salah A, El-Mahy S K, El-sayed O and Battisha I K 2020 Up-conversion behaviors of nano-structure BaTi0.9Sn0.1O3 activated by Er3+/Yb3+ ions *Optik* **209** 164571

[21] Tauc J, Grigorovici R and Vancu A 1966 Optical Properties and Electronic Structure of Amorphous Germanium *physica status solidi (b)* **15** 627-37

[22] Manea E, Pârvulescu C, Purica M, Budianu E and Florin C 2012 Antireflective Coatings with Nanostructured TiO2 Thin Films for Silicon Solar Cells *Journal of Nano Research* **21** 89-94

[23] Haider A, Najim A and Muhi M 2016 TiO2/Ni composite as antireflection coating for solar cell application *Optics Communications* **370** 263-6

[24] Dincer I and Zamfirescu C 2016 *Sustainable Hydrogen Production,* ed I Dincer and C Zamfirescu: Elsevier) pp 309-91

[25] Aouina A, Bensouici F, Bououdina M, Tala-Ighil R, Toubane M, Kezzoula F and Chebout K 2018 Effect of Er doping on the microstructural, optical, and photocatalytic activity of TiO2 thin films *Materials Research Express* **6** 016406

[26] Sharma D and Purohit G 2014 *Analysis of the Effect of Fill Factor on the Efficiency of Solar PV System for Improved Design of MPPT*

[27] Giribabu L, Chandrasekheram M, Kantham M L, Reddy V G, Satyanarayana D, Rao O S and Reddy P Y 2006 Conjugated organic dyes for dye-sensitized solar cells

[28] Rosana N T, Joshuaamarnath D, K. L V J and Sambandam A 2014 Mixed dye from nerium oleander and hibiscus flowers as a photosensitizer in dye sensitized solar cells *International Journal of ChemTech Research* **6** 5022-6

Chemical bath deposited Nickel oxide thin film as electrode material for pseudocapacitors

T V Sathyan[1, 2], Nygil Thomas[3], Jasmine Thomas[3], K. Deepa[4] and T L Remadevi[1]

1. School of Pure and Applied Physics, Dept. of Physics, Kannur University, Kerala, India.

2. Dept. of Physics, Nehru Arts and Science College, Kanhangad, Kerala. India.

3. Dept. of Chemistry, Nirmalagiri College, Kuthuparamba, Kerala, India.

4. Dept. of Physics, PRNSS College, Mattannur, Kerala, India

*sathyantv.tv@gmail.com

Abstract. We have synthesized thin films of nickel oxide (NiO) on silver and glass substrates, at very low temperature of 60^0C, by chemical bath deposition (CBD) method. The precursor used consists of nickel nitrate and aqueous ammonia. Structural characteristics were studied using x-ray diffraction (XRD) and morphological studies were done using scanning electron microscopy (SEM). Ultraviolet-visible (UV-Vis) spectroscopy was used for optical studies. To investigate electrochemical behaviour of thin film electrode materials, cyclic voltammetry (CV) measurements were conducted. For electrochemical studies the galvanostatic charge/discharge (GCD) tests were also conducted. The formation of face centred cubic NiO structure was confirmed using XRD. The scanning electron microscopy images show uniform distribution of worm-like porous morphology. CV measurements revealed the capacitive behaviour of the films.

1. Introduction

Nowadays we use renewable resources (solar/wind) as the main source of energy. But the renewable sources mainly depend on weather conditions. So we are in need of energy storage devices. In addition to batteries, electrochemical capacitors, also known as supercapacitors, have a reputable role[1,2]. Supercapacitors with metal oxide electrodes are called pseudocapacitors. Formation of electric double layer at or near the electrode electrolyte interface is the mechanism behind the charge storage in electric double layer capacitors (EDLCs). Where as in pseudocapacitors, fast and reversible redox reaction mainly causes faradaic pseudo capacitance, in addition to the formation of double layer at or near the interfaces between the electrode and electrolyte [3]. Selection of electrode and electrolyte, the voltage range etc. influence the charging and discharging process of pseudocapacitors. Among them, the selection of novel electrode materials has a key role. Electrochemically active transition metal oxides like ruthenium, nickel, manganese, copper, cobalt etc. were used as electrode materials, in which energy can be stored via faradaic charge transfer and the electrochemical processes.

Due to their outstanding chemical, thermal, physical, optical, electric and magnetic properties, for pseudocapacitor applications, we preferred to use metal oxide as electrode material. Moreover, nickel oxide generated greater interest because of the low cost of their raw materials, less toxicity and environmental benignity. It is extensively used as electrodes for pseudocapacitors and batteries, also used in portable electronics and electrical vehicles, electrochromic devices, smart windows, gas sensors, solar thermal absorbers etc. One of the main drawbacks of nickel oxide electrodes is its high resistivity. Surface morphologies of the films largely affects the value of the specific capacitance. NiO thin films with nano flake or worm-like morphology exhibit a good capacitive behaviour [4-7].

2. Materials and Methods

The precursor used for the synthesis of NiO thin films was nickel nitrate ($Ni(NO3)26H2O$) and ammonia. Substrates used were soda lime glass slides and silver sheets. The substrates were cleaned using extran (soap solution) and potassium dichromate solutions. 1.45 gm of nickel nitrate each was dissolved in three beakers containing 60, 70 and 80 ml of distilled water. Then 40, 30 and 20 ml of ammonia were added respectively to the above nickel nitrate solutions, so that the pH values of the precursors were about 12.2, 12.1 and 11.9 respectively. The substrates were placed vertically in the solutions. The optimum temperature during the deposition process was 60 ±1°C and the time of deposition was 6 h each. The as-prepared films were assigned the names as CNO6 6040, CNO6 7030 and CNO6 8020. Now the as-prepared samples were kept in a muffle furnace at a temperature of 400^0C for 1 h. The annealed samples were designated as CNO6A 6040, CNO6A 7030 and CNO6A 8020.

3. Results and discussions

3.1 X-Ray Diffraction Studies

Chemical bath deposition technique was adapted for the synthesis of thin films at various concentrations. On annealing at 400^0C for 1 h, the as-prepared films were converted to NiO. The as-prepared samples consist of peaks at 19.60, 33.50, 38.70, 52.20, 59.20 and 70.80^0 corresponding to the crystal planes (001), (100), (101), (102), (110), (103) respectively and are identified as nickel hydroxide [$Ni(OH)_2$] using the JCPDS data card number # 030177. On annealing, the peaks corresponding to $Ni(OH)_2$ disappeared and new peaks at 37.20, 43.20 and 62.70^0 corresponding to the planes (111), (200), (220) appeared, shown in figure 1. (a-f). The annealed samples are identified as face centered cubic Nickel oxide (NiO), using the JCPDS data card number # 780643.

3.2 Morphological studies

Scanning electron microscope (SEM) images of both the as-prepared and annealed samples were studied. Figure 1. (g-i) shows the SEM images of CNO6A 6040, CNO6A 7030 and CNO6A 8020. Annealing of the as-prepared samples did not appreciably influence the morphology of the samples. SEM images showed uniform, porous and interconnected worm-like structures on the substrates, which are in agreement with the literature [8,9].

3.3 Electrochemical studies

To investigate the electrochemical behaviour of NiO thin films three electrode system, with 3 molar potassium hydroxide electrolyte, was used. NiO-coated on silver sheet and Ag/AgCl were used as the working and reference electrodes. Cyclic Voltammograms were recorded in a potential range between -0.25 to +0.4 V, with 3 molar potassium hydroxide aqueous electrolyte. The Voltammogram obtained for CNO6A 7030 at a scan rate of 5 mV/s is shown in figure 2. (a). Specific capacitance obtained for CNO6A 7030 at 5 mV/s was 505 Fg^{-1}. Galvanostatic curves of CNO6A 7030 are shown in figure 2. (b). The discharge portions of the curve reveal that there are plateau in all curves, corresponding to faradaic discharging process [10]. At all scan rates, the cyclic votammograms shows identical shape (shown in figure 2. (c)), indicating a fine reversible character of the NiO films [11].The contributions from faradaic (redox reactions at or near the electrode surface) and non-faradaic process (due to adsorption or desorption of ionic species at or near the electrode-electrolyte interfaces) can be studied using CV curve [12,13]. The plot of specific capacitance versus the scan rate for CNO6A 7030 is shown in figure 2. (d).

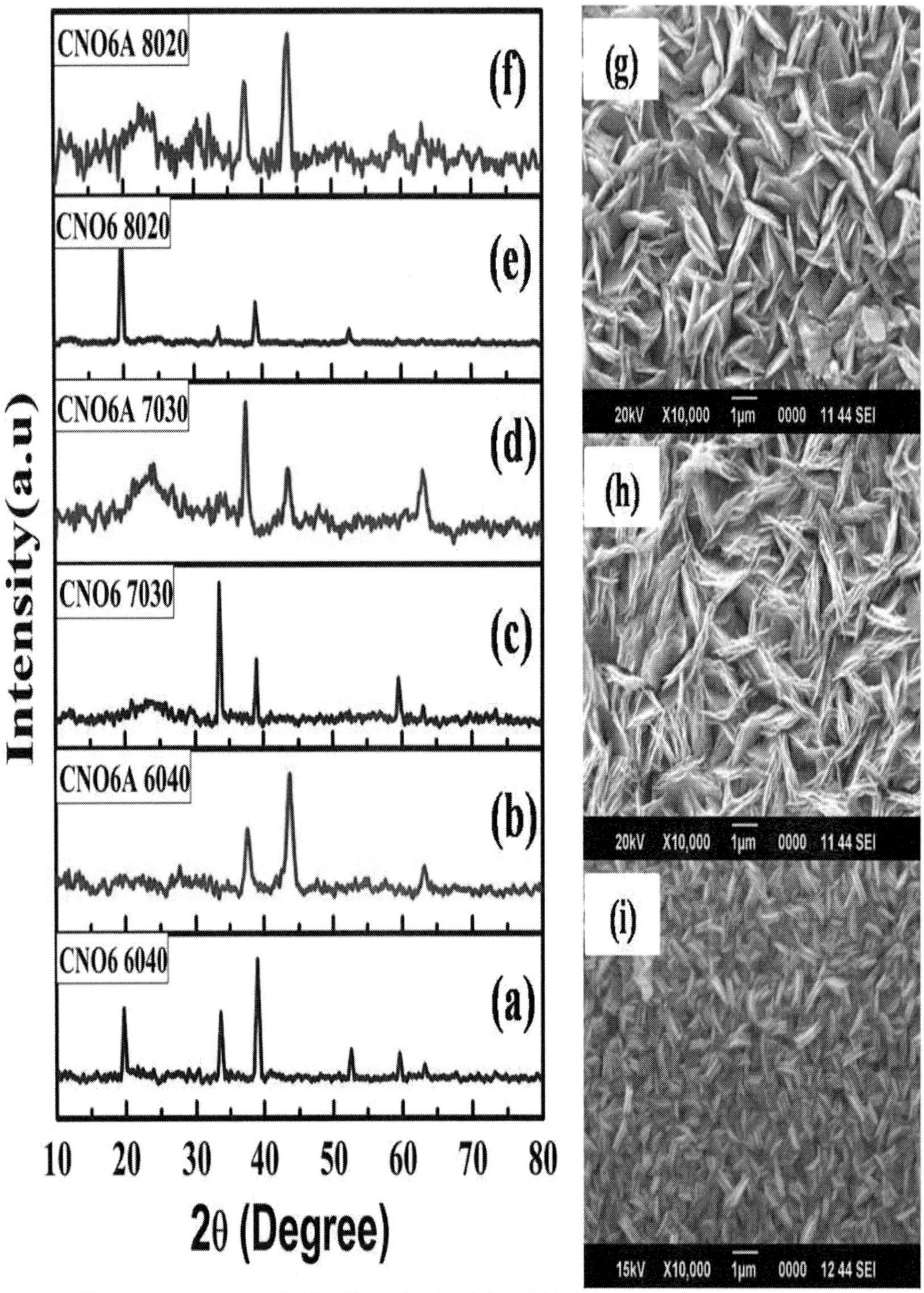

Figure 1. X-ray pattern of (a) CNO6 6040, (b) CNO6A 6040, (c) CNO6 7030, (d) CNO6A 7030, (e) CNO6 8030 and (f) CNO6A 8030. SEM images of (g) CNO6A 6040 (h) CNO6A 7030 and (i) CNO6A 8020.

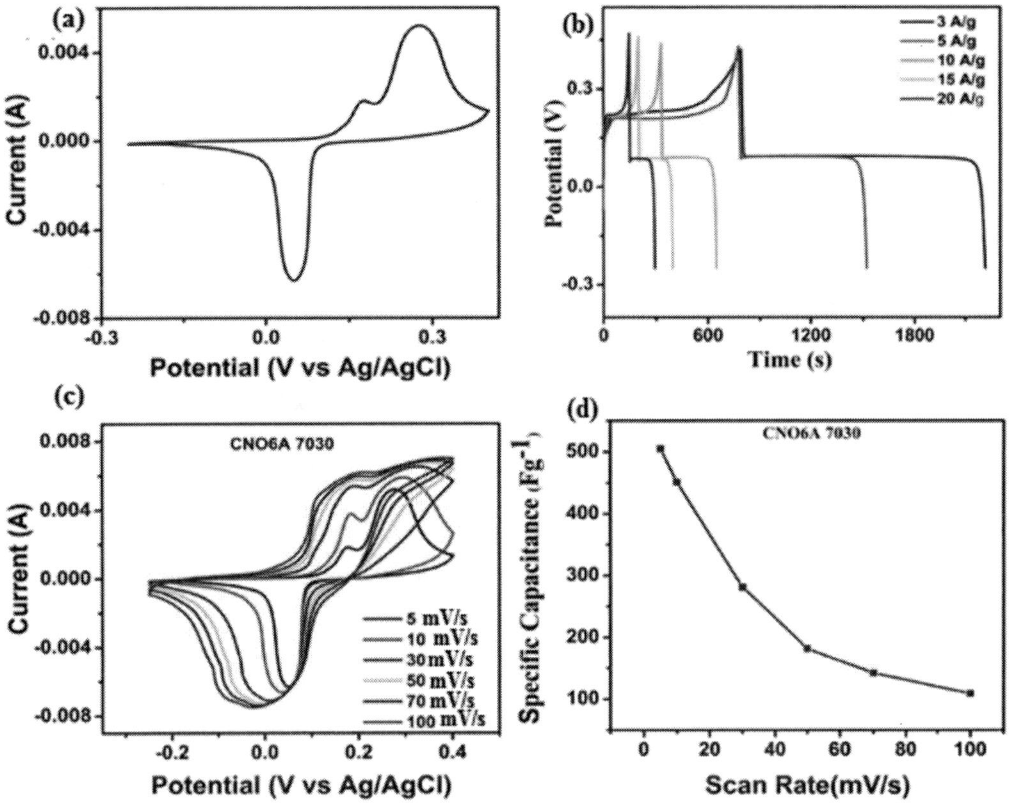

Figure 2. (a) CV plot of CNO6A 7030 at 5 mV/s, (b) GCD plot (c) CV plots of CNO6A 7030 and (d) Specific capacitance versus scan rate for CNO6A 7030.

4. Conclusions

Using CBD technique, we have successfully synthesized nickel hydroxide thin films, at low temperature of 60 ^{0}C, and converted the films to NiO. Sharp peaks in the XRD patterns exhibited the crystalline nature of the samples. SEM images showed well covered, porous and interconnected worm-like structures on the substrates. Electrochemical behaviour was analyzed using three-electrode system. Among the three samples studied for electrochemical behaviour, CNO6A 7030 exhibited comparatively large value of specific capacitance of 505 Fg^{-1} with 3 molar potassium hydroxide aqueous electrolyte.

References

[1] Jian Y, Afriyanti S, Eugene K and Pooi S L 2011 *Adv. Mater.* **23** 746-750.
[2] Rakhi R B, Wei C, Dongkyu C and Alshareef H N 2012 *Nano lett.* **12** 2559-2567.
[3] Young-Ha K and Soo-Jin P 2011 *Curr. Appl. Phys.* **11** 462-466.
[4] Purushothaman K K, Inbamany M B, Balasubramanian S and Gopalan M 2013 *ACS Applied Mater. Interfaces* **5** 10767-10773.
[5] Yan L, Li R, Li Z, Liu J, Fang Y, Wang G and Gu Z 2013 *Electrochim. Acta* **95** 146–154.
[6] Raid A I, Sa'ad G and Ghada A K 2013 *Appl. nanosci.* **3** 509-504.
[7] Maowen X, Lingbin K, Wenjia Z, and Hulin L 2007 *J. Phys. Chem* **111** 19141-19147.
[8] Patil U M, Gurav K V, Fulari V J, Lokhande C D and Oh S J 2009 *J. Power Sources* **188** 338-342.
[9] Martinez-Gil M, Pintor-Monroy M I, Cota-Leal M, Cabrera-German D, Garzon-Fontecha A A, Quevedo-Lopez M A and Sotelo-Lerma M 2017 *Mater. Sci. Semicond. Process* **72** 37-45.

[10] Kai W, Liwei L and Hongwei Z 2013 *Int. J. Electrochem. Sci.* **8** 4785-4791.
[11] Ashuthosh K S, Debasish S, Keshab K, Kalyan M and Gobinda G K 2016 *ACS Appl. Mater. Interfaces* **8** 20786-20792.
[12] Hainan W and Laurent P 2012 *Electrochim. Acta* **64** 130-139.
[13] Kirstin B, John W, Jan H, Christian R, Sven O S, Sarah H T, Bernd M S, Bruce D, and Torsten B 2010 *J. Am. Chem. Soc.* **132** 6982–6990.

Investigation of low-cost magnesium stannate transparent conductive oxide layer: optical, structural and electrical properties and photovoltaic applications

G. Kiruthiga[1, 5], K S Rajni[2*], T Raguram[2], Nandhakumar Eswaramoorthy[3], Selvakumar Pitchaiya[4]

[1]Department of Physics, Avinashilingam Institute for Home Science and Higher Education for Women,Coimbatore – 641 043, Tamil Nadu, India.

[2]Department of Sciences, Amrita School of Physical Sciences, Coimbatore, Amrita Vishwa Vidyapeetham, Tamil Nadu, India.

[3]School of Mechanical Engineering, Vellore Institute of Technology, Vellore-632014, Tamil Nadu, India.

[4]Department of Engineering and Science, Western Norway University of Applied Sciences, 5063 Bergen, Norway.

[5] Research and Development Centre, Bharathiar University, Coimbatore-641 046, TamilNadu, India.

kiruthiga_phy@avinuty.ac.in, ks_rajani@cb.amrita.edu

Abstract. In this research investigation we reveal the development of Magnesium Tin Oxide (MTO) as Transparent Conductive Oxide (TCO) material. It is the best replacement for the existing TCO materials. In the present work, Tin (II) Chloride and Magnesium Acetate are (MA: SC) taken in different ratios (0.1M: 0.1 M- S_1C, 0.1M: 0.2M- S_2C, 0.1M: 0.3M-S_3C, 0.1M: 0.4M-S_4C, 0.1M: 0.5M-S_5C) and the prepared solution is coated at the deposition temperature of 400° C by NSP technique. The deposited thin films are then annealed at a very high temperature of 500°C for three hours. A structural study explains that the prepared films exhibiting a strong diffraction peak, corresponding to the plane (105) magnesium tin oxide of rhombohedral structure. It is noted that the value of thickness is varied from 210nm to 480 nm when the molar concentration of Tin (II) chloride increases from 0.1M to 0.5M. The maximum transmittance obtained is more than 80% with a wider band gap of 3.89eV. FE-SEM shows improved crystallinity, development of grain size and the attainment of uniformity in grain distribution after annealing. From EDAX analysis, it is noted that when the concentration of Tin (II) Chloride as well as annealing temperature increases, the presence of unwanted elements is reduced and hence the purity is improved. FTIR result shows the presence of functional groups present in the prepared MTO thin films. From the studies of Hall Effect measurements, the value of the resistivity is measured and it is in the order of 10^{-3}(Ω cm). Photo-anodes and counter electrodes of DSSC are prepared with MTO as TCO substrate, and the cell efficiency is measured. The discussions explain that DSSC constructed with platinum coated on MTO (S_5C) as counter electrode and TiO_2 coated on MTO (S_5C) as photo anode shows a better power conversion efficiency of 3.28% than the rest of the other cells.

1. Introduction

In the beginning story of the solar cells industry, either silicon or selenium is used to make photovoltaic devices. Usually, p-n junction exists in all the photo voltaic devices, and they are utilized without any biasing. Focused on the charge separation concept at various conduction mechanisms in the interface of the two materials the fabricated devices are operated [1]. Owing to their possibly high conversion efficiency, flexibility and their lower production cost, DSSCs or Gratzel cells are more appealing over the last few decades. After the reach of mesoporous materials such as TiO2 and synthesized dyes, the efficiency of these cells can be improved. Gratzel and O-Regan checked 7% to 10% efficiency of solar cells by utilizing porous TiO2 electrodes with electrolytes of Iodine/I3 redox couple and Ruthenium based dye [2].

While keeping a better contact with electrolytes, TCO films of mesoporous materials in these solar cells outstandingly increase the light harvesting cross section by the sensitizers of surface anchored charge transfer. In such device ultrafast injection of electron from a photo excited dye into the conduction band of an semiconductor oxide and subsequently regeneration of dye and transportation of the hole in to the counter electrode, are in-charge for the electricity generation efficiently [3, 4]. DSSCs can attain 11.1% energy conversion efficiency at current status [5].Additionally, the development of DSSC is to bring forth long term stability at the temperature of about 80°C-85°C which is an essential demand for outstanding application of DSSC. In this invention, there was a constant approach to develop the stability and efficiency of these devices. Transparent conducting oxide (TCO) have been largely utilized for a different energy efficient windows, optoelectronic devices, Flat panel Display (FPD), light emitting (LEDs), Solar cells, storage type cathode ray tubes, photo catalysis surface layers in electroluminescent application and gas sensors [6].The two essential parameters of the material to be utilized as TCO in DSSC are (i) 80% transparency to allow the passage of optimum sunlight on the cell's effective surface area. (ii) Maximum value of electrical conductivity so as to have a better transfer rate of charge and minimized energy loss. Indium-doped tin oxide (ITO, In2O3: Sn) and fluorine-doped tin oxide (FTO, SnO2: F) are the commonly used substrate in DSSC. Usually, ITO films exhibiting the value of transmittance > 80% and the resistance value as 18 Ω/cm2 and the films of FTO exhibiting transmittance value which is very lower ~ 75% and 8.5 Ω/cm2 value of resistance [7]. In the present work MTO thin films are prepared by nebulizer spray pyrolysis technique and its characteristics are analyzed to find its suitability as TCO substrate for DSSC applications. K. Punitha et.al reported the paper for the preparation of MgSnO3 thin films [8].

V.K.Prem Kumar et.al analyzed electrochemical performances of hydrothermally synthesized cubic magnesium stannate (Mg2SnO4) nano particles [9]. Observation before and after photo-chromism and also ionization potential change of magnesium tin oxide films has been reported by Yutaro Suzuki et.al.[10]. G. Kiruthiga et.al already reported that the properties of MTO substrates annealed at 400°C and the solar device fabrication with prepared MTO as TCO substrates [11]. From the literature survey, it is noted that only a very few works are available in this material, and no one reported the application of MTO substrate in DSSC.

Nebulizer Spray Pyrolysis technique is used with the starting materials of (Mg: Sn) at a substrate temperature of (Ts) of 400°C and annealed at 500°C in the current research work, DSSC is fabricated by using the prepared MTO as substrate and its characteristics are analyzed. We examined the performances of DSSC with attention to transparent conducting oxide substrates. For ITO the value of sheet resistance is 52 Ω/sq and for FTO 8.5 Ω/sq will reflect major differences in internal global efficiency: from 2.24% for ITO to 9.6% for FTO [12]. But in our work, we are focused on the construction of DSSC with newer transparent conducting oxide substrate as Magnesium Tin oxide. This work shows the better novelty for the new try and the efficiency of the constructed DSSC varied to 3.28%. This percentage of efficiency is higher than ITO-based DSSC. Only a few literatures are available for the construction of magnesium based Transparent Conducting Oxide substrate [8, 9, 50, 54, and 55]. No prior reports for the fabrication of DSSC with constructed MTO as TCO material in the device assembling. Finding of new Transparent Conducting substrate is the major novelty of our Research Work.

2. Experimental

Preparation of TCO substrate

Tin (II) Chloride ($SnCl_2.2H_2O$), Magnesium acetate $(CH_3COO)_2 Mg_4H_2O$, 2-propanl ($CH_3CHOHCH_3$) are mixed and stirred well. Isopropyl alcohol is used as a solvent. In this present work, in 50 ml of the solvent, tin (II) chloride has been dissolved in five ratios such as 0.1M to 0.5M and Magnesium acetate is kept constant (0.1M ratio of Magnesium Acetate only dissolved in Isoproponal) and the solutions were mixed well by using the magnetic stirrer. The prepared solution is then sprayed into the glass substrates which are kept in hot plate at 400 °C. The temperature is controlled by the temperature controller. After preparing the films they are annealed at 500°C for three hours. The detailed preparation of MTO thin films such as substrate cleaning, optimized parameters during deposition of the films are explained in our previous paper [11,50,55].

Assembling of DSSC device

MTO substrate is utilized as TCO layer for DSSC applications. The samples S_3C, S_4C, S_5C exhibits better optical and electrical properties and the samples S_1C and S_2C exhibit only the optical properties it may due to the lower concentration of tin. Both the photo anodes and counter electrodes are prepared by using MTO as TCO substrate. The active surface area is fixed as 0.5 sq. cm. Using the paste of TiO_2, photo-anode (PA) is prepared by mixing Triton X- 100, Acetyl acetone (Qualigens) and TiO2 [P25 Degussa (20 nm) – Sigma Aldrich] with satisfactory proportion and the paste will be coated on to the constructed MTO conducting plate by the method of Doctor Blade. TiO_2 deposited on the surface of MTO substrates was retained in the furnace at the temperature of 450°C for the time of 45 minutes. After reaching room temperature the coated plates will be taken out from the furnace. This processing is for providing better adherence of TiO_2 paste into the surface of the MTO substrates. Platisol (T/SP_Solarnix) is used for the construction of platinum coated counter electrode (CE) and the layer is deposited on the surface of FTO and MTO substrates by the method of Doctor Blade and annealed at 500°C for 30 minutes. Then into the dye (N719) solution (0.5 mM in ethanol) (Solarnix) the coated photo anodes are immersed for 24 hours to obtain better absorption and with a counter electrode it is sandwiched. For capillary action in between the photo-anode and the counter-electrode, the electrolyte i.e., iodide-based electrolyte (Solarnoix, Iodolyte HI-30) is injected.

Characterization

Prepared MTO thin film properties are verified with UV-Vis Spectrophotometer, X-Ray diffraction studies, FE-SEM Analysis, Hall Effect measurement system, I-V, FTIR and Electrical Impedance Analysis by using the following Instruments. The structural property is analyzed using X- ray Diffractometer (PW3071/xx Bracket Diffractometer system=XPERT-PRO).Stylus Profilometer (ZYGO'S Optical Profilometer) as well as Micro gravimetric method is used for Thickness Measurement. Studies for Electrical analysis (Mobility, type of the film, sheet resistance) done by Hall Effect Measurements (Ecopia Instrument). For the study of optical behaviour like finding transmittance, optical band gap and absorption studies, UV-VIS Spectrophotometer (JASCO, V-670) is used. Morphological and Compositional analysis is characterized using Field Emission Scanning Electron Microscope (FESEM) with Energy Dispersive X-ray Spectrometer (EDX) (ZEISS, ΣIGMA HV, CARL ZEISS with Bruker Quantax 200 – Z10 with EDS Detector) and also for the analysis of elemental compositional the same device has been used. SHIMADZU with MIRACLE instrument is used for FTIR analysis. The EIS measurements and I – V characteristics are carried out by Keithley Instrument (Tektronix, 2650 Source Meter) and Electrochemical Workstation (ZIVE SP1 Won-ATech).Won-ATech).

3. Results and discussion

Thin film measurements

Among different thickness measurement methods, one of the flexible methods is gravimetric method. This method does not require any multiplex instruments to observe the value of thickness of the film like other measurement techniques. In this method the masses are measured by the digital weighing machine before and after deposition of the film on the surface of the substrate. During the measurements the influencing parameters were the mass of the deposited film (m) and its density (ρ) and the deposited area (A).Measurement of thin film thickness is carried out by the equation [11, 50, and 55].

$t = m/\rho A$

From the Figure 1, it is observed that when the concentration of tin increases from 0.1M to 0.5M then the value of thickness is also increased from 210 nm to 480 nm. The results of thickness values are tabulated in Table 1;

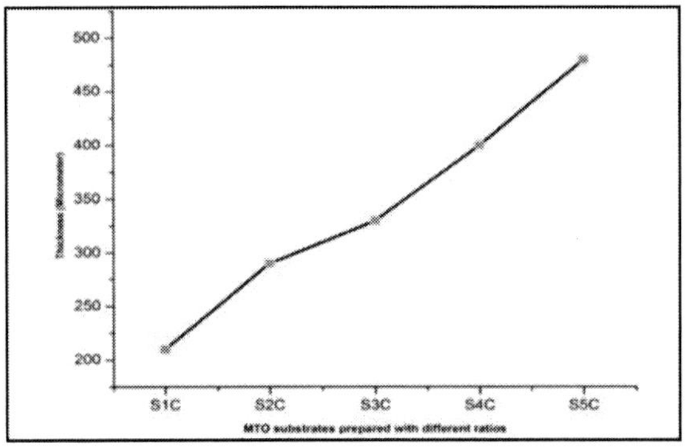

Figure 1. Variation of thickness with different MTO substrates annealed at 500°C.

Table1.Thickness of the $MgSnO_3$ thin films annealed at 500°C

Molarity Ratio(M)	Temperature (°C)	*(nm)*
(S_1C)	500	210
(S_2C)	500	290
(S_3C)	500	330
(S_4C)	500	400
(S_5C)	500	480

Due to the higher concentration of tin chloride, the thickness value is increased. In the case of spray pyrolysis, the thickness value is depending on some factors such as the concentration of solutions, the substrate's heat treatment and controlling spray duration. The nucleation process and the eventual growth are the two possible mechanisms that affect from the nucleation at the interface of substrate/film with the inclination of nuclei to work out a lowest configuration of free energy. The ending growth of the film results from the endurance of nuclei having a dynamically unsteady plane parallel to the surface of the substrate amidst oriented randomly nuclei owing to their divergent growth rates. This means that the orientation growth is formulated into one crystallographic direction of the minimum energy of the surface. Then, the grains became greater as the film fatten with minimum surface energy density. Subsequently, with improving molarity, the solution comprises more tin ions. As thickness calculated for the film deposited at higher molar concentrations are thicker as compared to films prepared at beginning molar ratios [13]. As the thickness of the film increased, the crystallinity also improved as evident from the intensity of peaks at (422). Also, it is noted that the thickness of films prepared by spray pyrolysis depends on several factors.

Analysis of structural parameters

Figure2 explains the XRD pattern of coated MTO thin films at five different ratios 0.1M: 0.1M (S_1C), 0.1M: 0.2M (S_2C), 0.1M: 0.3M (S_3C), 0.1M: 0.4M (S_4C) and 0.1M: 0.5M (S_5C). From the XRD results, we can conclude as-prepared film exhibits non-crystalline nature (amorphous) and after the annealing process the film exhibits crystalline nature. The obtained peaks are compared with JCPDS data of SnO_2 with card numbers of (21-1250) and $MgSnO_3$ (30-0798). The observed SnO_2 peak at (110) decreases with increase in the concentration of tin chloride. Due to the difference of the electron density of the doped atom with that of the neighbouring atoms change in intensity appears and this will make some more intensed peaks and other less intensed peaks. The peaks corresponding to the plane (110), (015) and (303) shows the presence of $MgSnO_3$ and the presence of Mg_2SnO_4 is noted from (422) plane. It is noted that at higher molar ratios of tin chloride, $MgSnO_3$ has been disproportionate into its other phases such as Mg_2SnO_4 Phase. Micro-structural parameters are measured and the values are tabulated. The radius of the tin atom is higher than that of a magnesium atom and this explains the depletion of the lattice parameters. The variation of lattice parameters with different MTO substrates is explained in Figure 3.

The lowering of lattice parameter values is thought to be the effect of stress undergone by thin film grains and may be due to a change in the nature and concentration of the native imperfections [13] which leads to the compression of the lattice parameters. It is noted that the Mg^{+2} has ionic radius of 0.67Å, which is close to the ionic radius of Sn^{+4}(0.71Å). Therefore, the replacement of Mg by Sn has a little effect on the lattice constants and crystal structure. Also, $MgSnO_3$ nanostructures may typically have a few defects such as oxygen vacancies, lattice disorders, etc. By annealing, these defects are removed and the dangling bonds on $MgSnO_3$ surface interact with oxygen ions from the atmosphere and due to this electrostatic attraction, lattice parameter is slightly contracted [13-15].

Several studies have reflected that post-annealing treatment can control the structural properties of MTO thin films which have been deposited on different substrates [16-20] by controlling the annealing temperature [21,22].The grain size is considered as a significant factor that controls the resistance of the material. In the literature, no one has reported the deposition of $Mg_xSn_{1-x}O_2$ thin films by spray pyrolysis. Table 2 shows the micro structural calculations of the samples calculated from the prominent peaks (105) and (422). The grain size is measured to vary from 62 nm to 69 nm for the substrates for the substrates S_1C. The peaks are compared with JCPDS values and it is tabulated from Table ST1 to Table ST5 (supplementary tables).

The micro-structural parameters like dislocation density and strain of the deposited thin films are measured to be directly proportional. The observed lattice parameters values of the thin films are roughly close to the standard values of $MgSnO_3$ (a = 5.2342° and c = 13. 662°) for the high intensed peak.The prominent peak at about 38° and 52° agree with the miller indices of (015) and (422) diffraction peaks of rhombohedra structure, and it is exposed by all as-grown samples which mention that orientation at c-axis to the substrates surface [14]. Owing to the tin atoms segregation near the boundaries ,the non-crystalline region of Mg-O bonds may exist and, in this case, tin atoms in the tetragonal lattice may replaced by Mg atoms and Mg ions may engage the interstitial sites of SnO2 [15, 16]. From the structural analysis measurements crystallinity of the deposited thin films developed and evidently grain size becomes greater that shows to enlarge in the surface roughness. By varying annealing temperature roughness can be reduced [24]. In the higher annealing temperature $MgSnO_3$ phase can be disproportionate in to its phases like Mg_2SnO_4 [8].

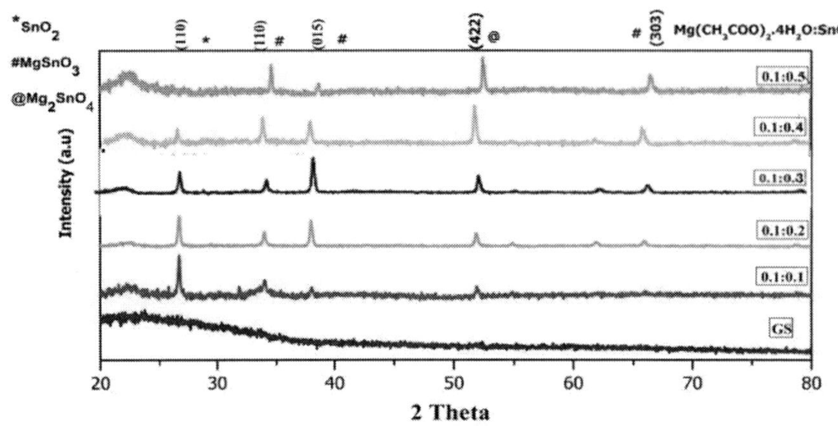

Figure 2. XRD pattern for the MTO substrates annealed at 500°C.

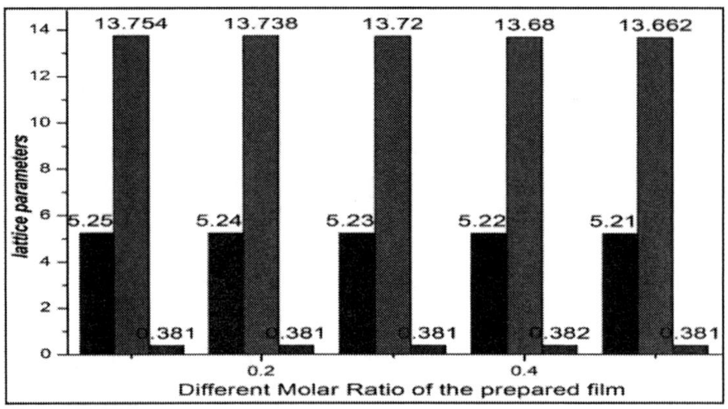

Figure 3. Variation of lattice parameters of the prepared MTO substrates annealed at 500°C

Table 2. Micro-structural parameters for MTO substrate annealed at 500 °C

Molarity ratio (M)	*FWHM (β)*	Grainsize (nm)	*Dislocation Density 10^{-14}*	*Micro strain Size (10^{-6})*	*a=b*	*C*	*a/c ratio*
0.1:0.1 M	0.2230	62.76	1.882	1.1821	5.252	13.754	0.381
0.1:0.2 M	0.1923	64.54	3.206	2.2101	5.242	13.738	0.381
0.1:0.3 M	0.3542	66.75	1.609	2.230	5.235	13.720	0.381
0.1:0.4 M	0.3011	68.56	1.692	1.655	5.223	13.680	0.382
0.1:0.5 M	0.1672	69.34	3.264	3.218	5.211	13.662	0.381

Figure3 shows that the variation of the lattice parameters with increasing molar ratios of the prepared substrates. In this case the lowering of lattice parameters is thought to be the effect of stress undergone by thin film grains and may be due to a change in the nature and concentration of the native imperfections [13] which leads to the compression of the lattice parameters. It is noted that the Mg+2 has ionic radius of 0.67Å, which is close to the ionic radius of Sn+4(0.71Å). Therefore, the replacement of Mg by Sn has a little effect on the lattice constants and crystal structure. Also, $MgSnO_3$ nanostructures may typically have a few defects such as oxygen vacancies, lattice disorders, etc. By annealing, these defects are removed and the dangling bonds on $MgSnO_3$ surface interact with oxygen ions from the atmosphere and due to this electrostatic attraction, lattice parameter is slightly contracted [13-15].The homogeneous nucleation of magnesium stannate particles tends to hinder the grain growth which in turn resulted in the reduced grain size for the substrates of lower ratios [22].

Morphological studies

Figure 4 shows the morphology of the prepared $MgSnO_3$ thin films by nebulizer spray pyrolysis technique by keeping the magnesium acetate constant and varying the tin chloride concentration. In the FESEM images, higher concentration of tin oxide results in better grain size with leafy structure compared to other lower ratios. From the FESEM analysis it is noted that the film was smooth, uniform in structure. In the lower ratios of tin chloride, in some places the crystallites are agglomerated, and some pin holes are observed. Due to the manual spraying some imperfections, voids may occur in the surface of the thin films. Similar type of observations noted for the $MgSnO_3$ films annealed at 400°C [11, 23].

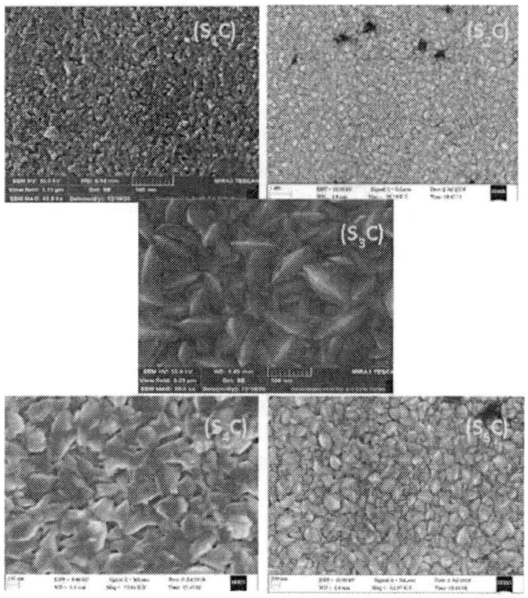

Figure 4. FESEM images of MTO substrates annealed at 500°C

Optical studies

Figure 5 a, b and c shows transmittance, absorbance and the variation of energy gap variation with various molar ratios correspondingly. The observation of transmission value is higher than 80% at tin oxide's starting molarity concentration. When DSSC is fabricated with titanium dioxide it is affected by the lower stability issue under the illumination of UV [25]. This problem might be controlled by tin with the proper amalgamation of other oxides. In our current research analysis the Figure 4 b. indicates the observation of wide band gap of MTO thin films in the value of 3.89 eV when the solution attains higher molar ratio of tin oxide. In the entire structure of DSSC the large band gap of MTO (Magnesium Tin Oxide) thin films (3.89 eV) will create lower oxidative holes and can develop the long term stability [26, 27]. With suitable ratio of Mg, it is possible to tune the band gap by doping SnO_2 [24, 25, 26].

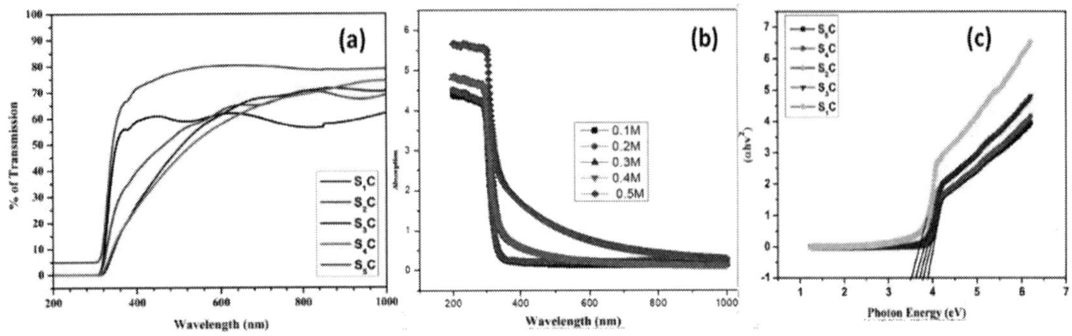

Figure 5. (a) Transmittance spectrum of the MTO substrates annealed at 500°C (b) Transmittance spectrum of the MTO substrates annealed at 500 0 C (c) Tauc's plot of the MTO substrates annealed at 500°C

Table 3. Transmission (%) values and band gap values for MTO substrate annealed at 500 C

Molarity Ratio(M)	Transmission (%) at 500°*C*	*Bandgap Values (eV) from Tauc's Plot for the samples annealed at 500 °C*
0.1:0.1 M (S_1C)	80.65	3.38
0.1:0.2 M (S_2C)	74.36	3.49
0.1:0.3 M (S_3C)	71.53	3.65
0.1:0.4 M (S_4C)	68.36	3.78
0.1:0.5 M (S_5C)	58.69	3.89

The widening of the band gap is usually observed for the semiconductor oxide materials doped with donors, and band gap abatement is happening if the material is doped with acceptors. The reducing value of band gap was attributing to the hole appearance of MgxSn1-xO2. For Every substitution in O2p state Magnesium atom will generate two holes due to the lower value of valence electron than Sn4+.Inside the forbidden gap region they create the impurity band. In this band the electrons in the valence band are moved and they `can be joining with the holes initially. However, they are unstable. The band gap shrinking is observed due to the recombination of the trapped electrons with the hole in the conduction band. At the higher annealing temperature MTO sample has a wider band gap value than the lower annealed MTO samples. It is due to the Mg interstitials due to the restricting solubility of Magnesium Acetate in Tin (II) Chloride [28]. The optical absorption coefficient (α) tends to obey the below mentioned relation for photon-energy (hν) is known as Tauc's relation (1)

$$\alpha h\nu = \left(h\nu - E_g\right)^{\frac{1}{n}} \quad .... (1)$$

Where 'Eg'- optical band gap and 'n' - the nature of the element transition [28]. Using this Tauc's relation (1) energy band gap is calculated and the value is varying from 3.38 eV (S1C) to 3.89 (S5C) eV. In the visible region the percentage of transmittance range is exceeded 80%.While the value of thickness is raised then the average transmittance value will be rising slightly which may be induced by free carrier absorption that maximizes coated thin film carrier concentration and provides the maximum transmission of light energy [29]. The coated films are actually become thicker with respect to the variations of the film transmittance. The calculated percentage of transmittance of the films were tabulated in Table 5 and the transmittance percentage values for the substrates S1C, S2C, S3C, S4C, S5C in the visible range was varied from 58.56 eV to 80.65 eV and the transitions are analyzed to be directly allowed transition. Because of the grain boundary scattering reduction and the deprivation of oxygen from the crystal can induce the further development in the possessions of MTO films due to the post-annealing temperature as well as post-deposition method.

FT-IR analysis

FT-IR analysis of MgSnO3 between the ranges from 600 to 4000 cm-1 is shown in Figure 6. The peaks observed at 659 and 955 cm^{-1} correspond to the O-Sn-O and O-Mg-O stretching vibrations [56,57]. The peaks observed at 1388 cm^{-1} correspond to asymmetric stretching vibrations of nitrate ions. The weak absorption bands at 2362and 2985 cm^{-1} are due to the C–H symmetric stretching vibrations of organic residue. The peak observed at 3736 cm^{-1} corresponds to the –OH-group-stretching vibrations [58]. This observation provides evidence for the presence of chemically bound H_2O in the magnesium hydroxide. A similar peak is also observed by other researchers [59, 60]. Each sample is absorbed a small amount of water and it is observed by the result. The appearance of hydrogen bonds is verified by the strong peak at 2362 cm^{-1} specifies the oscillations of O-H which might be owing to the water absorbed and groups of Sn-OH [33]. In the region1300-1400 cm^{-1}, the vibrations of bending H-O-H in water is examined to be consistent with the stretching of the magnesium stannite and stannate [34].

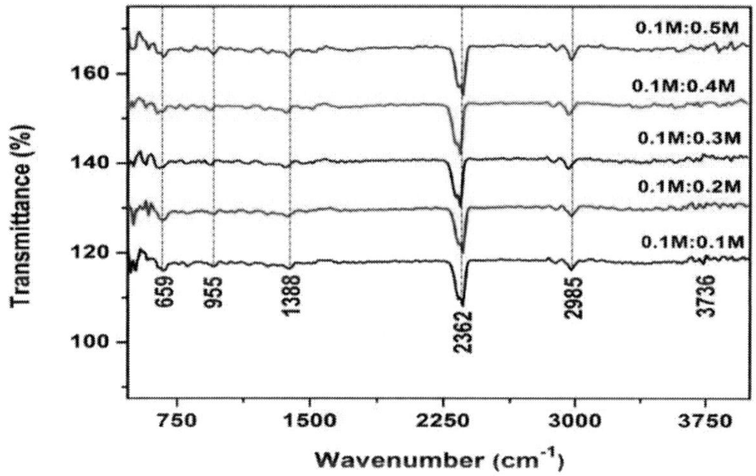

Figure 6. FTIR spectra of MTO substrates annealed at 500°C

Electrical studies

With small loss tangent and low permittivity values used for potential electronic ceramics, such as thermally stable capacitors, newly alkali earth stannate have been evaluated. At Maximum temperature and frequencies Magnesium stannate has been a better candidate for a large scale of applications. The behaviour of magnesium meta stannate ($MgSnO_3$) and magnesium Orthostannate (Mg_2SnO_4) is totally different from the corresponding counterparts of Ca, Sr and Ba. At high temperature $MgSnO_3$ is not stable and disproportionate in to its phases like Mg_2SnO_4 and tin oxide [35]. Relatively limited amount of research is available on the sintering behaviour of Mg-Sn-O system [36,37].Conversion of solar energy is the latest and most benefittable application of magnesium tin stannate, in which they act as transparent protective coatings as well as terminals to make connectors.

Huang et al. [38] reported that the magnesium tin composite oxides ($MgSnO_3$) have been prepared by heating $MgSn(OH)_6$ precursor. Because of the treatment of heat, the crystallites of the $MgSnO_3$products enlarge gradually with the heat energy and at the end it will decompose into SnO_2 and MgO. With the required size of 25x25 mm the substrates for Hall measurements were sprayed directly over sodium glass substrate .This work summarizes the dependence of the resistivity (r), Hall mobility (m) and carrier concentration (n) of MTO films on molar ratio with different thickness. The resistivity is about 1.11X $10^{-3}\Omega$ cm for a 480 nm film, and then gradually increases to 7.2X $10^{-3}\Omega$ cm for a 400 nm film. This phenomenon is directly related to the change of carrier concentration and Hall mobility according to the formula of resistivity $\rho = 1/(ne\mu)$. All carriers are possessing the carrier concentration of the order of 10^{20} $cm^3$for the samples of higher ratio tin, increase slightly as the thickness increases, reflecting that longer spraying time may cause more substantial $MgSnO_3$ or more oxygen vacancies. This is because the MTO film with reduced thickness is associated with poor crystallinity having various imperfections owing to large stress, and many free electrons then are caught by large numbers of traps formed by these defects, since the Mg concentration of all the films is about 0.1 wt% (determined by XRD, FESEM) [39-41].

The value of carrier concentration and Hall mobility raised to 10^{20} cm^3, 71.53 cm^2/Vs correspondingly. The resistivity gradually decreases to the minimum value in the order of $10^{-3}\Omega$ cm. The possible reason is that the annealing process has the effect of increasing grain size and crystallinity of the film, as mentioned before, which therefore results in less grain boundary scattering. On the other hand, loss of oxygen from the crystal will also produce the interstitial tin atoms which results in $Sn_{1+x}O$ in the matrix. This means that the intrinsic donor can be increased by the vacuum annealing process and thus, increase the conductivity [40, 41].

Table 4. *Electrical resistivity parameters for MTO substrate annealed at 500 C.*

Molarity ratio (M)+(AN)	*Bulk Concentration (cm^3)*	Mobility (μ) cm^2/Vs	*Resistivity (ρ) (Ω) x10^{-3}*	*Conductivity (ρ)*	*Sheet Resistance (Ω/sq)*
0.1:0.1 M (S_1C)	2.1174 ×10^{18}	80.65	3.0675	27.11	35
0.1:0.2 M (S_2C)	19.607 ×10^{19}	74.36	7.2655	50.08	27.75
0.1:0.3 M (S_3C)	1.7954×10^{20}	71.53	1.1100	77.63	15.13

Elemental compositional analysis

Table 5. *Elemental weights of Sn, O and Mg elements in MTO substrates annealed at 500C*

Composition of Mg:Sn (wt.%)	*Sample Code*	*Composition of prepared thin film*			
		Magnesium (wt %)	*Oxygen (wt.%)*	*Tin (wt. %)*	*Other elements (%)*
0.1M:0.1M	S_1C	11.39	47.67	29.84	Ca – 4.31 Na – 2.92
0.1M:0.2M	S_2C	11.71	27.67	59.85	C -2.24
0.1M:0.3M	S_3C	10.61	11.67	73.44	Ca-3.21
0.1M:0.4M	S_4C	11.71	11.45	77.11	Ca-5.14
0.1M:0.5M	S_5C	4.12	10.60	84.22	Na-3.12 Si -1.70

The unwanted elements presented are Ca, Na, C, in the values of 4.31%, 2.92%, 2.24%, 3.21%, Ca-5.14%, Na-3.12% and Si - 1.70%. While the ratio of the molarity is improved then the percentage of un-required elements will be reduced. It is noted Table 4. The elements Mg, Sn and O are present in the expected percentage while the ratio of tin is increased in the higher ratios (0.4M and 0.5M) and the values are tabulated.

Device performance

In these five substrates only higher ratio samples are exhibiting both electrical and optical properties. But the lower ratio samples only exhibiting optical properties. Figure 7 explains the analysis of J-V measurements for the constructed DSSC with different MTO substrates annealed at 500 °C DSSCs fabricated with these lower ratio substrates also and they are giving less efficiency. For analyzing the peculiar properties of DSSC impedance spectroscopy is one of the prime tool. In the junction in the middle of the electrolyte/counter electrodes (Rct1) of fabricated DSSC and also the interface between the TiO2/dye/electrolyte (Rct2) the electro catalytic resistance may analyzed EIS investigations were accomplished on DSSCs using the three constructed electrodes S3C based DSSC, S4C based DSSC, and S5C based DSSC primarily and the efficiency values are higher than compared to a lower ratio prepared electrode. An impedance measurement was executed at AC amplitude of 10 mV at the room temperature with an open voltage over the frequency range in between 0.1 Hz to 1 MHz in the dark circumference. Figure 9 shows the characteristics of J-V curve of the prepared DSSC's. Figure 8 shows EIS spectra of five different DSSC devices.

The photovoltaic J-V characteristics of the fabricated solar cell parameters such as open-circuit voltage (V_{OC}), short-circuit current density (J_{SC}), Fill factor (FF) and Efficiency (η %) can be obtained from the J-V curve through the given below equations [42-44].

$$FF = \frac{J_{max}\, X\, V_{max}}{J_{sc}\, X\, V_{oc}}$$

$$\eta = \frac{J_{sc}\, X\, V_{oc}\, X\, FF}{P_{in}}$$

Herein, 'P_{in} '- incident power (100 mW/cm^2).

Figure 8 (b, c, d) shows Nyquist plots of S_3C –DSSC, S_4C-DSSC, S_5C-DSSC and Table 5 shows the values of efficiency for every fabricated cell and all the measured parameters. Practically in these EIS spectra three characteristic semicircles has been represented by the Nyquist plot for a fabricated DSSC [40, 41]. The MHz region represented by small semicircle in the spectra and this lower frequency region allocated to the Nernst diffusion of I3- within the electrolyte. Usually in the centre frequency region presided by huge semicircle and the range for this region is usually in between the range of (10–100 Hz) is ascribed to that of charge transfer resistance at both the interfaces of Titanium dioxide/dye/electrolyte (R_{ct2}) and the semicircle in the higher frequency region (kHz) is allocated at the counter electrode/ electrolyte interface (R_{ct1}) to the charge transfer resistance [43-45].

In the range of high-frequency region the solution of the electrolyte's redox plane in where charge transfer resistance (Rct) will be revealed. In the EIS spectra two various distinguishing semicircles revealed for the all counter electrodes. From the observations of EIS spectrum, it is distinctly observed that in the region of higher frequency, semicircle is overlapped in higher ratio samples and also we can view in the middle frequency region a major portion of the semicircle. This may be owing to the tiny cracks of presence in the fabricated DSSC and it may cause the poor interconnection of the MTO substrate with the nano-particles of TiO2 [46, 47] and also in comparison with higher ratio prepared substrates the interfacial charge transfer resistance is increased for the lower ratio prepared substrate. The beginning point of semicircle of the maximum frequency region is considered to calculate interfacial resistance of the series resistance (R_s) between the MTO conducting glass substrate and the electrode material. The Nernst diffusion impedance (Z_N) for the red/ox commute in the entire solution of described by the minimum frequency region semicircle. In the constructed DSSCs there we can found the lowering of semicircle in the region of middle frequency in the sequence of S_3C>S_4C>S_5C due to the gently raising acceleration of the transfer of electron in the photo anode [48]. If the Rct_2 value is decreased due to the strengthening of the photon initiated electron assembling from the surface of TiO_2 to the MTO substrate (J_{sc}) and the data analysis of current value compete with the prior investigation [49].

The Rct value follows the order $S_3C>S_4C>S_5C$. The change in the charge transfer resistance values is due to the change in electronic conductivity and many electro catalytic represents series resistance (Rs). The change in difference of the values of interfacial charge transfer resistance is mainly due to the optimized optical and electrical properties. In the complete processing of DSSC excluding the MTO substrate the other used materials, components, the electrolyte and all other arrangements are identical. The values of Rs value is differed even we are focusing the identical components and it can be assigned to the various electrical conductivities and optical parameters of the proposed TCO in counter Electrodes shortly CEs.

In the final constructed DSSC the value of the series resistance (Rs) will drop and it may guide the varying fill factor percentage of (FF) while we are utilizing greatly conductive MTO placed CE. [50] The values of Rs is in change for the platinum coated MTOs which may utilized as the CE is compatible with above look in to the current -Voltage results, in which the value of FF of DSSC oriented on CE-MTO focused DSSCs is more than other DSSCs [51]. Because of the reduced Voc i.e., reduced redox potential the value of Fill factor is decremented for the lower ratio substrates and this parameter affects the dynamics of recombination between conduction band electrons and Lithium Iodide electrolyte [52]. The structural, Electrical and optical properties can influence the performance of MTO [53, 54].

From Table 5 the efficiency values are measured for DSSC/MTO with different molar ratios of MTO. For the lower ratios of MTO the efficiency value is very low and it is varying from 0.68% to 0.72%. For the Higher Molar ratios the value of efficiency is more than 3%.The better transmittance and conductivity values of these MTO substrates allows more electrons in the interface between the anodes and dye exhibiting more efficiency value when it is used with fabricated DSSC.

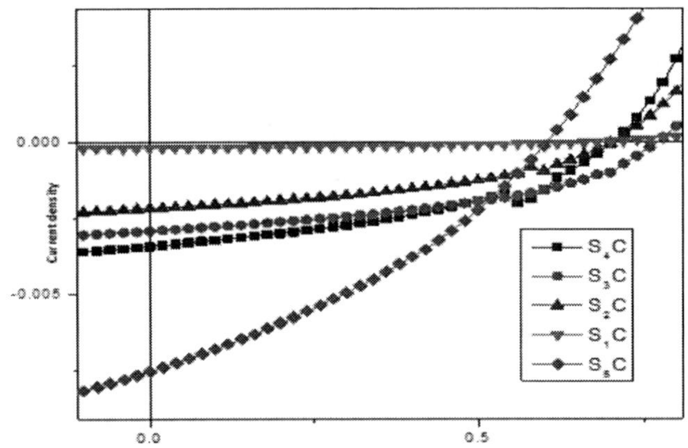

Figure7. J-V characteristics - MTO substrates annealed at 500°C

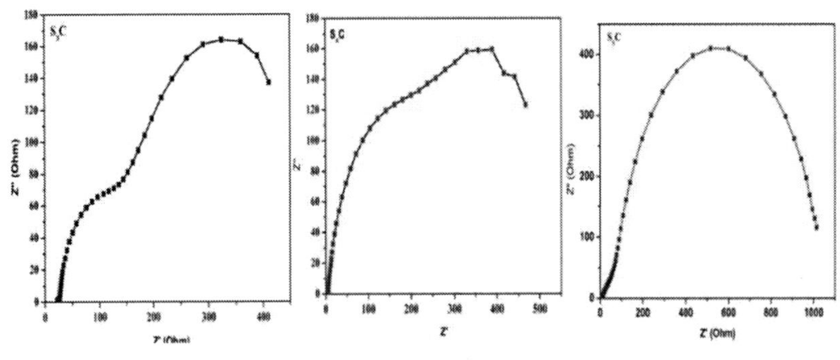

Figure 8. EIS Spectra - MTO substrates annealed at 500°C

IOP Conf. Series: Materials Science and Engineering 1263 (2022) 012020 doi:10.1088/1757-899X/1263/1/012020

4. Conclusion

In order to produce the cost-effective DSSC our research is focused. The Prepared MTO substrates were deposited at the temperature of T_s 400°C and annealed at T_A 500°C initially. The XRD analysis shows mixed phases in every concentration. This is one of the drawbacks of the samples which is prepared at this annealing temperature.The crystallite size is initially increased in comparison with previously annealed substrates. UV analysis explains good transmittance (more than 80%) and a larger band gap (about 3.89eV). The lowering value of resistivity with higher molar concentration is in the range of $x10^{-3}\Omega$/cm. These substrates then will be used for the fabrication of DSSC and the higher ratio of tin substrate (S5C) shows better efficiency (3.28%) than the lower ratio of tin substrates which is annealed for 500°C. To improve the efficiency of DSSC further the optimized parameters are planned to change during the preparation of MTO substrates.

SUPPLEMENTRY TABLES:

Table ST1. (S_1C) - (0.1M: 0.1M-500°C)
Table ST2. (S_2C) - (0.1M: 0.2M-500°C)
Table ST3. (S_3C) - (0.1M: 0.3M-500°C)
Table ST4. (S_4C) - (0.1M: 0.4M-500°C)
Table ST5.(S_5C) - (0.1M: 0.5M-500°C)

Table ST1. (S_1C) - (0.1M: 0.1M-500°C)

d(Å)	2θ(deg)	(hkl)	Compound
3.333	26.74	(11 0)	SnO2(21-1250)
2.635	34.01	(10 4)	MgSnO3(30-0798)
2.353	34.40	(31 1)	MgSnO3(30-0798)
1.762	51.89	(42 2)	Mg2SnO4(24-0723)

Table ST 2. (S_2C) - (0.1M: 0.2M-500°C)

d(Å)	2θ(deg)	(h kl)	Compound
3.254	27.40	(110)	SnO2(21-1250)
2.590	34.63	(104)	MgSnO3(30-0798)
2.453	34.40	(311)	MgSnO3(30-0798)
2.325	38.72	(015)	MgSnO3(30-0798)
1.76	51.90	(422)	Mg2SnO4(24-0723)
1.487	61.87	(300)	MgSnO3(30-0798)
1.406	64.50	(303)	MgSnO3(30-0798)

Table ST3. (S_3C)- (0.1M: 0.3M-500°C)

d(Å)	2θ(deg)	(hkl)	Compound
3.331	26.75	(110)	SnO2(21-1250)
2.613	34.01	(104)	MgSnO3(30-0798)
2.453	34.40	(311)	MgSnO3(30-0798)
2.366	38.13	(015)	MgSnO3(30-0798)
1.764	51.90	(422)	Mg2SnO4(24-0723)
1.497	61.87	(300)	MgSnO3(30-0798)
1.415	64.99	(303)	MgSnO3(30-0798)

Table ST4. (S_4C)- (0.1M: 0.4M-500°C)

d(A)	2θ(deg)	(hkl)	Compound
3.332	26.74	(11 0)	SnO2(21-1250)
2.638	33.97	(10 4)	MgSnO3(30-0798)
2.453	34.40	(31 1)	MgSnO3(30-0798)
2.364	38.05	(01 5)	MgSnO3(30-0798)
1.765	51.79	(42 2)	Mg2SnO4(74-2152)
1.417	64.90	(30 3)	MgSnO3(30-0798)

Table ST 5. (S_5C)- (0.1M: 0.5M-500°C)

d(A)	2θ(deg)	(hkl)	Compound
2.592	34.59	(10 4)	MgSnO3(30-0798)
2.453	34.40	(311)	MgSnO3(30-0798)
2.325	53.38	(20 5)	MgSnO3(30-0798)
1.764	51.90	(42 2)	Mg2SnO4(24-0723)
1.497	61.87	(30 0)	MgSnO3(30-0798)

References

[1] Kirchartz T, Bisquert J, Mora-Sero I and Garcia-Belmonte G 2015 Phy. Chemi. Chem. Phy 17 4007.
[2] Sharma K, Sharma V and Sharma SS 2018 Nanos. Res. Lett.13 1.
[3] Martin C, Ziółek M and Douhal A 2016 J. Photochem. and Photobio C: Photochem Rev26 1.
[4] Muñoz-García AB, Benesperi I, Boschloo G, Concepcion JJ, Delcamp JH, Gibson EA, Meyer GJ,Pavone M, Pettersson H, Hagfeldt A and Freitag M 2021 Chem. Soc. Rev.50 12450.
[5] Chiba Y, Islam A, Watanabe Y, Komiya R, Koide N and Han L 2006Jap. J. Appl. Phy 45 L638.
[6] Minami T 2005 Semicon. Sci. Tech20 S35.
[7] Mehmood U, Rahman SU, Harrabi K Hussein IA and Reddy BVS, 2014 Adv.Mat. Sci. and EngArticle ID 974782.
[8] Punitha K, Sivakumar R and Sanjeeviraja C 2012 Ener. Procel5 312.
[9] Premkumar VK and Sivakumar G 2017J. Mater. Sci: Mater. Electr28 14226.
[10] Suzuki Y, Takaki H, Inoue S and Matsumura Y 2021 AIP Adv11 085108.
[11] Kiruthiga G, Raguram T, Rajni KS, Selvakumar P and Nandhakumar E 2021 Mat. Sci: Mat. Electr32 22780.
[12] Sima C, Grigoriu C and Antohe S, 2010Th. Sol. Film519595.
[13] MH Francombe, H Sato Blue Bell, Pergamon Press19631964.
[14] Chen DY, and Hsu CY, 2008 Superlatt. and Microstr.44 742.
[15] Usseinov AB, Kotomin EA, Zhukovskii AT and Puans J2014 Th. Sol. Fil553 38.
[16] Chang J, Muhammad AZ, Wlodarski W and Waclawik ER 2013 Sens13 8445.
[17] T. Minami T 2000 MRS Bull.25 38.
[18] Ginley DS and Bright C 2000 MRS Bull.25 15.
[19] Lian J, Zhang D, Hong R, Qiu P, Lv T and Zhang D 2018 Nanomat.11 922.
[20] Ali A.H, Hassan Z and Shuhaimi A 2018 Appl. Surf. Sci443 544.
[21] Seong S, Jung YC, Lee T, Park IS and AhnJ 2018 Mater. Sci. Semi.Cond. Pro79 14.
[22] Abdulgafour HI, Yusof Y, Yam FK Adv 2013 Mater. Res620 132.
[23] F Wang MZ, Wu YY, Wang, YM Yu XM, Wu LJ, Zhugeb 2013 Vacc. 89 127.
[24] Dong BZ and Fang GJJour. Appl. Phy1012007.
[25] Sima C Grigoriu C and Antohe S 2010 Thin Sol. Film519 595-597.

[26] M. Qureshi 2015 J. Mater. Chem. A34291.
[27] Ramasamy E and Lee J 2010J. Phys. Chem. C11422032.
[28] Ali SM, Hussain ST, Bakar SA, Muhammad J and ur Rehman N 2013 In Jour. Phy.: Confer. Ser IOP Publishing439 012013.
[29] Qureshi M, Chetia TR, Ansari MS, Soni SS 2015J. Mater. Chem. A34291.
[30] Hao L, Diao X, Xu H, Gu B and Wang T 2008 Appl. Surf. Sci254 3504
[31] Kennedy J, Murmu PP, Gupta PS, Carder DA, Chong SV, Leveneur J and Rubanov S 2014 Mat Sci Semic. Proc 26561.
[32] Choi W, Termin A and Hoffmann MR 1994J. Phys. Chem9813669
[33] Wang C, Bahnemann DW and Dohrmann JK 2000 Chem. Communi161539.
[34] Ferhati H and Djeffal F 2020J. Comp. Electron19815.
[35] Azad AM, Shyan LLW and Yen PT1999 J. All. Comp282109.
[36] Azad AM. 2001 Mater. Res. Bull 36755.
[37] Huang F, Yuan Z, Zhou Y, Sun J 2004 Mater. Chem. Phys8316.
[38] Dong BZ and Fang GJ 2007 J. Appl. Phys101033713.
[39] Tong H and Deng ZH 2011 Appl Surf Sci257 4906e11.
[40] Islam MM, Ishizuka S, Yamada A, Matsubara K, Niki S and Sakurai T 2011 Appl Surf Sci2574026e30.
[41] Kim DH, Kim HR, Lee SH, Byon E and Lee GHJ 2010 Non-Crys. Sol 3561779e83.
[42] Raguram T, Rajni KS 2020 J. Sol. Sci. Tech93202.
[43] Kiruthiga G, Raguram T, Rajni K.S, P. Selvakumar, E. Nandhakumar (2021), Journal of Materialsscience: Material Electronics, https://doi.org/10.1007/s10854- 021-06754-0
[44] Aiswarya KM, Raguram T and Rajni KS 2019Polyhedron176114267.
[45] Ashok A, Vijayaraghavan SN, Unni GE, Nair SV and Shanmugam M 2018Nanotechn29175401.
[46] Tricoli A, Nasiri N, Chen H, WallerAS and Righettoni M 2016Sol. Ener136553.
[47] VittalR and Ho KC 2017Rene. Sust. Ener. Rev 70920.
[48] Bwana NN 2009 J. Nano. Res111917.
[49] Pitchaiya S, Eswaramoorthy N, Natarajan M, Santhanam A, Ramakrishnan VM, Asokan V, Palanichamy P, Palanisamy B, Kalimuthu A and Velauthapillai D 2020New J. Chem448422.
[50] G.Kiruthiga and SanjeevirajaChinnappanadar 2014Intern. Jour. Chem. Tech. Res.6 1942.
[51] Shang G, Wu J, Huang M, Lin J, Lan Z, Huang Y and Fan L 2012J. Phys. Chem. C11620140.
[52] Kumar R, Umar A, Kumar G, Nalwa HS, Kumar A and Akhtar MS 2017 J. Mater. Sci52 4743-4795.
[53] Lee KM, Suryanarayanan V and Ho KC 2006Sol. Ener. Mat. Sol. Cells902398.
[54] Kiruthiga Prabhu G, Raguram T and Rajni KS 2019 IOP Conf. Ser. Mater. Sci. Eng577012093.
[55] Kiruthiga G, Rajni K S, Raguram T, Nandhakumar Eswaramoorthy, Selvakumar Pitchaiya, "Indium-free $MgSnO_3$ transparent conductive oxide layer: investigation on structural, optical and electrical properties and photovoltaic performance analysis, Applied Nanoscience https://doi.org/10.1007/s13204-022-02353-5

Temperature stimulated bandgap tailoring in the smart chromogenic $WO_30.33H_2O$

M Manuja[1], Tintu Thomas[1] and Gijo Jose[1]*

[1] Post graduate and research department of Physics, St.Berchmanns college Changanasserry 686101, India
*Corresponding author. Mobile: 9446921753; E-mail: gijojose@sbcollege.ac.in

Abstract: The orthorhombic form of $WO_30.33H_2O$ is prepared hydrothermally and the thermochromic property of the material is identified using spectroradiometer with in a wavelength range of 325 nm to 1075 nm. The variation of reflectance with temperature is observed and it is accompanied with a change in bandgap. The absorbance relation with temperature is analyzed and the presence of Inter Valence Charge Transfer (IVCT) band is detected in the absorbance spectra. The IVCT bands illustrate the homovalent charge transfer mechanism behind the thermochromism taking place in the compound. The change in bandgap with temperature provides further supportive evidence to the thermochromic phenomenon observed in the compound.

Keywords: $WO_30.33H_2O$, the thermochromism, IVCT mechanism, bandgap tailoring.

1. Introduction

Transition metal chalcogenides possess layered structure, controllable nonzero band gap, which can be exfoliated even to monolayer [1]. The decrease of layer number by exfoliation progressively widens the band gap of material and switches from indirect to direct transitions [2,3]. Oxygen bonds in transition metal oxides constitute strongly correlated electron systems and provide tunable structural, electrical and optical properties. Unusual and useful properties of TMOs are due to incomplete electronic configuration in d orbital. The degeneracy of d electrons in transition metals losses when they create bonds with ligands to form complexes. The distribution of electrons in different energy levels depends on the structure and electronic configuration of combining ligand atoms.

The occurrence of IVCT mechanism, and existence of different oxidation states for transition metals etc are the key features observed in TMOs. TMO's finds potential applications in chromogenic devices [4], smart windows [5], photo catalytic degradation of organic materials, in catalysis [6], energy saving technologies [7,8] etc. It also shows structural distortion due to metal defect, oxygen vacancy creation and eventually could lead to interesting thermal, electrical and magnetic behaviors. They exhibit numerous attractive properties like super conductivity [9], colossal magneto resistance [10], piezo electricity [11], microelectronics [12], photonics etc.

Among different TMOs, WO_3 plays a distinct role in structural, electrical, thermal and optical studies. Various oxidation states ranging from $^{+}2$ to $^{+}6$ make it suitable for chromogenic applications. Unfilled and unpaired d orbitals in the valence shell contribute to its outstanding performance in photo, thermo and electro chromic behaviors [13]. In between the layers of the compound, H^+ ions move continuously giving proton conductivity which is referred to as Grotthhuss mechanism [14]. Present work concentrates on the temperature stimulated chromogenic property of $WO_30.33H_2O$ and introduces spectroradiometer as a powerful tool to analyse chromogenic properties in materials. The work highlights and elucidates the altering of band gap allied with temperature with proper theoretical supports.

Creation of oxygen vacancies leading to the nonstoichiometry and structural defects in the compound are the key factors which provides plenty of attractive behaviors in the hydrated WO_3. Because of its layered nature, foreign ions can easily intercalated by breaking the bonds and reduce the layer number which can be used effectively in lithium ion battery applications and shows better results in supercapacitor applications [15]. It can also perform as a better candidate in designing of smart windows, display system, antiglare mirrors, solar cell fabrication etc. On account of its special chemical features it is also suitable for calalysis, degradation of organic dye, sensing applications, fuel cells, photovoltaics etc. It is already proposed as a system for the generation of renewable energy due to its high efficiency, long life cycle and high energy storage density.

2. Experimental

2.1. Sample preparation

The orthorhombic phase of $WO_30.33H_2O$ is prepared hydrothermally in light of our previous reports from sodium tungstate precursors [16]. All reagents were of analytical grade and used without further purification. 0.1 M solution of tungstic acid is prepared by dissolving 1.32 g of sodium tungstate ($Na_2WO_4.2H_2O$) in 40 ml of distilled water and is subjected to room temperature stirring for 30 minutes to make it a homogenous mixture. The homogeneity of the solution provides uniform structure for the product obtained. 2 ml of HCl is added drop by drop during stirring to make the pH below 1. The procedure is pH sensitive and the very high acidic medium is required for the sample synthesis in order to get desired phase of the material. Gradual addition of HCl provides white colored precursor solution and is transferred to teflon lined stainless autoclave and is kept in an oven at 120 °C for 11 hrs. The obtained sample is centrifuged and washed several times using water and ethanol and dried in an oven at 80°C for 3 hrs. The procedure of sample preparation is shown in Figure 1.

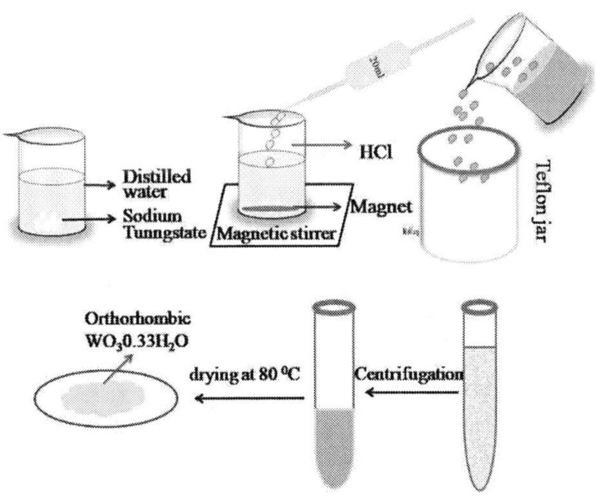

Figure 1. The schematic representation showing stage by stage procedure of the method of preparation of orthorhombic $WO_30.33H_2O$ via hydrothermal technique.

2.2. Characterization technique

The structural confirmation and phase purity of the prepared samples were done using x-ray diffraction spectroscopy (XRD) in Bruker D8 x-ray diffractometer having Cu Kα1 (λ=1.5406 Å) radiation with step size of 0.02 and a scan rate of 3⁰ per minute between 2θ values ranges from 10 to 70⁰. The thermochromic property of $WO_30.33H_2O$ is analyzed using a spectroradiometer with in a wavelength range of 325 nm to 1075 nm. The measurements are performed in a Field Spec spectroradiometer from ASD Inc. (model no FS HH 325-1075).

3. Results and discussions

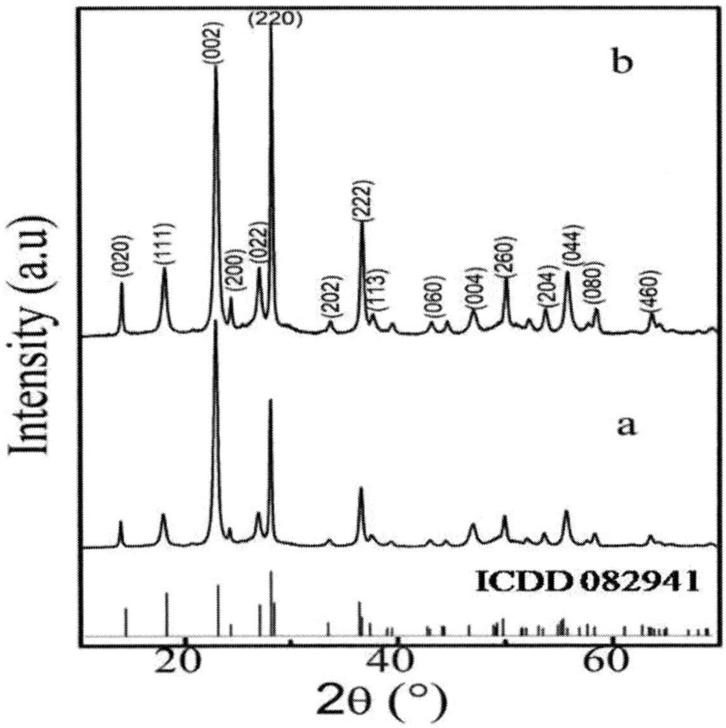

Figure 2. X-ray diffraction profiles of orthorhombic $WO_30.33H_2O$ (a) at room temperature, (b) at 200 °C with standard ICDD patterns at the bottom.

The phase and purity of the sample are confirmed from the recorded XRD pattern and is presented with respective ICDD profiles at the bottom in the Figure 2 (a). Diffraction profiles are compared with the standard values of ICDD card no 082941. All hkl planes corresponding to the 2θ values are indexed to the orthorhombic phase of $WO_30.33H_2O$. Figure 2 (b) indicates the temperature dependent XRD patterns of the sample at 200 °C. The matching peaks indicate that the sample retains its crystallographic phase even after it is treated at 200 °C. However the sample shows a color change with temperature due to the thermochromic property of the material.

Thermochromism is referred to as a reversible change in color when subjected to external stimuli of temperature [17]. Herein the temperature stimulated chromogenic mechanism of $WO_30.33H_2O$ is analyzed in both quantitative and qualitative way using a spectroradiometer. Throughout the procedure, the sample is placed on a hot plate where temperature can be controlled and the reflectance spectrum is recorded at different temperatures. The obtained spectra at different temperatures are shown in the Figure 3 (a).

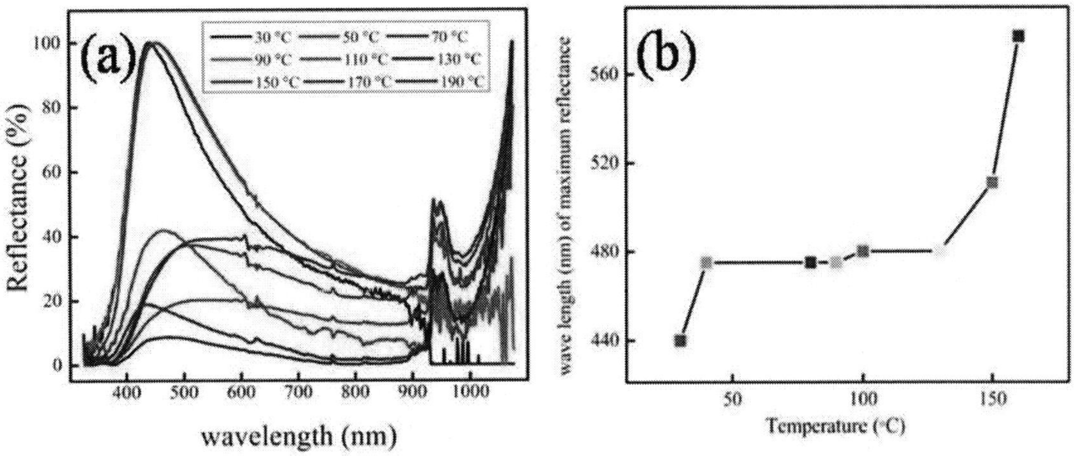

Figure 3 (a) Reflectance of the material with respect to wave length and (b) Graphical representation of wavelength corresponding to maximum reflectance at different temperatures.

The wavelength representing maximum reflectance at a constant temperature is shown graphically in the Figure 3 (b). The graph shows that the wavelength corresponding to maximum reflectance changes with temperature. The increase in reflectance with temperature is an indication of the color change in material when subjected to the application of external stimuli. Figure 4 (a-i) represents the reflectance spectra of the sample at different temperatures and the inset shows the photograph of material showing color change.

The influence of temperature in the band gap of the material is recognized from the tauc plots of reflection spectra in the temperature range 30-190 °C. Here the indirect band gap obtained from taucplots with $(\alpha h\upsilon)^{1/2}$ as ordinate and hυ as abscissa. Where the co efficient of reflection (α) is calculated using the relation

$$\alpha=\ln\left(\frac{R_{max}-R_{min}}{R-R_{min}}\right) \quad (1)$$

A straight line portion extrapolated to y=0 gives an indirect band gap. Figure 4 (a-i) also bears the tauc plots and the respective band gaps in the inset of the figures. This provides direct evidence of the color change with respect to temperature stimuli.

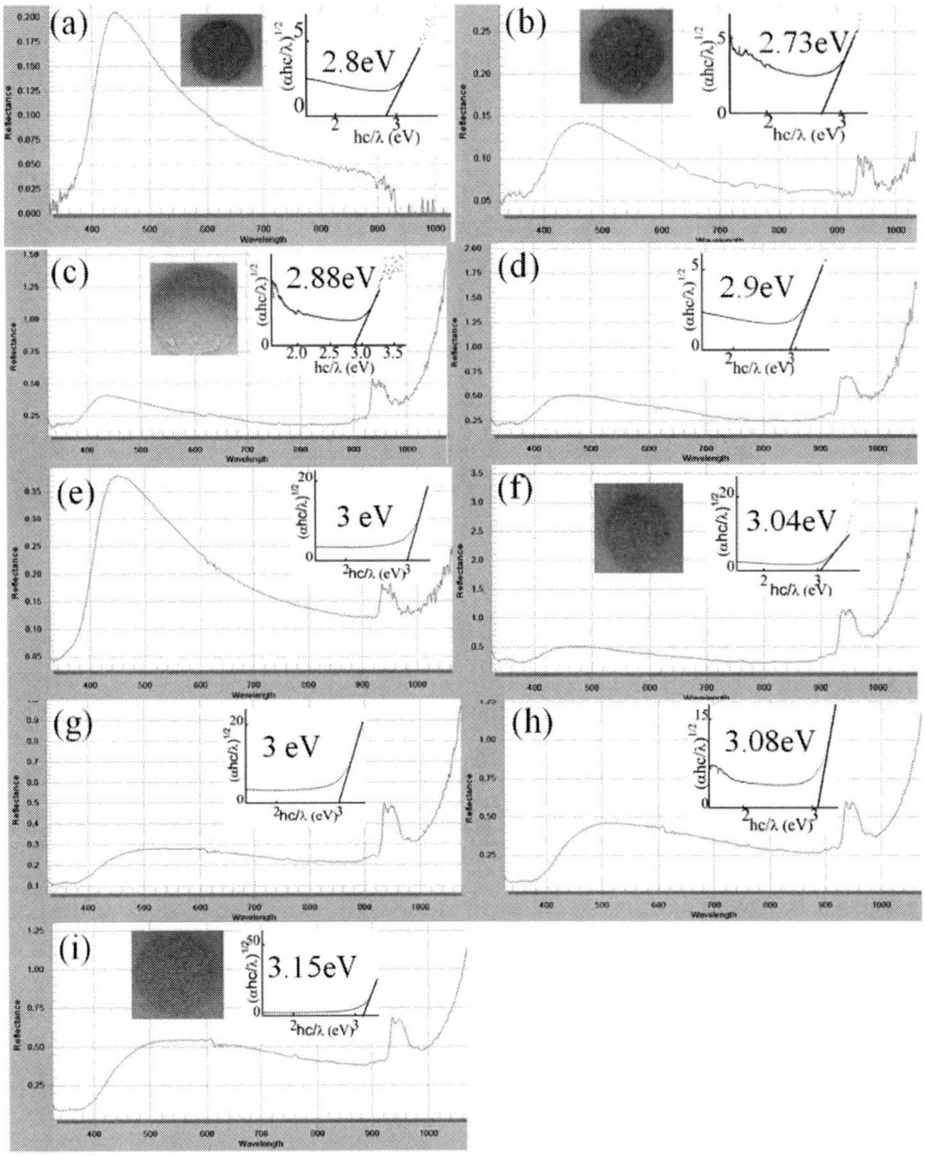

Figure 4 . Spectroradiometer measurements of $WO_30.33H_2O$. Reflectance versus wavelength plots at different temperatures (a) 30 ˚C, (b) 50 ˚C, (c) 70 ˚C, (d) 90 ˚C, (e) 110 ˚C, (f) 130 ˚C, (g) 150 ˚C, (h) 170 ˚C, and (i) 190 ˚C. Insets in each figure shows corresponding tauc plots with bandgaps and the color of samples. Variation of color with temperature is clearly visible from the photographs.

The theory behind the color change can be elucidated using the IVCT mechanism and it is observed in compounds having mixed valence states in central metals [18,19]. $WO_30.33H_2O$ has multiple valence states and they swap their oxidation states with each other by absorbing energy. The absorption spectra of material under UV-Visible/IR illumination can be used to analyze the IVCT mechanism in a compound [20,21,22]. The recorded reflectance (R) data is converted to absorbance (A) using the relation

$$A = log_{10}(1/_R) \quad (2)$$

and the derived absorbance spectra are plotted in the Figure 5. Here the presence of IVCT band is detected and is shown in the Figure 5 (a) and the enlarged peak is given in Figure 5 (b).

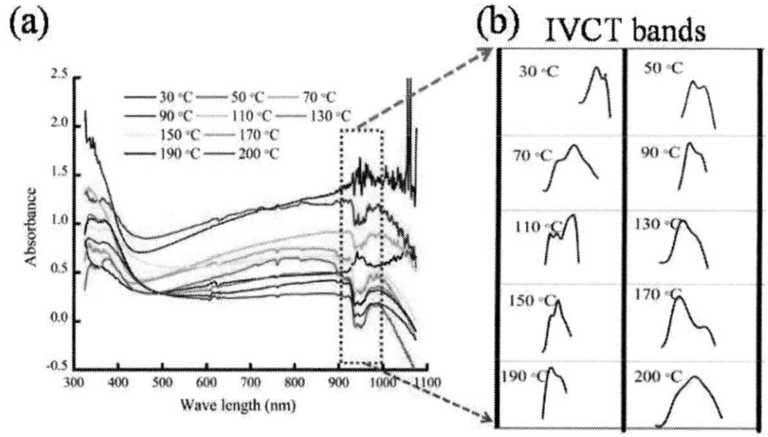

Figure 5 Derived absorbance spectra of $WO_30.33H_2O$ at varying temperatures. The enlarged portion of the marked part in the plots represents the IVCT band.

Due to the nonstoichiometry of tungsten, in addition to W^{6+}, the presence of W^{5+} is also observed in $WO_30.33H_2O$ [2]. These two states exchange their oxidation states on absorbing thermal energy. This mechanism represents as follows (3).

$$W_a^{6+} + W_b^{5+} \overset{h\nu}{\leftrightarrow} W_a^{5+} + W_b^{6+} \tag{3}$$

The reductant, oxidant pair (W^{6+} and W^{5+}) causes the metal to metal charge transfer and is referred to as precursor complexes in homovalent IVCT mechanism [23,24]. Due to the direct d-d transition, electrons hope between these cations and coloration occurs in the compound.

4. Conclusion

The thermochromism accompanied by the variation in bandgap is analyzed in orthorhombic $WO_30.33H_2O$ and is illustrated by adopting the concept of homovalent IVCT. The metal-to-metal charge transfer peak called IVCT band is observed in the absorbance spectra. Hopping of electron between the reductant oxidant pairs (W^{6+} and W^{5+}) constitute charge transfer and coloration.

Acknowledgement

Authors acknowledges department of environmental science of M.G. University for providing facility for spectroradiometer measurement. First author acknowledges Mahathma Gandhi University Kottayam, Kerala, India for providing university JRF 2017.

References

[1] Manuja M, Krishnan V S and Jose, G (2018, September) In IOP Conference Series: Mater. Sci. Eng. 360, 012015. IOP Publishing.
[2] Kuc A, Zibouche N and Heine T (2011) Phys. Rev. B, 83, 245213.

[3] Manuja M, Thomas T, Jose J and Jose G (2022) Materials Today: Proceedings.
[4] Granqvist C G, Green S, Niklasson G A, Mlyuka N R, Von Kraemer S and Georen P (2010) Thin Solid Films, 518, 3046-53.
[5] Granqvist C G (1990) Crit. Rev. Solid State Mater. Sci., 16, 291-308.
[6] Shifrina Z B, Matveeva V G and Bronstein L M (2019) Chem. Rev., 120, 1350-96.
[7] Cannavale A (2020) Clean. Technol., 2(4), 462-475.
[8] Granqvist C G (2014) J. Vac. Sci. Technol. B Nanotechnol. Microelectron., 32, 060801.
[9] Shen Z X and Dessau, D. S. (1995) Phys. Rep., 253(1-3), 1-162.
[10] Burgy J, Mayr M, Martin-Mayor V, Moreo A and Dagotto E (2001) Phys. Rev. Lett., 87, 277202.
[11] Kalantar-zadeh K, Ou J Z, Daeneke T, Mitchell A, Sasaki T and Fuhrer M S (2016) Appl. Mater. Today 5, 73-89.
[12] Darling R B and Iwanaga S (2009) Sadhana, 34, 531-542.
[13] Deb S K (2008) Sol. Energy Mater. Sol. Cells, 92, 245-258.
[14] Manuja M, Thomas T, Jose J, Jose G and George K C (2019), J. Alloys. Compd., 779, 15-21
[15] Manuja M, Thomas T, John S, Jose J and Jose G (2021) J. Alloys. Compd., 869, 159234.
[16] Manuja M, Sarath K V, Thomas T, Jose J and Jose G (2020) J. Electron. Mater., 49, 2556-67.
[17] Hage D S (2013). Reference module in chemistry, molecular sciences and chemical engineering. In Elsevier Inc..
[18] Miessler G L and Tarr D A (2010) Inorganic Chemistry 3rd ed., Pearson/Prentice Hall publisher, ISBN -13-035471-6.
[19] Bajaj H C, Shukla A D and Das A (2002). J. Chem. Sci., 114, 431-442.
[20] Hoffman A S (2013) Advanced drug delivery reviews, 65, 10-16.
[21] Carter K A, Shao S, Hoopes M I, Luo D, Ahsan B, Grigoryants V M and Lovell J F (2014) Nat. commun., 5, 1-11.
[22] Kelley E G, Albert J N, Sullivan M O and Epps III T H (2013) Chem. Soc. Rev., 42, 7057-71.
[23] Maji S, Sarkar B, Mobin S M, Fiedler J, Kaim W and Lahiri G K (2007) Dalton Trans., 23, 2411-18.
[24] Storm S L, Springsteen A and Ricker T M (1998) Tech. rep., Labsphere.

Supercapacitive performance of exfoliated graphitic carbon nitride nanoflakes

Veena Ragupathi[1]*, Abisha devaraj[1], Puspamitra Panigrahi[1] and N. Ganapathi Subramaniam

[1]Centre for Clean Energy and Nanoconvergence, Hindustan Institute of Technology and Science, Padur-603103, Chennai, India
[2]Quantum Functional Semiconductor Research Centre, Dongguk University, Seoul 100-715, South Korea

rveena@hindustanuniv.ac.in

Abstract. Recently, Exfoliated graphitic carbon nitride (E-gCN) has drawn significant interest in the field of energy generation and storage. In this study, exfoliated graphitic carbon nitride nanoflakes are synthesized by condensation followed by ultrasonic exfoliation. The supercapative behavior of exfoliated graphitic carbon nitride is analyzed. Structural analyses confirm the formation of thiazine and heptazine heterocycles. Scanning electron microscopy image shows flake-like morphology. The E-gCN exhibit the specific capacitance of 160 F g^{-1} at 1 A g^{-1} and retains 96.2% capacity at 3000 cycles. The presence of nitrogen in the two-dimensional layered structure significantly increases the conductivity and alters the electronic structure. The nano-flake morphology increases the charge diffusion kinetics, which improve the charge storage mechanism.

1. Introduction

In recent years, our society move towards highly capable sustainable and renewable energy storage technology like fuel cells, batteries and ultracapacitors. In these aspects, carbon-based material with porous morphologies is extensively utilized for electrical double layer capacitor. Generally, the performance and capacity of the energy storage devices are depend upon the electrode materials. Hence more research work has been focused on capable electrode material for ultracapacitors. In this concept, environment-friendly, graphitic carbon nitride is best option and has attractive features like tuneable band structure, abundant, less toxic and stable material [1]. Carbon nitrogen frameworks are successfully used in hydrogen production, sensors, pollutant degradation and electrochemical energy storage devices [1-3]. The presence of nitrogen and exfoliation provides a unique electronic structure that improves conductivity and surface polarity. However, the utilization of graphitic-carbon nitride material in supercapacitors are still limited owing to its low electrical conductivity and also exploration of g-C_3N_4 in supercapacitors is in primary stages. David Adekoya et al. reviewed the different types of carbon nitrogen framework in electrochemical energy storage devices [4]. Ghaemmaghami et al. studied carbon nitride as next generation supercapacitor materials [5]. Commonly, Nano-architectures significantly improves the surface area of the material, which promotes ion transport and charge storage mechanism. Here, Exfoliated graphitic carbon nitride (E-gCN) material is produced by polycondensation followed by ultrasonification and their supercapacitive behavior is studied.

2. Experimental Procedure

Exfoliated graphitic-carbon nitrogen (E-gCN) was produced by ultrasonication. Initially, 6g of thioacetamide precursor was heated to 550 °C for a period of 2 h. Then, 0.5 g of as-synthesized material was dissolvedin 1:1 ratio of propanol and distilled water and ultra-sonicated for 6 h. The solution was filtered and dried. To evaporate residual propanol, E-gCN was slowly heated to 250 °C under air for 2h.

2.1 Characterization

Structural and morphology measurements were evaluated using Rigaku Smart Lab X-ray diffraction measurement, Fourier transform infrared spectrometer (Bruker) and FEI Quanta 400, scanning electron microscopy

Supercapacitive behaviour of the E-gCN material was analyzed by three electrode configurations (VersaSTAT 3, Princeton Applied Research). Glassy carbon, Platinum wire and Ag/AgCl were used as working, counter and reference electrodes. Potassium hydroxide (2M) was used as electrolyte. E-gCN coated on the glassy carbon using 15μL Nafion solution. Electrochemical measurements were recorded between 0-0.8V. Electrochemical impedance spectroscopy (EIS) was recorded with the potential amplitude of 1 mV and the frequency range of 100 kHz to 10MHz.

3. Results and Discussion

XRD pattern of E-gCN material is shown in Fig. 1a and the results accorded with JCPDS file no 87-1526. The appearance of (100) and (002) plane validates the existence of tri-s-triazine and aromatic units [6]. Fig.1b depicts the FTIR spectra of E-gCN and the peak at 1642, 1569 and 1409 and 809 cm^{-1} corresponds to C-N stretching and triazine group vibrations. The C-NH-C vibration modes were observed at 1320 and 1240 cm^{-1} [7].

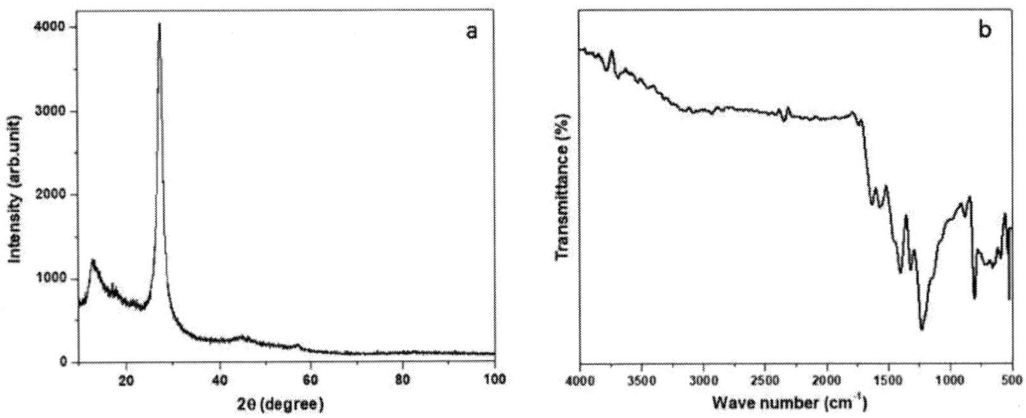

Fig. 1 a) XRD and b) FTIR spectra of E-gCN material

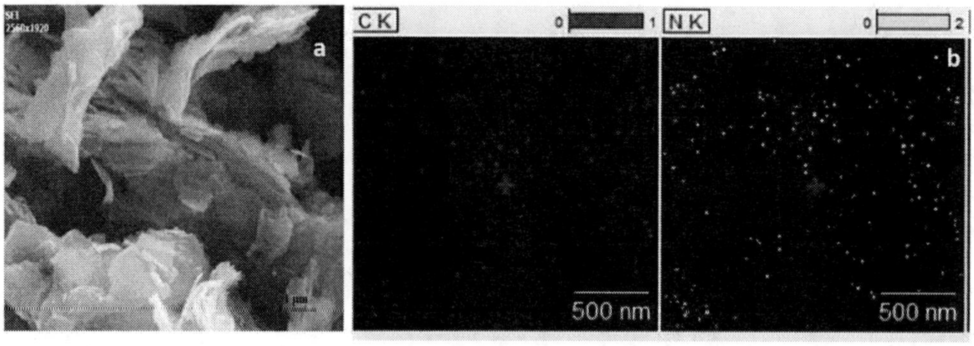

Fig. 2 a) SEM and b) EDS mapping of E g-CN material

SEM image of E-gCN and exhibit flake structure (Fig.2a). Generally, nanostructure provides a high surface area. In this study, the exfoliation process increases the distance between the flakes and generates more active sites, which significantly improves charge storage and electrolyte penetration. Fig.2b represents the EDS mapping of E-gCN and reveals the stoichiometric ratio of carbon and nitrogen.

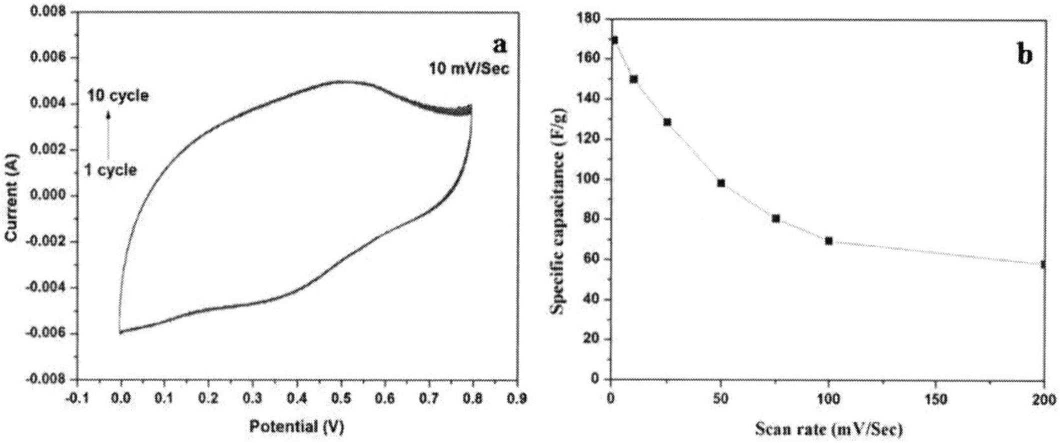

Fig. 3 a) Cyclic Voltammogram (CV) and b) Capacitance *vs.* scan rate of E-gCN.

CV plot at 10 mV s^{-1} is illustrated in Fig. 3a. The rectangular profile indicates the supercapacitive performance of E-gCN and also reveals the pseudocapacitive behaviour. Specific capacitance versus scan rates is plotted in Fig 3b. The E-gCN exhibits the specific capacitance of 171.81 F g^{-1} at 1mV s^{-1}.

Fig. 4a displays the Galvanostatic charge-discharge (GCD) measurements of E-gCN nanoflake and the calculated specific capacitances are displayed in Fig. 4b and the E-gCN nanoflakes delivers the specific capacitance of 211 F g^{-1} at 200 mA g^{-1}. Roger Gonçalves et al. described the specific capacitance of graphitic carbon nitride (117 F g^{-1} at 200 mA g^{-1}) [8]. The GCD measurements of E-gCN nanoflakes at 1000 mA g^{-1} is plotted in Fig 4c and indicates triangle charge discharge behaviour with less ohmic loss. Cyclic stability of E-gCN nanoflakes is plotted in Fig. 4d. E-gCN delivers 160 F g^{-1} (1000 mA g^{-1}) at

3000 cycles and possess 96.2 % capacity retention which confirms better stability and reversibility of E-gCN material. The exfoliation layers grasp more charges into its layered structure and also improvethe electrolyte penetration which significantly improves the electrochemical performance of E-gCN.

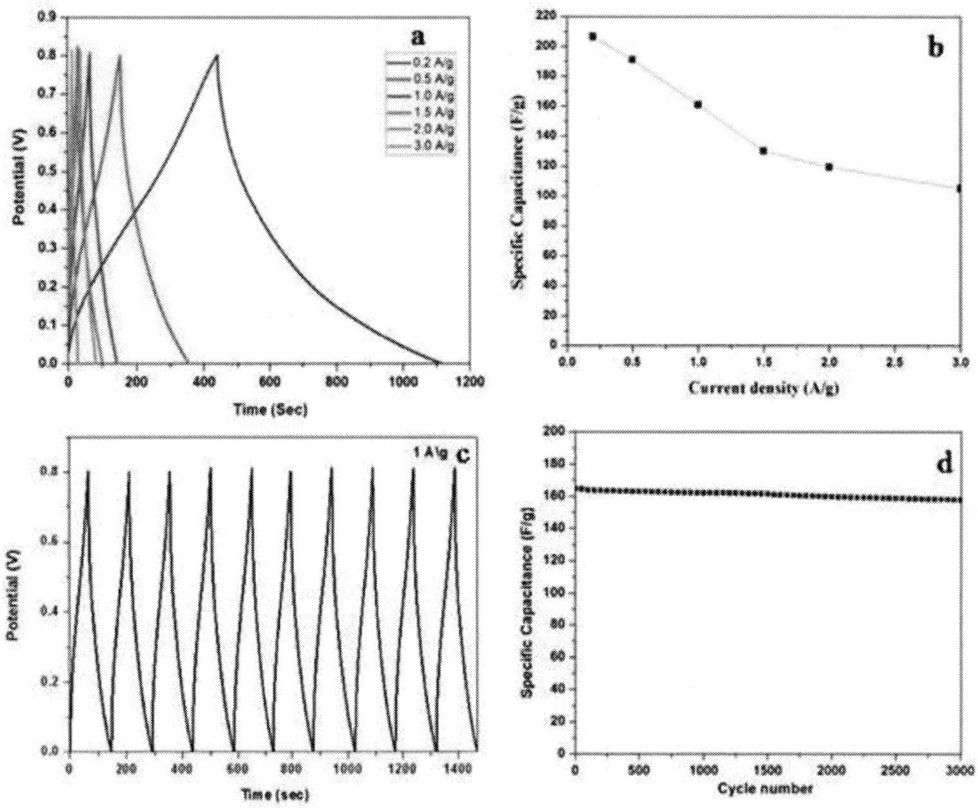

Fig. 4 a) GCD at different current density, b) Specific capacitance *vs.* current density, c) GCD at 1000 mA g^{-1} and d) Cyclic stability of E-gCN electrode.

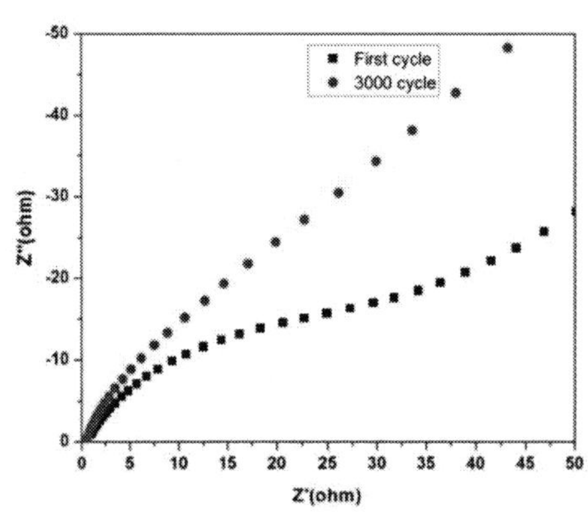

Fig. 5 Electrochemical impedance spectra of E-gCN electrode

Electrochemical Impedance spectroscopy (EIS) of the electrode was measured and the resulted Nyquist plot at the first and 3000 cycles is shown in Fig. 5. Charge transfer resistance (Rct) of the electrode was calculated from equivalent circuit model. The Rct values at the first and 3000 cycles were 20 Ω and 5 Ω respectively. The lower charge transfer resistance at the 3000 cycle reveals continuous charge discharge cycle could lead to the further activation of the electrode. The lone pair of electrons offers additional charges which improve the supercapacitive performance as well as the conductivity of the material.

4. Conclusions

In this work, cost-effective polycondensation and exfoliation was adopted to synthesize E-gCN material and its supercapacitive behavior was analyzed. XRD pattern confirms the formation of tri-s-triazine units. FTIR result indicates the presence of CN heterocycle. SEM result shows nanoflakes Electrochemical measurements result reveals excellent supercapacitive behavior and cyclic stability.. The E-gCN delivers 170 F g^{-1} and 96.2% capacity retention at 3000 cycles. The flake-like morphology increases the surface area and create more active site in the surface which improves the charge storage capacity.

Acknowledgment

Author thanks, the research funding from the Science and Engineering Research Board (SERB), Govt. of India for the TARE – SERB Project (TAR/2019/000125).

Declaration of Interest

None.

References

1. J. Wang, S. Wang, A critical review on graphitic carbon nitride (g-C3N4)-based materials: Preparation, modification and environmental application, Coord. Chem. Rev. 453 (2022) 214338.

2. T. Meenakshi, D. Pritam, Recent progress in research on multifunctional graphitic carbon nitride: An emerging wonder material beyond catalyst, Carbon. 192 (2022) 308-331

3. M. Ismael, A review on graphitic carbon nitride (g-C3N4) based nanocomposites: Synthesis, categories, and their application in photocatalysis, J. Alloys Compd. 846 (2020) 156446.

4. D. Adekoya, S. Qian, X. Gu, W. Wen, D. Li, J. Ma, S. Zhang, DFT-Guided Design and Fabrication of Carbon-Nitride-Based Materials for Energy Storage Devices: A Review, Nano-Micro Lett. 13 (2020).

5. M. Ghaemmaghami, R. Mohammadi, Carbon nitride as a new way to facilitate the next generation of carbon-based supercapacitors, Sustain. Energy Fuels. 3 (2019) 2176–2204.

6. V. Ragupathi, P. Panigrahi, N. Ganapathi Subramaniam, Bandgap engineering in graphitic carbon nitride: Effect of precursors, Optik (Stuttg). 202 (2020) 163601.

7. H. Katsumata, F. Higashi, Y Kobayashi, I. Tateishi, M. Furukawa, S. Kaneco, Dual-defect-modified graphitic carbon nitride with boosted photocatalytic activity under visible light, Sci. Rep. 9 (2019) 14873

8. R. Gonçalves, T.M. Lima, M.W. Paixão, E.C. Pereira, Pristine carbon nitride as active material for high-performance metal-free supercapacitors: simple, easy and cheap, RSC Adv. 8 (2018) 35327–35336.

IOP Conf. Series: Materials Science and Engineering 1263 (2022) 012023 doi:10.1088/1757-899X/1263/1/012023

Study of the capacitance and conductance (C - V – F & G – V – F) of the Thin Film based Cu/p-SnSe Schottky Barrier Junction

Hirenkumar Shantilal Jagani[1*], Abhishek B. Patel[2**], C. U. Vyas[2], Mayuri Navapariya[1], Karan Bhoraniya[1] and V. M. Pathak[1]

[1] Department of Physics, Sardar Patel University, Vallabh Vidyanagar, Gujarat, 388120 India.
[2] Department of Physics, A. N. Patel Post Graduate Institute of Science and Research, Anand, 388001, India.

* Corresponding authors: hirenjagani308@gmail.com

** Corresponding authors: abhip785@gmail.com

Abstract. SnSe, the well-known transition metal chalcogenide family member is perceived to be preferable for its tremendous device applications. Here, the authors have tried to fabricate a p-SnSe/Cu Schottky junction diode. The Capacitance(C)–Voltage (V) & Conductance(C)–Voltage(V) characteristics with different frequency(f) of the fabricated diode were studied at the applied bias voltage -1 to 1 V in f range from the 0.1 MHz to 1 MHz at room temperature. Effect of applied Frequencies on various parameter: Series Resistance (R_s), Insulator layer capacitance (C_{ox}), and Interface States density (N_{ss}) were evaluated by means of maximum capacitance (C_m) along with maximum conductance (G_m) in the region were strong gathering region. From the results confirm negative resistance at low frequencies due to negative reactance, but at high frequencies resistance becomes positive, which depicts novel capacitive properties which can be applicable for novel applications of SnSe-based diode.

Keywords. SnSe, *Negative conductance, thin films, Schottky diode, series resistance.*

1. Introduction:

Widely, the metal-semiconductor (M-S) structures play a vital role in constructing many advantageous devices in present era of technological field. Schottky diode device fabrication has optimistic future electronics. Moreover, transistors, FETs, MISFET, MESFET can also have variable applications due to the special kind of junction normally known as Schottky. Diodes based on such junctional interface with comparably short barrier height are preferred for device applications create suitability of operated under the condition of cryogenic temperatures and other like IR-detectors or sensors, radars systems, switching circuits etc.[1] Such diodes can emerge out as relatively fast charge reveled as quick-electrical responses.

IOP Conf. Series: Materials Science and Engineering 1263 (2022) 012023 doi:10.1088/1757-899X/1263/1/012023

However, inhomogeneity of the junction interface, defects, grain boundaries, porosity, etc. will also be present in the thin film and restrict the functional parameters of diodes. Additionally, recent research has observed negative capacitance behavior in the diodes. By studying the [2] literature, it is observed that the all devices have different physical mechanism for negative capacitance behavior such as injection of minority carriers, instrumental errors, parasitic inductance, pure distribution of electrostatic charge, hopping to localized interface states etc., but meticulous physical mechanisms for negative capacitance behavior has not been clearly identified yet.[3] Recently, Transition metal chalcogenides (TMC) based Schottky diode study[4] is the interest of research. So, in the present study, we have discussed the C-V & (G/ω)-V relative response in-terms of graphs of fabricated of *p*-SnSe (thin film)/Cu (thin film) diode at a different f.

2. *Experimental Detail:*

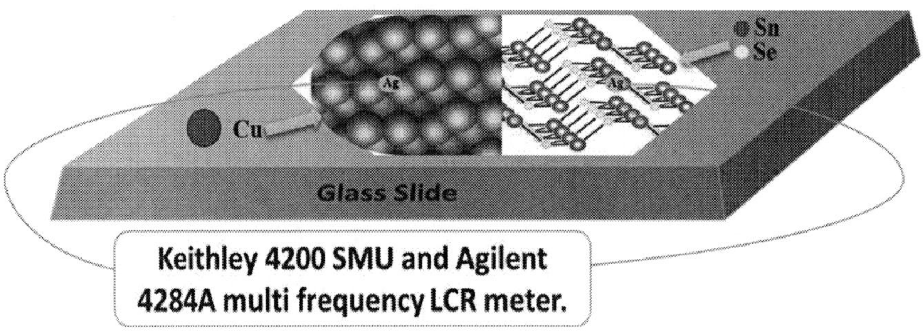

Figure 1. The Schematic diagram of the atomic arrangement and experimental setup of the manufactured diode

Fig.1 describes the schematic structure of the fabricated diode. Firstly, the SnSe compound was grown using the direct vapour transport technique. Further, the grown compound was collected from the furnace and fine powder of the compound was made using mortar-pestle. This fine powder was then characterized by SEM, XRD, TEM, etc. sophisticated instruments to study the chemical confirmation and structural properties. After characterizing, the powder was used to grow the thin film on the glass substrate using a Physical vapour deposition unit (Hind HighVacuum). Some part of the SnSe thin film having a thickness of ~5kÅ was covered by a mica sheet after growth to develop the junction and to fabricate the Cu/p-SnSe Schottky device. A copper (Cu) thin film was deposited on top of the tin-selenide (SnSe) thin film having a thickness of ~5kÅ. Contacts were taken on the surfaces of the thin films using conducting silver paste (Ag), as shown in fig.1. Article including the Cu/p-SnSe characterization and device applications have been published by the authors.[5] C-V & G-V characteristics of the fabricated diode were analyzed using Keithley 4200 SMU and Agilent 4284A LCR meter setup at room temperature. C-V & G/*w*-V characteristics of the fabricated diode were observed within the range of 0.1 MHz to 1 MHz frequency by the experimental setup revealed in fig.1.

3. Results and discussions:

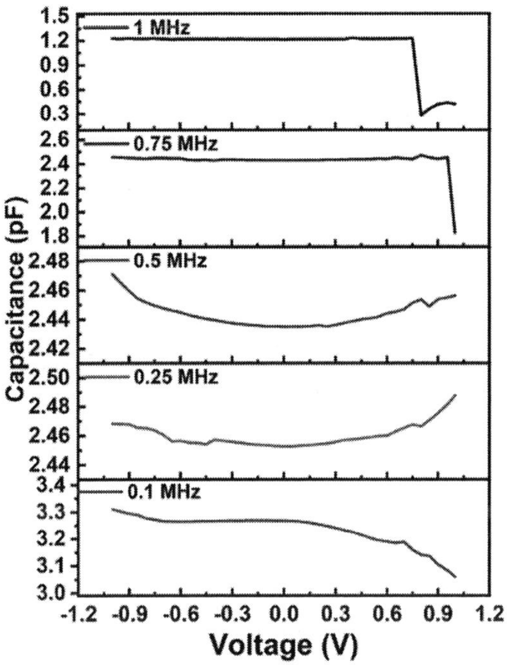

Figure.2. C-V characteristics of thin-films based Schottky diode by Cu/p-SnSe.

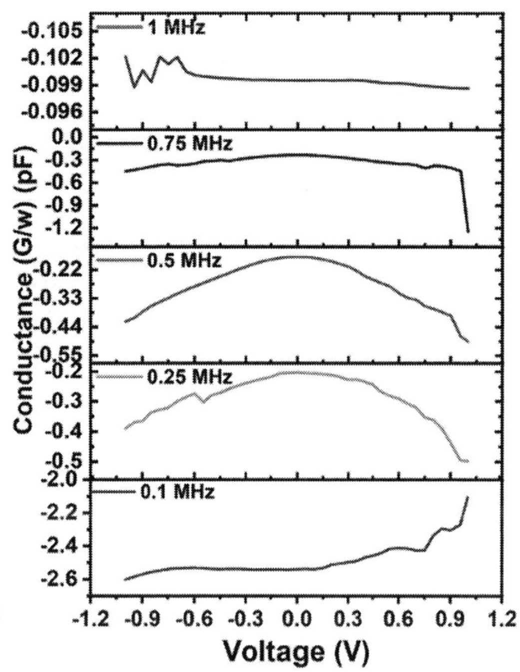

Figure.3. G/w-V characteristics of thin-films based Schottky diode by Cu/p-SnSe.

C-V and G/*w*-V characteristics of Cu/*p*-SnSe M-S thin film Schottky junction diode fabricated on the glass surface was carried-out in the mentioned range of f with help of SMU Keithely 4200 at ambient condition of Laboratory and plotted in figure 2 and 3 respectively. Some parameters can be evaluated from the plots (Figures 2 and 3) and equations given below.

$$\mathbf{Y_M = \frac{1}{Z_M} = G_m + j\omega C_m} \quad \textbf{(1)}$$

where, G_m, C_m, and ω are the highest measured value of conductance at the accumulation region, the maximum capacitance at the accumulation region, and the angular frequency of the diode respectively. The value of the R_S works as real part in admittance can be obtained from equation 1, rewrite as under:

$$R_S = \frac{G_m}{{G_m}^2 + \omega {C_m}^2} \quad (2)$$

The G_m and C_m can be used to evaluate the capacitance of the non-conducting layer noted as C_{ox} by following equation:

$$C_{OX} = C_m[1 - \left(\frac{G_m}{\omega C_m}\right)^2] \quad (3)$$

The one of the prime parameters of the Schottky diode is density distribution with variation in applied frequency at the interface state (N_{SS}) can be obtained by:

$$N_{SS} = \frac{2}{qA} \frac{\frac{G_m}{\omega}}{\{\left[\left(\frac{G_m}{\omega}\right) C_{ox}\right]^2 + \left[1 - \frac{C_m}{C_{ox}}\right]^2\}} \quad (4)$$

Where R_S is the series resistance, C_{ox} is the insulator layer capacitance, A is the area of the diode, q is the electron charge and N_{SS} is the density of the interface state.[6] The evaluated parameters are tabulated in table 1.

Table.1. Comparative study of the C Vs V and G/*w* Vs V graphs along with f.

Present work						References		
						[7]	[8]	[3]
Freq. Hz (MHz)	**0.1**	**0.25**	**0.5**	**0.75**	**1**	**1**	**1**	**1**
C_m (pF)	3.32	2.49	2.47	2.46	1.22	~50	-5	-10nF
G_m/w (pF)	-2.29	-0.20	-0.18	-0.23	-0.10	~50 µF	-0.1	1 nF
R_s (MΩ)	-1.40	-0.32	-0.29	-0.37	-0.67	0.02	-	1
C_{ox} (pF)	1.74	2.47	2.46	2.44	1.21	-	-	-
N_{ss} (eV^{-1} cm^{-2}) ($x10^{23}$)	2.71	48.00	52.50	40.60	22.80	2.00	-	2×10^{12}

The capacitance decreases with increasing the frequency as shown in figure 3. This can be considered as proof of the existence of interface state density. Such behavior of C indicates, rise in the polarization density creates observed fall in the capacitance, as a results large number of carriers were developed inside the structure. Ideally, specifically at high frequencies, both graphs for C–V as well as G/w–V of fabricated device normally shows not dependency over frequency as presented in Figures 2 and 3.

Here, from figure.2. We observed the capacitance exhibits increasing behavior in accordance to gradual decrement of reverse biased voltage a t frequency value 1 MHz, reveled variation in the width of the depletion layer for the applied biasing voltage. Both C verses V and G/ω were exhibits decreasing nature ascending value of frequency but at lower value of frequency, the variation in interface states in accordance with the a. c. signal, which yields as increasing in the value of capacitance as well as conductance due to the dependency over frequency. For f > 1MHz in such case device exhibits not dependency of the interface states with the a. c. signal, reducing the contribution of interface states to the total capacitance. Studied range of frequency represents an inhomogeneous layer formed at the semiconductor over Metal interface. From the figure. 2 & 3 behavior of resistance and conductance obtained value of capacitance with positive sine.
From table 1, the decay measured N_{SS} describes the large accountable change observed in the interfacial state density with the rising value of frequency. At 0.5 MHz value for frequency density of states shows measure decrement as compare to 1 MHz, exhibits the frequency modulation with the charge carrier conductions mechanism of device current. Observed carrier recombination is emerge out due to relative changes between both. Nss and frequency. In addition, density distribution formed at the interfacial site have its own importance in the field of solid-state devices as direct or indirect involvement in measured parameter like Rs of junction admittance, capacitance, conductance in Schottky junction Cu/*p*-SnSe. Cox indicates abnormal behavior evince at the high operating frequency. Negative Rs and Gm occurs due to negative reactance. Negative resistance or conductance has applications as high order active filters. Highest measured capacitance indicates the goodness of the junction between the Copper and SnSe thin-film interface.[9] Table 1 shows the comparison of parameters with reported articles.

4. Conclusions:

C-V & G/w/V characteristics of the p-SnSe (thin film)/Cu (thin film) Schottky junction diode were analyzed in the frequency ranging from the 0.1 MHz to 1 MHz. Capacitance behaves ideally with a change in frequency. Negative conductance and resistance were generated due to negative reactance and applicable as high order active filters. At high frequencies, the interface state density creates dominance of carrier recombination and rise the series-resistance

(Rs) and admittance of the under studied diode. Finally, negative conductance of presented Device emerging out as most vital feature for its utilization for the applications.

Acknowledgement:

Corresponding author expresses gratitude to the Gujarat government for giving financial support through the SHODH project.

References:

[1] Jagani H S, Patel A, Gohil J and Pathak V M 2022 Self-powered anisotropic photo-responsive properties of tin mono-selenide (SnSe) photodetector *Opt Mater (Amst)* **132** 112756

[2] Horide T, Nakamura K, Hirayama Y, Morishita K, Ishimaru M and Matsumoto K 2021 Thermoelectric Property of n-Type Bismuth-Doped SnSe Film: Influence of Characteristic Film Defect *ACS Applied Energy Materials* **4** 9563–71

[3] Bilkan Ç, Gümüş A and Altindal Ş 2015 The source of negative capacitance and anomalous peak in the forward bias capacitance-voltage in Cr/p-si Schottky barrier diodes (SBDs) *Materials Science in Semiconductor Processing* **39** 484–91

[4] Patel H, Patel K, Patel A, Jagani H, Patel K D, Solanki G K and Pathak V M 2021 Temperature-Dependent I–V Characteristics of In/p-SnSe Schottky Diode *Journal of Electronic Materials*

[5] Jagani H S, Gupta S U, Bhoraniya K, Navapariya M, Pathak V M, Solanki G K and Patel H 2022 Photosensitive Schottky Barrier Diode Based on Cu/p-SnSe Thin Film Fabricated by Thermal Evaporation *Materials Advances*

[6] Shiwakoti N, Bobby A, Asokan K and Antony B 2016 Temperature dependent dielectric studies of Ni/n-GaP Schottky diodes by capacitance and conductance measurements *Materials Science in Semiconductor Processing* **42** 378–82

[7] Padma R and Reddy V R 2014 Electrical properties of Ir/n-InGaN/Ti/Al schottky barrier diode in a wide temperature range *Advanced Materials Letters* **5** 31–8

[8] Kim H 2016 Capacitance-voltage (C-V) characteristics of Cu/n-type InP schottky diodes *Transactions on Electrical and Electronic Materials* **17** 293–6

[9] Patel A, Pathak V M, Solanki G K, Patel K D and Pataniya P 2020 The influence of antimony doping on I–V, C–V-f and (G/w)-V-f characteristics of indium/ SbXW1-XSe2 (X=0, 0.1, 0.5) alloy Schottky diodes *Superlattices and Microstructures* **137**

IOP Conf. Series: Materials Science and Engineering 1263 (2022) 012024 doi:10.1088/1757-899X/1263/1/012024

Doped poly 3-methylthiophene device exhibits negative-differential resistance

Shobith M Shanbogh[1*], P Anjaneyulu[1*]

[1]*REVA University, Bengaluru, India, pincode:560064*

*Corresponding author. E-mail: shobishanbogh@gmail.com, anjaniisc@gmail.com

Abstract Poly 3-methylthiophene (P3MT) polymer is electrochemically deposited on stainless steel substrate and a sandwich device structure (SS/P3MT/Ag) is realized by placing a top metal contact to fabricate a two-terminal device. The polymer is first doped with PF_6^- & ClO_4^- dopants and then de-doped for 30 seconds. The current-voltage (I-V) measurement is carried out on a de-doped P3MT device to probe the charge-transport and negative-differential resistance (NDR). In the present experiment, NDR and Charge transport mechanism varies with the dopant. The magnitude of NDR, i.e., peak-valley current (PVCR) depends on the voltage swept and dopants. We propose the reason for anomaly NDR is dopant-induced trap-states.

1. Introduction

When the voltage is swept with the increase in steps, current decreases, and is referred to as NDR. NDR was first discovered by Esaki in a germanium device[1], and NDR has applications in the oscillator, logic gates, and memory device (binary 0 and 1)[2-4]. NDR is reported in many devices like inorganic, organic, biomolecule, composite, polymer, hybrid, heterostructure, etc[5-13], but polymer devices have the advantage over other conventional devices like ease of synthesis, flexibility, cost-effectiveness, and more. tuning and controlling NDR is quite a challenge and P3MT is one of the promising candidates among many devices in the same. P3MT doped with PF_6^- & ClO_4^- are electrochemically synthesized in a two-electrode customized cell by passing constant current and later de-doped. De-doping is a process where we reverse the polarity of the electrode and supply current for the removal of dopants at the surface. Ag is used as top contact to complete the device geometry SS/P3MT/Ag. This de-doped P3MT device show NDR, and is tunable and controllable by various external parameters like work function of the electrode, dopants and doping concentration, applied voltage, and sweep direction [14,15]. In this study, current-voltage measurement is carried out for the P3MT device de-doped for 30 seconds to probe the NDR and charge transport mechanism in the device.

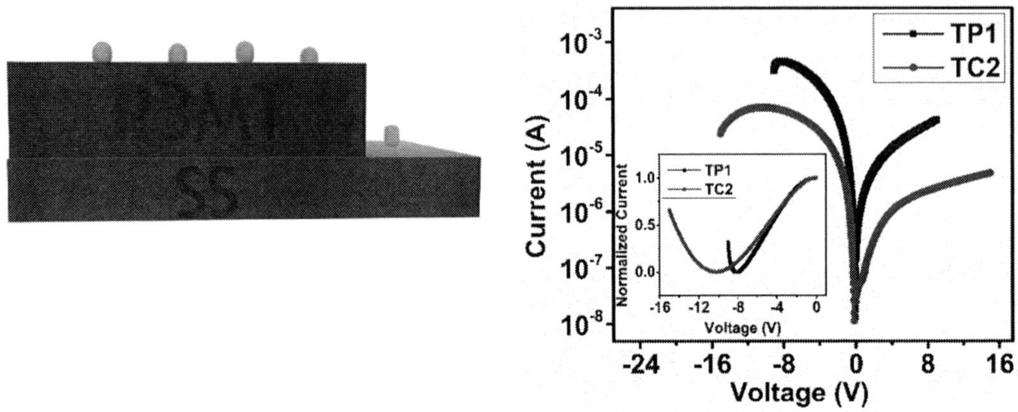

Figure 1. (a & b) (a) Shows the schematic diagram of two terminal device, stainless steel (SS) bottom electrode, P3MT as the active layer, and Silver (Ag) as the top contact. (b) I-V graph of P3MT doped with TP1 and TP2 respectively.

Dopant	**PVCR In negative bias**	**Current ratio (I_n/I_p)**	**voltage**	**Charge transport model**
PF_6^-	1.487	10.18	9 V	T-SCLC
ClO_4^-	2.78	15.08	15 V	T-SCLC

I_n-current in negative bias, I_p-current in positive bias

Table 1 shows comparative studies of PVCR, current ratio, and conduction mechanism.

2. Experimental section

P3MT thin film is deposited on SS substrate using the electrochemical method. 60 millimolar concentration of 3-methylthiophene monomer with each dopant PF_6^- & ClO_4^- are dissolved in an organic solvent i.e., propylene carbonate, and the solution is used as an electrolyte for thin film deposition. Bottom electrode SS is cleaned using Acetone, and isopropyl alcohol thoroughly and dried, Cleaned SS substrates are dipped into the electrolyte solution and 2.5 mA/cm^2 current is passed for 3 minutes for film deposition. We use two electrode systems and SS is chosen to be the electrode on either side. De-doping is the process to increase the resistance in P3MT film, we change the polarity of the electrode and supply 0.8 mA/cm^2 for 30 seconds for the same. Semi-dry silver paste is used as top contact to complete the device geometry. SS/P3MT/Ag device geometry is further used to probe the electrical property.

3. Result and discussion

Figure 1. (a) shows the schematic of SS/P3MT/Ag device geometry and I-V for TP1 (P3MT doped with PF_6^-) and TC2 (P3MT doped with ClO_4^-) by connecting the anode of the source meter to top contact (Ag) throughout the measurement. Figure 1. (b) is an I-V study for TP1, and TC2 devices, and the inset is a normalized I-V in the negative bias region (NDR region). TP1 is swept from -9 V to 9 V, similarly, TC2 is swept from -15 to 15 V and both the devices show NDR in the negative bias region. TP1 device gets shorted if the voltage is enhanced greater than 9 V. TP1 is relatively conductive than the TC2 device, the maximum current ratio I_n/I_p for TP1 and TC2 is 10.18 and 15.08 respectively. The magnitude of NDR is measured in peak to valley current ratio (PVCR) and it is observed that TC2 shows relatively larger NDR with PVCR of 2.78 and PVCR of TP1 is 1.48. The peak voltage of TP1 and TC2 devices are -8.13 and -10.18 V respectively. From the results, it is evident that NDR peak voltage can be tuned by varying the dopant, and applied bias.

Figure 2 (a & b) I-V fitting is done to acquire knowledge of the conduction mechanism in the device. Figure 2 (a) double logarithmic of (I-V) is plotted for device TP1 in the negative bias region (0 to -9 V) and it shows trap-assisted space charge limited current (T-SCLC) from 0 to -0.4 V and is confirmed by observing the slope value of ~ 2.44. With the further rise in voltage from -0.4 to -2.5 V slope is 2.08, i.e. the mechanism is shifted to space charge limited current (SCLC). For the bias of -2.5 to -5.7 V, the slope is found to be 1.69 and this infers that there is a transition from SCLC to Ohmic conduction, with further increase in the applied bias slope is negative and this attributes to negative differential resistance (NDR). When device TP1 is swept in the positive voltage (0 to 9 V), log (I) vs log (V) is plotted for the same and it is shown in the inset of Figure 2 (a). The slope is varying from 1.5 to 0.9 hence showing Ohmic behavior. I-V fitting of device TC2 in negative bias (0 to -15 V) revealed that there is a transition from trap assisted space charge limited current (T-SCLC) to Ohmic when the voltage is increased from 0.18 V to 7.44 V with further increase in the bias, the device shows NDR. Similarly, from the inset of Figure 2 (b) when the device is swept in the positive bias region (0 to 15 V), it is fitted with $lnI \propto \sqrt{v}$ and is inferred as Schottky emission at lower applied bias $\sim \leq 1$ V. When the device is swept from 1 to 15 V there is a transition from I α V^2 to V α I and attributes to Ohmic conduction at higher applied bias. From I-V fitting and previous reports, it is evident that the conduction mechanism involved in doped P3MT devices is by trapping and de-trapping of charge carriers across the polymer/electrode interface and bulk. NDR in PF_6^- doped P3MT is previously studied by varying carrier density, and work function of the electrode, and observed that NDR in polymer devices is due to the trapping and de-trapping of charge carriers[14,15]. The process of de-doping enhances the NDR in P3MT, is due to long-lived traps present in the device, and is an inherent property of the de-doped P3MT device. NDR can be tuned by carrier density and electrode work function and is well known in P3MT devices, but in this study, we explored the tuning of NDR, operation voltage, and PVCR by using different dopants and happens to show a slight difference in the conduction mechanism.

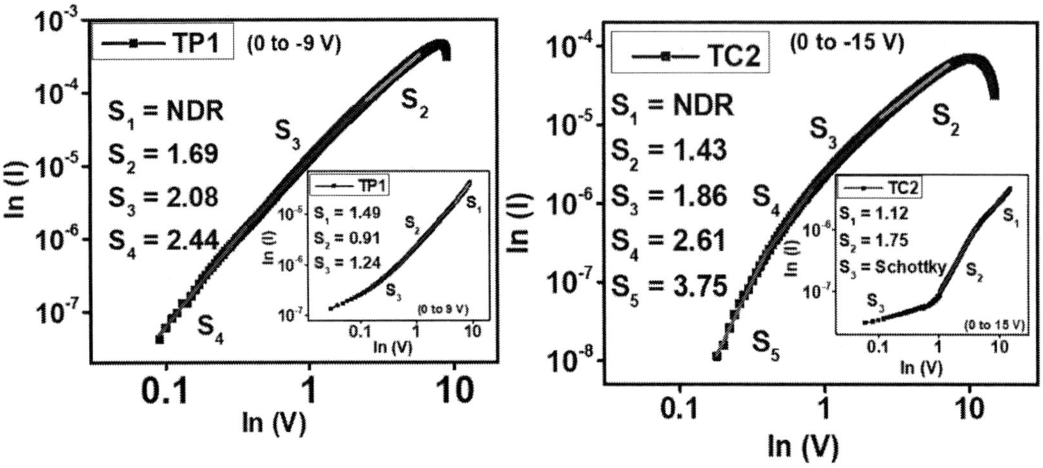

Figure 2 (a & b) (a) Shows charge transport in TP1 device in negative bias and the inset shows the mechanism in positive bias. (b) Shows charge transport in TC2 device in negative bias and the inset shows the mechanism in positive bias.

4. Conclusion

Device TP1 is relatively conductive when compared to TC2 hence the operation voltage of TP1 cannot be increased beyond 9 Volts, TC2 can be swept to 15 Volts. The peak voltage and PVCR of the NDR are greater for device TC2 than TP1. NDR can be tuned by varying the applied bias and dopant and its concentration. Conduction mechanism results revealed that there is a possibility of trap formation in the device which may be responsible for the NDR mechanism in these two devices.

Author information

Corresponding Author

*Shobith M Shanbogh

Department of Physics, School of Applied Sciences, REVA University, Bengaluru-560064, India.

Email: shobishanbogh@gmail.com

Mob no: 7090929942

ORCID: https://orcid.org/0000-0001-6833-6545

*Dr. Anjaneyulu Ponnam

Department of Physics, School of Applied Sciences, REVA University, Bengaluru-560064, India

Email: anjaniisc@gmail.com;

Mob no: 9989036960

ORCID: https://orcid.org/0000-0002-1777-8017

Acknowledgment
The authors acknowledge the support from REVA University for the facilities provided to carry out the research.

Reference

[1] Esaki L 1958 New phenomenon in narrow germanium p-n junctions *Phys. Rev.* **109** 603–4

[2] Oberoi D, Dagar P, Shankar U, Vyas G, Kumar A, Sahu S and Bandyopadhyay A 2018 Design, synthesis, and characterization of an Fe(ii)-polymer of a redox non-innocent, heteroatomic, polydentate Schiff's base ligand: negative differential resistance and memory behaviour *New J. Chem.* **42** 19090–100

[3] Gan K J, Huang C H, Yeh W K, Guo C Y and Lu J J 2018 Design of multi-threshold threshold gate using MOS-NDR circuits suitable for CMOS process *Analog Integr. Circuits Signal Process.* **96** 409–16

[4] Ferreira G C A, Napporn T W, Kokoh K B and Varela H 2017 Complex Oscillatory Kinetics in the Electro-Oxidation of Glucose on Gold *J. Electrochem. Soc.* **164** H603–7

[5] Zheng J, Zhang J, Wang Z, Zhong L, Sun Y, Liang Z, Li Y, Jiang L, Chen X and Chi L 2018 Programmable Negative Differential Resistance Effects Based on Self-Assembled Au@PPy Core–Shell Nanoparticle Arrays *Adv. Mater.* **30** 1–8

[6] Zheng J, Zhang J, Wang Z, Zhong L, Sun Y, Liang Z, Li Y, Jiang L, Chen X and Chi L 2018 Programmable Negative Differential Resistance Effects Based on Self-Assembled Au@PPy Core–Shell Nanoparticle Arrays *Adv. Mater.* **30** 1–8

[7] Hu X, Wang W, Sun B, Wang Y, Li J and Zhou G 2021 Refining the Negative Differential Resistance Effect in a TiOx-Based Memristor *J. Phys. Chem. Lett.* **12** 5377–83

[8] Nenna G, Masala S, Bizzarro V, Re M, Pesce E, Minarini C and Di Luccio T 2012 Particle size dependence of resonant-tunneling effect induced by CdS nanoparticles in a poly(N-vinylcarbazole) polymer matrix *J. Appl. Phys.* **112** 044508

[9] Guisinger N P, Greene M E, Basu R, Baluch A S and Hersam M C 2004 Room Temperature Negative Differential Resistance through Individual Organic Molecules on Silicon Surfaces *Nano Lett.* **4** 55–9

[10] Mandal D, Routh P and Nandi A K 2018 A New Facile Synthesis of Tungsten Oxide from Tungsten Disulfide: Structure Dependent Supercapacitor and Negative Differential Resistance Properties *Small* **14** 1–13

[11] Zhou G, Duan S, Li P, Sun B, Wu B, Yao Y, Yang X, Han J, Wu J, Wang G, Liao L, Lin C, Hu W, Xu C, Liu D, Chen T, Chen L, Zhou A and Song Q 2018 Coexistence of Negative Differential Resistance and Resistive Switching Memory at Room Temperature in TiOx Modulated by Moisture *Adv. Electron. Mater.* **4** 1–12

[12] Zeng C, Wang H, Wang B, Yang J and Hou J G 2000 Negative differential-resistance device involving two C60 molecules *Appl. Phys. Lett.* **77** 3595–7

[13] Dong X F, Zhao Y, Zheng T T, Li X, Wang C W, Li W M, Shao Y and Li Y 2021 Coexistence of Bipolar Resistive Switching and the Negative Differential Resistance Effect from a Kesterite Memristor *J. Phys. Chem. C* **125** 923–30

[14] Anjaneyulu P, Varade V, Sangeeth C S S and Menon R 2020 Anomalous current-voltage and impedance behaviour in doped Poly 3-methylthiophene devices *J. Phys. D. Appl. Phys.* **53** 295301

[15] Anjaneyulu P, Suchand Sangeeth C S and Menon R 2010 Negative differential resistance in doped poly(3-methylthiophene) devices *J. Phys. D. Appl. Phys.* **43** 425103

Experimental and First-Principles Thermoelectric studies of Bulk ZnO

Hashir P[1], P.P Pradyumnan[1], Aadil Fayaz Wani[2], Kulwinder Kaur[2]

[1] Department of Physics, University of Calicut, Calicut, 673635, India
[2] Department of Applied Sciences, Punjab Engineering College, Chandigarh, 160012, India

hashirp.916@gmail.com

Abstract. The Thermoelectric perspective to produce electricity from waste heat has obtained great attention over the last few years. However, the fulfillment of energy requirement of the contemporary world by the thermoelectric method can be achieved by developing good thermoelectric materials of high conversion efficiency. Density functional theory (DFT) is widely used simulation technique in the materials science field for computing electronic properties of the materials. In our DFT calculation Quantum Espresso (QE) package were used to investigate the electronic band structure as well as electronic density of states of bulk ZnO sample. To express core electrons, projector-augmented wave (PAW) pseudopotentials were chosen and to optimize band structure LDA+U method of DFT approximation was opted. Our DFT calculations give direct band gap 3.2004 eV and the experimental value is 3.24 eV. Our works are found to be good acceptance with previously reported values and the DFT study via QE and BoltzTraP codes are suitable for predicting the thermoelectric properties of semiconductor materials.

1. Introduction

Thermoelectricity have fascinated a great amount of interest due to its application in the field of scavenging industrial and automobile exhaust heat and significant in solar power production application [1,2]. The efficiency of all thermoelectric(TE) materials are optimized by a term called figure of merit $ZT= S^2\sigma T/(K_l+K_e)$, the terms are S- seebeck coefficient , σ- electrical conductivity, T- absolute temperature, k_e- electrical thermal conductivity and K_l- lattice thermal conductivity [3]. ZnO is one of the viable candidates for TE materials because of its great thermal and mechanical stability, oxidation resistance, affordability, and lack of toxicity. The n type semiconductor material ZnO has a large band gap of 3.3 eV [4].

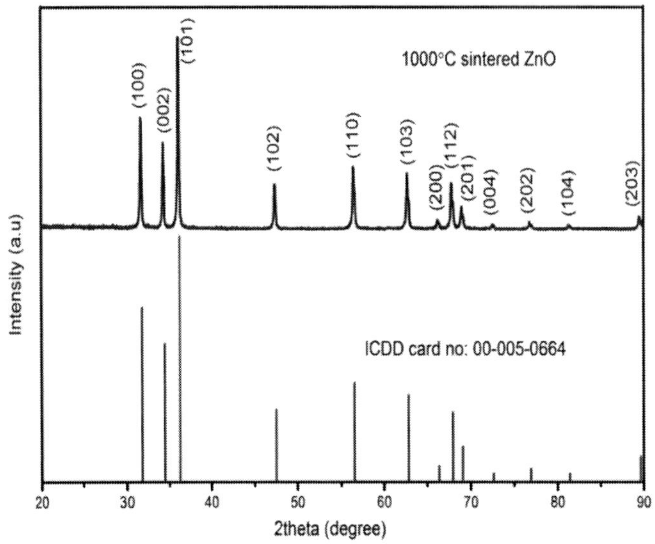

Figure 1. XRD pattern of synthesized ZnO powder.

In our study, we simultaneously used experimental and DFT approaches to examine the viability of n type bulk ZnO sample as a high temperature TE material. We utilize this combination to explore the band structure, optical and TE characteristics of the ZnO sample. In the first-principles study we used Hubbard correction to Local Density Approximation (LDA+U) for band structure calculation and TE calculations were performed based on Boltzmann transport equation with fixed value of relaxation time [5]. In order to get reliable TE DFT value, first we need good band structure which can be achieved by repeated band gap calculation using SCF iteration. Once the band structure is optimized go for the TE calculation using BoltzTraP software these are the steps to follow. Theoretical TE data were extracted based on chemical potential and the final data were compared with the experimental observations. All our TE results compared with previous reports.

2. Experimental method

2.1. Sample preparation

The pure ZnO samples were synthesized experimentally by solid state reaction route technique using commercial Zinc Oxide powder (Merck Emplura). For pelletizing ZnO, 5% PVA were added as binder, the mixture was pressed in to cylindrical pellet of 13 mm diameter and thickness 2.84 mm using hydrolytic pelletizer with a pressure 90 Kg/cm^2. The prepared pellets kept at 1000 ^{0}C for sintering with the aid of a high temperature programmable furnace for 4 hour at a rate of 5 ^{0}C/ min. The post sintered pellets and its powder were taken for the material characterization and TE analysis.

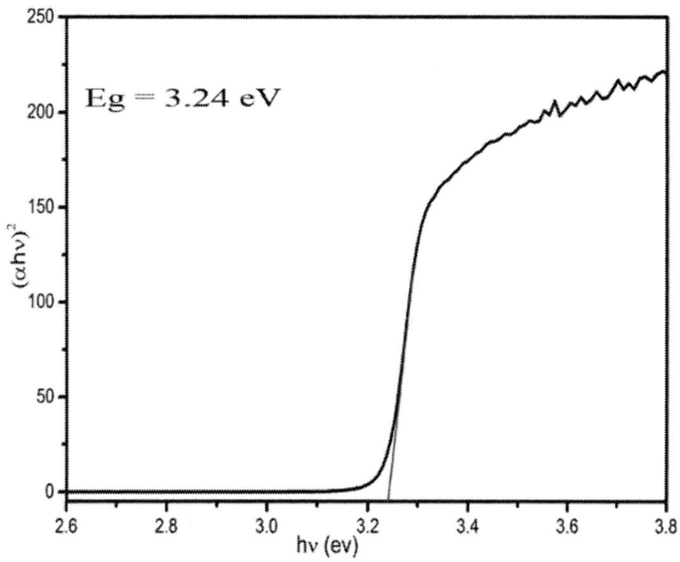

Figure 2. The optical band gap of synthesized ZnO powder.

2.2. Characterization

The structural characterization was carried out by the aid of Rigaku MiniFlex 600 having source radiation Cu Kα (λ=1.540 Å at 40 KV and 15 mA) and the rate of operating speed 10 ^{0}/min and 2Θ ranges from 10 ^{0} to 90 ^{0}. The TE studies were performed using ULVAC-ZEM3 TE measurement unit at Helium atmosphere and the temperature ranges from 300 K to 950 K [6]. The repeated TE measurement shows reproducible results for the same sample. The optical properties were analyzed by means of UV-Vis spectroscopy (JASCO V-550) in DRS mode.

3. Computational method

The overall DFT simulations were performed using open source Quantum Espresso package [7] and in order to tune DFT band gap value we used LDA+U approximation as exchange correlation functional [8]. For getting similar ZnO hexagonal wurtzite structure CIF file ID mp-2133 was taken from the materials project site [9]. The ZnO primitive cell contains two Zn and two O atoms, the Projector Augmented Wave (PAW) pseudo potential were used to represent core electrons [10,11]. The converged ground state energy gives optimized energy cutoff value for charge density that is fixed to 70 Ry similarly energy cutoff value for wave function is fixed to 560 Ry. In the similar way the converged energy value gives 4x4x4 brillouin zone k point grid.

All TE properties were calculated for a fixed value of relaxation time τ, computational measurements are carried out by using open source package BoltzTraP in connection with Quantum Espresso [12]. In order to get τ value of sample, experimental room temperature electron mobility value was taken from the literature [6]. In the present study, due to the computational complexity we took our research

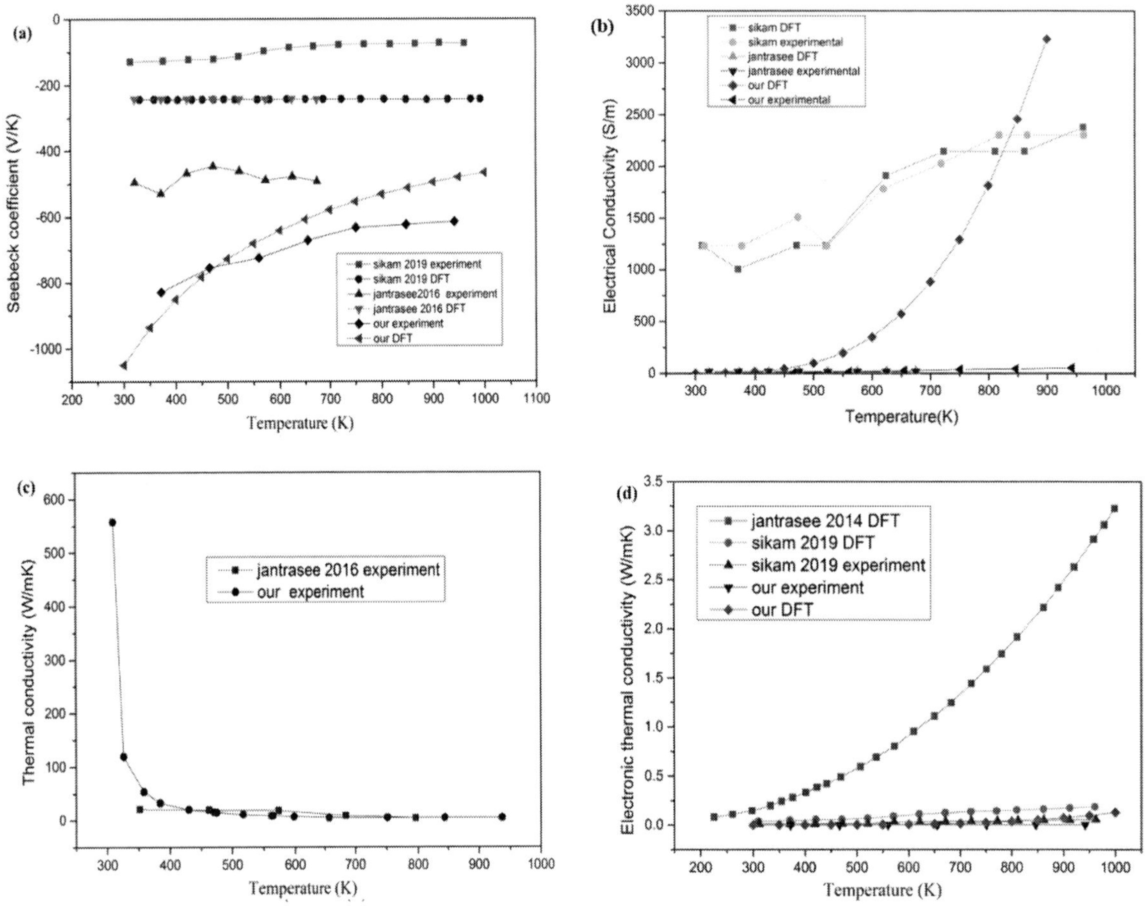

Figure 3. TE properties of ZnO : (a) Seebeck Coefficient, (b) Electrical conductivity, (c) Total thermal conductivity and (d) Electronic thermal conductivity.

group's experimental thermal conductivity ($K=K_l+K_e$) data for the calculation of figure of merit [13].

4. Results and discussion

X-ray diffraction analysis of the prepared ZnO sample exactly matches with ICDD card No- 000-005-0664 of ZnO phase without any impurity peaks shown in the figure 1. The peaks of the XRD pattern indicates the wurtzite hexagonal structure of P 63mc space group of ZnO and the calculated lattice constant values are obtained as a= 3.254 Å, b= 3.254 Å and c= 5.212 Å which are found to be good agreement with previous results [5,13,14].

The optical band gap value of ZnO samples were investigated using Tauc plot with photon energy (hυ) against Kubelka Munk function ($(\alpha h\upsilon)^2$), the terms indicates α- absorption coefficient, h- Planck's constant and υ- frequency of photon. By extrapolating the linear region of the plot gives large band gap value of 3.24 eV showed in the figure 2.

4.1. Thermoelectric properties

Using ULVAC ZEM-3 TE unit, the thermoelectric properties of ZnO sample, including Seebeck coefficient (S) and electrical conductivity (σ) were calculated. The temperature versus Seebeck coefficient studies of our work shows improved result compared with previous works were shown in the figure 3(a) [5,13,14]. Our experimental Seebeck coefficient studies are in good accordance with DFT studies. The n type semiconductor behaviour of the pure ZnO sample was guaranteed by the negative sign of the Seebeck coefficient. A comparative experimental and DFT study was performed between temperatures versus electrical conductivity shown in the figure 3(b) [5,13,14]. Even though Seebeck coefficient shows decreasing trend with temperature, the increasing trend of the electrical conductivity shows the semiconducting behavior and It results in an improvement of the power factor ($S^2\sigma$), which is seen in figure 4(a) [13,14].

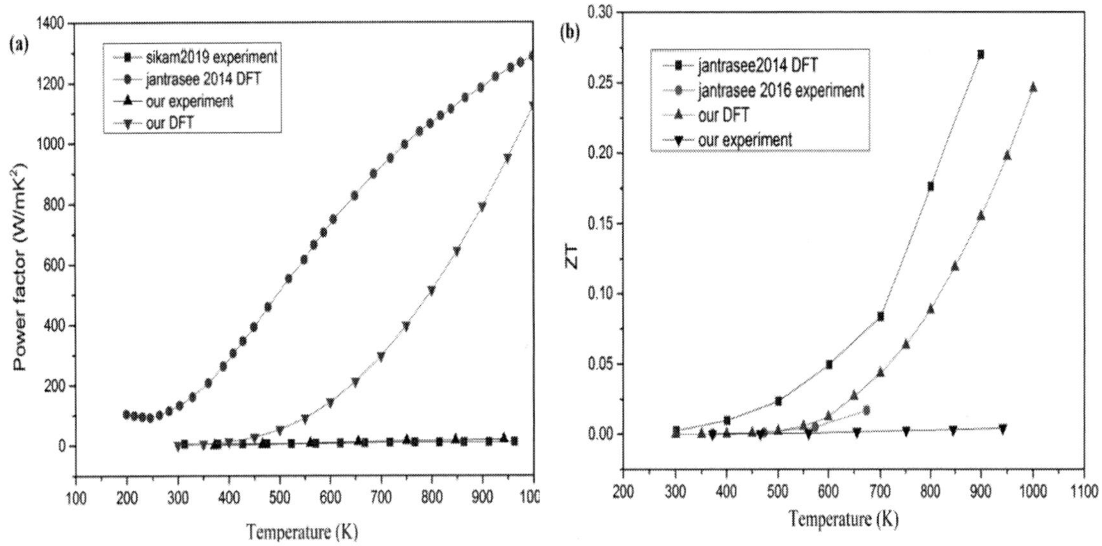

Figure 4. Thermoelectric properties of ZnO: (a) Power factor and (b) Figure of merit

The total thermal conductivity of the ZnO pellet was studied experimentally with temperature shows decreasing trend plotted in the figure 3(c). Due to the sample's lower electrical conductivity, the lattice thermal conductivity component dominates the electronic thermal conductivity term, which is verified by Wiedemann Franz law [15], $K_e = L\sigma T$, where L is the Lorentz factor and σ from the experimental results presented in figure 3(d). The lowest value of thermal conductivity at 942 K is 4.582 W/mK. Figure 4(b) illustrates the experimental ZT values increasing trend with temperature. The ZT is found to have a maximum value 0.0041 at 900 K. A comparable ZT value 0.0016 is obtained at 650 K and the same reported by Zi Hua Wu et.al at 680 K [16].

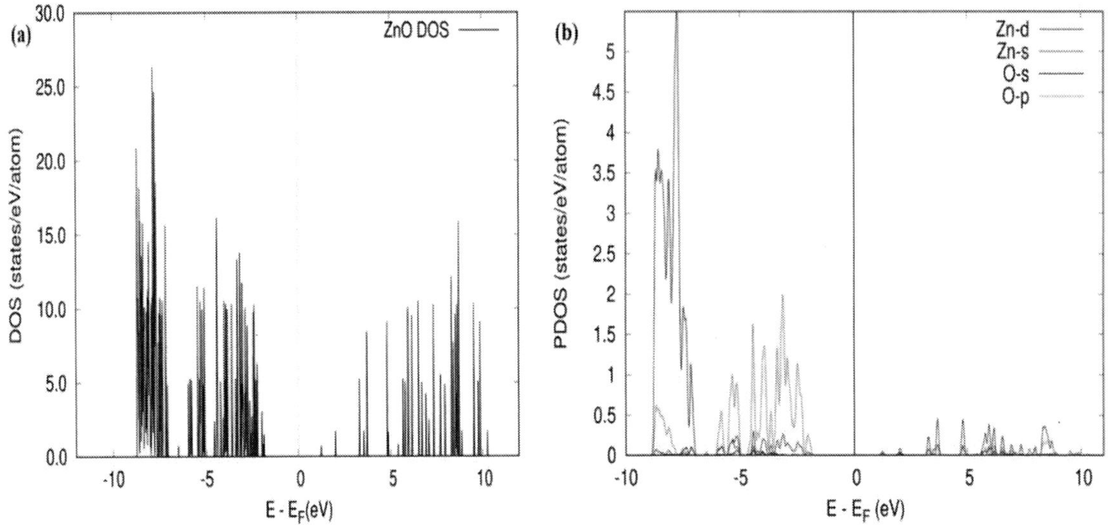

Figure 5. DFT study of ZnO (a) Density of states and (b) Projected density of states.

4.2. Calculation

The optimized hexagonal wurtzite structure in the DFT calculation gives lattice constants a= 3.286 Å, b= 3.286 Å and c= 5.258 Å which show a strong correlation with the experimental results. In the absence of Hubbard correction to LDA gives band gap value 0.7 eV [17,18]. In our study we varied Hubbard correction term for Zn-3d state by choosing U from 7 eV to 11 eV and J = 1 eV, similarly for O-2p state U from 3 eV to 8 eV and J=1. The optimized value Zn 3d state U_{Zn} = 8 eV and for O-2p state U_O = 7 eV which yields a band gap of 3.2004 eV, which is in good agreement with the value of our optical band gap.

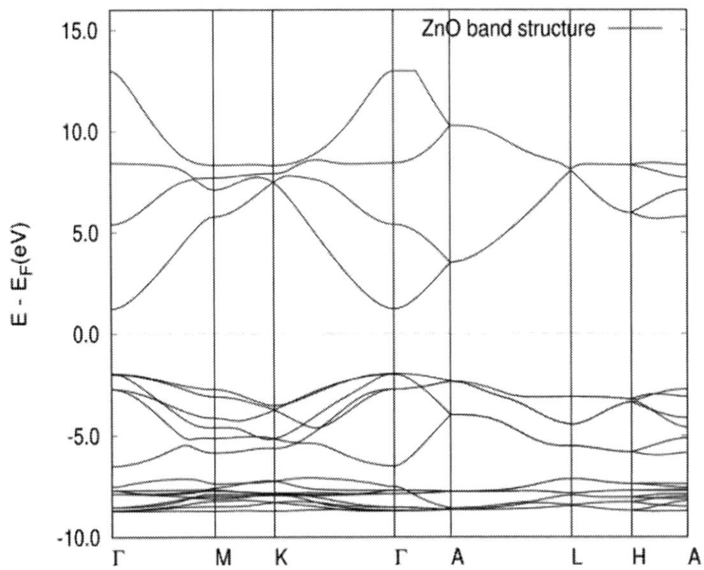

Figure 6. DFT band structure with E_g = 3.2004 eV

Figure 5(a) displays the density of states (DOS), and the Fermi level, which is located between CB and VB, indicates that the material is semiconducting. Understanding the role that each orbital contribution plays in the band structure, Figure 5(b) displays the projected density of states (PDOS). It is evident that the valance band can be separated into two regions, namely the lower valance band region (-10 to -6 eV) and the higher valance band region (-6 to -2 eV). The upper valance band was provided by O 2p states, and the bottom valance band was owned by Zn 3d states. In the conduction band, majority contribution take part by Zn 4s and a small contribution of O 2p states were also observed.

Our DFT Non-SCF calculations give direct band gap 3.2004 eV for the simulated ZnO structure and the shift in the Fermi level of the band structure shows n type semiconductor behaviour of the simulated structure shown in the figure 6. The Direct Band Gap is observed when the Conduction Band Minimum and Valance Band Maximum are at the Same K Point Γ [19]. A comparative lattice constants (a, c), band gap (E_g) results were shown in the Table1 including both experimental as well as DFT results. A comparative study of DFT methods also included in the Table1. We compared our experimental value to the BoltzTraP simulated Seebeck coefficient (S), electrical conductivity (σ) and electronic thermal conductivity (K_e) values and further checked with other previous works were shown in the figures 3(a), (b) & (d) [5, 13, 14]. We took TE data correspond to chemical potential $\mu = 0.55885$ Ry (7.6035 eV) and the constant relaxation time $\tau = 27.21 \times 10^{-15}$ s [6] but the actual values of relaxation time is temperature dependent [15, 20].

Table1. Comparison of experimental and calculated lattice constants a & c, band gap E_g of bulk ZnO with previous reports.

Parameters	Our work *Expt.*	*DFT*	Ref. 5 *Expt.*	*DFT*	Ref. 13 *Expt.*	*DFT*	Ref. 14 *Expt.*	*DFT*
a (Å)	3.254	3.286	3.249	3.250	------	3.258	------	6.508
c (Å)	5.212	5.258	5.212	5.212	------	5.214	------	10.472
E_g (eV)	3.240	3.200	3.150	1.750	------	1.700	3.180	1.800
DFT Method		*LDA+U (QE)*		*LDA+U (ABINIT)*		*LDA+U (ABINIT)*		*GGA+U (VASP)*

At higher temperature range phonon interaction and phonon transportation dominates, it is not considered in the DFT calculation. In addition with this in DFT studies we considered constant relaxation time and hence the variation observed between experimental and DFT electrical conductivity curve. Our comparative electronic thermal conductivity results are found to be good accordance with previous reports [13,14]. Due to the complexity for total thermal conductivity (K) by DFT calculation and also the BoltzTraP packages are not able to calculate K, hence we used our experimental K values for ZT calculation.

5. Conclusion

This study used experimental and first-principles methods to evaluate the structural, optical, and thermoelectric properties of bulk ZnO. The ZnO sample was created in the experimental section utilising a solid state reaction method. The hexagonal wurtzite structure of ZnO is confirmed by the XRD analysis, and there is no impurity phases found. LDA+U approximation is used for DFT study, through open source Quantum Espresso code, the Fermi level of calculated band structures and The n type character of ZnO is guaranteed by the Seebeck coefficient's negative value and the similar observation is found in DOS and PDOS calculation. The DFT TE studies of bulk ZnO were performed using BoltzTraP code, which is correlated with our experimental results. Our calculations are found to have good agreement with the outcomes from our experiments. The LDA+U method via Quantum Espresso and BoltzTraP codes are very suitable to predict the thermoelectric properties of the semiconductor materials.

Acknowledgements

The research facilities were provided by UGC-SAP and FIST2 (DST, Government of India) and DST SERB major research Project SB/EMEQ-002/2013 (Government of India), in the Department of Physics, University of Calicut, which the authors gratefully acknowledge. The authors thankful to Central sophisticated Instrumentation Facility (CSIF), University of Calicut, for providing high performance computational and characterization facilities.

References

[1] Bell, L.E. Cooling, heating, generating power, and recovering waste heat with thermoelectric systems. Science, 2008, 321: 1457-1461.
[2] Synder, G. J. & Toberer, E.S. Complex thermoelectric materials. Nat.Mater., 2008, 7: 105-114.
[3] Yang J, Xi L, Qiu W, et al. On the tuning of electrical and thermal transport in thermoelectrics: An integrated theory experiment perspective. npj Comput Mater., 2016, 2: 15015.
[4] Ohtaki M, Tsubota T, Eguchi K, et al. High-temperature thermoelectric properties of $(Zn_{1-x}Al_x)O$, 1996, 79(3): 1816.
[5] Jantrasee S, Moontragoon P, Pinitsoontorn S, Thermoelectric properties of Al-doped ZnO: experiment and simulation, J. Semicond., 2016, 37: 9.
[6] Anju Paulson, Muhammed Sabeer N.A, Pradyumnan P.P, A synergetic approach of band gap engineering and reduced lattice thermal conductivity for the enhanced thermoelectric property in Dy ion doped ZnO, J. Alloys Compd., 2019, 786 : 581-587.
[7] Giannozzi P, Baroni S, Bonini N, et al. QUANTUM ESPRESSO: a modular and open-source software project for quantum simulations of materials. J Phys Condens Matter., 2009, 21: 395502.
[8] Anupati Telugu Raghavender, Mudunuri Chaitanya Varma, Subimal Deb, et al., Tuning the band-gap of zinc oxide by first principles studies, AIP Conf Proc., 2017, 1832: 120012.
[9] Klinton Davis, Ryan Yarbrough, Michael Froeschle, et al., Band gap engineered zinc oxide nanostructures via a sol–gel synthesis of solvent driven shapecontrolled crystal growth, RSC Adv., 2019, 9: 14638.
[10] Anubhav Jain, Shyue Ping Ong, Geoffroy Hautier, et al., Commentary: The Materials Project: A materials genome approach to accelerating materials innovation, APL Mater., 2013, 1: 011002.
[11] Perdew JP, Burke K, Ernzerhof M. Generalized gradient approximation made simple.,Phys Rev Lett., 1996, 77: 3865-3868.
[12] Madsen GKH, Singh DJ., BoltzTraP. A code for calculating band-structure dependent quantities., Comput Phys Commun., 2006, 175: 67-71.
[13] Jantrasee S, Pinitsoontorn S, Moontragoon P., First-principles study of the electronic structure and thermoelectric properties of Al-doped ZnO, J Electron Mater, 2014, 43(6): 1689.
[14] Sikam P, Moontragoon P, Ikonic Z, et al., The study of structural, morphological and optical properties of (Al, Ga)-doped ZnO: DFT and experimental approaches, Appl. Surf. Sci., 2019, 480: 621-635.
[15] Tritt T M, Subramanian M A. Thermoelectric materials, phenomena, and applications: a bird' s eye view. MRS Bulletin, 2006, 31: 188.
[16] Zi-Hua Wu, Hua-Qing Xie, Yong-Biao Zhai, Preparation and Thermoelectric Properties of Co-Doped ZnO Synthesized by Sol–Gel, J. Nanosci. Nanotechnol., 2015, 15: 3147-3150.

[17] Sheetz R. M., Ponomareva I, Richter E, et al. Defect-induced optical absorption in the visible range in ZnO nanowires. Phys. Rev. B, 2009, 80: 195105.
[18] Janotti A., Van de Walle C. G., LDA+U and hybrid functional calculations for defects in ZnO, SnO2, and TiO2, Phys. Status Solidi B, 2011, 248: 799 - 804.
[19] Park K, Seong J K, Nahm S., Improvement of thermoelectric properties with the addition of Sb to ZnO, J Alloys Compd., 2008, 455: 331.
[20] Aadil Fayas Wani, Bindu Rani, Sharopov U.B, et.al, Thermoelectric investigation of transition metal oxide NiO2: A first principles study, Int J Energy Res., 2022, 1–9.

Ab initio investigation of electronic structure and topological features in ErNiSb and ErSb compounds

A V Lukoyanov[1,2] **and S T Baidak**[1,2]

[1]M.N. Mikheev Institute of Metal Physics of the Ural Branch of Russian Academy of Sciences, 18, S. Kovalevskaya str., 620108 Ekaterinburg, Russia
[2]Ural Federal University named after the first President of Russia B. N. Yeltsin, 19, Mira str., 620002 Ekaterinburg, Russia

E-mail: lukoyanov@imp.uran.ru

Abstract. This manuscript is devoted to the electronic structure, as well as magnetic properties, investigations of the ternary ErNiSb and binary ErSb intermetallic compounds using GGA+*U* within so called ab initio approach. Our detailed study of the band structure obtained with accounting for electronic correlations in the narrow-gap semiconductor ErNiSb and semimetal ErSb is performed in order to identify topological features.

1. Introduction

*R*NiSb intermetallics are comprised of *R* – rare earth elements, *T* – 3d /4d/5d transition metals, and *X* standing for p elements, these compounds belong to the *RTX* family with a plethora of unique properties and phenomena promising for multifunctional applications [1]. Many compounds from of the RTX family demonstrate remarkable magnetic, electrical, thermoelectric properties for different temperatures [2]. Some *RTX* are found to be characterized by a large magnetocaloric effect, i.e. MCE, as well as magnetoresistance, i.e. MR [1,3,4]. The large MCE here is caused by temperature dependence of magnetization and big values of magnetic moments [4]. In *R*NiSb with the half-Heusler crystal structure with some *R*, high mobility ratio and high-temperature power factor were revealed [5,6]. The effect of Ni substitution in ErNiSb was investigated and found to enhance the thermoelectric figure of merit [7]. On the other hand, some binary *R*Sb with the same crystal structure, including LaSb and CeSb compounds, are topological semimetals with unusual Dirac-cone-like states observed in angle-resolved photoemission spectroscopy (ARPES) studies [8]. In this work, we investigate and compare the electronic and band structures of ErNiSb and ErSb with similar crystal structures.

2. Crystal structure and computational details

The intermetallic compounds *RN*iSb, including ErNiSb, are crystallized in the MgAgAs-type, i.e., space group *F-43m*, # 216, half-Heusler structure [5,9]. The ErNiSb intermetallic compound has the lattice parameters: a = b = c = 6.247 Å with Er in 4a (0; 0; 0), Ni in 4c (1/4; 1/4; 1/4) and Sb in 4b (1/2; 1/2; 1/2) positions [9]. For ErSb; a = b = c = 6.110 Å [10], it has the NaCl-type (space group *Fm-3m*, # 225). The atomic positions for Er and Sb are the same as in ErNiSb. To study the electronic structure of the ErNiSb and ErSb, the LSDA+U [11] method in the GGA+U version was employed. It is widely used to include strong electron correlations of the 4f electrons in the shell of rare-earth ions [12]. The calculations were done in the Quantum ESPRESSO package [13]. In GGA+U, the electron correlations are accounted for in Er with the direct Coulomb interaction U equal to 6.5 eV, Hund's exchange parameter J equal to 0.7 eV [4,14]. The ferromagnetic ordering of the Er moments is assumed in our calculations. For ErNiSb and ErSb, the total magnetic of the compound consists of the magnetic moments of Er, the moments of Ni and Sb are zero, similar to Rh in *R*Rh*X* [1]. The calculated GGA+U spin moment of Er is 3 μ_B. But in order to get the effective magnetic moment of erbium from our results, let us take into account that L = 6 for Er as for R^{3+} [4], then the effective magnetic moment can be calculated as 9.58 μ_B, cf. to the experimental value of 9.7(3) μ_B [9].

3. Electronic and band structures of ErNiSb

In figure 1, the partial densities and summed total for the electronic states (DOS) of ErNiSb are plotted for the majority (upper panels) and minority (lower panels) spin directions. The Fermi level is at zero of the energy axis, it is located within the energy gap. Several intense peaks of the total DOS of ErNiSb in figure 1a are at -8.3 to -7.2 eV, then two peaks at -6.2 eV and -5.6 eV, as well as near 2.0 eV in the conduction band. These peaks of DOS are stemmed from the Er 4*f* states. A wide band from -4.2 eV till -0.5 eV in figure 1b is due to the non-spin-polarized Ni 3*d* states. One can notice that due to the structure, hybridization and Sb, the Ni 3*d* states in ErNiSb are fully unoccupied in distinction with the other Ni-based *R*-Ni [14]. For example, in $ErNi_5$ and $HoNi_5$, the Ni ions are characterized by the magnetic moment 0.2 μ_B and provide states at the Fermi level [14]. The Er 5*d* are also shown in figure 1b as broad and almost unoccupied states in both spin projections. The Sb 5*p* states in figure 1c and other not shown electronic states contribute negligibly to the total DOS of ErNiSb.

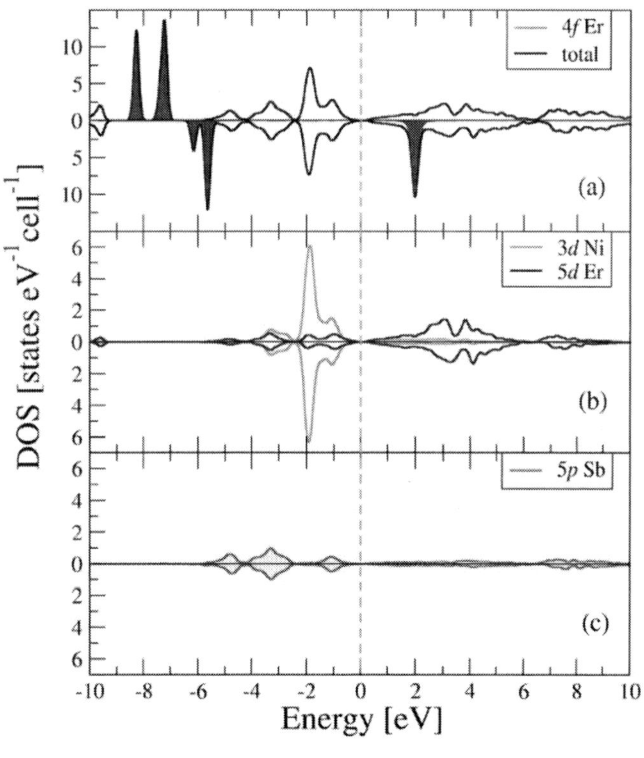

Figure 1. Total (a) and partial (b,c) densities of states of ErNiSb compound from GGA+U.

The band structure of ErNiSb is plotted in figure 2 for the majority (a) and minority (b) spin projections. In both projections the energy gap is clearly seen with 0.34 eV gap in one spin projection, and 0.25 eV in the opposite one. Thus, the final energy gap is indirect between Γ and X points of 0.25 eV. The narrow peaks of the 4*f* erbium ions are manifested as very flat bands at the discussed energies. Remarkably, the valence band of ErNiSb exhibits the presence of the occupied bands next to Γ along the L-Γ-X and K-Γ directions at the Fermi energy. The lowest unoccupied band in ErNiSb is next to X along the Γ-X-W direction.

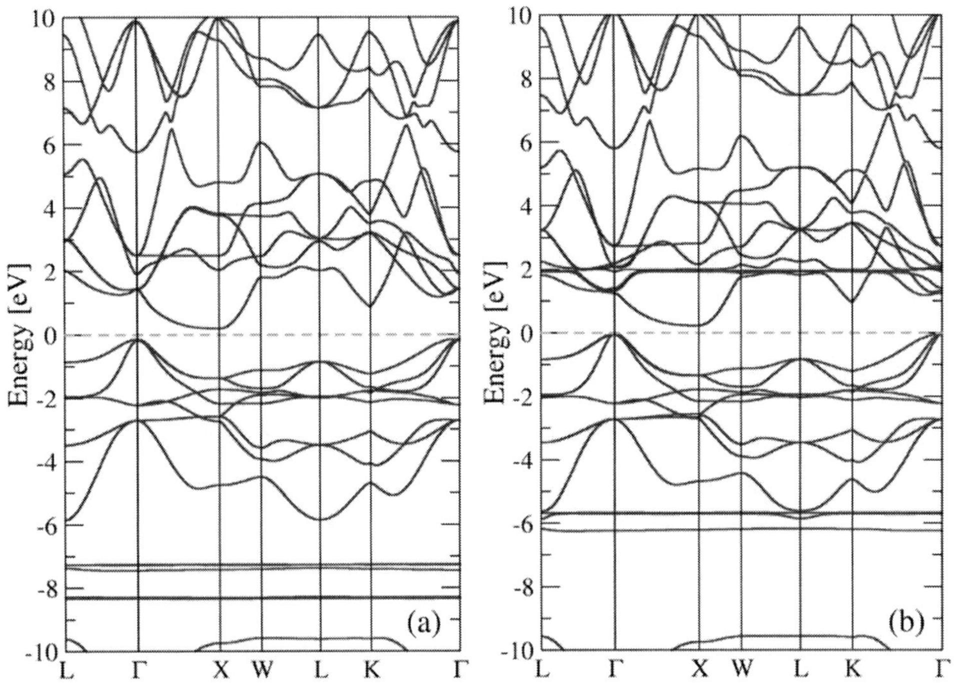

Figure 2. Band structure of ErNiSb for the majority (a) and minority (b) spin projections.

4. Electronic and band structures of ErSb

In the panels a-c of figure 3, the partial and summed total DOS for ErSb are plotted. The Fermi level is at zero of the energy axis, but the densities of states at the Fermi energy (E_F) are not zero in both spin projections. Again, in figure 3a the largest peaks in DOS belong to the Er 4*f* states. The Er 5*d* are shown in figure 3b as broad and almost unoccupied and symmetrical states in both spin projections. The Sb 5*p* states, see figure 3c, have small contributions near E_F.

In the calculate band structure of ErSb, see figure 4, one can find the hole pockets next to Γ (directions L-Γ-X and K-Γ) and an electron pocket next to X (direction Γ-X-W) formed by these bands discussed above in ErNiSb. These pockets do not cross and form a semimetallic state in ErSb. This result motivates further studies of the intermediate cases with vacancies of Ni in ErNiSb, a case of the bands approaching the Fermi level with a zero band gap can provide type-II Weyl semimetal or spin gapless semiconductor situations for changing volume or external impacts.

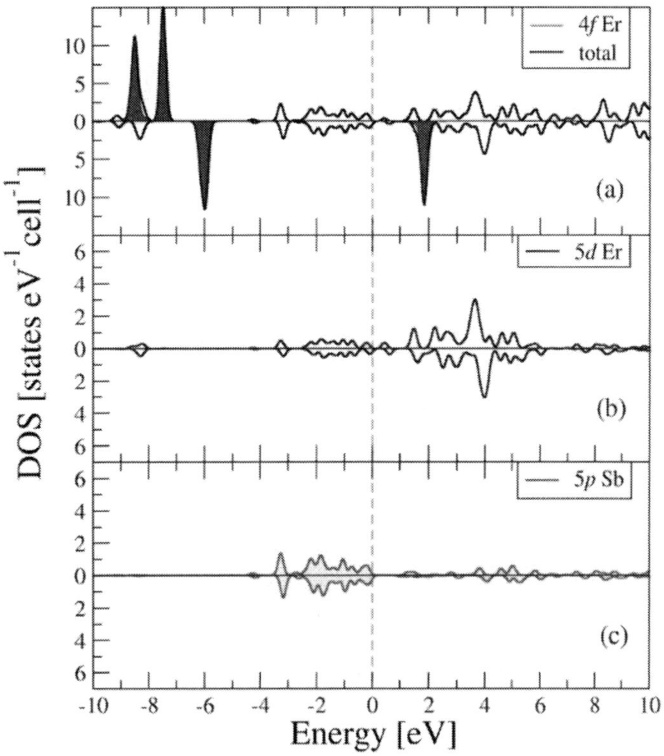

Figure 3. Total (a) and partial (b,c) DOS of ErSb compound from GGA+*U*.

5. Conclusions

Thus, here the electronic structure for both ErNiSb and ErSb compounds are investigated in GGA+*U* method based on density functional theory and additional accounting for strong correlations of the 4*f* electrons of Er. The first compound, ErNiSb, is found to be a narrow gap semiconductor with the indirect gap in the electronic structure in both spin projections. In contrast, the ErSb compounds, which crystallizes in the same cubic structure and Er, Sb positions but without Ni, is obtained with the band structure of a semimetal. The band structure of ErNiSb exhibits the presence of occupied bands which form the hole pockets next to Γ, directions L-Γ-X and K-Γ, at the Fermi energy in ErSb. The unoccupied bands in ErNiSb have the nonsymmetric band next to X, direction Γ-X-W, and which forms an electron pocket in ErSb. The calculated magnetic properties are solely caused by the magnetic moments of Er in these compounds and provide a good agreement with the published in the literature previous experimental results.

Acknowledgments

Our study was supported by the grant of Russian Science Foundation No 22-42-02021.

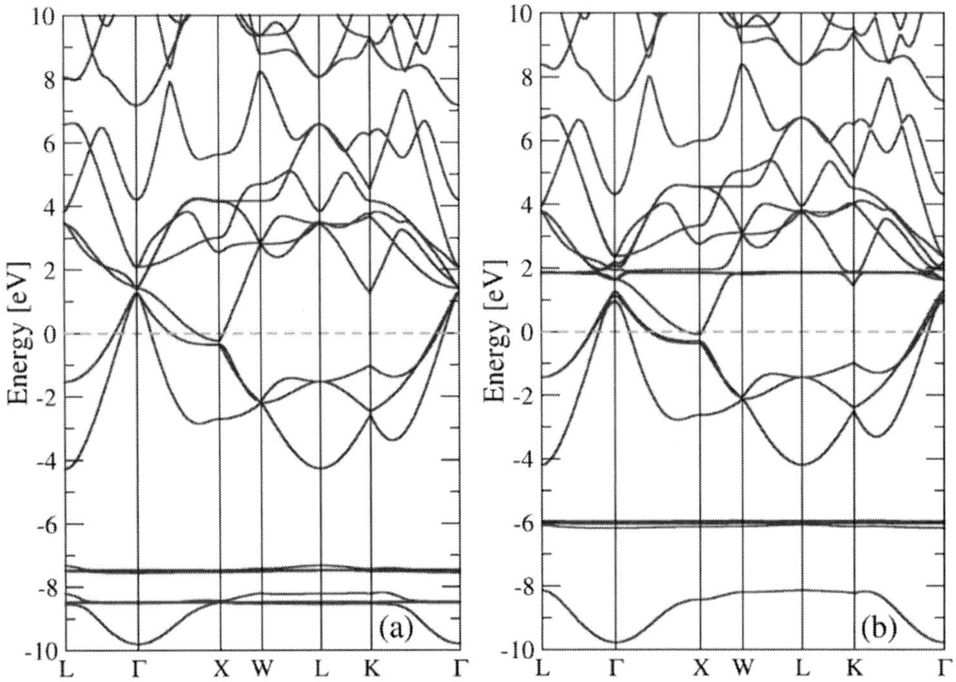

Figure 4. Band structure of ErSb for the majority (a) and minority (b) spin projections.

References

[1] Gupta S et al 2014 *J. Phys. D: Appl. Phys.* **47** 365002 https://doi.org/10.1088/0022-3727/47/36/365002

[2] Winiarski M J and Bilińska K 2019 *Intermet.* **108** 55 https://doi.org/10.1016/j.intermet.2019.02.009

[3] Gupta S et al 2021 *J. Alloys Compd.* **888** 161493 https://doi.org/10.1016/j.jallcom.2021.161493

[4] Gupta S, Suresh K G, Nigam A K and Lukoyanov A V 2015 *J. Alloys Compd.* **640** 56 https://doi.org/10.1016/j.jallcom.2015.02.126

[5] Ciesielski K et al 2020 *J. Alloys Compd.* **816** 152596 https://doi.org/10.1016/j.jallcom.2019.152596

[6] Kawano K et al 2007 *Appl. Phys. Lett.* **91** 062115 https://doi.org/10.1063/1.2769398

[7] Kawano K et al 2008 *J. Appl. Phys.* **104** 013714 https://doi.org/10.1063/1.2956699

[8] Oinuma H et al 2017 *Phys. Rev. B* **96** 041120 https://doi.org/10.1103/PhysRevB.96.041120

[9] Hartjes K and Jeitschko W *J. Alloys Compd.* **226** (1995) 81

[10] Abdusalyamova M N et al 1990 *J. Less-Common Metals* **166** 221

[11] Anisimov V I, Aryasetiawan F and Lichtenstein A I 1997 *J. Phys.: Cond. Mat.* **9** 767

[12] Anisimov V I, Lukoyanov A V and Skornyakov S L 2018 *Phys. Metals Metallogr.* **119** 1254 https://doi.org/10.1134/S0031918X18130161

[13] Giannozzi P et al 2017 *J. Phys.: Condens. Matter* **29** 465901 https://doi.org/10.1088/1361-648X/aa8f79

[14] Knyazev Yu V et al 2012 *Phys. Status Solidi B* **249** 824 https://doi.org/10.1002/pssb.201147342

IOP Conf. Series: Materials Science and Engineering 1263 (2022) 012027 doi:10.1088/1757-899X/1263/1/012027

Screen printed ZnO thick films for NH_3 gas sensing

***Vaishali T. Salunke[1], P.B. Buchade[2], A.D. Shaligram[3] and R.Y. Borse[4]**
[1]M.S.G. Arts, Science and Commerce College Malegaon Camp, Dist. Nasik, Maharashtra, India.
[2]MES Abasaheb Garware College, Pune, India.
[3]Department of Electronic Science, SPPU Pune, India.
[4]M.J.M. Arts, Commerce, and Science College, Karanjali (Peth), Nasik. India

*Corresponding author's e-mail address tvsvaishali12@gmail.com

Abstract: The paper reports the synthesis of ZnO powder by self-propagation solution combustion method and the development of screen-printed ZnO thick films for sensing ammonia gas. The surface and structural examination of the thick film was studied by using SEM and XRD techniques. The particle and grain size of the thick film were determined using SEM and XRD respectively. The temperature coefficient of resistance (TCR), electrical, and NH_3 gas sensing characteristics of ZnO thick film were observed with varying temperatures. Thick films show the inverse relations of resistance with respective temperatures. The sensitivity, response, and recovery time toward NH3 gas sensing were discussed.

1. Introduction

Metal oxide semiconducting n-type wurtzite hexagonal ZnO is a fascinating material. ZnO is a chemically as well as thermally stable material having a high band gap energy (3.37eV) at room temperature. For the last 50 years, surface electronic properties of ZnO have been examined and studied for different applications [1]. At moderate temperatures, ZnO is sensitive to different reducing gases. With different synthesis approaches ZnO powder has been used for different applications. Because of its high exciton binding energy (60meV), electron mobility, thermal stability, and non-toxicity[2-4], ZnO is a promising material possessing a wide variety of applications such as in food packaging, medicine, biomedical applications, antimicrobial agent against borne diseases, cosmetics (talcum powder), optical devices (LEDs), electrical devices, piezoelectric devices, photo-detectors, surface acoustics devices, gas sensors, etc. [5-9].

In this paper, screen-printed ZnO thick film was used for NH_3 gas sensing. Self- propagation solution combustion approach at a high temperature of 450 °C was used to synthesize ZnO powder. In day to day life, the application of NH_3 gas sensors has increased in different fields like food industries, chemical industries, and interpretation of medical analysis, industrial processes, and protection of the environment by various methods. Excess amount of NH_3 gas is dangerous to health sometimes it can cause death. The gas sensors available in the market are costly therefore the characteristics of ZnO thick films prepared using screen printing were discussed for NH_3 gas sensing.

2. Experimental

2.1 Synthesis of ZnO powder:

The ZnO nano-powder was synthesized by using the self-propagation solution combustion method at 450 °C. The main precursor, zinc nitrate hexahydrate works as an oxidizer, and for purpose of fuel, dextrose was used. 1.35 M zinc nitrate hexahydrate and 0.79 M dextrose were dissolved in 25 ml purified water. The mixture was kept at 70 °C on a magnetic stirrer. When the solution was converted into a gel-like structure, it was placed in a preheated furnace at 450 °C. The reaction in the furnace was completed within 15 minutes. The solution boils, ignites and combustion takes place. The powder was then removed from the furnace and calcinated at 600 °C for one hour to remove the carbon residues from the synthesized powder. The various steps adopted during the synthesis of ZnO powder displayed in Fig.1

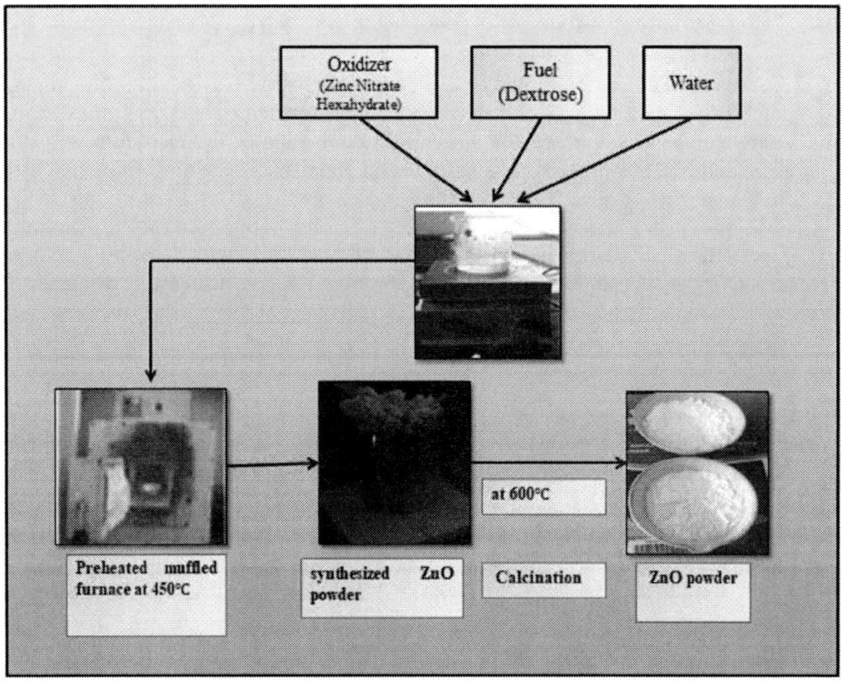

Fig. 1: Steps for the synthesis of ZnO powder

Fig. 2 represents the XRD pattern of the synthesized powder that confirms the formation of ZnO powder. Many peaks in the XRD pattern indicate the polycrystalline nature of synthesized ZnO powder [11]. This synthesized powder was used for the development of the thick film gas sensors.

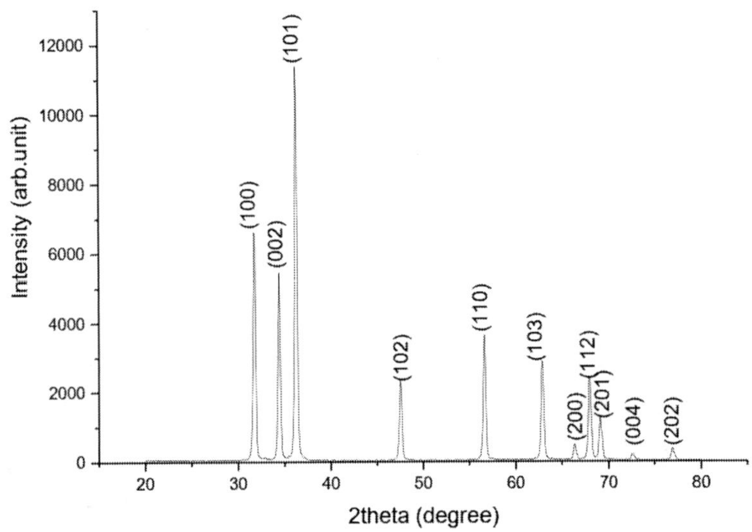

Fig. 2: XRD of synthesized ZnO powder

The observed XRD patterns of synthesized powder match with the JCPDS 36-1451 card. The peaks show the strongest X-ray diffraction peaks at 36.23 °, and the FWHM (β) =0.2095. The average crystallite size (D) = 35.25 nm was obtained by using the Debye Scherrer formula [10, 11]. The XRD pattern shows the formation of ZnO powder with no impurity.

2.2 Development of ZnO thick film sensors:

The screen printed ZnO thick film sensor samples on alumina substrate was accomplished using the paste of ZnO powder in three different steps as displayed in Fig. 3(a), (b), (c) and Fig.3 (d) shows the actual screen printing setup. For this, a nylon screen of 140 mesh size was used. As a permanent binder glass frit (70 wt. % PbO, 18 wt% Al_2O_3, 9 wt% SiO_2 3wt % B_2O_3), provisional binder ethyl cellulose (EC) and Butyl Carbitol Acetate (BCA) as a vehicle which was used for the preparation of thick film paste. For ZnO paste, the organic to the inorganic ratio of 30:70 was maintained. The organic part consists of EC and BCA in a ratio of 8:92 added drop by drop to make thixotropic pasted whereas the inorganic part contains functional ZnO powder and glass frit having a 95:5 ratio. Using the fine ZnO powder paste, thick film samples were prepared on alumina substrates of size 2.5 cm x 1.25cm through the mask on a nylon screen. After drying the samples in an air atmosphere for 20 to 30 minutes under an IR lamp, the films were fired at 500 °C for 45 minutes in the furnace to make the films more sticky and ready to use for characterization and sensing measurement.

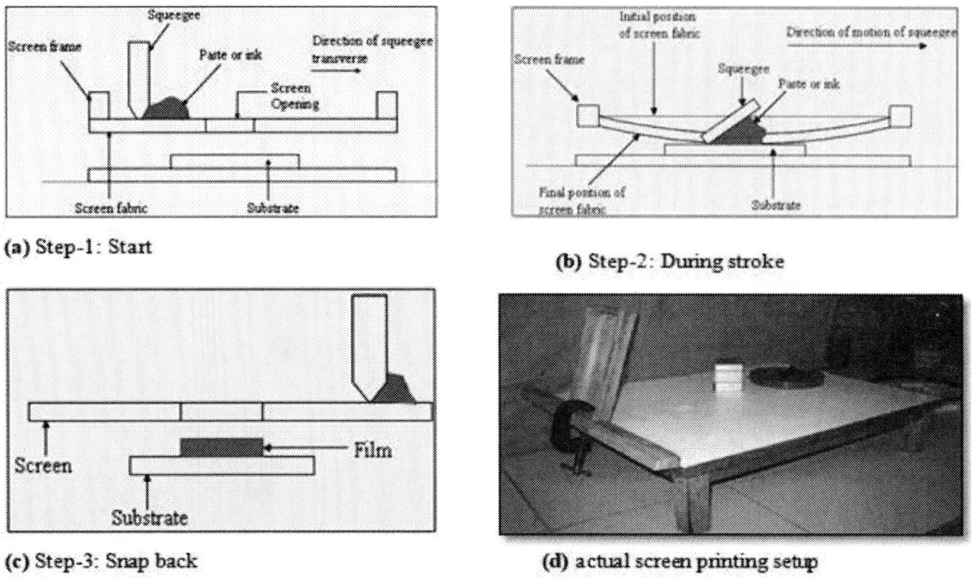

Fig. 3: Steps of screen printing for thick film samples

The electrical and gas sensing characteristics were studied using a static gas sensing measurement system in which resistance of the film was calculated with respective varying temperatures from room temperature to 400 °C.

3. Results:

3.1 Structural characterization of thick film

The structural characterization of screen-printed ZnO thick film sensors was carried out and analyzed by XRD and SEM.

3.1.1 XRD study

The XRD analysis was performed in a 2θ angle range of 20 ° to 80 °. The XRD of ZnO films shown in Fig. 4 shows polycrystalline hexagonal nature since the peaks resemble the reflection from (100), (002), (101), (102), (110), (103), (200), (112), (201) and (202) planes. The observed XRD pattern is in tune with JCPDS 36-1451 card. The peaks represented by 'x' in the XRD pattern of Fig. 4 show the peaks for the alumina substrate on which the ZnO screen printed thick film pattern was developed.

The XRD peak shows the preferred orientation for the ZnO particle of the thick film along the axis of the (101) plane [10, 11] since the XRD patterns show the strong X-ray diffraction peaks at $2\theta = 36.25$ °, and the FWHM (β) =0.25. The average crystallite size (D) = 34.34 nm was obtained by using the Debye Scherrer formula [10, 11] as in eq. (1)

$$D = \frac{0.9\lambda}{\beta cos\theta} \quad (1)$$

where β is full width at half maximum (FWHM) in radian of the diffraction peak intensity and wavelength of X-ray radiation is denoted by λ. The Scherrer's constant is equal to 0.94. (in general, denoted by the 'k').

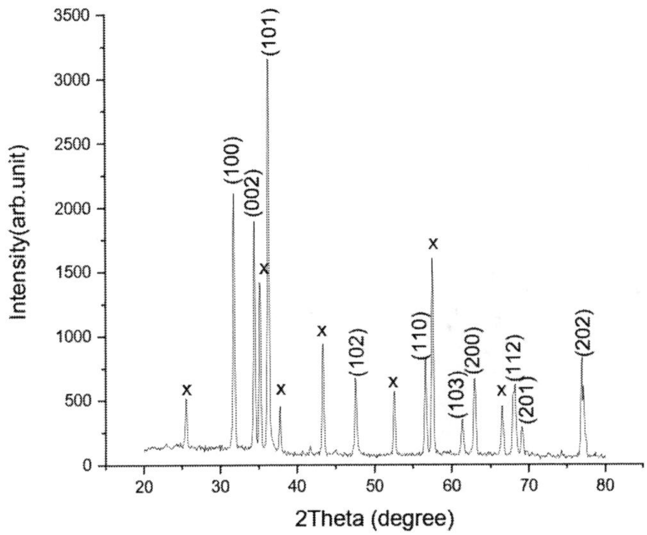

Fig. 4 XRD pattern of thick film

To interpret the lattice parameters of the ZnO thick film following equation (2) was used [10,11],

$$\frac{1}{d^2{}_{(101)}} = \frac{4}{3}\left(\frac{1}{a^2}\right) + \frac{1}{c^2} \quad (2)$$

In this equation d = interplanar distance, a & c = lattice constant. The Table 1 shows the calculated lattice constant values and lattice constant values recorded in JCPDS 36-1451 card. The values of lattice constant moderately vary because ZnO is slightly dependent on its basicity of the ratio of precursors that takes parts in the formation of ZnO powder and then thick film paste. This appropriation was confirmed from the EDAX graph.

Table 1: Lattice constant of ZnO thick film

Firing Temperature (500 ^{0}C)	**Lattice Constants**	
	a (nm)	**c (nm)**
ZnO Thick film (calculated)	0.3242	0.5292
JCPDS 36-1451 card	0.3249	0.5205

3.1.2 Surface Morphology of thick Film sensor

SEM study: The surface morphology of the prepared ZnO thick film sensor was studied using Scanning Electron Microscopy (Model JEOL 6300LA Germany). Fig. 5 represents the SEM image of the microstructure of the screen printed ZnO thick film sensor. It shows that the microstructure is non-uniform and composed of a mixture of spherical and hexagonal shapes and clusters of particles with clearly seen voids or porosity on the surface. The clusters of some particles are also visible. The surface was without cracks. The observed particle size was 1.25 μm with the specific surface area [12] of 0.856 m^2/g which was calculated using the formula represented in equation (3),

$$S = \frac{6}{\rho d}, \quad (3)$$

where the diameter is indicated by 'd' and ρ is the particle density.

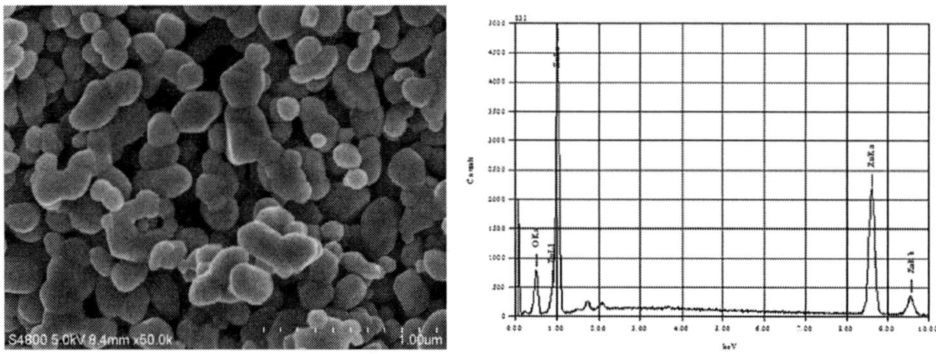

Fig. 5: SEM and EDAX picture of screen printed ZnO thick film sensor

The elemental composition analysis in the form of atomic and mass percentages as are shown in Table 2

Table 2: Elemental composition analysis of ZnO thick film fired at 500 °C

Firing Temperature	Element	At. Wt. %	Mass %
500 °C	Zn O	77.33 22.67	93.47 6.53

3.2 Electrical and gas sensing characterization of screen printed ZnO thick film sensor:

For electrical and gas sensing characterization of ZnO thick film samples, the D.C. resistance of the ZnO thick film samples was measured using the half-bridge method [13-15] as a function of temperature. The system consists of a glass chamber (25 liters and ~12" diameter) and a 1000 W nichrome wire heater (having resistance ~120 ohms at room temperature). The heater was used to change the temperature of ZnO thick film samples from room temperature to 400 °C with a step of 10 °C by varying its voltage using dimmer-stat (maximum current limit up to ~ 8 A). The electrical terminals were brought out from ZnO thick film samples by using insulated feedthrough mounted on the stainless steel base plate. For external contacts, aluminum foil with pressure contact was used. Indicator cum controller with the help of Cr-Al thermocouple was used for measuring the temperature. The thick film resistance (DC) friction of ZnO film sensor fired at 500 °C temperature in air (R_a) and NH_3 gas (R_g) (at 1000 ppm) atmosphere was shown in Fig. 6(a). This Fig.6(a) shows that the resistance dropped with an increase in temperature. This shows the semiconducting behavior of ZnO thick films obeying the relation $R = R_0 e^{-\Delta E/KT}$ in the temperature range of 50 to 400 °C. Nature of both resistance (R_a and R_g) vary w.r.t temperature was same. Initially, resistance falls suddenly then linearly decreases up to a certain temperature and then decreases exponentially with the increase in temperature and finally reaches a steady saturation level. Initially, variation of R_g resistance in presence of a gas environment shows some increase and decrease of resistance due to humidity. Fig. 6(b) shows the sensitivity of ZnO thick film for a target NH_3 gas at different concentrations like 100 ppm, 200 ppm, 400 ppm, 800 ppm, and 1000 ppm observed with varying temperatures. The sensitivity was calculated using relation= $\frac{Ra}{R_g}$, where the resistances of thick film in air and gas environment are represented by 'R_a 'and ' R_g ' respectively. The observed operating temperature for NH_3 gas at different concentrations was 260 °C having maximum sensitivity of 7.88 as shown in Fig. 6(b). In the process of NH_3 gas sensing, ZnO acts as an oxidizing agent whereas NH_3 gas plays the role of a reducing agent. When molecules of NH_3 gas are present on the surface of ZnO thick film, it contacts with the negatively charged O^-, the electrons are trapped and returned to the conduction band of the ZnO thick film sensor, and then NH_3 gas reduces the absorbed oxygen molecule from the surface of ZnO thick film, due to this mechanism the resistance of the ZnO thick film decreases in presence of NH_3 gas.

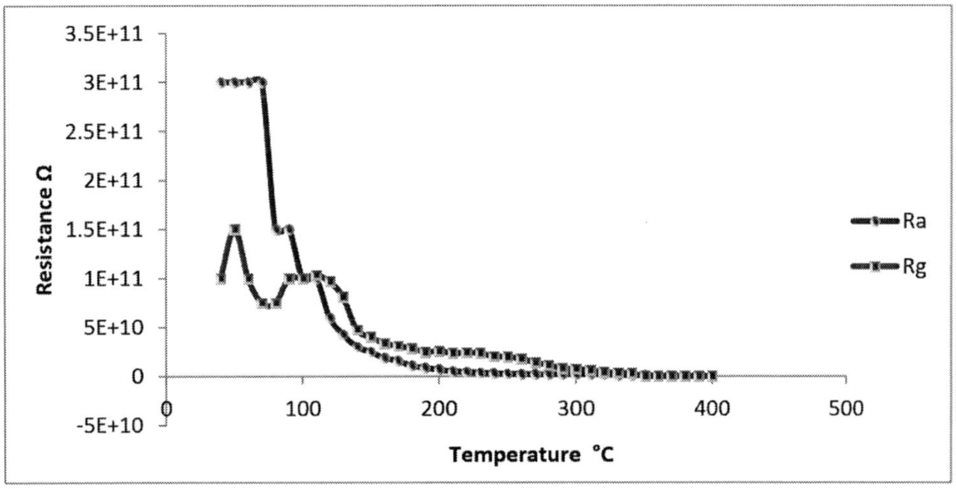

Fig.6 (a)

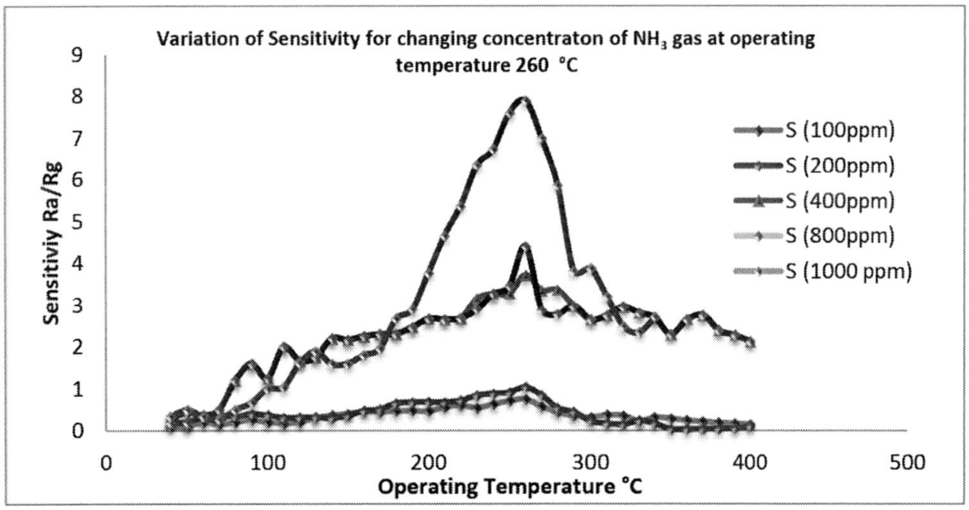

Fig. 6 (b)

Fig. 6: (a) Variation of Resistance of thick film w.r.t. to the temperature in air and NH_3 gas environment (b) Variation in sensitivity of ZnO thick film for different concentrations of NH_3 gas in ppm at operating temperature 260 °C

It was observed from Fig. 6(b) that at an operating temperature of 260 °C the sensitivity of ZnO thick film increases with an increase in the concentration of NH_3 gas at ppm level. In the presence of an NH_3 gas environment, the resistance of thick film changes due to the oxidation-reduction reaction that takes place between ZnO and NH_3 gas as shown in the following reaction (4) and (5)

$$3\,Zn^{II} + 6\,e^- \rightarrow 3\,Zn^0\ (reduction\ of\ Zn) \quad (4)$$
$$2\,N^{III} - 6\,e^- \rightarrow 2\,N^0\ (Oxidation\ of\ N) \quad (5)$$

The observed response and recovery time shown in Fig. 7(a) and (b) for operating temperature 250 °C was 90 seconds and 150 seconds respectively in presence of a 1000 ppm NH_3 gas environment.

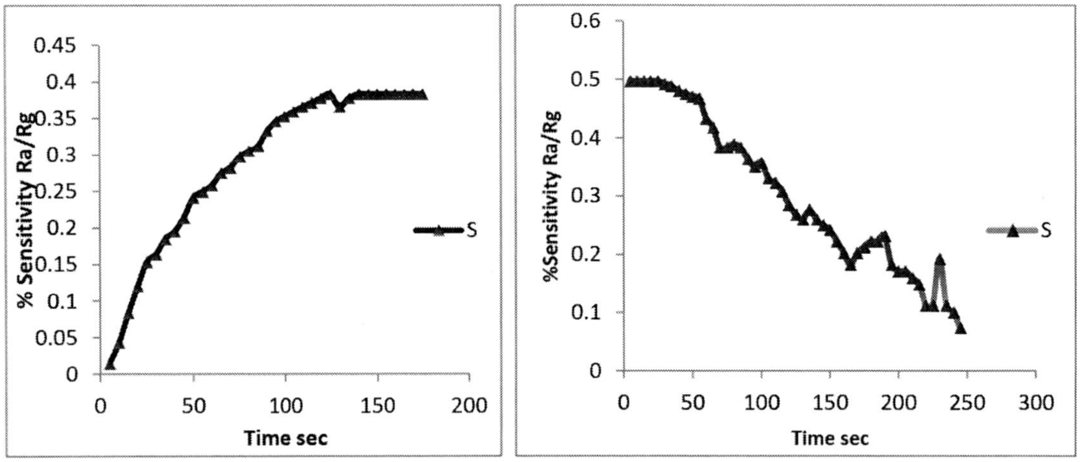

(a) Response time **(b)** Recovery time

Fig. 7 ***Response and recovery time***

The irritation of the eyes, nose, and throat is observed at 50 ppm without any irreversible effect on human health. Saroj D.Patil et.al [16] reported that the variation of ammonia gas sensing response up to 2500 ppm increases with increasing operating temperature. At 400 °C they reported the sensitivity towards NH_3 gas was only 19.64%. The increase in sensitivity and decrease in operating temperature as shown in Fig. 6(b) was due to the use of synthesized ZnO powder for the development of ZnO thick films. The different researchers tested ammonia for different ppm by changing the parameters of the ZnO gas sensors and obtained different results [16, 17, 18]. This health report [19] stated that for up to 30 minutes at 500 ppm, human can tolerate the NH_3 gas without seriously affecting his/her body or life. This paper discussed the effect of the synthesis of ZnO powder to increase the sensitivity toward NH_3 gas sensing and decrease the operating temperature with lower response and recovery time without affecting human health.

The temperature coefficient of resistance (TCR) and the activation energy was determined from the electrical DC resistance variance concerning the temperature in the air atmosphere.

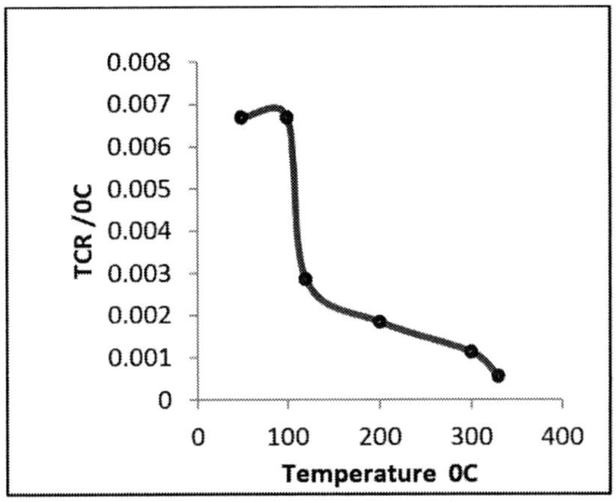

(a) TCR Versus Temperature

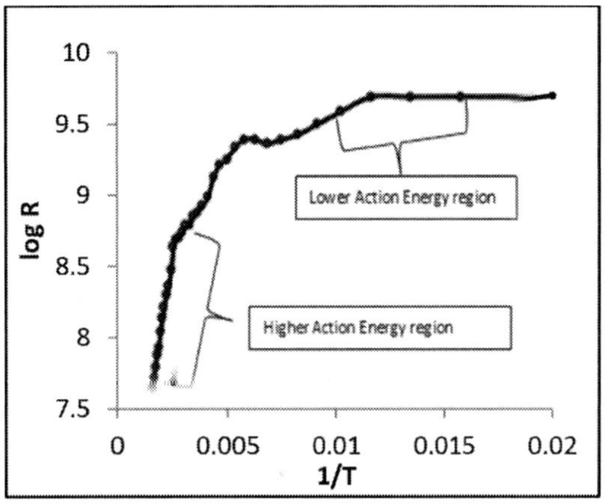

(b) Activation curve (Arrhenius Plot)

Fig.8 TCR and activation energy

Fig. 8(a) shows the dependence of TCR of ZnO films on the operating temperature, it goes on to decrease with increasing temperature indicating that the process of electron emission improved w.r.t. the increase in temperature. The lower and higher activation energy was determined from the Log R versus 1/T shown in Fig. 8(b). The value of activation energy is listed in Table 3.

Table 3 Activation energy

Synthesis Temp=450 °C Firing Temperature °C	Activation Energy(eV)	
	Lower temperature region	Higher temperature region
500	0.0035	0.0846

At higher temperatures activation energy increases compared to lower temperature regions but the activation energy comparatively less [20]. The surface reaction of thick film between the target gas and adsorbed oxygen species shows the dependence of activation energy. The sensitivity of the film surface reaction with target gas increases with the lower value of activation energy [21].

4. Conclusion

ZnO (ZnO) material is a promising material for various applications. ZnO-based thick film sensor shows the sensitivity towards NH_3 gas at 260 °C. The sensitivity of the ZnO thick film sensor was increased with the concentration of NH_3 gas in ppm. The effect of synthesized ZnO powder leads to an increase in sensitivity and lowers operating temperature. This paper explains both the synthesis of ZnO powder and the development of the NH_3 gas thick film sensor. In the future, we will study the effect of other additive semiconducting materials in the ZnO powder synthesis to minimize the operating temperature for reducing gases.

Acknowledgments

The author wishes to acknowledge the authority of M.S.G. College for constant support and encouragement for research work. Also thanks to the department of Electronic Science and Physics SPPU, Pune for providing the facilities for structural characterization.

References:

[1] Heiland, G., Kunstman, P. *Polar surfaces of ZnO crystals.* Surf. Sci. 13, 72–84 (1969)

[2] S. Kundu, U. Nithiyanantham, DNA-mediated fast synthesis of shape-selective ZnO nanostructures and their potential applications in catalysis and dye-sensitized solar cells, Ind. Eng. Chem. Res. 53 (2014) 13667-13679.

[3] Z.L. Wang, *Splendid one-dimensional nanostructures of ZnO: A new nanomaterial family for nanotechnology*, Acs Nano. 2 (2008) 1987-1992.

[4] R. Sankar Ganesh, E. Durgadevi, M. Navaneethan, V.L. Patil, S. Ponnusamy, C. Muthamizhchelvan, et al., *Low temperature ammonia gas sensor based on Mn-doped ZnO nanoparticle decorated microspheres*, J. Alloy. Compd. 721 (2017) 182-190.

[5] R. Saravanan, K. Santhi, N. Sivakumar, V. Narayanan, A. Stephen, *Synthesis and 23 characterization of ZnO and Ni doped ZnO nanorods by thermal decomposition method for spintronics application*, Mater. Charact. 67 (2012) 10–16.doi:10.1016/j.matchar.2012.02.015.

[6] R. Mohamed, J. Rouhi, M.F. Malek, A.S. Ismail, a H. Salman, *Sol Gel Synthesized Zinc Oxide Nanorods on Single And Co- doped ZnO Seed Layer Templates : Morphological , Optical and Electrical Properties,* Int. J. Electrochem. Sci. 11 (2016) 2197–2204

[7] S.J. Soenen, W.J. Parak, J. Rejman, B. Manshian, (Intra) *Cellular Stability of Inorganic Nanoparticles : E ff ects on Cytotoxicity ,* Particle Functionality , and Biomedical Applications, Chem. Rev. 115 (2015) 2109–2135. doi:10.1021/cr400714j.

[8] D.H. Kim, J.H. Park, T. Il Lee, J.M. Myoung, *Superhydrophobic Al-doped ZnO nanorods-based electrically conductive and self-cleanable antireflecting window layer for thin film solar cell, Sol.* Energy Mater. Sol. Cells. 150 (2016) 65–70. doi:10.1016/j.solmat.2016.01.041.

[9] H. Yadav, N. Sinha, S. Goel, B. Kumar, *Eu-doped ZnO nanoparticles for dielectric, ferroelectric and piezoelectric application*s, J. Alloys Compd. 689 (2016) 333–341. doi:10.1016/j.jallcom.2016.07.329.

[10] B.D. Cullity, book having title *Elements of X-ray diffraction 2nd Edition,* Addison Wesley Publishing Company Inc., Phillippines, 1978, pp 50-65.

[11] C.F.Holder, *Tutorial on Powder X-ray Diffraction for Characterizing Nanoscale Materials* ACS Publications 2019 DOI: 10.1021/acsnano.9b05157 ACS Nano 2019, 13,7359–7365 https://pubs.acs.org/doi/pdf/10.1021/acsnano.9b05157

[12] Gao L, Li Q, Song J, Wang J, *Preparation of nan0-scale thick film and its oxygen sensitivity,* Sensor and Actuators B 71(2000) 179-183.

[13] G. Sarala Devi, S. Manoramma and V.J. Rao, *Gas sensitivity of SnO2/CuO Hetrocotacts,* J. of Electrochemical Society, 142, 8 (1995)2574-2557.

[14] Jain G.H., Patil L.A., *Gas Sensing properties of CuO and Cr activated BST thick film,* Bulletin of Materials Science, 29(4),August 2006, 403-411, Doi:10.1007/bf0270414

[15] Dayan, NJ. et.al, *On the highly selective ZnO:Al2O3 based thick ®lm hydrogen sensors,*Journal of Materials Science Letters (1997) 16:1952-1954. https://doi.org/10.1023/A:1018503104557.

[16] Saroj D. Patil and et.al , *Synthesis, Characterization and Ammonia Sensing Properties of Mn Doped ZnO Nano-Composite,* International Journal of Science and Research (IJSR), ISSN(Online):2319-7064. Index CopernicusValue (2013):6.14 Volume 5, Issue 5, May 2016,1640-1643. Paper ID:NOV163741

[17] K.Ravichandran et.al, *Enhanced ammonia sensing by cost-effective ZnO thin films through Yttrium doping* https://doi.org/10.21203/rs.3.rs-607950/v1

[18] Dinesh Kumar Chaudhary et.al,*Sensing Performance of a ZnO-based Ammonia Sensor,* Journal of Physical Science, Vol. 33(1), 97–108, 2022, https://doi.org/10.21315/jps2022.33.1.7

[19] Health Effects of Ammonia by the Fertilizer Institute,Nourish,Replenish, Grow , https://www.tfi.org/sites/default/files/documents/HealthAmmoniaFINAL.pdf

[20] B.Ismail, M.Abaab, B.Rezig, *Structural and electricalproperties of ZnO films prepared by screen printing technique,Thin Solid Films 383(2001)92-94*

[21] Tynee Bhowmick, Arnab Banerjee, Sudip Nag and Subhasish Basu Majumder,*Gas sensinging characteristics in ZnO thin film explicated through the analysis of conductance transients and the concept of activation energy,*2018 IEEE, 978-1-5386-4707-3/18/$31.00 ©2018 IEE

Synthesis and characterization of bismuth ferrite- barium titanate nano composites

Sharon V.S[1], Malini K.A[1*],Arun K.J[2]

[1]Department of Physics ,Vimala College Thrissur-9, Kerala, India.
[2]Department of Physics ,Sree Kerala Varma College Thrissur-11, Kerala, India

Email:malinijayaram@gmail.com

Abstract: Bismuth ferrite and Strontium doped bismuth ferrite($Bi_{1-x}Sr_xFeO_3$(x=0.0,0.3,0.5,0.7) samples are synthesized by the modified sol-gel technique which is a simple and economic technique.Composites of bismuth ferrite and barium titanate in the ratio 2:1 and 1:2 and $Bi_{1-x}Sr_xFeO_3$ – $BaTiO_3$ (x=0.3,0.5,0.7) with the ratio 2:1 are synthesized by solid-state reaction technique. The formation of composites of bismuth ferrite with rhombohedral structure and space group R3c and barium titanate with tetragonal structure and space group P4mm is identified using XRD. The dielectric and ferroelectric properties of the composites are investigated at room temperature and are reported in this paper.

Keywords: Sol-gel method; ferroelectricity

1. INTRODUCTION

Multiferroic materials are of large interest to researchers because of their interesting basic physics and promising application for magnetoelectric instruments [1–3]. Bismuth ferrite ($BiFeO_3$) belongs to the multiferroic family, possesses the structure of rhombohedral perovskite with the space group of R3c and exhibits multiferroic properties at room temperature[1,2]. It shows weak magnetism because of the magnetic moment with spin cycloid, and the Fe^{3+} to Fe^{2+} reductions produce the oxygen vacancies. These oxygen vacancies cause the leakage current and thus limiting its use in device manufacturing. For minimizing this leakage current the substitution of rare earth and transitional metal atoms is attempted at the bismuth ferrite A and B sites. Recent research works focus on finding lead-free electro ceramics as the replacement materials for lead-based ferroelectrics such lead zirconate titanate. $BiFeO_3$ is an eco-friendly material as it does not contain lead and is also used for high-temperature piezoelectric applications due to its high Curie temperature. Barium Titanate($BaTiO_3$) is a famous ferroelectric material that possesses low leakage current and is environmentally friendly. Depending upon the temperature $BaTiO_3$ shows polymorphic character. The tetragonal polymorph (t-$BaTiO_3$) has the more fascinating characteristics because of the ferroelectric and piezoelectric characteristics. c-$BaTiO_3$ (cubic polymorph) is paraelectric in nature. At the Curie temperature, TC ~130^0 C barium titanate undergoes transition from tetragonal to cubic[4,5]. $BiFeO_3$ –$BaTiO_3$ composites are expected as a delicate magnetoelectric material because of the outstanding properties of their components. In our present work structural and electrical characteristics of Bismuth Ferrite prepared by the Sol-gel technique are described. This paper also describes the synthesis of composites based on $BiFeO_3$-$BaTiO_3$ (BF: BTO) in various proportions such as (1:2, 2:1), $Bi_{1-x}Sr_xFeO_3$ - $BaTiO_3$ (x=0.3,0.5,0.7) with the ratio 2:1.

2. EXPERIMENTAL

2.1. *Material Synthesis*

The Bismuth ferrite ($BiFeO_3$) samples were synthesized by the modified sol-gel technique. The precursor materials used for the synthesis are bismuth nitrate and iron nitrate solutions with appropriate concentration levels. Solutions of 1M bismuth nitrate, 1M iron nitrate and 2M citric acid were prepared. After proper mixing , Citric acid was added into the solution and the mixture is stirred for complete dissolution. Then the solution is heated at 80°C with continuous stirring for 30 minutes, after which it is placed on a hot plate to form a dark viscous gel. Auto combustion of dried resin happened with the continuous heating and evolution of large quantities of gases. It is further heated for 5-10 minutes to the complete combustion of the material. After reducing the temperature, it is removed from the chamber and ground to get a fine powder. This is a modified sol-gel technique as Citric acid is added as a fuel for the combustion as compared to conventional ethylene glycol method [6]. The ferroelectric phase $BaTiO_3$ with a tetragonal structure is directly purchased from Nano Research Elements. The required amounts of the components namely bismuth ferrite and barium titanate are used to prepare composites in the molecular mass ratio 1:2 and 2:1. Strontium doped bismuth ferrite and barium titanate are taken in the ratio 2:1. Then these are mixed well using a mortar and pestle with acetone as a homogenizing medium. The samples are then calcinated at 1000°C for three hours and slowly cooled to room temperature.

2.2. *Characterization*

The structural characterization of synthesized samples $BiFeO_3$ and $BaTiO_3$ is done by XRD. The wavelength of 1.54Å is used for the X-ray diffraction. The average crystallite size is calculated using Scherrer formula.

$$D = \frac{0.9\lambda}{\beta\cos\theta} \quad (1)$$

where β is full-width at half-maxima of the strongest intensity diffraction peak, λ is the wavelength of the radiation and θ the angle of the strongest characteristic peak.

The dielectric characterization of the nanoparticles is carried out by HP 4285 LCR meter at room temperature with frequencies ranging from 100kHz-5MHz. The calcined pellets of 12mm diameter are used for the dielectric characterization.

The lattice parameters of the $BiFeO_3$ samples are analyzed by the formula

$$d = \frac{a}{\sqrt{\frac{4(h^2+k^2+hk)}{3}+\frac{a^2l^2}{c^2}}} \quad (2)$$

$$d = \frac{1}{\sqrt{\frac{h^2}{a^2}+\frac{k^2}{b^2}+\frac{l^2}{c^2}}} \quad (3)$$

The lattice parameters of the $BaTiO_3$ samples were calculated using the formula

$$\frac{1}{d^2} = \frac{(h^2+k^2)}{a^2} + \frac{l^2}{c^2} \quad (4)$$

Where a, b, c :lattice constant , d : Inter planar distance, (h,k,l) : The miller indices

3. Results and Discussions

3.1. *Structural studies*

The XRD pattern of $BaTiO_3$ (BTO) and $BiFeO_3$ (BFO) in the ratio 1:2 and 2:1 as well as $BaTiO_3$ with $Bi_{1-x}Sr_xFeO_3$ in the ratio 1:2 are shown in Fig 1. The formation of bismuth ferrite with rhombohedral structure with space group R3c and barium titanate with tetragonal structure with space group P4mm is confirmed by the diffraction peaks represented in the standard PCPDF file(86-1518) and JCPDS file (05-0626)[7] respectively. The XRD show some impurity peaks of $Bi_2Fe_4O_9$ PCPDF file (72-1832) and $Bi_{24}(Bi_{1.04}Fe_{.84})O_{40}$ PCPDF file(82-1316). The lattice constant is tabulated in table 1. The tetragonal phase of the samples is determined from calculating the c/a ratio ~1 [8]. c/a ratio for the bismuth ferrite phase increases with strontium doping because of the higher ionic radius of Sr^{2+} (1.18Å) compared to Bi^{3+} (1.03Å) ions. Debye-Scherrer formula is used to calculate the average crystallite size of the samples and are tabulated in table1[9].

Table 1. Parameters obtained from the XRD analysis of the samples

Composition	Crystallite Size D(nm)	Lattice parameter Bismuth Ferrite phase(Å)	Lattice parameter Ferroelectric phase (Barium titanate) (Å)	c/a ratio tetragonality	c/a ratio for bismuth ferrite
BTO:BFO-2:1	32.83	a =5.66 c =13.06	a =4.005 c =3.808	0.950	2.307
BTO:BFO-1:2	31.39	a =5.92 c =13.98	a =4.054 c =4.029	0.993	2.361
BSFO-0.3:BTO-2:1	24.76	a =5.64 c =13.8	a =3.988 c =4.15	1.04	2.446
BSFO-0.5:BTO-2:1	15.15	a =5.64 c =13.8	a =3.959 c =4.070	1.03	2.446
BSFO-0.7:BTO-2:1	1.79	a =5.56 c =13.88	a =3.931 c =4.004	1.01	2.496

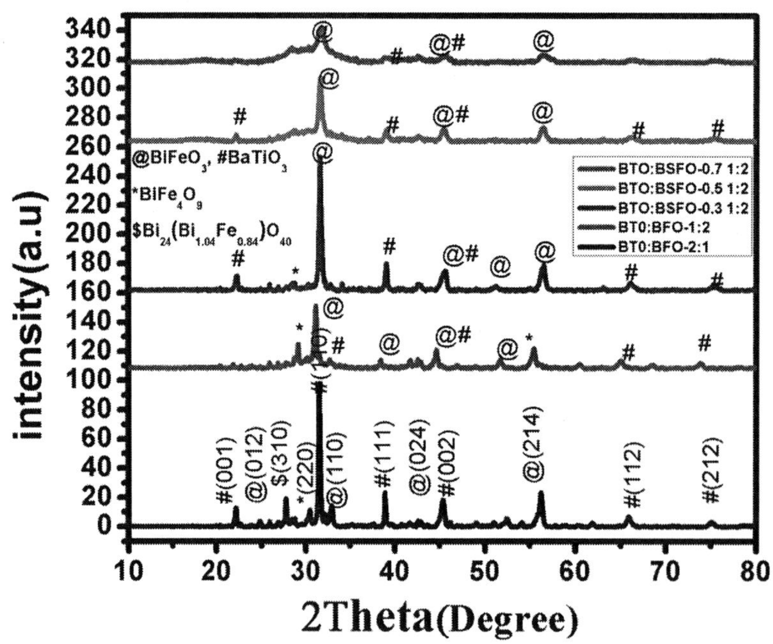

Fig1.XRD pattern of all samples

3.2. *Dielectric Property Analysis*

The variation of dielectric constant with frequency is shown in Fig 2. There are two distinct regions representing the dielectric constant dependence on frequency. A region (5kHz to 0.1MHz) with decreasing dielectric constant with increasing frequency and another region where the dielectric constant doesn't vary with frequency (in the range 0.1MHz to 1MHz). The dielectric constant variation in these frequency regions are related to bismuth ferrite and barium titanate phases. The permittivity below to 0.1MHz is mainly due to bismuth ferrite content. The dielectric constant below to 0.1MHz and above 0.1MHz is related to two polarization mechanisms. The polarization below to 0.1MHz is the interfacial polarization that arises when two compounds have distinct conductivities. The bismuth ferrite has a conductivity larger than barium titanate. At a specific applied electric field, the polarons move into the interface with barium titanate and it is called low-frequency dispersion. This kind of polarization happens below the frequency to 0.1MHz region. The second polarization is the cause of the stable permittivity in the range of 0.1MHz to 1MHz. The delay between the dielectric polarization and the frequency of the applied electric field is called relaxation. The rate of oscillation of the field is greater than the rate of movement of charge in the higher frequencies. So the polarons cannot move through the bismuth ferrite grains. So the total electric polarization is canceled and this is the cause for the decrement in the dielectric constant value [10]. The dielectric constant decreases with increasing frequency is because of the Maxwell-Wagner type interfacial polarization[11] and space charge polarization and agree with the Koop's phenomenological theory[12]. The value of dielectric constant and low value of dielectric loss is close to the reported values [13].

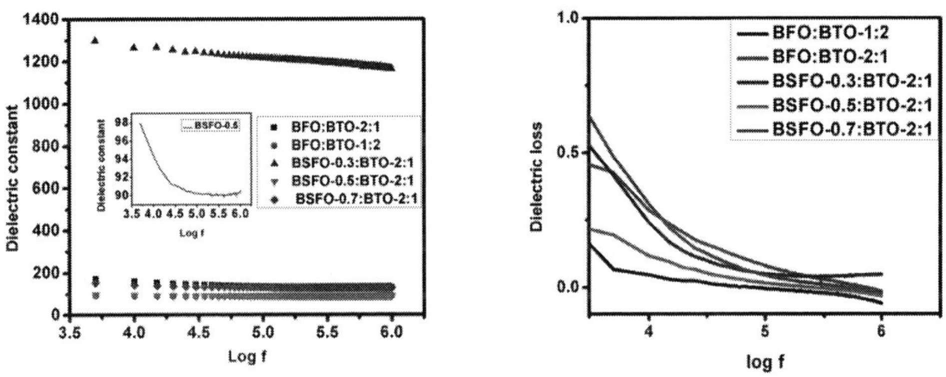

Fig 2. Variation of dielectric constant and dielectric loss in the company of frequency for the samples.

The dielectric constant value is high for BSFO-0.3: BTO samples. When the strontium is doped into the sample the value of the dielectric constant increases to higher values. The dielectric constant value is high for all the samples. So these materials are used in capacitor dielectrics [14]. Fig 2 also shows the frequency variation for dielectric loss at room temperature. With increasing frequency, the dielectric loss decreases. At larger frequencies the hopping electrons cannot follow the applied field and this is the cause of the decrement in the dielectric parameters.

3.3. *Ferroelectric Property Analysis*

Fig 3 represents the polarization with the electric field (P-E) loops . Ferroelectric properties are explained by measuring the polarization(P) against the electric field(E) up to 20KV/cm.

IOP Conf. Series: Materials Science and Engineering 1263 (2022) 012028 doi:10.1088/1757-899X/1263/1/012028

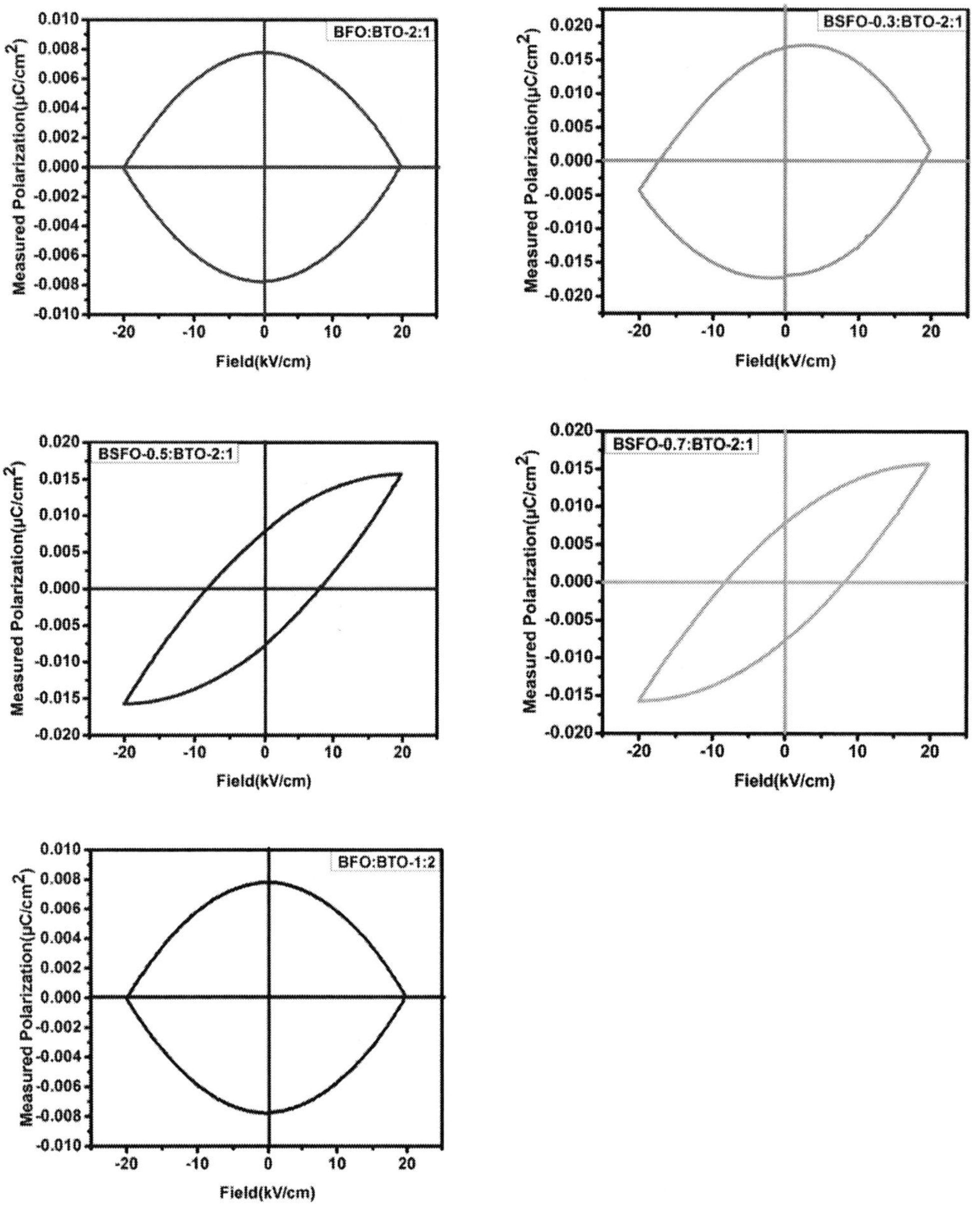

Fig 3. Polarization (P) against electric field(E) for all composites

From the above ferroelectric hysteresis loop, it is clear that all samples show the ferroelectric behavior . From the XRD, it is clear that the impurities are present for BFO:BTO (2:1), BFO:BTO(1:2) and BSFO-0.3:BTO samples. The impurities leads to increase the conductivity and leakage current. BFO: BTO (2:1) and BSFO-0.3: BTO show an enlarge shape which assigns to high leakage current density[15]. But for BSFO-0.5: BTO and BSFO-0.7:BTO have suppressed the leakage current because there is no impurities [16]. The value of measured polarization value is smaller than the reported values[17]. Ferroelectric properties are tabulated in table 2.

Table2. Dielectric constant, Dielectric loss, Saturation polarization and Remanent Polarization for all compositions and Barium Titanate.

Composition	Dielectric constant	Dielectric loss	Saturation polarization($\mu C/cm^2$)	Remanent Polarization($\mu C/cm^2$)
BTO:BFO-2:1	175	0.4615	$2.10*10^{-4}$	0.0078
BTO:BFO-1:2	93	0.1571	$2.59*10^{-4}$	0.0078
BSFO-0.3:BTO-2:1	1300	0.5288	0.0017	0.0168
BSFO-0.5:BTO-2:1	100	0.2190	0.0158	0.0081
BSFO-0.7:BTO-2:1	151	0.6337	0.0156	0.0081

4. Conclusion

A series of $BiFeO_3$-$BaTiO_3$ (BFO: BTO) in various proportions such as (1:2, 2:1), $Bi_{1-x}Sr_xFeO_3$ - $BaTiO_3$ (x=0.3,0.5,0.7) with the ratio 2:1 are successfully prepared. XRD studies confirms pure tetragonal perovskite structure of $BaTiO_3$ and rhombohedral structure for pure bismuth ferrite as well as for strontium doped samples. The dielectric studies reveal that with increasing frequency the dielectric constant value decreases. The value of the dielectric constant for the prepared samples are high when compared to the reported values and it can be used for manufacturing of capacitor dielectrics and gate dielectrics.

Acknowledgement

The authors wish to thank the support from DST, sanctioned to Vimala College Thrissur, (SR/FST/College-046/2011) and St,.Thomas college Thrissur, for structural characterization.

References

[1] H. Basantakumar Sharma, Ferroelectrics 516 (2017) 90–97.
[2] A. Pakalniškis, A. Lukowiak, G. Niaura, P. Głuchowski, D. V. Karpinsky, D.O. Alikin, A.S. Abramov, A. Zhaludkevich, M. Silibin, A.L. Kholkin, R. Skaudžius, W. Strek, A. Kareiva, J. Alloys Compd. 830 (2020) 1–22.
[3] N. Wang, X. Luo, L. Han, Z. Zhang, R. Zhang, H. Olin, Y. Yang, Nano-Micro Lett. 12 (2020).
[4] R. Chauhan, R.C. Srivastava, Pramana - J. Phys. 87 (2016) 2–7.
[5] L. V. Leonel, A. Righi, W.N. Mussel, J.B. Silva, N.D.S. Mohallem, Ceram. Int. 37 (2011) 1259–1264.
[6] S. V.S, V.E. Gopalan, I.A. Al-Omari, K.A. Malini, J. Supercond. Nov. Magn. 2021 (2022) 1–10.
[7] M.M. Vijatovic Petrovic, A. Dzunuzovic, J.D. Bobic, N. Ilic, I. Stijepovic, B.D. Stojanovic, Process. Appl. Ceram. 14 (2020) 9–18.
[8] N.M. Zali, C.S. Mahmood, S.M. Mohamad, C.T. Foo, J.A. Murshidi, AIP Conf. Proc. 1584 (2014) 160–163.
[9] T. Hussain, S.A. Siddiqi, S. Atiq, M.S. Awan, Prog. Nat. Sci. Mater. Int. 23 (2013) 487–492.
[10] J.P. Martínez-Pérez, A.M. Bolarín-Miró, C.A. Cortés-Escobedo, F. Sánchez-De Jesús, Ceram. Int. (2021).
[11] W. Spies, A. Maller, J. Linkemann, A. Frank, M. Wagner, C. Kozhuharov, B. Franzke, K. Beckert, F. Bosch, H. Eickhoff, M. Jung, O. Klepper, W. König, P.H. Mokler, R. Moshammer, F. Nolden, U. Schaaf, P. Spädtke, M. Steck, P. Zimmerer, N. Gran, W. Scheid, M.S. Pindzola, N.R. Badnell, Phys. Rev. Lett. 69 (1992) 2768–2771.
[12] T.M. Meaz, S.M. Attia, A.M. Abo El Ata, J. Magn. Magn. Mater. 257 (2003) 296–305.
[13] A. Baji, M. Abtahi, Adv. Nano Res. 1 (2013) 183–192.
[14] R. Singh, R.K. Ulrich, Electrochem. Soc. Interface 8 (1999) 26–30.
[15] H. Naganuma, Y. Inoue, S. Okamura, J. Ceram. Soc. Japan 118 (2010) 656–658.
[16] H. Naganuma, Y. Inoue, S. Okamura, IEEE Trans. Ultrason. Ferroelectr. Freq. Control 55 (2008) 1046–1050.
[17] T. Zheng, J. Wu, J. Alloys Compd. 676 (2016) 505–512.

Low Temperature Thermal Properties of Al_2O_3

Vinu T P

Assistant Professor, NSS Hindu College, Changanacherry, Kerala, INDIA-686102

drvinutp@gmail.com

Abstract. There are three Second Order Elastic Constants and six Third Order Elastic Constants for Al_2O_3 system. We calculate all the second and third Elastic Constants using Strain Elasticity theory. At standard temperature, the thermal properties of Al_2O_3 are theoretically analyzed. Grüneisen Parameters of the elastic waves at different angles of Al_2O_3 are evaluated using the elastic constants. The Brugger Gamma and normal-temperature Grüneisen Gamma are calculated by the method adopted by Menon and Ramji Rao. The volume expansion for Al_2O_3 system is positive since the normal-temperature value of Grüneisen Gamma is positive.

Keywords: Cubic, Elastic Constants, Grüneisen Parameters

1. Introduction

Using the elastic constants and pressure derivatives, calculated the mode Grüneisen Parameters. Grüneisen Parameters provide a clear picture of the powerful elastic-magneto bonding at the antiferromagnetic-paramagnetic transition [1]. Invar effect is the best-known effect in Magnetism. [2-3]. The Grüneisen parameters and their volume dependence are very interesting [4-6]. The knowledge of intermolecular interactions is very important in understanding the properties of solids [7-8]. The unharmonicity of a crystal lattice can be studied using Gruneisen Parameters, which represent the relative strain dependence of elastic wave velocity and can shed more light on the thermal and mechanical properties of materials. Elastic constants link specific heat, Gruneisen parameters, and thermal expansion. The objective of this work is to find the elastic, mechanical, and thermal properties of Al_2O_3 under normal conditions. Under normal conditions, Al_2O_3 shows a cubic crystal structure.

2. Theory

2.1. Elasticity of Al_2O_3

Murnaghan's strain elasticity theory is used to find the third-order elastic constants of Al_2O_3 [9]. The theory developed by Ramji Rao and Rajput for the strained crystal in a cubic system is used to find the elastic constants of Al_2O_3 [10]. Al_2O_3 has 3 different 2nd and 6 different 3rd order elastic constants and are given in Table 1. The second-order elastic constants are positive, while all the third-order elastic constants are negative.

Table 1. Elastic constants of Al_2O_3 in GPa.

Reference	C_{11}	C_{12}	C_{44}	C_{111}	C_{112}	C_{155}	C_{123}	C_{144}	C_{456}
Calculated Value	94.2	38.9	38.9	-881	-228	-228	-127	-127	-127

2.2 Thermal properties of Al_2O_3

Coefficient of linear thermal expansion (α) is expressed as

$$V\alpha = [(S_{11} + 2S_{12})\, \overline{\gamma}_L(T)]\, C_v$$
$$= \gamma^{Br} C_v \chi^{iso} \quad (1)$$

S_{ij} - elastic compliance coefficients, V - molar volume, C_v - molar specific heat and χ^{iso} - isothermal compressibility. $\overline{\gamma}_L(T)$ - normal-temperature Grüneisen functions. γ^{Br} - Brugger Gamma [8]. The Grüneisen function is expressed by

$$\overline{\gamma}(T) = \left[\Sigma_{qj}\, \gamma(q,j) C_v(q,j)\right]\left[\Sigma_{qj}\, C_v(q,j)\right]^{-1} \quad (2)$$

The Grüneisen functions at low temperature

$$\overline{\gamma}(-3) = \left[\int \Sigma_{j=1}^{3} \gamma_i\,(\theta,\varphi) V_i^{-3}(\theta,\varphi) d\Omega\right]^{-1} \quad (3)$$

$V_j(\theta,\varphi)$ - elastic waves wave velocity in the direction (θ,φ). γ_j - the Grüneisen parameter. The Grüneisen parameter for acoustic modes is calculated, by the method adopted by Menon and Ramji Rao [11]. Gps and acoustic wave velocities of cubic crystal are depending on θ and not the azimuth φ.

The Brugger and Fritz (1) Grüneisen parameters are expressed as

$$\gamma^{Br} =\rightleftarrows [(S_{11} + 2S_{12})\overline{\gamma}]\chi_{iso}^{-1} \quad (4)$$

The wave direction equation is given by [12]

$$\rho_0\omega^2 u_i = 4\pi^2 \Sigma_{kjl}\, u_j Y_l Y_k \left[C_{ik,jl} + \Sigma_{mn}\, \varepsilon_{mn}\left(C_{ik,jl,mn} + C_{ik,nl}\delta_{mj} + C_{nk,jl}\delta_{mi} + C_{kl,mn}\delta ij\right)\right] \quad (5)$$

Y_i's - component of the wave propagating, u_i - displacement's component. ω - angular frequency and ρ_0- unstrained crystal density. $C_{ij,kl}$ and $C_{kl,mn}$ – 2nd and 3rd order elastic constants. In terms of strain component ε, expressions for 2nd and 3rd order elastic constants are written as

$$C_{11}^{'} = C_{11} + \left[(C_{111} + 2C_{112} + 3C_{11} + 2C_{12})\frac{\varepsilon^{'}}{3}\right]$$

$$C_{12}^{'} = C_{12} + \left[(2C_{112} + C_{123} - C_{11})\frac{\varepsilon^{'}}{3}\right]$$

$$C_{44}^{'} = C_{44} + \left[(2C_{155} + C_{144} + 2C_{12} + C_{11} + 2C_{44})\frac{\varepsilon^{'}}{3}\right] \quad (6).$$

The Grüneisen parameter from the equation (4) is

$$\gamma_i = \frac{-1}{2\overline{X}_j}\left\{\frac{\left[\overline{X}_j\frac{\partial}{\partial\varepsilon}(A+B)\right] - \left[\frac{\partial}{\partial\varepsilon}(AB - C^2)\right]}{\left[2\overline{X}_j - (\overline{A}_0 + \overline{B}_0)\right]}\right\} \quad (7)$$

where

$$A = C_{11}^{'} \sin^2\theta + C_{44}^{'} \cos^2\theta,$$

$$B = C_{44}^{'} \sin^2\theta + C_{11}^{'} \cos^2\theta,$$

$$C = \sin\theta\cos\theta\left(C_{12}^{'} + C_{44}^{'}\right)$$

and

$$X_j = \rho_0 V_j^2(\theta,\varphi).$$

Table 2. Grüneisen Parameters for elastic waves at different angles θ to the crystal axis in the Al_2O_3.

θ	γ_1	$\rho_0 v_1^2$	γ_2	$\rho_0 v_2^2$	γ_3	$\rho_0 v_3^2$
0	5.2	94.2	4.3	38.9	-4.3	38.9
5	5.2	94.6	4.1	38.9	-4.3	38.5
15	5.3	97.4	3.0	38.9	-3.9	35.7
25	5.4	101.2	1.4	38.9	-3.4	31.8
35	5.5	104.3	-0.1	38.9	-2.9	28.8
45	5.5	105.4	-0.7	38.9	-2.7	27.6
55	5.5	104.3	-0.1	38.9	-2.9	28.8
65	5.4	101.2	1.4	38.9	-3.4	31.8
75	5.3	97.4	3.0	38.9	-3.9	35.7
85	5.2	94.6	4.1	38.9	-4.3	38.5
90	5.2	94.2	4.3	38.9	-4.3	38.9

3. Results and Discussion

The variation of elastic wave velocities through Al_2O_3 for the three acoustic branches is collected in Table 2, and the corresponding variations of the mode Gruneisen Parameters are shown in Figure 1. The longitudinal acoustic mode γ_1 has a minimum value of 5.2 at the angles $\theta = 0^0$ and 90^0 and a maximum value of 5.5 at $\theta = 45^0$. Here all the values are positive and this mode shows maximum anisotropy. While the transverse acoustic mode γ_2 has a maximum value of 4.3, which occurs both at the angles $\theta = 0^0$ and 90^0. -0.7 is the minimum value of γ_2 of Al_2O_3 at an angle $\theta = 45^0$. The transverse acoustic modes of γ_3 of the cubic crystal Al_2O_3 are negative. The maximum value of γ_3 for Al_2O_3 is -4.3 which occurs at both the angles 0^0 and 90^0, and a minimum value -2.7, which occurs at 45^0. Here all the values are negative and this shows a minimum anisotropy. The value for normal temperature Grüneisen Parameter γ_L is 1.5, and the Brugger Gamma is 0.5.

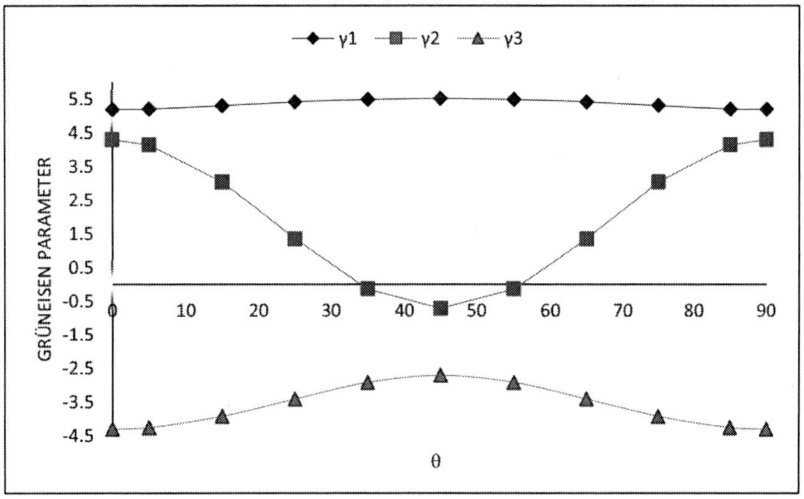

Figure 1 Variation of the Generalized Grüneisen parameters γ_j (θ) as a function of angle θ of the Al_2O_3 system.

4. Conclusion

The longitudinal acoustic mode γ_1 varies from 5.5 to 5.2. While the transverse acoustic modes γ_2 varies from 4.3 to -0.72 and γ_3 varies from -2.7 to -4.3 respectively. Thus, the anisotropy of Gruneisen Parameter decreases as we go from γ_1 to γ_3.

References

[1] Metcalfe R D, Saunders G A, Kankurtarn M and Alberts H L, *Phi. Magn. B.* 79 (2013), 663.
[2] Leonid Dubrovinsky, Dubrovinskaia N and Borje Johansson, *Phys. Rev. Lett.* 86 (2001), 4851.
[3] Manosa L I, Saunders G A, Cankurtarn M and Albert H L, *Phys. Rev. B.* 45 (1992), 2224.
[4] Singh A V, Sharma J C and Shankar J, *Physica.* 94 B (1978), 331.
[5] Perrin G and Delannoy M J -Coutrins, *J. Phys. Chem. Solids.* 49 (1998), 1397.
[6] Gopala Rao R V and Venkatesh R, *J. Phys. Chem. Solids.* 58 (1997), 939.
[7] Mary Anne White, MerinGasat G and David W I F, *Sol. Stat. Commn.* 94 (1995),481.
[8] Brugger K and Fritz T C, *Phys. Rev. A* 157 (1967), 524.
[9] Murnaghan F D, '*Finite Deformation of an Elastic Solid*'. Wiley, New York, 1951.
[10] Ramji Rao and Rajput, *Phy. Stat. Sol.* (b) 94 (1974), 691.
[11] Menon C S and Ramji Rao R, *J. Phys. Chem. Solids* 33 (1972), 2129.
[12] Thurston R N and Brugger K, *Phys. Rev.* 133, 6A (1964), A1604.More references

Structural Properties of Mercapto Stabilizers on an Autocatalytic Pure Copper Metal Deposition

P Balaramesh[*, 1], S Jayalakshmi[2], V Anitha[3], Absara Fdo[4] and P Venkatesh[5]

***Corresponding Author: P Balaramesh, email -pbr.sh@rmkec.ac.in**

[1]Department of Chemistry, R.M.K.Engineering College, Chennai, Tamil Nadu- 601206, India.
[2]Department of Chemistry, VISTAS, Chennai, Tamil Nadu-600117, India.
[3]Department of Chemistry, Velammal Engineering College, Chennai, Tamil Nadu -600066.
[4]Department of Chemistry, R.M.K. College of Engineering and Technology, Chennai, India.
[5]Department of Chemistry, Pachaiyappa's College, Chennai, Tamil Nadu- 600030, India.

Abstract. This article focuses on the effect of mercapto additives on electroless pure copper thin film deposition. The copper deposits produced by the autocatalytic bath comprising xylitol, glyoxylic acid, and potassium hydroxide as complexing agents, reducing agents, and pH adjusters, respectively, were of superior grade. pH 13.0 ± 0.25 and 45°C were ideal bathing conditions. In order to improve the thermal stability and the good take hold off with copper, a trace quantity of methanesulphonic acid was used. Nitrogen and sulphur containing heterocyclic compounds such as 2-mercaptopyridine and 2-mercaptopyrimidine were used as the bath stabilizers. 1 ppm of the mercapto stabilizers stabilizes the bath conditions and their inhibiting potential was studied. The influence of the fundamental bath parameters on autocatalytic pure copper deposition have been investigated in our study. Physical properties and stability were characterized by the gravimetric method. The diffraction method was used to examine the structural characteristics of the copper deposits.
Key words: glyoxylic acid, mercapto additives, methanesulphonic acid, pure copper, xylitol

1. Introduction

In the recent years, forty-six methods of metal deposition techniques have been regulated and recognized by scientists. For the metal coating process, electro plating is the most supporting principle among all the available techniques. Owing to the pronounced physical and electrochemical properties, thin film coating technology has garnered significant attention in the field of electronic industry [1-4]. Electroless plating process has fulfilled the expected demand in the fabrication of decorative articles, semiconductors, integrated circuits and through-hole plating in the printed circuit boards [5-8]. Emerging applications of this technique lie in areas such as, fabrication of electromagnetic interference shielding materials, ceramic or polymeric nanoparticles, energy conversion, aerospace, biomedical and automotive industries etc. [9-12].

Initially, Bernard, Brashear, and Wurtz [13-17] were interested in silver and nickel metals. F.D. Chattway successfully coated glass with copper in 1907 using a combination of copper and formaldehyde [18]. Due to its reduced electrical resistivity and stronger electro migration resistance, copper is envisioned as the present and future connection material in high-end microprocessors and memory devices [19-21]. Moreover, electroless copper coatings provide protection for common metal surfaces that are prone to corrosion. Selection of suitable complexing agent, reducing agent and pH controller is the most important criteria for electroless or autocatalytic process for achieving finest metal deposits [22-23].

In this work, biodegradable pentahydroxylic xylitol is used as an environmentally friendly chelating agent [24], since it provides better stability and possesses good chelating properties for Cu (II) ion in alkaline medium.

Glyoxylic acid is a good reducing agent for electroless copper baths, which is capable of completely reducing divalent copper to metallic copper, and not to intermediate cuprous oxide [25]. A little quantity of methanesulphonic acid acts as a potential electrolyte in this coating process. Table 1 shows the applications and the uses of methanesulphonic acid in various fields [26].

Table 1. Applications of methanesulphonic acid in various fields.

Field	Applications
Metallurgy	Electro polishing
Batteries	Electrolyte for high energy density
Advanced material	Surface modification reaction
Polymer composites	Synthesis of nanocomposites
Pharmaceutical industry	Efficient acid catalyst
High performance acidic cleaner	Rust removal
Electroless plating	Electrolytes

Heterocyclic compounds such as 2-mercaptopyridine and 2-mercaptopyrimidine are utilized as bath stabilizers and modifiers for copper deposition as well. Table 2 shows the autocatalytic bath compositions and the required conditions.

Table 2. Composition for xylitol based optimized electroless plating bath.

Bath contains	Xylitol Plain bath	Stabilizers used bath
CuMS (II) ion contacting salt	3 g/L	3 g/L
Xylitol	20 g/L	20 g/L
Glyoxylic acid	10 g/L	10 g/L
KOH (pH)	13.0 ± 0.25	13.0 ± 0.25
Temperature	45 °C	45 °C
Stabilizers	0 ppm	1 ppm
2-Mercaptopyriminde (2-MPm), and 2-Mercaptopyridine (2-MPy)		

2. Methodology

Analytical-grade chemicals were used to create an eco-friendly electrolyte. On an epoxy sheet (2.0 X 2.0 X 0.1 cm), the electroless Cu deposition was carried out in a 100 ml beaker. The substrate was polished with fine grit paper before being rinsing with double-distilled water in preparation for deposition. After rinsing with distilled water, the substrate was surface etched using a solution of $KMnO_4$ and $H2SO_4$. To facilitate improved deposition rate and to improve adhesive properties of the Cu thin film, the surface was sensitized using SnCl2 solution (SnCl2 mixed with HCl) and activated by dipping in a solution of HCl and $PdCl_2$. The substrate surface has to be pre coated with palladium prior electroless deposition process to activate the substrate surface. The stannous ions reduce the palladium ions to finely divided metallic palladium nuclei on the surface of the substrate according to the equation.

$$Sn^{2+} + Pd^{2+} \longrightarrow Sn^{4+} + Pd \quad (1)$$

The palladium nuclei should then initiate the autocatalytic plating process.
The complete set of reactions and mechanisms for electroless plating process is given below,

$$CHOCOOH + OH^- \xrightarrow{Pd} H_2 \uparrow + CHOCOO^- \quad (2)$$

$$Cu^{2+} + H_2 + 2OH^- \longrightarrow Cu + 2H_2O \quad (3)$$

$$CHOCOOH + OH^- \xrightarrow{Cu} H_2 \uparrow + CHOCOO^- \quad (4)$$

Equations (2) and (4) resemble each other, except in the fact that the catalyst Pd is replaced by Cu, hence the reactions proceed auto catalytically. Glyoxylic acid is an appropriate reducing agent for electroless copper plating.

The overall reaction is,

$$Cu^{2+} + 2CHOCOOH + 4OH^- \rightarrow Cu + 2HC_2O_3^- + 2H_2O + H_2 \uparrow \quad (5)$$

Similarly, the overall reaction of xylitol based methanesulphonate in the plating process is represented below.

$$CuMsXy(OH)_3^{2-} + 2CHOCOOH + 4OH^- \rightarrow Cu + H_2 \uparrow + 2CHOCOO^- + 2H_2O + MsXy^- \quad (6)$$

2.1 Formula for Physical properties

$$Deposition\ rate\left(\frac{\mu m}{h}\right)T = \frac{W \times 10^4}{dAt} \quad (7)$$

Where 'W' is the deposit's mass (g), 'd' is the film material's density (g/cm^3), 'A' is the film's coated surface area (cm^3), and 't' is the coating time (h).

2.2 Effect of bath parameters

The following bath parameters and their influence on autocatalytic copper deposition were studied.

- Concentration of copper
- pH
- Reducing agent
- Temperature
- Stability

2.3 Formulae for Structural property - X-ray diffraction studies

The Scherer equation [27] is written as follows to determine the particle size:

$$D = \frac{K\lambda}{\beta \cos\theta} \quad (8)$$

'K' is the Scherer constant, and is the wavelength of the light used in the diffraction. The angle is measured at the 'Full-Width Half Maximum' of the sharp peaks. The shape of the particle is described by the Scherer constant (K) in the formula above, which is often assigned a value of 0.89. Determination of crystallite size 'D' was done using Hall-Williamson method [28]. The plot gives straight line with slope and intercept.

$$\beta \cos\theta = \frac{K\lambda}{D} + \eta \sin\theta \quad (9)$$

The formula is used to determine the specific surface area of copper deposits.

$$S = \frac{6 \times 10^3}{dD} \quad (10)$$

'D' is the crystallite size in nanometers, and'd' is the assumed density of copper in cubic centimeters (8.96 g/cm^3). Frequently, the percent of crystallinity "Xc" is computed by

$$X_c = \left\{\frac{0.24}{\beta}\right\}^3 \quad (11)$$

The following relation may be used to determine the micro strain.

$$(\varepsilon) = \frac{\beta \cos\theta}{4} \quad (12)$$

It is possible to determine the dislocation density's value by

$$(\delta) = \frac{1}{D^2} \quad (13)$$

The unit volume $V = 0.865\ a^2c$ (14)

Where 'a' and 'c' are lattice constant.

3. Results and Discussion

3.1 Bath parameter effects on copper deposition rate

The effect of bath parameters such as concentration of copper, pH, reducing agent, temperature and the stability were studied. In order to optimize the electroless bath, chelating agent and reducing agent were prepared in different concentrations. Following the systematic procedures, the bath condition was observed, recorded and the deposition rate was calculated. On interpreting the data from Table 3, figure 1, 2 and 3, it is clear that the deposition rate also increases as the concentration of copper and glyoxylic acid rises. But, from the stability point of view, the copper concentration at 3g/L and glyoxylic acid at 10g/L gives a more stable bath, than the other concentrated baths. The concentration of the metal ion is variable depending on the nature of the reducing agents and bath constituents. The bath composition is fixed on a trial-and-error method.

Table 3. Deposition rate of copper deposits on the effect of concentration of copper, pH, and reducing agent.

Effect of concentration of copper		**Effect of pH**		**Effect of reducing agent**		**Bath condition**
Concentration of copper (g/L)	**Deposition rate (µm/h)**	**pH**	**Deposition rate (µm/h)**	**Glyoxylic acid (g/L)**	**Deposition rate (µm/h)**	
1	0.86	12.50	1.25	1	0.92	Stable
2	1.92	12.75	2.32	5	2.56	Stable
3	3.02	13.0	3.02	10	3.02	More Stable
4	4.36	13.25	2.58	15	4.68	Less Stable
5	5.18	13.50	1.82	20	5.82	Un Stable

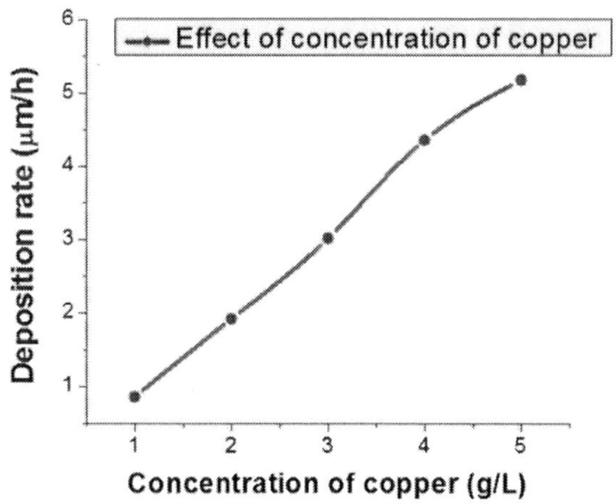

Figure 1. Effect of copper concentration in an electroless bath containing xylitol.

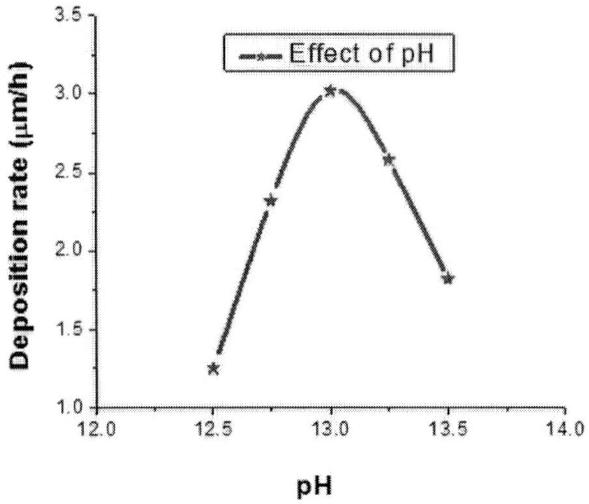

Figure 2. Effects of pH in an electroless bath containing xylitol.

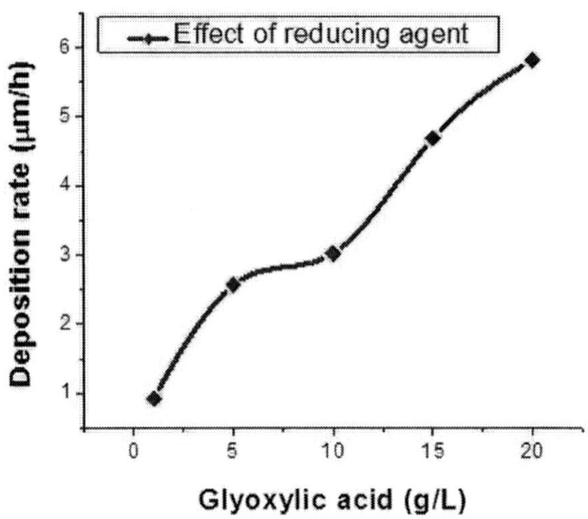

Figure 3. Effect of glyoxylic acid concentration in xylitol containing electroless bath

The pH has a major role in the electroless deposition bath. A methanesulphonate bath that contains xylitol has enhanced copper deposition in alkaline media with pH values above 12.0. Using potassium hydroxide as the pH adjuster, the pH was increased by a difference of 0.25 from 12.50 to 13.50. Initially, the deposition rate increases on increasing the pH, but at pH 13.0, the deposition rate reached a maximum rate of 3.02 μm/h and the bath condition was observed to be more stable. In general, the electroless copper plating starts at an alkaline pH, increases with pH and reaches the maximum deposition rate. Further increase in the pH may lead to bath decomposition and hence the deposition gets affected. Nevertheless, on increasing the pH beyond 13.0, a decrease in the deposition rate was observed and the electroless bath conditions also turned out to be unstable.

3.2 The effect of temperature on bath condition

Since glyoxylic acid functions as both an electron donor and a reducing agent in the autocatalytic bath, the effect of temperature plays a key role in this work. Glyoxylic acid was not favored in supplying electrons at a room temperature of 30 °C and the stability was also questionable. By increasing the temperature, glyoxylic acid enhanced the supply of electrons and the deposition rate has changed drastically. Table 4 and figure 4 show that the deposition rate and the bath condition have been favored in the temperature range from 45°C to 60°C. However, more stable bath was observed at 45 °C and a considerable deposition rate has also been observed.

Table 4. Values of copper deposit on the effect of temperature on Xylitol containing methanesulphonate bath.

Effect of temperature						
Temperature (°C)		**30**	**45**	**60**	**75**	**90**
Bath condition		Stable	Stable	Less Stable	Unstable	Unstable
Xylitol plain bath	Deposition rate (μm/h)	1.12	3.02	3.48	4.62	5.80
Stabilizers used bath	Bath condition	Stable	More Stable	stable	Less stable	Unstable
2-Mercaptopyridine	Deposition rate (μm/h)	0.82	2.78	3.21	4.28	5.32
2-Mercaptopyriminde		0.78	2.62	3.08	4.16	5.16

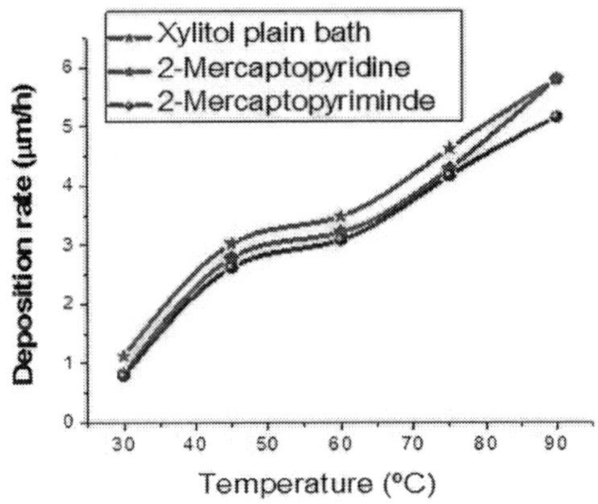

Figure 4. Effect of temperature in xylitol containing electroless bath.

3.3 Effect of concentration of additives on bath stability

Heterocyclic organic stabilizers such as the 2-mercaptopyridine (2-MPy) and 2-mercaptopyrimidine (2-MPm) are used as stabilizers in this work. Addition of small amount of additives modified the deposition rate and structure of copper deposits. Furthermore, the purity of the metal deposits was also enhanced.

In general, in an autocatalytic bath, an additive can act either as an inhibitor or as an accelerator. The accelerating or inhibiting potential of an additive is confirmed by comparing the calculated data of deposition rate with the respective plain bath.

Usually, addition of an accelerator leads to an enhanced deposition rate than the plain bath, where as inclusion of an inhibitor results in reduced deposition rate than the plain bath. In this work, both 2-MPy and 2-MPm have acted as inhibitors, since these organic compounds are having a lone pair of electron such as nitrogen and sulphur.

These heteroatoms get adsorbed more on the substrate and further, they decrease the rate of plating. The presence of nitrogen atom influences the conjugation effect and the presence of sulphur atom enhances the chemisorption on the substrate.

3.4 The effect of copper deposits by increasing time

The deposition rate of xylitol plain bath (i.e.) without the addition of stabilizers was observed as 3.02 (μm/h) at 60 minutes. However, in Table 5 and 6, figure 4, 5, 6 and 7 shows that the rate of deposition decreased after the addition of 0.1 ppm concentration of 2-MPy and 2-MPm at the same 60 minutes time period of deposition. Upon increasing the concentration of stabilizers up to 1 ppm, a drop off in the deposition rate was noted. There were no significant changes in deposition at higher concentration of additives beyond 1 ppm at 60 minutes. But, the deposition rate drastically changed by increasing the time upto 120 minutes with a time interval of 15 minutes.

Lower concentrated 2-Mpy and 2-MPm were stable upto 120 minutes and no significant changes were observed by further increase in time. At higher concentration (5 ppm and 10 ppm) of 2-Mpy and 2-MPm, no significant change in deposition rate was observed at 60 minutes and also further increase in time has shown no much effect on the deposition, while comparing the bath with 1 ppm concentration. The chemisorptions and conjugation effect on the substrate was favorable only at lower concentration.

Table 5. Values of copper deposits on the stability of bath at Elevated temperature and higher concentration of 2-MPy (ppm)

2-Mercaptopyridine (ppm)	Time (minutes)						Bath stability
	60	75	90	105	120	135	
0.1	2.92	4.12	5.36	6.58	7.16	No significant	
0.5	2.84	3.92	4.96	6.12	6.76	change in deposition	
1.0	2.78	3.86	4.48	5.56	6.28	7.56	Stable
5	No significant	2.86	3.56	4.32	4.92	5.78	
10	changes in deposition	2.82	3.26	4.28	4.56	5.12	

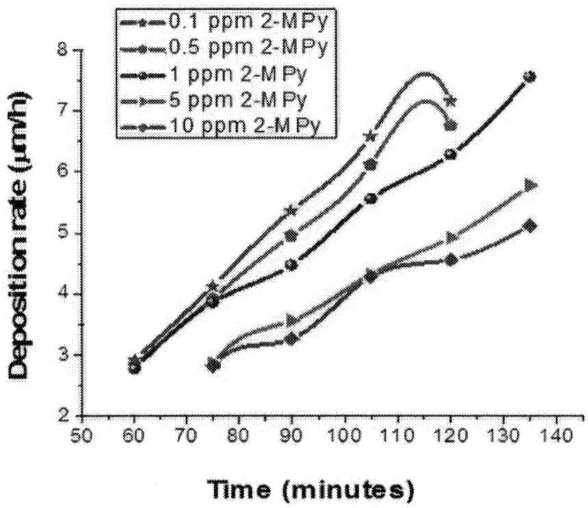

Figure 5. Stability of bath at higher concentration of 2-MPy (1 ppm) at different time intervals.

The copper ion in xylitol containing methanesulphonate bath has actively gained the electron from the glyoxylic acid donor. 2-Mpy and 2-MPm act as modifiers to change the deposition rate at higher concentration. Moreover, 2-Mpy and 2-MPm have soft sulphur donor atoms, which can easily combine with copper ion to give larger complexes and hence, steric factor is also a contributing factor for reduced deposition rate.

The mobility of copper ion was stationary at higher ppm and above 120 minutes. So, it was concluded that 2-Mpy and 2-MPm stabilize the bath at all concentration. But, excellent deposition rate and bath optimization were observed only at 1 ppm.

Table 6. Values of copper deposits on the stability of bath at Elevated temperature and higher concentration of 2-MPm (ppm)

2-Mercaptopyrimidine (ppm)	**Time (minutes)** 60	75	90	105	120	135	**Bath stability**
0.1	2.86	3.96	5.16	6.36	6.96	No significant change in deposition	Stable
0.5	2.74	3.82	4.86	5.92	6.42		
1.0	2.62	3.64	4.28	5.12	6.28	7.16	
5	No significant changes in deposition	2.96	3.28	4.12	4.76	5.26	
10		2.68	3.12	3.96	4.36	4.86	

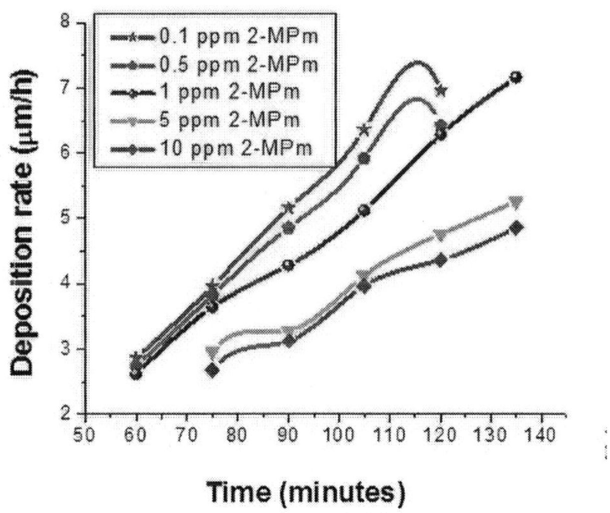

Figure 6. Stability of bath at higher concentration of 2-MPm. (1 ppm).

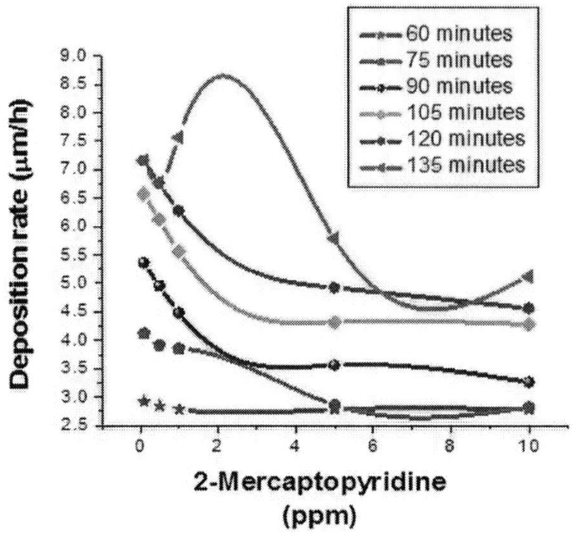

Figure 7. Effect of copper deposits by increasing time in xylitol containing electroless bath with 2-MPy.

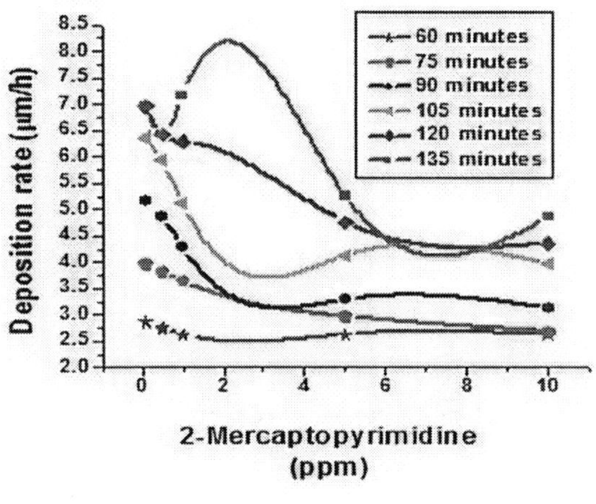

Figure 8. Increase in time increases the rate of copper deposition in a 2-MPm electroless bath containing xylitol.

3.5 Structural properties

Structural properties of copper deposits were assessed by analyzing the peaks at (111), (200) and (220) planes. Table 7 and figure 9 and 10 shows that the texture of copper usually has a preferred orientation of (111) plane with FCC structure. Conversely, in our work, the nature of high conductivity and the solubility of biodegradable methanesulphonic acid have shifted the orientation from lower plane (111) to higher plane (200). Hall-Williamson method is better than the usually used Debye-Scherer equation for crystallite size. Crystallite size can be calculated by relating FWHM and cosθ values.

Table 7. Structural properties on xylitol containing methanesulphonic acid with stabilizers at 1 ppm.

Structural properties	Xylitol plain bath	Xylitol with 2.-mercaptopyridine	Xylitol with 2-mercaptopyrimidine
Crystallite size (nm) (Debye-Scherer)	121	92	86
Crystallite size (nm) (Hall-Williamson)	121.86	91.82	85.98
Intercept value (Hall-Williamson)	2.252 x10^{-3}	2.989 x10^{-3}	3.192 x10^{-3}
Dislocation density (ρ in m /m^3)	6.734 x 10^{-5}	1.186 x 10^{-4}	1.353 x 10^{-4}
Fraction of crystallinity (g/cm^3)	0.8784 x 10^3	0.3885 x 10^3	0.318 x 10^3
Micro strain (10^{-3}lin^{2}m^{-4})	0.6265 x 10^{-3}	0.8222 x 10^{-3}	0.8788 x 10^{-3}
Specific surface area (m^2/g)	5.495	7.293	7.788
Unit cell volume (A^3)	47.674	47.595	47.124

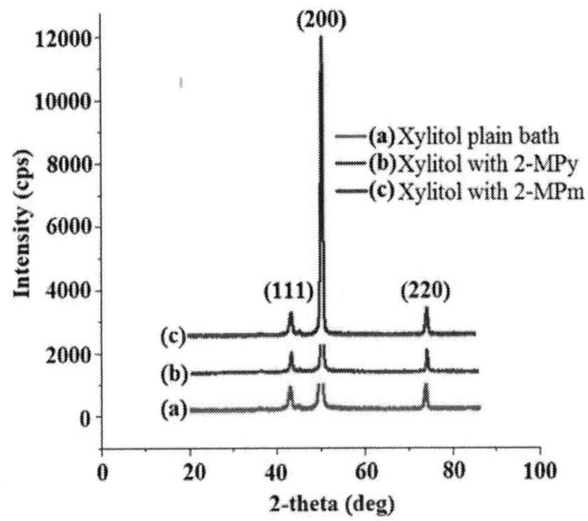

Figure 9. XRD pattern of xylitol plain bath with 2-Mpy and 2-MPm at 1 ppm.

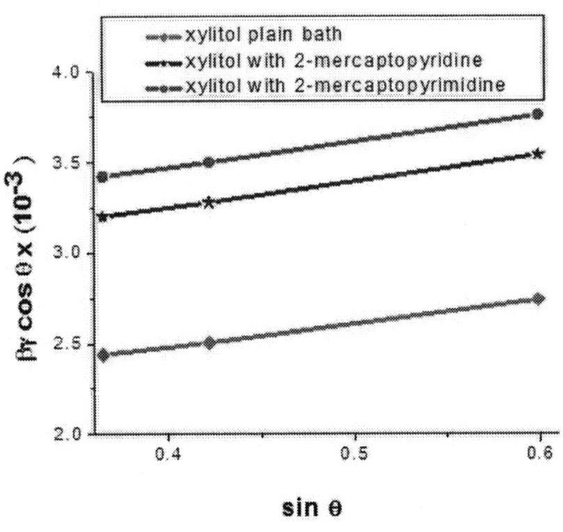

Figure 10. Hall-Williamson plot for electroless coated copper deposits to Xylitol plain bath with 2-Mpy and 2-MPm at 1 ppm.

In general, line width and crystallite size have an inverse relationship with specific surface area value, which is directly proportional to line width. Based on the crystallite size, d-spacing and theoretical density of the copper the lattice parameters were calculated to be, a = b = c = 0.361491 nm and standard unit cell volume (V) was 47.238 for pure copper deposit. On comparing our experimental data with the standard values, it is evident that volume of plain bath deposit (47.674), 2-MPy deposit (47.595) and 2-MPm deposit (47.124) matches with the ASTM & standard JCPDS card no. 04-0836.

4. Conclusions

- Xylitol containing methane sulphonated bath favored copper deposition in an alkaline medium at pH above 12.0. The deposition rate reached a maximum rate of 3.02 μm/h at pH 13.0 and more stable bath was observed at 45 °C by increasing the temperature.
- Even though, increase in concentration of copper and glyoxylic acid resulted in an enhanced deposition rate, copper concentration at 3g/L and glyoxylic acid at 10g/L has been noted to result in a more stable bath, than the other concentrated baths.
- The addition of stabilizers 2-MPy and 2-MPm up to 1 ppm eventually caused the deposition rate to be lower than the deposition rate of xylitol plain bath for deposition period of 60 minutes. This shows that both 2-MPy and 2-MPm act as inhibitors. Besides, no significant changes were recognized in deposition rate at higher concentration of additives beyond 1 ppm.
- Organic compounds having lone pair of electrons, such as, nitrogen and sulphur have greater adsorption onto the substrate surface. Nitrogen atom influences the conjugation effect and sulphur atom enhances the chemisorptions on the substrate. These factors contribute to the inhibiting effect of 2-MPy and 2-MPm.
- Higher concentration of 2-MPy and 2-MPm at 60 minutes resulted in higher deposition rate and no significant changes in deposition was witnessed, when the deposition duration was increased to 120 minutes.
- 2-MPy and 2-MPm were stabilizing the bath at all concentration. Steric factor influence decreases the deposition rate at a higher concentration.
- Hall-Williamson method is better than the usually used Debye-Scherer equation for crystallite size. Calculated unit cell volume and lattice parameters are in good agreement with the standard values as that of ASTM & standard JCPDS card no. 04-0836.

References

[1] Tseng W T, Lo C H, Lee S C 2001 *J Electrochem. Soc* **148** C327-C332.
[2] Hong-Hui Hsu, Kun-Hsin Lin, Su-Jien Lin, Jien-Wei Yeh 2001 *J Electrochem. Soc* **148** C47-C53.
[3] Yagi S, Nakanishi H, Matsubara E, Ichitsubo T, Hosoya K 2008 *J. Electrochem. Soc* **155** D474-D479.
[4] Dev A, Tandon S, Jha P 2020 *Sadhana* **45** 156-160.
[5] Guo R H, Jiang S Q, Yuen C W, Ng M C F 2009 *Surf. Engin* **25** 101-105.
[6] Milowska K Z, Burda M, Wolanicka L, Bristowe P D, Koziol K K 2019 *nanoscale* **11** 145–157.
[7] Lahiri A, Borisenko N, Olschewski M, Pulletikurthi G, Endres F 2018 *Faraday Discuss* **206** 339–351.
[8] Qin Guangchao, Zhang Yu, Yuan Manman, Chen Rui Liu Youhao 2019 *J. Mat. Sci.Electronics* **30** 9767-9774.
[9] Uraz C, Macit S 2018 *J. of Sci. & Engin* **20** 369-375.
[10] Martins J I, Nunes M C 2016 *Surf. Engi* **32** 363-371.
[11] Faraji S, Faraji A H, Noori S R, Ani F N 2015 *Surf. Eng* **31** 179-188.
[12] Coombs Jr C F. 2001 printed Circuit Handbook McGraw-Hill, New York, United States, 5th edition.
[13] Bernard S 1798 'The Repertory of Arts and Manufactures' **5** 71-81.

[14] Justus Von Liebig 1835 *Ann. D. Pharm* **14** 134-144.
[15] Roux F A. U. S. Patent 1,207,218, 1916
[16] Saubestre EB 1959 'Tech. Proc. of the Golden Jubilee convention of American Electroplater Societ, Electroless copper plating **46** 264-265.
[17] Brenner A R, Riddell G E 1946 *J. Res. Natl. Bur* **37** 31-34.
[18] Chattaway F D 1907 *Proc. Roy. Soc.,* London **80 - A** 88-92.
[19] Yokomine K, Shimizu N, Miyamoto Y, Iwata Y, Love D, Newman K 2001 'IEEE Electronic Components and Technology Conference, 51st proceedings 1384-1394.
[20] Cho Sang Jin, Nguyen Trieu, Boo Jin Hyo 2011 *J. of Nanosci. & Nanotech* **11** 5328-5333.
[21] Oh K W, Kim D J, Kim S H 2002 *J of App.Poly. Sci* **84** 1369-1379.
[22] Xu L, Zhou K, Xu H, Huang L 2001 *App. Suf.Sci* **183** 58-61.
[23] Shukla S, Seal S, Akesson J 2001 *App. Suf. Sci* **181** 35-50.
[24] Balaramesh P et.al 2014 Int. *J. of Inno. Res. and studies* 3 167-181.
[25] Lu Yu, Lian Guo, Robert Preisser, Rohan Akolkar 2013 *J.Electrochem. Soc* **60** D3004-D 3008.
[26] Kshatriya R B, Machi J K, Nazeruddin G M 2014 *Orient J. of chem* **30** 857-862.
[27] Debye P, Scherer P 1916 *Phy. Ziet* **17** 277-283.
[28] Williamson G K, Hall W 1953 *Acta Metallurgica* **1** 22-26.

Extraction and Hydrolysis of Naringin from Citrus fruit peels

Akrati Sant[1], Imran Ahmad[1], Sonika Bhatia[*1]

[1]Department of Chemistry, Isabella Thoburn College, Lucknow 226007, UP, India

*Email: sonikaitc2@gmail.com

Abstract. Naringenin, a flavonoid belonging to the flavanones subclass has been reported to have several promising biological activities like antioxidant, antitumor, anticancer, antiviral, anti-inflammatory & estrogenic activities. Naringin is found in the glycosidic form in citrus fruits like grapefruit, orange, and lemons. Naringenin is obtained by the hydrolysis of the glycoside naringin. In the present study, environmentally benign extraction methods have been reported for the extraction of naringin from the peels of grapefruit (Citrus X paradisi), an agricultural waste of the fruit juice industry. Successful isolation of naringin from both fresh and dry albedo of grapefruit has been carried out under three different conditions to yield pure white crystalline naringin. Further, simple acidic hydrolysis under three different conditions has been standardized to yield naringenin in a relatively good yield. Characterization of both naringin and naringenin has been done using NMR and thin layer chromatography.

Keywords: naringin, extraction, hydrolysis, naringenin

1. Introduction

In today's growing world, the waste output is increasing in huge volumes on a daily basis, affecting the ecosystem and eventually human health. Citrus fruits are one of the most extensively grown fruits the world over, resulting in an enormous number of byproducts that are rich in flavonoids, cellulose, pectin, soluble sugars, polyphenols, dietary fibers, and essentialoils [1,2]. Unfortunately, a substantial number of leftovers from citrus fruits end up as garbagein farm fields and disposal bins. Every year, the citrus processing industry generates massive volumes of trash, with citrus peel waste accounting for over half of the wet fruit mass [2]. The waste citrus fruit peels are of great interest among researchers and scientists as they are a rich source of phytochemicals that are beneficial in treating various long-standing diseases. Flavonoids are potent phytochemicals present in vegetables and fruits with many healthbenefits. Subclasses of flavonoids are flavanols, flavones, flavanones, flavonols, anthocyanins and isoflavones [3]. One of the promising phytochemicals is naringin and its a-glycolate form naringenin. They are flavanones, a subclass of flavonoids, and possess many biological activities like anticancer, antidiabetic, anti-inflammatory, antimicrobial, antiosteoporosis, anti-estrogenic, anti-oxidant, and have been found to be effective in treating cardio and neurovascular diseases [4]. Applications of flavonoids are also reported in the pharmaceuticals, medicinal, nutraceutical and cosmetic industries [5]. Various flavonoids are found in grapefruit, lemon, oranges, and lime, naringin being one of them [4]. Grapefruit which is the result of the crossing of pomelo and the sweet orange is a rich source of naringin [6]. Naringin has been extracted from waste grapefruit peels by cold extraction and Soxhlet extraction. Extraction of natural products is quite challenging as they contain heat-labile linkages and some essential oils. In literature, enzymatic hydrolysis of naringin has been used to convert it into it's a-aglycone form naringenin [7]. Simple and efficient hydrolysis of naringin under different conditions can also be carried out [8,9]. In this work, hydrolysis of naringin has been carried out by 3 methods to yield the a-aglycone naringenin. In this study, we standardized 3 ways of extraction and hydrolysis methods under different conditions.

2. Materials and Method

2.1 Chemicals and instruments

Commercially available ethanol, methanol, chloroform, (all solvents from Rankem, India), and sulfuric acid (Rankem, India) were used in the process. The extraction process and reactions were monitored using TLC plates. ^{1}H NMR spectra were recorded at Avll HD-300(FT NMR) on Bruker equipment (Avance) using deuterated methanol and acetone as a solvent.

2.2 Grapefruits and Grapefruit peels

Fresh grapefruits (*Citrus x paradisi L.*) were purchased and grapefruit peels were also collected from juice centers of Dehradun, Uttarakhand. The albedo (inner white spongy part) from the grapefruit peels was separated from the rest of the peel which is flavedo (orange exterior). The albedo was then air-dried for 4-5 days. The fresh albedos were also hand-sliced into small pieces and churned in a grinder for the direct extraction process.

2.3 Extraction of Naringin

The extraction of naringin from the albedos of grapefruit (Figure 1) was carried out with some modifications to the methods described in the literature [6]. The extraction process was carried out by three different methods to get a better yield of naringin using both dry and fresh albedo.

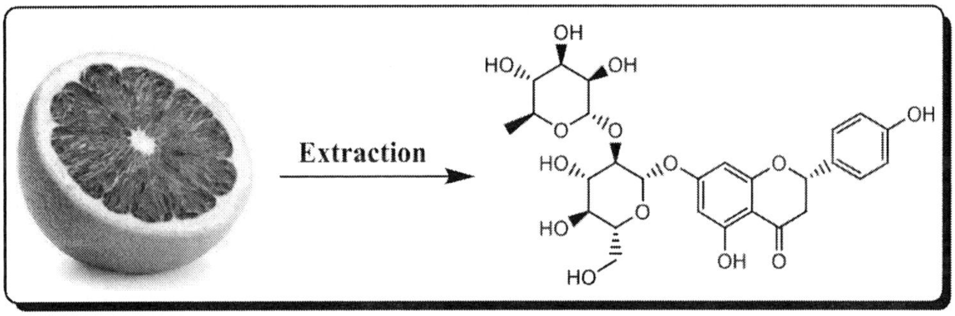

Figure 1: Extraction of Naringin from grapefruit albedo

2.3.1 Method 1: Soxhlet extraction using dry albedo in methanol: The extraction was carried out using the Soxhlet apparatus with 40g of the dried albedo of grapefruit (figure 2). The solvent used for Soxhlet extraction was methanol and temperature was maintained at 55-65 °C for approximately 3 h. After leaving the extract overnight, colourless crystals of pectin (figure 3) were collected from the extract and the remaining total methanolic extract was reduced to 10-12 g under reduced pressure at 45-50 °C and 20-25 cm^3 of water added to that extract. After stirring for 30 min at 60-70 °C, this methanolic extract was left for 3 days in a stoppered flask after adding 3 cm^3 of chloroform in it. On standing for 3 days, fine naringin crystals were formed and were filtered out using sintered crucible and collected. The progress of extraction was monitored and the purity of the obtained compound was checked using glass TLC plates coated with silica gel-G by qualigens in the solvent system methanol, water, and acetic acid (5:4:1) as shown in figure 4 and validated using NMR spectroscopy (figure 5).

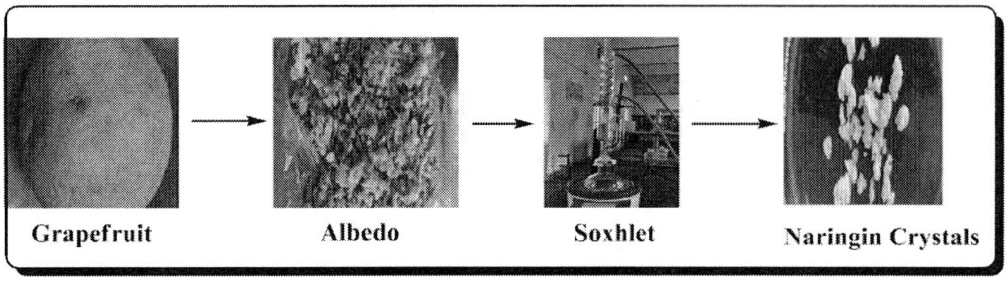

Figure 2: Pictorial representation of the conducted experiment for the extraction

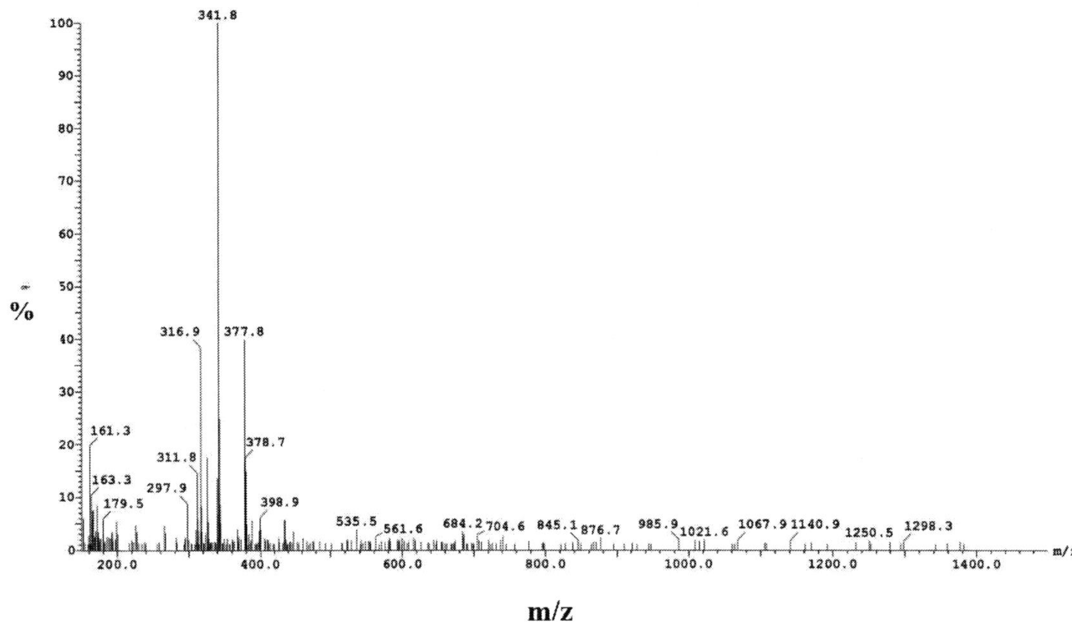

Figure 3: Mass Spectra of Pectin

2.3.2 Method 2: Soxhlet extraction using fresh albedo in methanol: The extraction was carried out using the Soxhlet apparatus with 40 g of the fresh albedo of grapefruit. The solvent used for Soxhlet extraction was methanol and the temperature was maintained at 55-65 °C for approximately 3 h After that methanolic extract was reduced to 10-12 g under reduced pressure at 45-50 °C, and 20-25 cm^3 of water was added to the extract. After stirring for 30 min at 60-70 °C this methanolic extract was left for 3 days in a stoppered flask after adding 3 cm^3 of chloroform in it. After 3 days, fine naringin crystals were filtered using sintered and collected. Characterization was done as described in method 1.

2.3.3 Method 3: Cold extraction of dry albedo: Cold extraction using 30g of the dried albedo of grapefruit has been carried out in methanol. The albedo was immersed in methanol and left for 4 days in a stoppered flask. After four days, the methanolic extract was decanted and reduced to 10-12 cm^3 under reduced pressure of 45-50 °C. After the addition of 20-25 cm^3 water to the methanolic extract, it was stirred for 30 min at 60-70 °C temperature. The methanolic extract was left undisturbed for 3 days in a stoppered flask after adding 3 cm^3 of chloroform. After 3 days, naringin crystals were filtered using sintered and collected. The characterization was done as described in method 1.

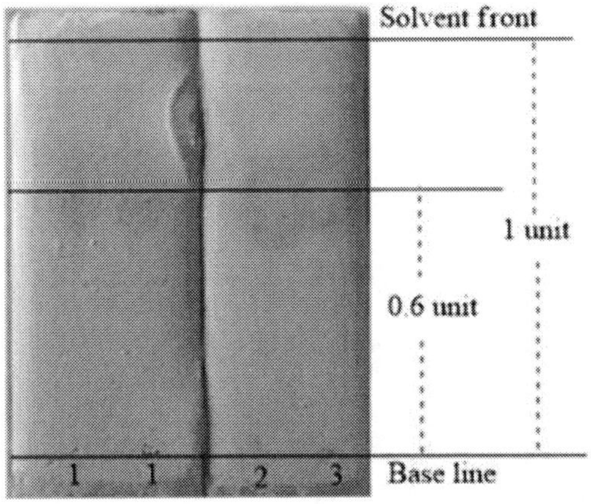

*Solvent System- Methanol: Water: Acetic Acid (5:4:1)

*R_f = 0.6

1-Soxhlet extraction of naringin from Method 1
2-Soxhlet extraction of naringin from Method 2
3-Cold extraction of naringin from Method 3

Figure 4. Comparative TLC of naringin extracted by methods 1,2 & 3

2.3.4 Analytical data of Naringin: White solid, M.P- 169.1°C- 170°C. ^{1}H NMR (MeOD, 300 MHz): δ 1.3 (dd, J= 6.3 Hz, 3H), 2.8-2.7 (dd, J = 17.1 Hz and 3 Hz, 1H), 3.9-3.1 (m, 10H), 3.89(dd, 1H), 5.25 (s,1H), 5.1 (dd, 1H), 5.35 (dd, J = 13.5Hz and 11.7 Hz, 1H), 6.18 (dd, J = 2.1 Hz, 1H), 6.15 (dd, J = 4.8 Hz, 1H), 6.85 (d, J = 7.2 Hz, 2H), 7.35 (d, J = 7.2 Hz, 2H).

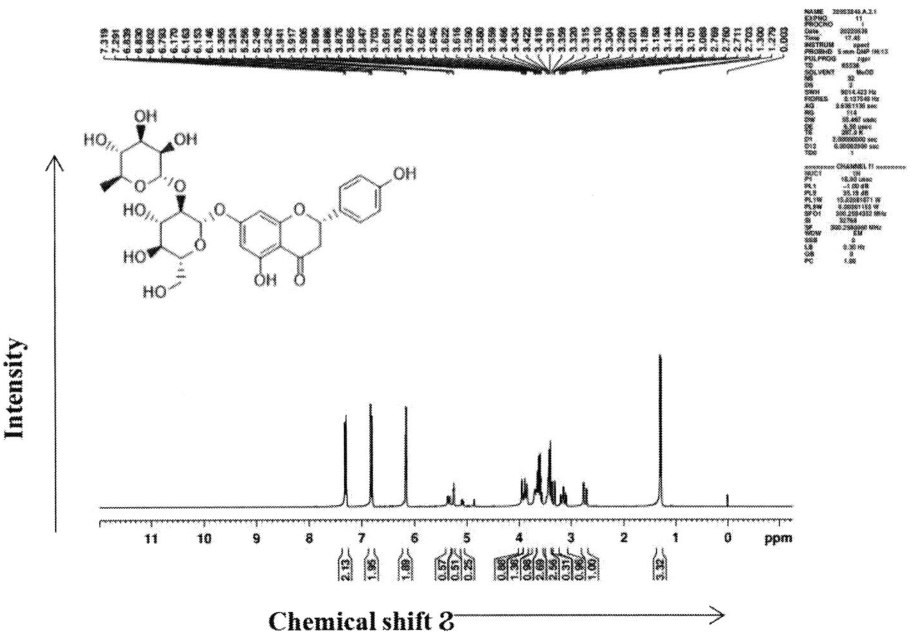

Figure 5: ^{1}H NMR of Naringin obtained from grapefruit albedo

2.4 Hydrolysis of Naringin

Naringenin is derived from the hydrolysis of naringin (figure 6). Literature shows enzymatic hydrolysis of naringin to yield naringenin. Simple and efficient hydrolysis of naringin under different conditions can also be carried out to get a better yield without further purification.

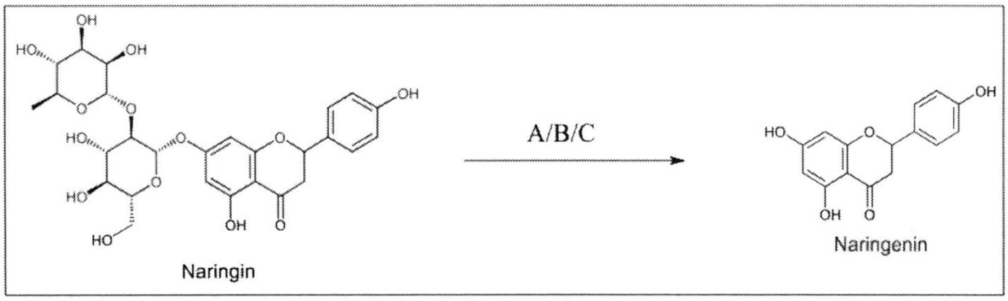

Figure 6: Hydrolysis of Naringin into Naringenin

2.4.1 : Method A: Acidic Hydrolysis in Ethanol. 2% 15 cm^3 H_2SO_4 ethanolic solution was added to 0.1 g of naringin in the round bottom flask. The mixture was then stirred and refluxed at 80 °C to 85 °C for 13h. The progress of the reaction was monitored via TLC. The reaction was monitored on glass TLC plates coated with silica gel-G using chloroform and methanol (9:1) as a solvent. The reaction was run until a single spot-on TLC was obtained, as shown in figure 7. The overall yield of 65 % was obtained and purification was done by column chromatography using ethyl acetate and hexane (50:50) as solvent. The purity of the product was checked using thin layer chromatography (solvent system) with an authentic sample of naringenin (Tokyo Chemical Company/Japan). Further validation was done by NMR spectroscopy (figure 8).

2.4.2 : Method B: Acidic Hydrolysis in Water. 2% 15 cm^3 H_2SO_4 water solution was added to 0.1 g of naringin in a round bottom flask. The mixture was then stirred and refluxed at 81°C to 85 °C for 14 h. Progress of the reaction was monitored via TLC. Characterization of the compound was done as described in method A. Purification of the product was done by column chromatography. The overall yield obtained was 45 %.

2.4.3 : Method C: Acidic Hydrolysis using the biphasic system. 2% 50 cm^3 H_2SO_4 water solution was added to 0.1 g of naringin in a round bottom flask with 100 cm^3 chloroform in it. The mixture was stirred and refluxed at 81 °C to 85 °C for 5h. The progress of the reaction was monitored via TLC until a single spot came. Characterization of the compound was done as described in method A. White crystalline product was obtained requiring no further purification. The overall yield from this method was 67 %. Comparative TLC of hydrolysis of naringin into naringenin by methods A, B & C is shown in figure 7.

IOP Conf. Series: Materials Science and Engineering 1263 (2022) 012031 doi:10.1088/1757-899X/1263/1/012031

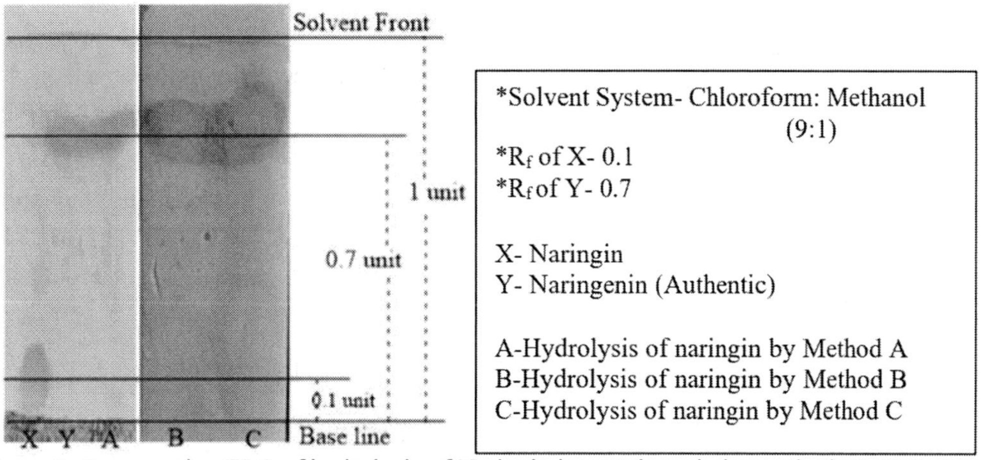

Figure 7: Comparative TLC of hydrolysis of Naringin into naringenin by methods A, B & C

2.4.4 : Analytical data of Naringenin: White solid, M.P- 247°C- 248°C. ^{1}H NMR (Acetone, 300 MHz) δ 2.7 (dd, J = 17.1 Hz, 1H), 3.2 (m, J = 12 Hz, 1H), 5.5 (dd, J = 12.9 Hz, 1H), 5.93 (s, 2H), 6.9 (dd, J = 2.7 Hz and 1.8 Hz, 2H), 7.4 (dd, J = 8.7 Hz, 2H).

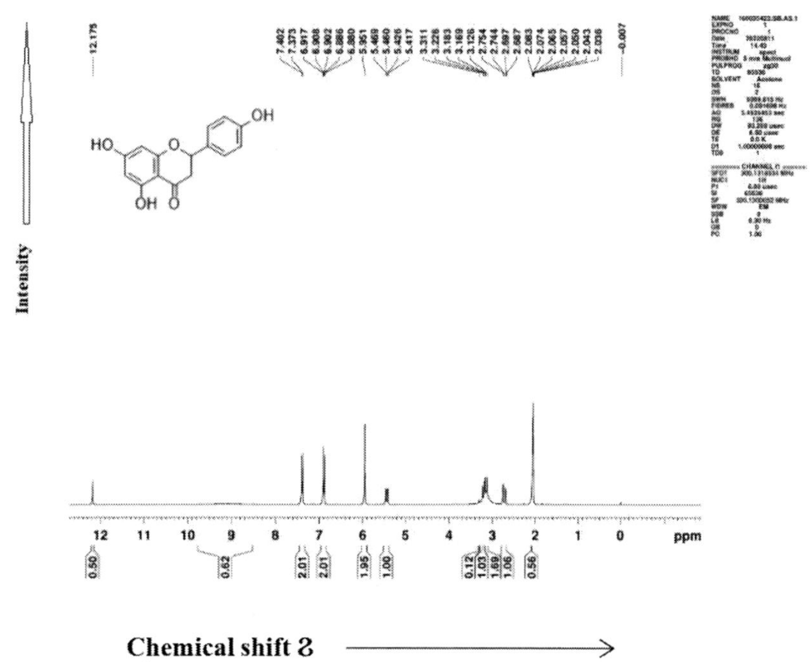

Figure 8: ^{1}H NMR (Acetone, 300 MHz) of Naringenin

3. Results & Discussion

Naringenin, the aglycon form of naringin has shown many biological activities like anti-cancer, anti-diabetic, anti-inflammatory, anti-microbial, anti-osteoporosis, anti-estrogenic, anti-oxidant, and in treating cardio and neurovascular diseases. It is thus a promising phytochemical. The derivatives of naringenin are easy to synthesize as compared to the glycolate naringin because naringin contains glucose units that are heat-labile, so the reactions which require high temperatures are less favourable.

Thus, naringenin is a better starting material for the derivatization and further development of pharmaceuticals.

In this study, firstly we validated the different extraction and hydrolysis methods of naringin from grapefruit peels and then made minor changes in conditions to improve the yield. In extraction *Method A*, along with naringin, we also got pectin thus it is a one-pot extraction of two very useful phytochemicals naringin and pectin. The extraction from the fresh albedo gave marginally more yield than the dry albedo which is 19.75 mg/gm. In the hydrolysis process, Biphasic-acidic hydrolysis yielded a pure compound in comparison to single-phase acid hydrolysis thus eliminating the need for further purification.

Table 1: Standardization of different extraction methods of Naringin from grapefruit albedo

S.No	Conditions	Solvent	Yield (Naringin/Albedo) (mg/g)	Yield reported in [6] (Naringin/Albedo) (mg/g)	Yield Pectin/Albedo (mg/g)
1.	Soxhlet extraction from Dry Albedo	Methanol	18	26	164
2.	Soxhlet extraction from Fresh Albedo	Methanol	19.75	10	negligible
3.	Cold extraction of Dry albedo	Methanol	11	22	negligible

Table 2: Standardisation of different methods of hydrolysis of naringenin

S. No.	Conditions	Yield (%)
A	Acidic Hydrolysis (Water)	45
B	Acidic Hydrolysis (ethanolic)	64
C	Bi-phasic Acidic Hydrolysis	67

4. Conclusion

From this study, it can be concluded that although extraction of naringin from wet albedo gave a better yield, though extraction from the dry albedo is more favorable as the content of essential oils is negligible in dry albedo so the naringin obtained requires less purification. Handling and storage of dry albedo are much easier as compared to wet albedo which can develop fungal growth on keeping. Biphasic acid hydrolysis is the preferred technique in comparison to single-phase as it yields a pure white crystalline product. So, from the waste, the best can be extracted. Naringin & its aglycone naringenin can be used in treating various chronic illnesses and pectin can be used in the food industry.

References

[1] Chavan P, Singh AK, Kaur G. Recent progress in the utilization of industrial waste and by-products of citrus fruits: A review. J Food Process Eng. 2018 Dec;41(8):e12895.
[2] Sharma K, Mahato N, Cho MH, Lee YR. Converting citrus wastes into value-added products: Economic and environmentally friendly approaches. Nutrition. 2017 Feb;34:29–46.
[3] Falcone Ferreyra ML, Rius SP, Casati P. Flavonoids: biosynthesis, biological functions, and biotechnological applications. Front Plant Sci [Internet]. 2012 [cited 2022 Feb 20];3. Available from: http://journal.frontiersin.org/article/10.3389/fpls.2012.00222/abstract.
[4] Patel K, Singh GK, Patel DK. A Review on Pharmacological and Analytical Aspects of Naringenin. Chin J Integr Med. 2018 Jul;24(7):551–60.
[5] Joshi R, Kulkarni YA, Wairkar S. Pharmacokinetic, pharmacodynamic and formulations aspects of Naringenin: An update. Life Sci. 2018 Dec;215:43–56.
[6] Victor MM, David JM, Sakukuma MCK, França EL, Nunes AVJ. A simple and efficient process for the extraction of naringin from grapefruit peel waste. 2017 Dec
[7] Ribeiro IA, Rocha J, Sepodes B, Mota-Filipe H, Ribeiro MH. Effect of naringin enzymatic hydrolysis towards naringenin on the anti-inflammatory activity of both compounds. J Mol Catal B Enzym. 2008 Jun;52–53:13–8.
[8] Guohua X, Pan R, Ge Y, Zhou C, Shen Y. Rapid Quantitative Analysis of Naringenin in the Fruit Bodies of Inonotus vaninii by Two-phase Acid Hydrolysis Followed by Reversed Phase-high Performance Liquid Chromatography-ultra Violet. Pharmacogn Mag. 2017;13(52):4.
[9] Min KY, Kim HJ, Lee KA, Kim KT, Paik HD. Antimicrobial activity of acid-hydrolyzed Citrus unshiu peel extract in milk. J Dairy Sci. 2014 Apr;97(4):1955–60.

Cyto-toxic Effect of Nano Ceria bio fabricated with DNA

Prabha Jyothi P S[1,2] and Nisha J Tharayil[1]

[1] Department of Physics, SN College for Women, Kollam, Research Centre, University of Kerala, Thiruvananthapuram
[2] Corresponding author: prabhajyothi79@gmail.com

Abstract. Cancer is a condition arising from the deregulation of several genes which causes change in normal cells to cancerous ones. The objective of all cancer treatment research is to eradicate cancer with little effect on normal cells. Nanostructured ceria of very small dimension (≈5nm) synthesized by co-precipitation method using deoxyribo nucleic acid (DNA) as capping agent has shown a promising antioxidant activity over almost all free radicals. Excessive reactive oxygen species have significant influence in the origination and development of numerous ailments, including cancer. So, the cyto-toxic effect of synthesized nanoceria on normal cells as well as on colon cancer cells is investigated. Inverted phase contrast microscope succeeded by MTT assay method were used to observe the survivability of cells. The investigation reveals a significant decline in the viability of cells when nanoceria, in the concentration range of 6.25–100μg/ml, was used on human cancer cells for 24,48 and 72 hours. The results showed that the activity of nanostructured ceria significantly depends on dose and time. For normal cells the reduction is less i.e., more than 75% of the cells are viable even if the concentration increases to 100μg/ml. But for cancer cells the percentage of viability decreases. Our study come up with a result that DNA assisted synthesized nanoceria has considerable cytotoxic effect, which seems likely to be effective as an anticancer agent while protecting healthy tissues.

1. Introduction

Cancer is a state arising due to changes in gene expression, which give rise to the mutation of normal cells to malignant ones [1]. These days cancer treatments use radiation and chemotherapy which have many side effects, because they not only affect the cancer cells, but also the healthy parts of our body. Chemo-therapies are linked with several disadvantages like toxic effects on normal cells, no target specificity, resistance to multidrug, etc. [2]. A large interdisciplinary research project known as Laser Activated Nanoparticles for Tumor Elimination (LANTERN) between physicists, doctors and biologists is developing a new method to treat the cancer that only affects cancer tumors locally. One of the nonsurgical methods for the removal of tumor that is being examined, which finds promise, is tumor destruction through the use of nanoshells [3]. To reduce the aftereffects and to enhance quality of life during recovery, several research works are trying to reach target-based anticancer drug delivery with nanoparticles. The objective of all these studies is to eradicate cancer with little effect on healthy tissue. Cancer is the main reason of death in entire world, even with the recent progress in research on molecular oncology and target-based therapies. Several studies have reported on the anticancer effect of nanostructured ceria in different cells synthesized through other methods [3–12].

Nano therapeutics is also an emerging alternative to the many side effects and demerits of chemotherapy in cancer treatment [13]. Nanotechnology has briskly turned up in the field of biotechnology, medicine, genetics, microbiology and nanorobots systems that are extensively used in the diagnosis, treatment, and precaution of disease. In this study, we have examined the efficacy of nanoceria on normal as well as colon cancer cell lines. Nanoceria of very small dimension (≈5 nm) bio fabricated using deoxyribonucleic acid as agent to reduce the size has shown a promising antioxidant activity over almost all free radicals [14]. Excessive reactive oxygen species have a significant role in the origination and development of numerous diseases, including cancer. Being a good scavenger of free radicals, the synthesized particle may show anticancer effect. So, we extended our studies to the cyto-toxic effect of synthesized nanoceria on the normal and colon cancer cells.

2. Experimental

2.1. Synthesis

The starting precursor used was Cerium (III) nitrate hexahydrate and the precipitating agent was sodium hydroxide (Merck). DNA powder used as capping agent was from Sigma Aldrich. Aqueous solution of 0.4 M sodium hydroxide and 0.1 M cerium nitrate hexa hydrate were added to an aqueous solution of DNA powder, drop wise, under constant stirring. After 5 hours of stirring, the precipitate was washed with deionized water and kept to dry naturally. Then, the grained hydroxide powder was annealed at 400°C for 3 hours in a furnace to get pale yellow coloured cerium oxide nanoparticles.

2.2. Cell Culture

The L929 fibroblast cell line from mouse and DLD-1 isolated from the large intestine of a colon adenocarcinoma patient were kept in Dulbecco's Modified Eagles medium (DMEM) and procured from Sigma Aldrich. A tissue culture flask was used for culturing of the cell line, with DMEM supplemented with antibiotic solutions of 100 µg/ml streptomycin, 100 U/ml Penicillin and 2.5 µg/ml Amphotericin B and 10% FBS, L-glutamine, sodium bicarbonate. After culturing, these were maintained in a humidified 5% Carbon dioxide containing incubator which was purchased from NBS Eppendorf, Germany at a temperature of 37° C. After two days, this confluent monolayer was trypsinized and 5000 cells/well was seeded in tissue culture plate of 96 wells. After that, it is again incubated in 5% Carbon dioxide atmosphere. Using a cyclomixer, 1 milligram of nanoceria which was dissolved in 1 mL DMEM and was filtered using 0.22 µm Millipore syringe filter.

2.3. Cytotoxic Evaluation

The medium used for culturing the cell lines was taken away after 24 hours. Then the wells containing cell lines were treated with nanoceria dissolved in DMEM of following concentrations: 6.25 µg/ml, 12.5 µg/ml, 25 µg/ml, 50 µg/ml and 100 µg/ml. The experiment was done in triplicates. The control cells which were not treated also kept for reference. Inverted phase contrast microscope was used to observe the viability of cells and then by MTT assay method. The MTT assay is rapid, simple, and cost-effective method, it become a very suitable technique for the quantification of living cells in culture. For the measurement, 15 mg of MTT (Sigma, M-5655) was reconstituted in 3ml phosphate-buffered saline (PBS) until completely dissolved and sterilized by filter sterilization. After an incubation of 24 hours, the specimen in wells were taken out. Then 0.03 ml of this MTT solution was poured into all test and cell control wells. The plate was delicately shaken and again incubated in a humidified 5% CO_2 atmosphere at 37°C for 4 hours. After this, the supernatant was detached and 0.1 ml Dimethyl sulphoxide (DMSO) was poured to each cell. The wells were mixed quietly by pipetting up and down in order to completely dissolve the purple formazan product. The absorbance values of this colored solution at 540 nm were measured using a microplate reader. Finally, cell viability was estimated as percentage relative to untreated control cells. Usually, the experiment was done in dark because MTT reagent is very sensitive when exposed to light.

3. Results

3.1. Structural Characterization of the powder sample obtained

Powder X-ray diffraction has been done and the pattern obtained is depicted in Figure.1. The analysis of the pattern shows that it can be indexed to face centred cubic single-phased fluorite CeO_2 structure. The peaks have been noted at 28.56°, 33.08°, 47.46°, 56.28°, 69.40° and 76.69° corresponding to (h k l) planes (111), (200), (220), (311), (222), (400) and (331) respectively (ICDD file no: 89-8436) of CeO_2. Broad peaks in the pattern indicates that average crystallite size is small [15]. The average crystallite size calculated using Scherrer formula comes out to be 5.28 nm.

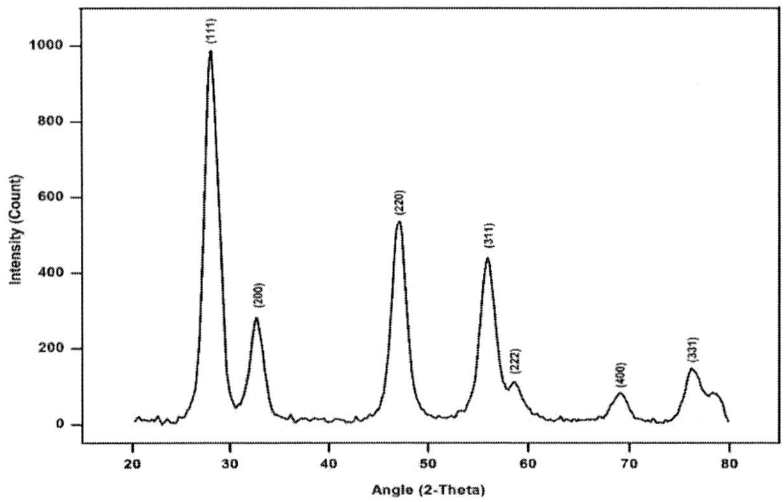

Figure 1. XRD pattern of the powder sample

The morphology of synthesized sample has been further investigated with transmission electron micrograph (TEM). In figure 2, the particles seem to be spherical with size in the range of 5±1 nm. The tiny particles with less aggregation indicate the efficient capping of double helix structured DNA.

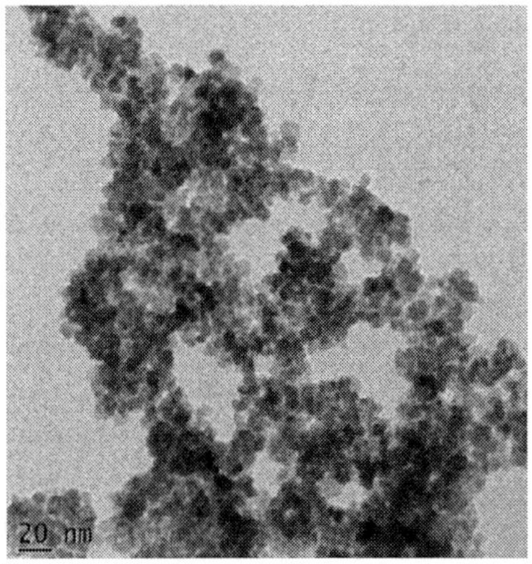

Figure 2 TEM image of the synthesized nanoceria

3.2. Cytotoxicity measurement by Microscopic Observation

After adding nanoceria of different concentrations, the whole plate was kept for one day (24 hours) and viewed directly by inverted phase contrast tissue culture microscope (Olympus CKX41 with Optika Pro5 CCD camera).

The phase contrast images of normal fibroblast cells are shown in Fig. 3. Any noticeable structural changes such as rounding, cell shrinkage, granulation and formation of vacuoles in the cytoplasm were considered as the measures of cytotoxicity. At lower concentrations of nanoceria, the change in morphology is negligible compared to the control cells (non-treated cells). It indicates that at lower concentrations nanostructured ceria is not making harm to normal cells. There is no evident change in morphology as the concentration increases. So, the cyto-toxic studies were conducted on human colon cancer cells at these concentrations to check whether they can be used as a cancer drug.

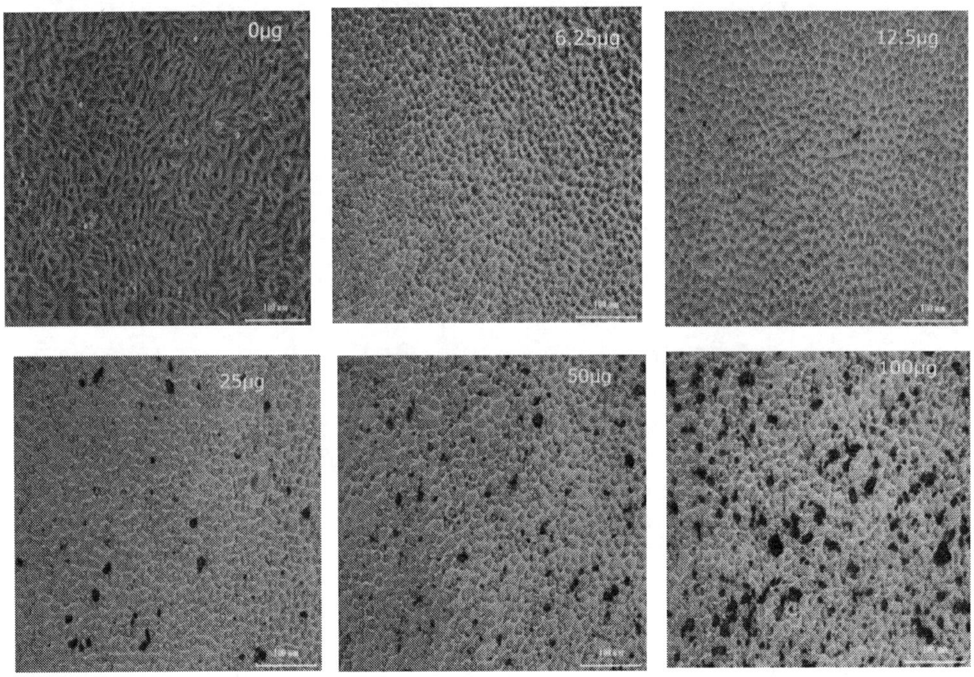

Figure 3. Phase contrast images of normal fibroblast cells

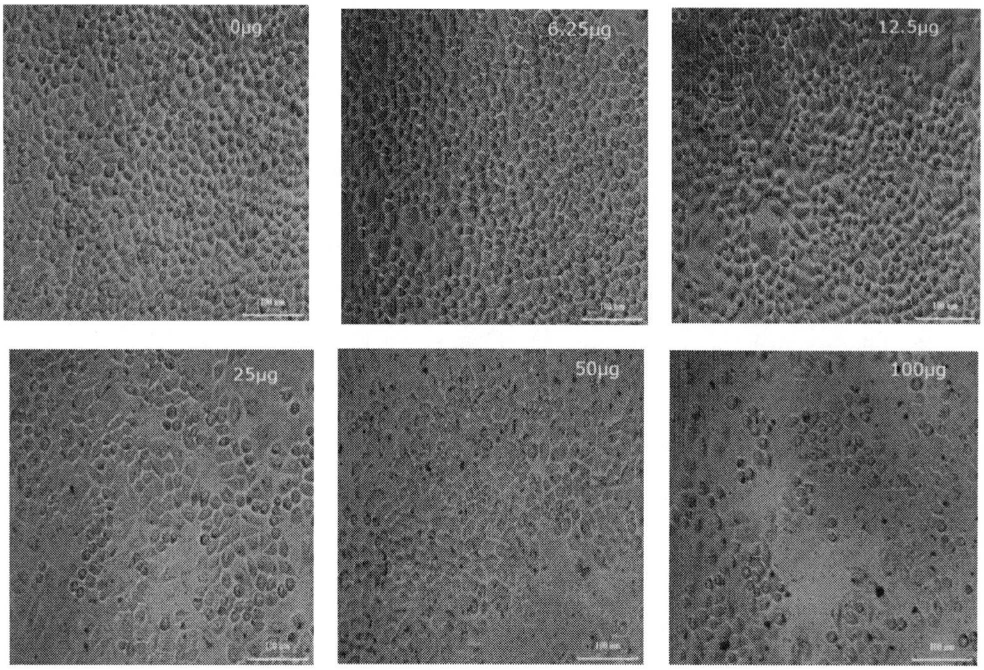

Figure 4. Phase contrast images of human Colorectal Adenocarcinoma (DLD-1) cells

The phase contrast images of human colorectal adenocarcinoma (DLD-1) cells after 24 hours of treatment is shown in Fig. 4. Even though cytotoxicity of nanoceria is small at lower concentration, as the concentration increases viability of the cancer cells decreases considerably as shown in the images. This means that it can kill the cancer cells to a great extent with cyto-protection on the normal cells.

3.3. Cytotoxicity Assay by MTT Method

The viability was again verified by the MTT dye 3- (4, 5- dimethylthiazol-2-yl) -2, 5-diphenyltetrazoliumbromide assay [16] in a dose as well as time dependent manner. This a quantitative method of determining the amount of a chemical present in a solution with the help of a color reagent for evaluating metabolic activity of the cell [17–19].

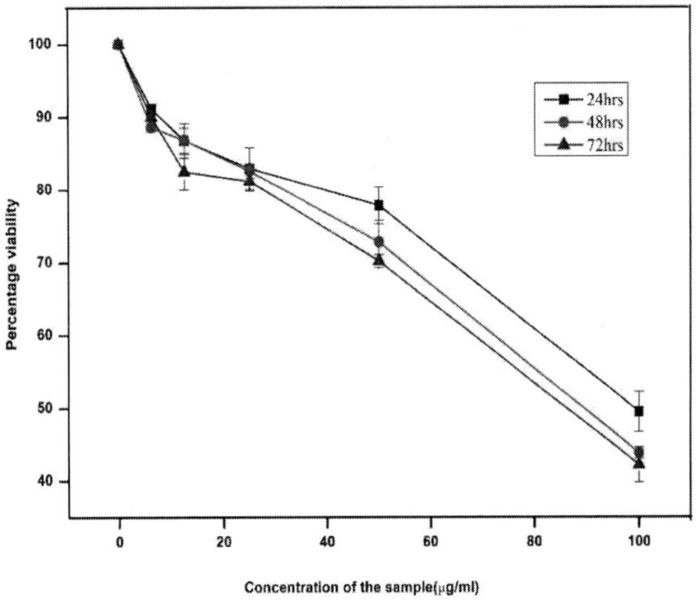

Figure 5. Cytotoxic effect of nanoceria on DLD-1 cells at 24, 48 and 72 hours of treatment

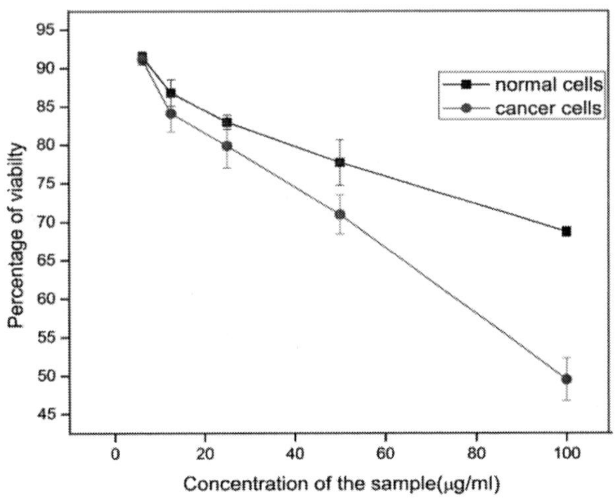

Figure 6. Percentage viability of normal as well as human colon cancer cells after 24 hours.

The viability of the cell (percentage) can be calculated as:

Viability (percentage) = (Mean absorbance of samples x100) / Mean absorbance of control group

Fig. 5 shows cytotoxic effect of nanoceria on DLD-1 cells at 24, 48 and 72 hours of treatment in a dose dependent manner from 6.25–100 µg/ml. Each point in the graph is the mean value of three replicates with standard deviation. Dimethyl sulphoxide (0.1%) was used as negative control. The results showed that the activity of nanostructured ceria significantly depends on dose and time. A significant reduction in cell viability of cancer cell was observed as the concentration of nanoparticle and time of exposure increases. The percentage of viability should be more for particles showing cyto-protection while it should be less for cytotoxicity. From Fig. 6, it is clear that cytotoxicity against cancer cells increases with concentration while it is comparatively less for normal cells. It means that synthesized nanoceria provides cyto-protection towards healthy living cells from free radicals but destroys the malignant cells via generating reactive oxygen species.

4. Discussion

In healthy cells (at physiological pH), nanoceria scavenges reactive oxygen species and protects the cells by acting as an antioxidant. But in malignant cells (low pH), it behaves as pro-oxidant by generating reactive species and destroys the cells [20]. Higher acidic environment of cancer cells in comparison with healthy cells is due to the acceleration of glycolysis and production of lactic acid [21]. In the low pH acidic environment, nanostructured ceria cannot exhibit the cyto-protective (antioxidant) nature and behaves as a cyto-toxic (pro-oxidant) which induces oxidative stress and thereby causes cell death [22]. Nanostructured ceria shows cyto-toxic nature in malignant cell by piercing into it and get released from the endosome into the cytoplasm. The superoxide dismutase (SOD) mimetic activity of the cerium oxide nanoparticles was triggered by this acidic intracellular pH of malignant or cancer cells. This process reduce superoxide into hydrogen peroxide, but inhibits its catalase (CAT) mimetic activity resulting in the aggregation of the massive amount of hydrogen peroxide in cells that are malignant. Furthermore, these reactive species cause mitochondrial destruction, oxidation of protein, and splitting of strand in DNA that results in death of cells. But nanostructured ceria shows cyto-protective effect in normal cell by piercing into the cell and scavenges free radicals with oxygen species due to superoxide dismutase activity. Due to this reaction, superoxide is the cell reduces into hydrogen peroxide. In physiological pH, Catalase activity is also taking place in which hydrogen peroxide gets further degraded into water and thereby reduces the accumulation of hydrogen peroxide. Henceforth, it saves the normal cell from death. Table 1 summarizes the anti-oxidant and pro-oxidant effects of DNA assisted synthesized nanoceria.

Table 1. Antioxidant and pro-oxidant effects of nanostructured ceria.

Antioxidant effect	**Pro-oxidant effect**
Normal cell (Physiological pH)	Cancer cell (Acidic pH)
Superoxide dismutase activity $O_2^{\bullet-} + Ce^{3+} + 2H^+ \longrightarrow Ce^{4+} + H_2O_2$	Superoxide dismutase activity $O_2^{\bullet-} + Ce^{3+} + 2H^+ \longrightarrow Ce^{4+} + H_2O_2$
Catalase activity $Ce^{3+} + H_2O_2 + H^+ \longrightarrow Ce^{4+} + 2H_2O$	No Catalase activity

For Superoxide dismutase activity, a larger proportion of Ce^{3+}/Ce^{4+} is an important criterion, while for Catalase activity, a larger proportion of Ce^{4+}/Ce^{3+} plays a vital role. As nanoceria has the ability to toggle its +4 and +3 oxidation states, it will neutralize both free radicals whenever needed [22]. Nevertheless, acidic pH in malignant cells enhances superoxide dismutase activity of nanostructured ceria yet hinders its catalase activity. This results in the aggregation of huge quantity of free radicals with oxygen species. So, nanostructured ceria shows toxic effect towards cancer cells [23]. The enhancement of efficacy and diminution of toxicity of a cancer drug can be done by directing it to the site and preserve its concentration for a particular time at the destination

5. Conclusion

When human colon cancer cells were treated with DNA assisted synthesized nanostructured ceria in concentration range 6.25–100 µg/ml for 24, 48 and 72 hours, a significant reduction in viability with time and increase in dose was detected. But for normal cells the reduction is less. The present study suggests that the fabricated nanoceria has considerable cytotoxic effect, which seems likely to be an anticancer agent while protecting the normal cells. A promising therapeutic strategy comes out to be by unifying nanoceria with anticancer drug. In healthy cells, with physiological pH, it behaves as cyto-protective agent by scavenging reactive oxygen species and thereby protecting them. But in malignant cells, under low pH environment, it shows cyto-toxic nature by generating reactive oxygen species and destroys them. The enhancement of efficacy and diminution of toxicity of a cancer drug can be done by directing it to its destination and preserve it for a particular time for medicinal action to take effect at the site.

References

[1] Zein R, Alghoraibi I, Soukkarieh C, Salman A and Alahmad A 2020 *Heliyon* **6** e04594
[2] Kukowska-Latallo JF, Candido KA, Cao Z, Nigavekar SS, Majoros IJ, Thomas TP, Balogh LP, Khan MK, Baker JR 2005 *Jr. Cancer Res.* **65(12)** 5317-24
[3] Dimendra J P, Pratik A M, Jatin J P, 2012 *Int. J. Drug Dev.& Res.* **4(1)** 14-27
[4] Asati A, Santra S, Kaittanis C, Perez 2010 *JM ACS Nano* **4(9)** 5321–31
[5] Lin W, Huang Y-W, Zhou X-D, Ma Y,2006 *Int. J. Toxicol.* **25(6),** 451–57
[6] De Marzi L, Monaco A, De Lapuente J 2013 *Int. J. Mol. Sci.* **14(2)** 3065–77
[7] Renu G, Divya RVV, Nair SV, Subramanian KRV, Lakshmanan VK 2012 *Adv Sci Lett.* **6** 17–25,
[8] Hijaz M, Das S, Mert I, Gupta A, Al-wahab Z, Tebbe C 2016 *BMC Cancer.***16(1)** 220
[9] Jana SK, Banerjee P, Das S, Seal S, Chaudhury K. 2014 *J nanoparticle Res.* **16(6)**
[10] Kumari M, Singh SP, Chinde S,Rahman MF, Mahboob M, Grover P 2014 *Int J Toxicol.* **33(2)**86
[11] Nourmohammadi E, Khoshdel-sarkarizi H, Nedaeinia R, Sadeghnia HR, Hasanzadeh L, Darroudi M, *J Cell Physiol.* 2019 **234(4)** 4987–96,
[12] Giri S, Karakoti A, Graham RP, Maguire JL, Reilly CM 3and Seal S, 2013 *PLoS ONE.* **8** 1.
[13] Brannon-Peppas L and Blanchette JO 2004 Adv. *Drug Delivery Rev.* **56** 1649-59.
[14] Prabha Jyothi P S, Nisha J Tharayil 2020 *J. Phy. and Chem. of Solids*, **141** 109421,
[15] Cullity B D, Graham C D, 2009, *Introduction to magnetic materials*, J Wiley and Sons, New York
[16] Darroudi M, Hakimi M,Sarani M, Kazemi oskuee R,Khorsand zak L and Gholami A L 2013 *Ceramics International* **39** 6917–21
[17] Stockert JC,Blázquez-Castro A, CañeteM,Horobin RW,Villanueva A 2012 *Acta Histochemica* **114** 785-96
[18] Stockert JC, Horobin RW,Colombo LL,Blázquez-Castro A 2018 *Acta Histochemica* **120** 159-67
[19] Sylvester PW 2011 *Methods Mol Biol.* **716** 157-68
[20] NeelamThakur, Prasenjit Manna, Joydeep Das 2019 J. of Nanobiotech. **17** 84
[21] Perez JM, Asati A, Nath S, Kaittanis C 2008 *Small* **4(5)**552–6.
[22] Xu C, Qu X 2014 *NPG Asia Mater.* **6(3)**e90
[23] Wason MS, Colon J, Das S, Seal S, Turkson J, Zhao J 2013 *Biol Med.* **9(4)**558–69

Synthesis of nanohybrid reinforced electrospun methylcellulose/ polyvinyl alcohol /polyethylene glycol nanofiber: study of material properties for possible biomedical applications

Mir Sahidul Ali[1], Mir Sahanur Ali[1,2], Jonathan Tersur Orasugh[3,4*], Dipankar Chattopadhyay[1,2*]

[1]Department of Polymer Science and Technology, University of Calcutta, 92 A.P.C. Road, Kolkata -700 009, West Bengal, India.
[2]Centre for Research in Nanoscience and Nanotechnology, Acharya Prafulla Chandra Roy Sikhsha Prangan, University of Calcutta, JD-2, Sector-III, Saltlake City, Kolkata-700098, West Bengal, India
[3]DST-CSIR National Centre for Nanostructured Materials, Council for Scientific and Industrial Research, Pretoria 0001, South Africa.
[4]Department of Chemical Sciences, University of Johannesburg, Doorfontein, Johannesburg 2028, South Africa.

Corresponding author email address: dipankar.chattopadhyay@gmail.com

Abstract. Over the past few epochs, emerging transdermal drug delivery systems (TDDSs) have gotten major devotion through incessant level of interest. The effort of this work is to understand the influence of nano-reinforcing agent on the morphology, property and its drug carrying capacity of the nanohybrid reinforced ketorolac tromethamine (KT) drug loaded electrospun nanofibrous web. In this study, cellulose nanocrystals (CNCs) extracted successfully from jute fibres (JF) and nanocollagen (NCG) was isolated from waste fish scales for the assembling of CNC-NCG reinforced MC/PVA/PEG electrospun nanofibrous bio-nanocomposites (BNCs) mat for transdermal drug delivery applications. The isolated nanoparticles (CNC & NCG) and the synthesized electrospun bio-nanocomposite were characterized by Fourier transform infrared (FTIR) spectroscopy, X-ray diffraction (XRD), Scanning electron microscopy (SEM), optical microscopy, Field emission scanning electron microscopy (FESEM).

Keywords: *Cellulose nanocrystals (CNCs), Nanocollagen (NCG), Bio-nanocomposites (BNCs) electrospinning, Nanofiber, Biomedical applications.*

1. Introduction

Nanoscale materials with nano-dimensions present various physical, mechanical, chemical, and biological properties compare to the macroscale materials, owing to the high surface to volume ratio, interactions of atoms and molecules [1]. Due to the unique features of nanofibers give an opportunity for using them potentially in the field of biomedical and healthcare applications [2]. The electrospinning technique is an easy, versatile and unique technique which has drawn significant attention to the production of nanofibrous structures with diameters less than one micrometer (μM) from polymer solutions [3]. In recent decades, the synthesis of nanocellulose (NC) and its reinforced polymer composite materials have received tremendous devotion due to their remarkable mechanical, biological and physiochemical properties [3]. Cellulose nanocrystals (CNCs) (Fig. 1d) and nanocollagen (NCG) are biocompatible, biodegradable green nano-dimensional fillers with amazing drug loading and releasing properties, which make them a good candidate for utilization in the various biomedical platform [3,4]. Extensive research has been done on the extraction of CNCs and NCG from various bio-resources. The chemical along with mechanical approaches are mainly adopted to isolate the CNCs and NCG nanofiller agents and their reinforced polymer nanocomposites. Nanocollagen and nanocellulose (NC) blended composites offer numerous advantages in biomedical applications e.g., carrier systems for protein, gene, and pharmaceutical drugs [3,5-7]. CNCs is common cellulose based reinforcing agent with remarkable biological properties widely used in the health care sector [7] as well as a carrier agent widely used in biomedical nanotechnology applications [6]. Recently nanohybrid grafted composite materials have been explored for pharmaceutical applications. Methylcellulose (MC) (structure shown in Fig. 1b) [3] and polyvinyl alcohol (PVA) (structure shown in Fig. 1 ai & aii) have various biomedical applications like wound healing and tissue engineering [3]. Ketorolac tromethamine (KT) (structure shown in Fig. 1c) is a pyrrolizine carboxylic acid derivative, nonsteroidal anti-inflammatory drugs (NSAIDs) possess analgesic as well as adequate anti-inflammatory actions by hindering prostaglandin synthesis, which widely prescribed because it not concomitant with any repugnant central nervous system (CNS) effects or probable addiction potential. Therefore, KT is quite more promising therapeutic medicine for the managing of endurable to severe pain [3]. The biological half-life of KT is 4-6 hours, so frequent dosing is required to sustain the action of drug to relieve the pain [6]. The drug KT, when deliver by conventional oral administration it has upper abdominal pain and gastrointestinal ulceration. To avoid such adverse side effect due to oral administration and problem of recurrent dosing, alternative transdermal drug delivery system (TDDS) has been developed. Electrospun nanofiber drug carriers, with excellent drug carrying and releasing properties with different formulation can be an alternative opportunity to overcome such problems [6].

In this study we synthesized CNCs from waste JF and NCG isolated from waste fish scales. These two nanomaterials were chosen as nano-reinforcing fillers as well as nano drug carrier due to their remarkable reinforcing and elegant nano-carrying properties. Biocompatible polymers MC and PVA were used as the matrix materials for the synthesis of nanofibers. These polymers have been extensively used in the biomedical field for the fabrication of various devices. The key goal of this study was to synthesis of CNC-NCG-loaded MC/PVA/PEG electrospun nanofibrous bio-nanocomposite for transdermal drug delivery applications. Moreover, the property and structural elucidation of the BNC nanofibrous web was performed by FTIR and field emission scanning electron microscopy (FESEM). This work defines the prospect of the synthesized drug loaded electrospun bio-nanocomposites nanofibers in advanced emerging biomedical fields.

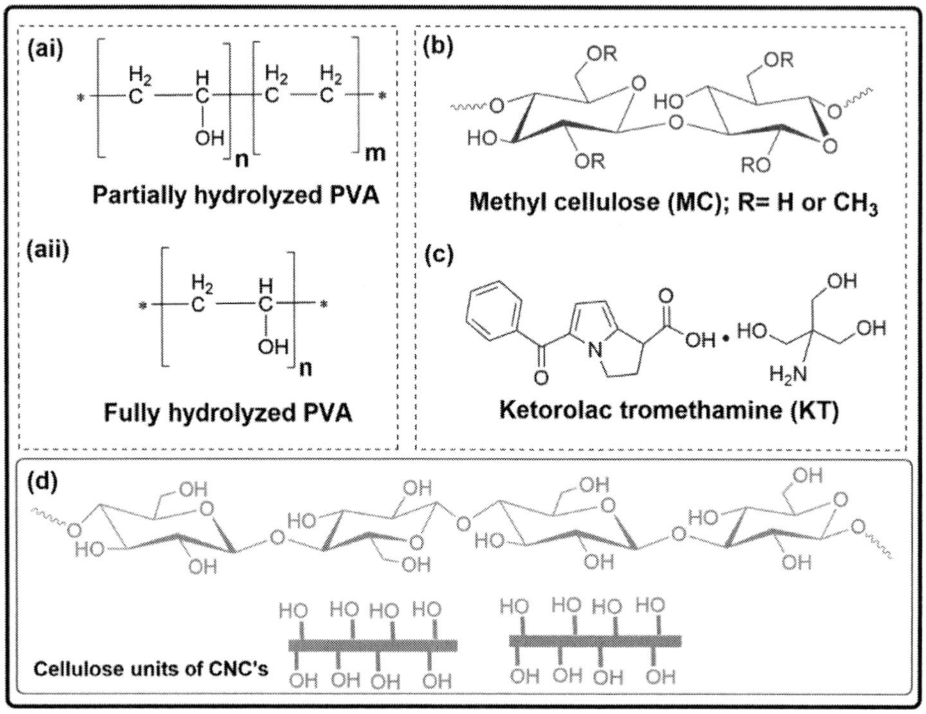

Fig. 1. Chemical structures of (ai & aii) partially and fully hydrolyzed PVA (b) Methyl cellulose (MC) (c) Ketorolac tromethamine (KT) drug (d) structure of cellulose for CNC's.

2. Experimental

2.1. Materials

Bio derived cellulose nanocrystals (CNCs) was isolated from jute fibers according to our previous report [6] and Nanocollagen (NCG) was isolated in our laboratory [3]. Sulphuric acid (H_2SO_4), sodium chlorite (NaOCl), Methylcellulose (MC), acetic acid (CH_3COOH), polyethylene glycol (PEG), sodium hydroxide (NaOH), nitric acid (HNO_3) and hydrogen peroxide (H_2O_2) were bought from Merk Specialties Pvt. Limited, Mumbai, India. Polyvinyl alcohol (PVA) was bought from Sigma-Aldrich, USA. Waste fish scales purchased from Rajabazar, Kolkata, West Bengal, India. Ketorolac tromethamine (KT) was gotten as a gift sample from Unichem Labs Ltd., Mumbai, India.

2.2. Procedures

2.2.1. Extraction of CNCs

Jute fibers (JF) were digested with 40% (v/v) H_2SO_4 and 2% (v/v) H_2O_2 solution to soften the fiber structure. Then, the digested jute was heated at 85 °C for 1 h in an oil bath under vigorous stirring. The sample was then filtered and treated with 10% (wt./v) sodium hydroxide solution at 90 °C for delignification and then washed with 3% (wt./v) sodium chlorite ($NaClO_2$) for 1 hr. The pure cellulose fibers are filtered repeatedly to obtain whitish cellulosic fibers and put under a hot air oven overnight to dry. The treated cellulose fibers were then break by acid hydrolysis with 50% H_2SO_4 at 50 °C for 3 hours to obtain CNCs suspension and then neutralized by washing several times with triple distilled water (TDW) by centrifugation by centrifuge machine and then lyophilized it (freeze-drying) to get the dry CNCs powder [6]. The schematic diagram of CNCs synthesis is shown in Fig. 2.

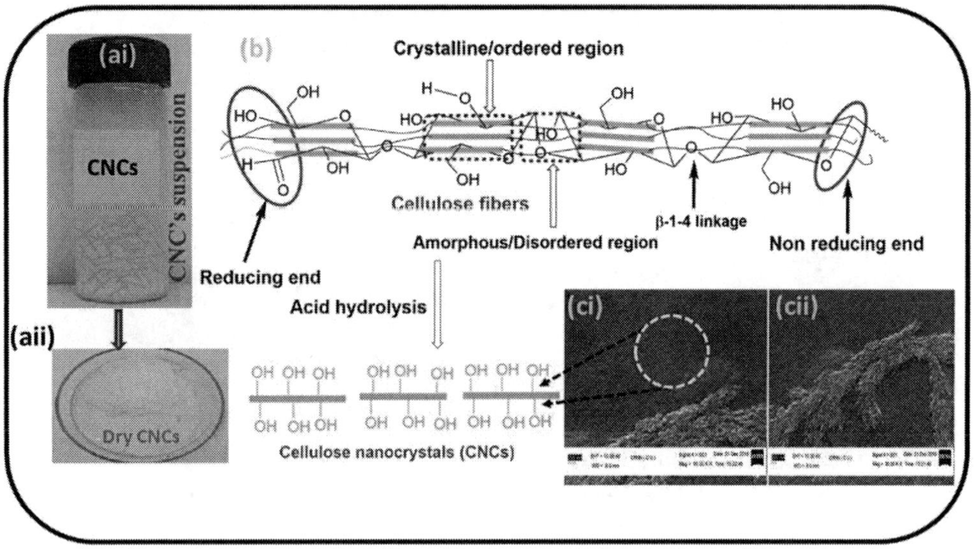

Fig. 2. (ai) CNC's suspension (aii) dry CNCs (b) Extraction process of CNCs from JF (ci & cii) SEM image of CNC's.

2.2.2. Isolation of nanocollagen (NCG)

Initially, 50 gm of waste fish scales (FS) were treated with 2 % (wt./v) sodium hydroxide (NaOH) solution for 1.5 hr. at ~70°C. Then the alkali treated weak fish scales were washed repeatedly. Then, the treated FS was put into 3% H_2O_2 (v/v) at a temperature of 75°C. After this, the solution was heated again with NaOH (5%) for 1-2 hours at 70°C and then repetitively washed for neutralization. Then it was additionally subjected with acetic acid 0.5% (v/v) solution for 10 hr. followed by washing to neutralize. The product was then again treated with 1% NaCl (wt./v) for 4 hours and then centrifugation with TDW to neutralize and freeze-drying to getting nanocollagen (NCG) as final product [3]. This entire process is depicted in Fig. 3.

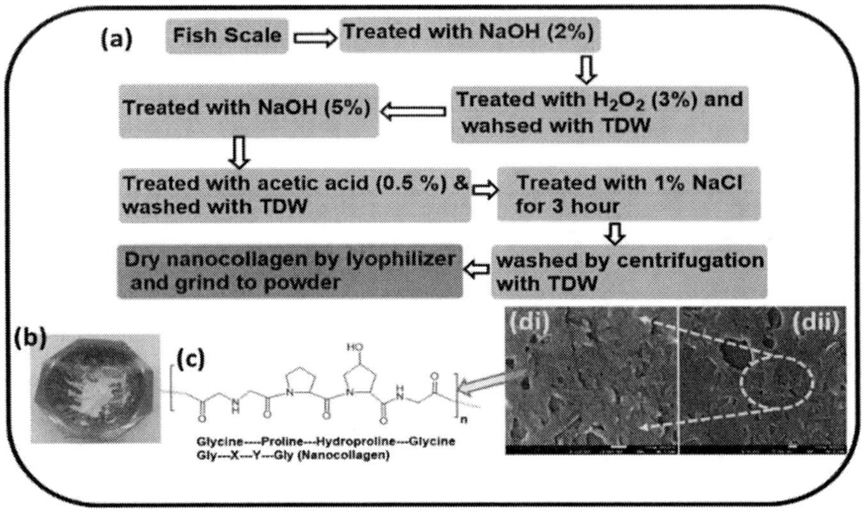

Fig. 3. (a) The Schematic representation of nanocollagen (NCG) isolation process from FS (b) Dry NCG (c) Chemical structure of NCG, and (d) FESEM image of NCG.

2.2.3. Fabrication of BNC formulation

For the fabrication of the nanofibers, at first 1wt% (with respect to polymers) nanofiller containing CNC-NCG were add in TDW and after this KT drug was added (5 wt% w.r.t polymers) to it then sonicated under bath sonication for 3 h [3]. A polymer solution containing 2% (wt/v) MC, 10% (wt/v) PVA and 5% PEG was prepared for BNC nanofiber synthesis [3]. The drug (KT) incorporated reinforcing nanomaterials were mixed with the polymer solution. The mixture was afterward heated to around 75 °C along with vigorous stirring (450 rpm) for 2 h. The solutions were afterward kept in the refrigerator for 1 day (at 5-10 °C) to obtain a clear viscous solution and then the polymeric formulations were used for the electrospun NF development by utilizing ESPIN– NANO, Chennai India. The optimized condition for bead-free electrospun mats were applied voltage (V): 27 kV; gap between tip and collector plate: 8 cm; flow rate 0.8 mL/h and the metallic plate collector (Al sheet) with dimension 20 x 20 cm^2; relative humidity: 48%; temperature: 25 °C. Though the concentration of the solution remained the same as aforementioned. We observed during the optimization process of the electrospinning that an increase in voltage led to decrease in the electrospun diameter of the nanofibres and vice-versa. The same trend followed for the distance between the needle tip and the collector plate. Though a direct relationship was observed for the flow rate where an increase in flow-rate led to a corresponding increase in the fibers diameter and vice-versa. The nanofibrous web preparation technique is depicted in Fig. 4.

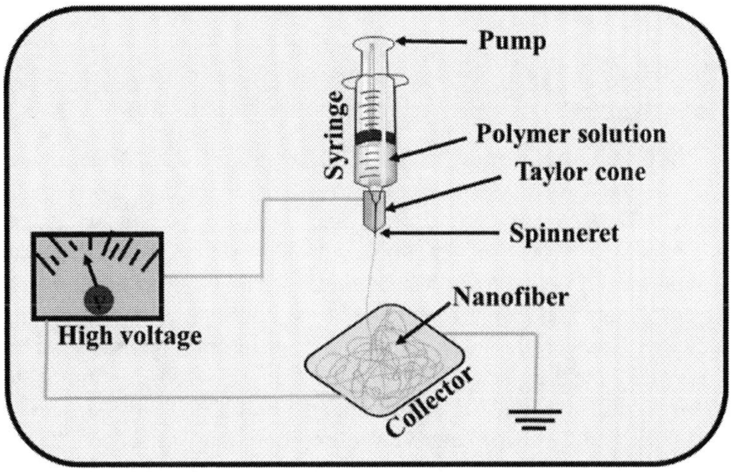

Fig. 4. Electrospinning technique for the preparation of nanofibers.

3. *Characterization*

3.1. *FTIR spectroscopy*

Fourier transform infrared spectroscopy (FTIR) of the Jute cellulose (JC), MC, PVA, ketorolac tromethamine (KT) drug and the prepared CNCs, NCG, and their electrospun nanohybrid bio-nanocomposite (BNC) was determined by using KBr pellet with Perkin Elmer spectrum Two FT-IR spectrometer over the range of wavenumber 4000-450 cm^{-1}.

3.2. *SEM analysis of CNCs*

The dried CNCs powder dispersions were prepared using TDW and sonicated for 2 h. The dispersed suspension was then cast on an aluminum (Al) sheet and dried overnight and further dry in an IR lamp before going for SEM analysis. The sample was coated with platinum (Pt) and afterward attached to the SEM sample holder, then surface morphology of the CNCs was then inspected by a ZEISS EVO 18 scanning electron microscope (SEM).

3.3. *X-ray diffraction (XRD) of Jute cellulose and CNCs*

CNC's crystalline property was analyzed by X-PERT-PRO Panalytical diffractometer by Cu Kα (λ = 1.5406 Å) as the X-ray generator, the scanning rate was 10°/min, and 2θ between 10 to 60 °.

3.4. *Optical microscopy (OM) analysis of nanofibers*

The electrospun nanohybrid reinforced bio-nanocomposite nanofibers morphology was observed by using a Leitz LABROLUX 12 POL S microscope.

3.5. *FESEM analysis of NCG and nanofibers*

The surface morphology of NCG and CNC-NCG reinforced drug loaded nanohybrid electrospun bio-nanocomposite (BNC) nanofibrous structure were examined by using a JEOL FESEM microscope, operated at 15 kV accelerating voltage. All the syntheized/prepared samples were coated with gold in a sputter coater afore being scrutinized by the FESEM.

IOP Conf. Series: Materials Science and Engineering 1263 (2022) 012033 doi:10.1088/1757-899X/1263/1/012033

4. Results and discussion

4.1. FTIR spectroscopy results

As shown in Fig. 5, jute cellulose exhibits peaks at 3410 cm^{-1} for -OH stretching, 2900 cm^{-1} for -CH stretching, and 1055 cm^{-1} for C-O-C stretching due to glucoside linkage. The amide I C=O stretching, as well as the amide N-H stretching, are at 1632 and 3443 cm^{-1}, respectively, with a shift due to multiple H-bonding interface creation of the amide nitrogen in the electrospun nanocomposite fibers present due to the inclusion of NCGs. The broadening, as well as drop in intensity of the IR peak at roughly 3805-3031 cm^{-1} in the nanocomposite, is due to H-bonding in the nanocomposites, confirming the interfacial interaction between the matrices and the reinforcing nanofillers. The indication of KT drug inclusion is revealed by the peak at 1560 cm^{-1} from KT (corresponding to -C=O (carbonyl stretching) [3,6]. This establishes that KT is present in MC/PVA/PEG/CNCNCG-KT BNC. The IR band at 1475 cm^{-1} is owing to C=C aromatic vibration (stretching) in KT [3]. The chemical structure of the KT drug was established by the occurrence of the band at 775 and 730 cm^{-1} which is associated with C-H bending in aromatic rings [3,6]. The peak at 1388 cm^{-1} defines the C-N bond vibration frequency, while the peak at 1045 cm^{-1} defines KT alcoholic -OH groups bending. The inclusion of KT in BNCs is also validated by the existence of 775 and 730 cm^{-1} arising from C-H bending vibration of aromatic rings. Therefore, the FTIR results assured that there is no covalent bond type development or interface amongst the drug, polymers, or both. As per the FTIR findings, only noncovalent type interactions appear in the nanofibrous bio-nanocomposite transdermal patch.

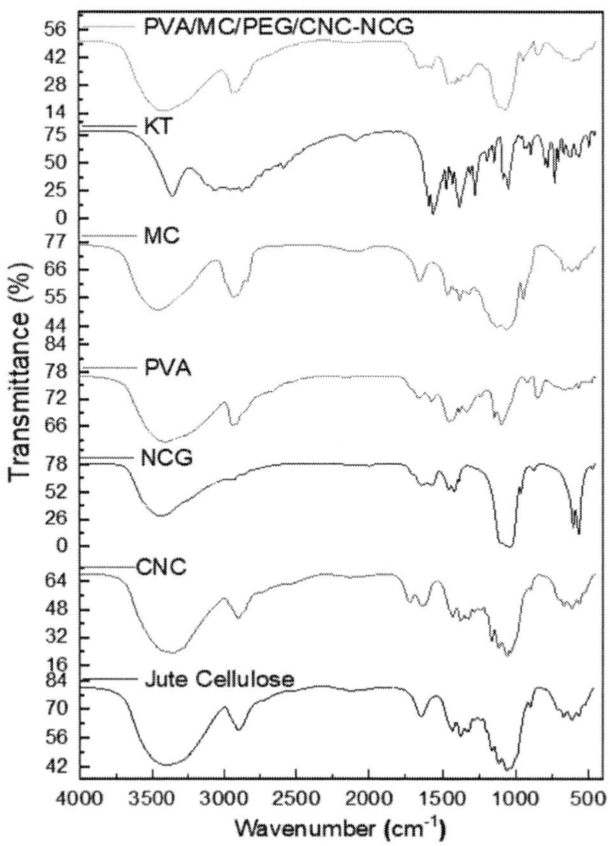

Fig. 5. FTIR spectra of Jute cellulose, CNCs, NCG, PVA, MC, KT, and bio-nanocomposite.

4.2. SEM results

The SEM micrograph of isolated CNC's shown in Fig. 2c. The rice like nanocrystalline network structure of CNCs which was extracted from jute fibers by acid hydrolysis technique.

4.3. XRD results

The XRD findings of Jute cellulose and CNC (shown in Fig. 6) revealed that jute cellulose peaks are obtained at 14.90, 16.05, 20.05, 22.56, and 34.38° for Miller indices of $(1\bar{1}0)$, (110), (102), (020), and (004), respectively. CNC peaks were found at 15.00, 16.35, 20.59, 22.98, as well as 34.88 correspondingly. Jute cellulose and CNC have cellulose II peaks at 20.05 as well as 20.59°, respectively. NaOH (mercerization) or acid treatment results in the creation of cellulose two (II). The peak intensity of CNCs is higher than jute cellulose due to the high crystallinity/ordered structure of CNCs.

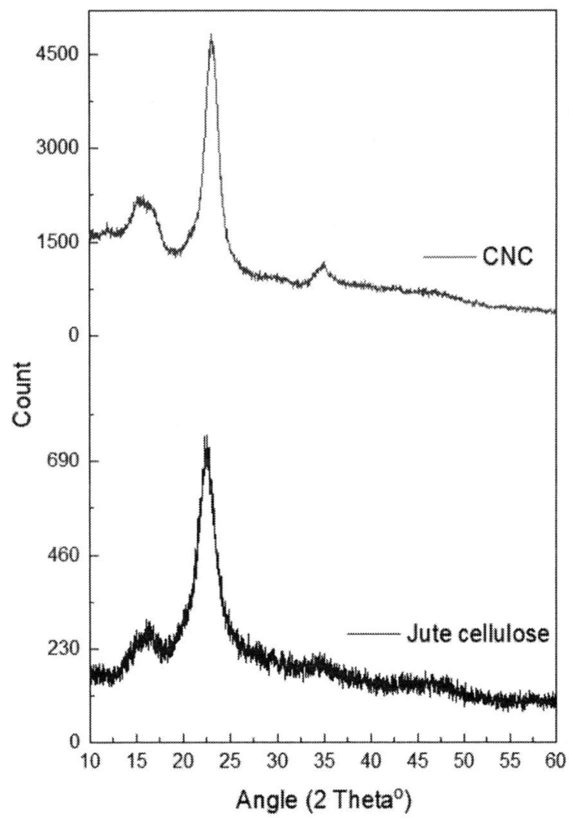

Fig. 6. X-ray diffraction patterns of Jute cellulose, and CNC.

4.4. Optical microscopy (OM) results of nanofibers

The surface morphology of the electrospun nano-hybrid reinforced bio-nanocomposite nanofibers were observed to be of fine networked architecture as shown in Fig. 7a. The structure agrees well with the FESEM images.

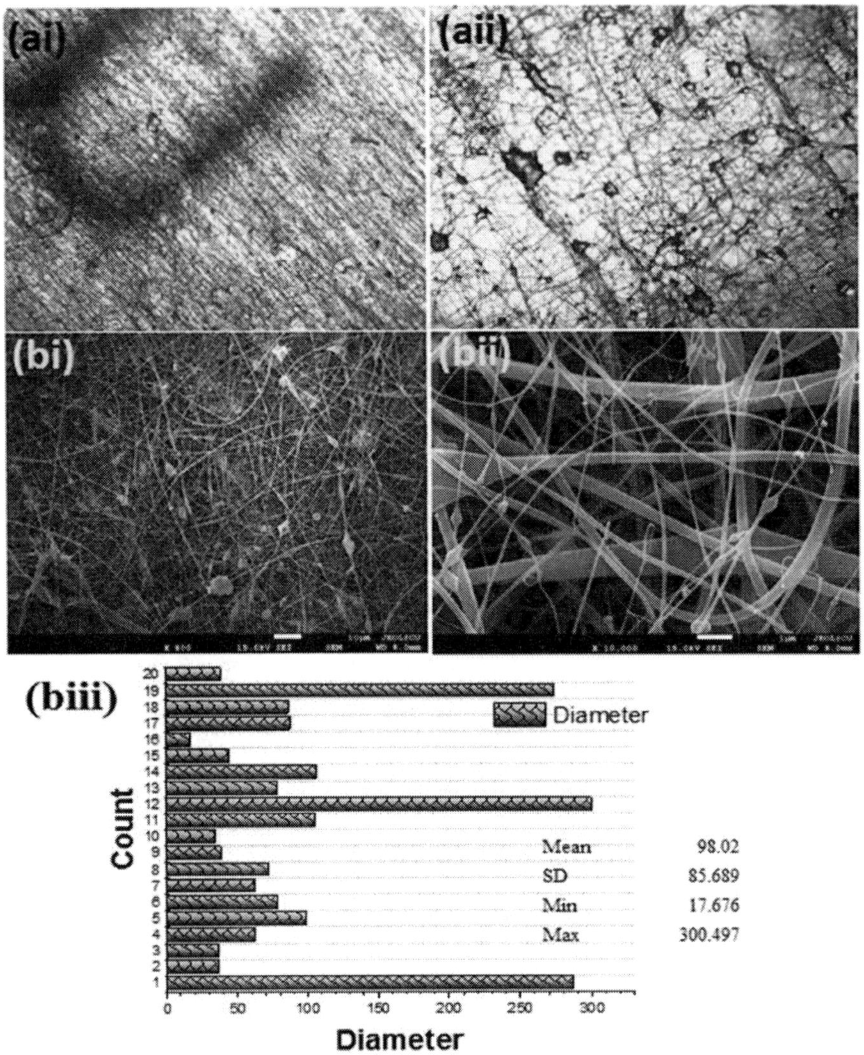

Fig. 7. (ai & aii) The Optical microscopy images (bi & bii) FESEM images of electrospun bio-nanocomposites fibers and (biii) diameter size distribution of nanofibers.

4.5. FESEM results

The FE-SEM micrograph of the electrospun nanostructured materials, as represented in Fig. 7 b, displays a nanofiber network with a diameter of approximately between 17.676 and 300.497 nm (with a mean diameter of 98.02 nm) and the length of several mm. This finding supports the effective fabrication of unique concept of an electrospun KT-loaded bio-nanocomposite system for prospective drug delivery applications. Other researchers' reports have demonstrated electrospun analogous nanofibrous web of PVA-based BNC fibers, as well as a known structural shape of electrospun nanofibers [1-3,7-8].

5. Conclusion

In this study we have presented the preparation of significant green CNCs and NCGs nanofillers/nanocarriers and their utilization to synthesize the novel bio-nanocomposite nanofibers by electrospinning technique. Successfully encapsulation and compatibility of the KT drug with the matrix polymers/fillers ensured by FTIR analyses. Through the ESPIN technique, we have shown that how we can easily develop a nanohybrid transdermal drug delivery system (TDDS) for administering KT transdermally via a fabricated nanofibrous transdermal system with novel properties, and hence we can avoid the drug-based side effects. The surface morphology revealed that the nanofibrous BNC having diameter within the range 17.36 to 300.4 nm and mean diameter of the fibrous network is 98.02 nm. The nanofibrous mat containing KT drug showed good surface morphology, drug-polymer compatibility which are suitable for TDD applications as well as other niches of biomaterials.

Acknowledgment

The authors wish to thank the Centre for Research in Nanoscience and Nanotechnology (CRNN), University of Calcutta for their all-around support.

Declaration

The authors have no conflict of interest

References

[1] Orasugh J, Ghosh S, and Chattopadhyay D. 2021 Cellulose nanofibrils in bio-nanocomposite films and their applications. In *Biopolymer-Based Nano Films* **(pp. 173-189)** *Elsevier.*
[2] Zelkó R, Lamprou D A, and Sebe I. 2019 Recent development of electrospinning for drug delivery. *Pharmaceutics* **12 (1)** 5.
[3] Samanta A P, Ali M S, Orasugh J T, Ghosh S K, and Chattopadhyay D. 2022 Crosslinked nanocollagen-cellulose nanofibrils reinforced electrospun polyvinyl alcohol/methylcellulose/polyethylene glycol bionanocomposites: Study of material properties and sustained release of ketorolac tromethamine. *Carbohydrate Polymer Technologies and Applications* **3** 100195.
[4] Barrientos I J H, Paladino E, Szabó P, Brozio S, Hall P J, Oseghale C I, Passarelli M K, Moug S J, Black R A, Wilson C G, Zelkó R. and Lamprou D A. 2017 Electrospun collagen-based nanofibres: A sustainable material for improved antibiotic utilisation in tissue engineering applications. *International journal of pharmaceutics* **531 (1)** 67-79.
[5] Sebe I, Szabó P, Kállai-Szabó B, and Zelkó R. 2015 Incorporating small molecules or biologics into nanofibers for optimized drug release: A review. *International Journal of Pharmaceutics* **494(1)** 516-530.
[6] Ali M S, Bhunia P, Samanta A P, Orasugh J T, and Chattopadhyay D 2022 Transdermal therapeutic system: Study of cellulose nanocrystals influenced methylcellulose-chitosan bionanocomposites. *International Journal of Biological Macromolecules* **218** 556-567.
[7] Czibulya Z, Csík A, Tóth F, Pál P, Csarnovics I, Zelkó R, and Hegedűs C. 2021 The Effect of the PVA/Chitosan/Citric Acid Ratio on the Hydrophilicity of Electrospun Nanofiber Meshes. *Polymers* **13(20)** 3557.
[8] Zelkó R. 2021 Supramolecular Structure and Stability of Nanofibrous Drug Delivery Systems. *ACTA PHARMACEUTICA HUNGARICA* **91 (3-4)** 126-127.

Natural radioactivity assessment of surface soil collected from Poovar village of Kerala, India

S R Soniya, P J Jojo

Research & Postgraduate Department of Physics,
Fatima Mata National College (Autonomous), Kollam, India
soniyasr04@gmail.com

Abstract. Making use of gamma ray spectrometric analysis method, the activities of soil-borne radio-nuclides viz. ^{226}Ra, ^{232}Th and ^{40}K in the surface soil samples from a specific village in coastal county has been determined. The surface soil of living environment in the Poovar village was used for the study. The activity concentration is used for evaluating various radiologically vital parameters such as levels of radium equivalent activity (Ra_{eq}), external hazard index (H_{ex}), internal hazard index (H_{in}), absorbed gamma dose rate (D), outdoor and indoor annual effective dose (AED), representative gamma radioactivity level index (Iγ) and alpha index (Iα) in the region. The estimated radioactivity concentrations of ^{226}Ra, ^{232}Th and ^{40}K was observed to fluctuate from below detectable level (BDL) of the instrument to 9 Bqkg^{-1}, 21 Bqkg^{-1} to 36 Bqkg^{-1} and 453 Bqkg^{-1} to 585 Bqkg^{-1}, respectively. Since all of the samples investigated in the study are within the advised limit, there are no radiation threats to the human beings in the region. The obtained information in this research can be used for future radiological mapping and impact assessments.

1. Introduction

The ambient radioactivity on earth originates from primordial radio-nuclides as well as from extraterrestrial sources such as isotopes produced by cosmic ray interactions. The terrestrial radioactivity is associated with radio-nuclides occurring naturally ^{226}Ra, ^{232}Th, and ^{40}K present in the earth[1]. The primeval radio-nuclides other than ^{226}Ra, ^{232}Th, and ^{40}K are found in the environment at low levels and hence their influence to the dose is considered negligible[2]. The contribution of primordial radio-nuclides and their daughter products in the natural environment is related to chemical properties of the radio-nuclides as well as the physical factors of the environment[3]. Long term exposure of the mankind to the natural radiation can result in various types of health hazard effects[4]. The exposure to ionizing radiation can cause lung cancer, which is known from many decades by longevity study of Japanese atomic bomb survivors[5]. Therefore, the period of exposure will have an important role, even though the exposure dose is small. The amount of energy transferred by the exposure of the materials to radiation is termed as absorbed dose[6]. According to the report of UNSCEAR 2008, the world-wide average value of dose from natural radiation to mankind is approximated as 0.3-1.0 mSv/year[7].

The various types of studies conducted worldwide shows the fact that the uranium (^{238}U), and its progeny in soil and rocks and thorium (^{232}Th) in monazite bearing sands are the major sources of radiation in HBRA (High Background Radiation Area)[8]. The aim of this study is to estimate the concentration of natural radionuclide concentration in the soil around the Poovar area. The objectives are to assess various radiologically important parameters namely radium equivalent activity, absorbed dose rate, annual gamma effective dose rate, internal and external hazard indices, gamma radioactivity level index and alpha index. The study of the research topic is significant in the context of exposure of the population to radiation resulting from the primordial radio-nuclides. Hence the result can be used for epidemiological studies and to establish a reference data for the region under study.

2. Materials and methods

The measurement of natural radionuclide was done from the collected soil samples of Poovar region in the Thiruvananthapuram district. Poovar is located at 8°19' N and 77°4' E. Total of twelve samples of soil were selected for the study. Mass of the each sample is taken as 0.45 kg. The samples were passed through a sieve and the homogeneous sample was heated at 110°C to make it dry. Each sample was placed inside an airtight calibrated container having a volume 305 cm^3. The sample containers were shelved as such for 30 days to attain radioactive equilibrium. Entire samples were examined by a $\gamma-$ray spectrometer having a crystal size of 3" × 3" NaI(Tl) scintillation detector (SPA 3), made in U.S.A by Thermal Fleisher Company and the crystal is manufactured by Saint Gobain, USA. The efficiency of the spectrometer for the concerned ^{226}Ra, ^{232}Th and ^{40}K was estimated to be 3.5 %, 1.18 % and 2.8 % respectively. The calibration of energy was found out using ^{137}Cs peak at 662 keV and two peaks of ^{60}Co. The energy peaks of ^{60}Co was observed at 1176.6 keV and 1332.8 keV respectively. The radioactivity of radium was estimated from the 1.764 MeV gamma line of ^{214}Bi and thorium from the 2.610 MeV gamma line of ^{208}Tl radionuclide. The activity concentration of potassium was analysed from 1460 keV gamma rays. The total time period taken for counting the sample was 10000 seconds. The gamma ray spectrums recorded were stored in a PC attached with a multi-channel analyzer. The specific radioactive levels of radioisotopes in the soil samples were assessed using the software.

Detectable limits of the radioisotopes for the detection system assessed were 4.7 $Bqkg^{-1}$for ^{226}Ra, 6.5 $Bqkg^{-1}$ for ^{232}Th and 27.18 $Bqkg^{-1}$ for ^{40}K.

3. Result and discussion

3.1 Estimation of specific activity

For estimating the specific activity of the radio-nuclides such as ^{226}Ra, ^{232}Th and ^{40}K in the samples, the equation (1)[9] was used. In the equation, *cps* denotes the net count per second given out by the samples, *BI* is the gamma intensity branching ratio and E_{ff} is the efficiency of the detector and w is the mass of the sample in kg.

$$\text{Specific activity } (Bqkg^{-1}) = \frac{\text{cps}}{\text{BI} \times \text{E}_{\text{ff}} \times \text{W}} \quad (1)$$

The specific radioactivity of radio-nuclides ^{226}Ra, ^{232}Th, and ^{40}K present in the samples used for the study are given in the Table 1. The specific activities of ^{226}Ra was observed to vary up to 9 $Bqkg^{-1}$ from the below detectable level (BDL), ^{232}Th varied from 21 $Bqkg^{-1}$ to 36 $Bqkg^{-1}$ and ^{40}K varied from 453 $Bqkg^{-1}$ to an extreme concentration of 585 $Bqkg^{-1}$. The outcomes obtained show that the radioactivity concentration of ^{226}Ra is lower in comparison with the world-wide average of 35 $BqKg^{-1}$. Radioactivity concentration of ^{232}Th is fairly comparable with the world-average concentration of 30 $BqKg^{-1}$. Radioactivity concentration of potassium is above the average value of 400 $BqKg^{-1}$

The figure 1 makes it evident that for the examined samples, concentration of activity of ^{40}K is the highest and that of ^{226}Ra is the lowest. The specific activity of ^{232}Th in the samples demonstrates that it is distributed in a narrow range. The major limitation of the estimations of radiological parameters in the following sections is that for samples which show specific activity of ^{226}Ra below detectable level, the value of 5 $Bqkg^{-1}$ (the detectable limit) was used for all the subsequent calculations. Therefore, the corresponding values of C_{Ra} and Ra_{eq} and their averages in the Table 1 and all parameters for these samples in Table 2 are most likely overestimated.

IOP Conf. Series: Materials Science and Engineering 1263 (2022) 012034 doi:10.1088/1757-899X/1263/1/012034

3.2 Radium equivalent activities of samples

A term "radium equivalent activity" (Ra_{eq}) has been established to represent net effect of the individual activities of ^{226}Ra, ^{232}Th, and ^{40}K by a single entity. The mathematical expression to evaluate the radium equivalent activity is[10]

$$Ra_{eq}(Bq\ kg^{-1}) = C_{Ra} + 1.43C_{Th} + 0.0077\ C_K \quad (2)$$

Here the symbols C_{Ra}, C_{Th}, and C_k denote the activity concentration of ^{226}Ra, ^{232}Th, and ^{40}K in $Bqkg^{-1}$, respectively. According to the United Nations Scientific Committee Report on the Effects of Atomic Radiation, 2000, the maximum value of Ra_{eq} activity must be less than 370 $Bqkg^{-1}$ while considering safety[2]. From the table 1 it can be understood that the Ra_{eq} value of soil samples from this region varies from $76 \pm 12Bqkg^{-1}$ to $101 \pm 15Bqkg^{-1}$ which is well below the maximum permissible value. Hence it is concluded that the entire sample selected for this study would not cause any significant radiation hazard to the population in the region.

3.3 Assessment of absorbed gamma dose rate

The gamma dose rates (D) in the atmospheric air above the soil surface absorbed by human beings for the uniform distribution of the radio-nuclides (^{226}Ra, ^{232}Th and ^{40}K) were estimated by means of the equation[11]:

$$D(nGyh^{-1}) = (0.462\ C_{Ra} + 0.621\ C_{Th}\ + 0.0417\ C_K) \quad (3)$$

From the analysis of data in the table 2, it can be observed that the estimated absorbed dose rate for ^{226}Ra, ^{232}Th, and ^{40}K varies from 37.14 to 48.20 $nGyh^{-1}$.

3.4 Assessment of hazard indices

The value of hazard index due to external gamma dose exposure must be less than or equal to one for a harmless margin of Ra_{eq} (upper limit370 $Bqkg^{-1}$). The equation used for the estimation of external hazard index, H_{ex} is[12],

$$H_{ex} = \frac{C_{Ra}}{370(Bqkg^{-1})} + \frac{C_{Th}}{259(Bqkg^{-1})} + \frac{C_K}{4810(Bqkg^{-1})} \leq 1 \quad (4)$$

The internal hazard index is envisioned to indicate a measure of internal exposure to ^{222}Rn and its radioactive daughter products and it should not exceed unity given by the equation[13]

$$H_{in} = \frac{C_{Ra}}{185(Bqkg^{-1})} + \frac{C_{Th}}{259(Bqkg^{-1})} + \frac{C_K}{4810(Bqkg^{-1})} \leq 1 \quad (5)$$

As can be perceived from the table 2, the radiation hazard and radioactivity level indices are within the limit of unity which shows that examined samples are safe to use.

3.5 Assessment of annual effective dose rate

To evaluate the annual effective dose (AED) rate owing to the gamma rays, the effective dose conversion factor of 0.7 $SvGy^{-1}$ suggested by UNSCEAR 2000 was employed[2]. Another vital factor for the assessment of AED, is the occupancy factor. This factor indicates the part of the time a human being spent indoors and outdoors during a day [7]. The occupancy factor used in the present estimation was 0.8 for indoor and 0.2 for outdoor [7]. If the absorbed dose rate D ($nGyh^{-1}$) is known, then the annual effective dose for indoor and outdoor exposures were calculated on the basis of the equation[14].

$$AED[Indoor]\ (mSvy^{-1}) = D \times 8760\ hy^{-1} \times 0.8 \times 0.7 \times 10^{-6} \quad (6)$$

$$AED[Outdoor](mSvy^{-1}) = D \times 8760\ hy^{-1} \times 0.2 \times 0.7 \times 10^{-6} \quad (7)$$

The annual effective radiation dose rates for indoor and outdoor environments have an average value of 0.21 $mSvy^{-1}$ and 0.05 $mSvy^{-1}$. The overall values of each sample are lower than the permissible annual limit of 1 mSv [7].

3.6 Estimation of index of radioactivity level (Iγ)

Index of radioactivity level, whose upper limit is unity, describes the radiation hazards owing to natural radio-nuclides in the surface soil is given by the equation[15]

$$I\gamma = \frac{C_{Ra}}{150(Bqkg^{-1})} + \frac{C_{Th}}{100(Bqkg^{-1})} + \frac{C_K}{1500(Bqkg^{-1})} \leq 1 \qquad (8)$$

Table 2 lists the estimated values of the gamma indices, which have a mean value of 0.68 and is within a relatively small range. The values are less than unity which demonstrates that the soil samples chosen for the investigation have low levels of gamma radiation.

3.7 Estimation of alpha index

Alpha index (Iα) is an important parameter used to evaluate alpha radiation resulted from excess radon inhalation originating from the soil under study. It should be always less than one while considering safety purposes. Estimation of the alpha index is based on the radioctivity concentration of radium C_{Ra} using the equation[16],

$$I\alpha = \frac{C_{Ra}}{200(Bqkg^{-1})} \qquad (9)$$

The recommended limit of specific activity for radium is 200 $Bqkg^{-1}$ since larger values may result in increased radon concentration from the sample[17]. The studied region is quite safe from the perspective of environmental radiation concerns being the observed values of the alpha index less than unity.

Table 1: Estimated activity concentrations of ^{226}Ra, ^{232}Th, ^{40}K and Radium equivalent activity.

No. of Soil Samples	^{226}Ra ($Bqkg^{-1}$)	^{232}Th ($Bqkg^{-1}$)	^{40}K ($BqKg^{-1}$)	Ra_{eq} ($BqKg^{-1}$)
01	< 5	36 ± 5	585 ± 179	101 ± 15
02	< 5	32 ± 7	525 ± 160	90 ± 13
03	5 ± 1	27 ± 4	560 ± 174	87 ± 13
04	< 5	36 ± 5	574 ± 179	101 ± 15
05	< 5	33 ± 5	475 ± 149	89 ± 13
06	9 ± 2	28 ± 4	505 ± 157	89 ± 13
07	< 5	27 ± 4	453 ± 140	78 ± 11
08	< 5	25 ± 4	490 ± 149	78 ± 12
09	8 ± 2	21 ± 3	497 ± 154	76 ± 12
10	< 5	28 ± 4	512 ± 159	84 ± 13
11	< 5	32 ± 5	525 ± 162	90 ± 14
12	< 5	30 ± 4	502 ± 155	87 ± 13
Average	7*	30	517	88
SD	2	4	40	8

* The average was calculated only from measurable values.

Radium, thorium, and potassium concentrations in the studied samples are depicted as a bar graph in figure 1.

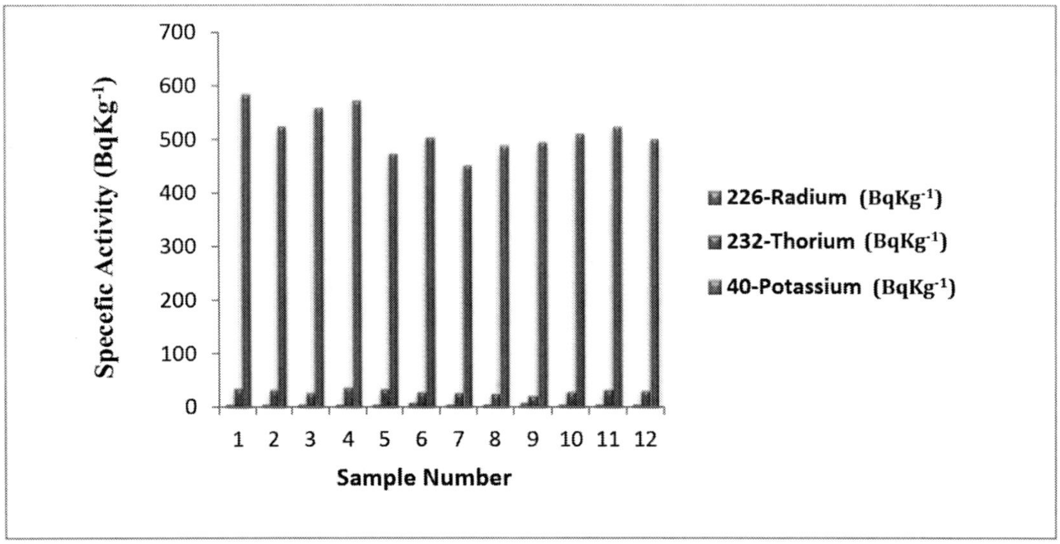

Figure 1 Histogram graph showing the concentration of radio-nuclides in different samples.

Table 2 : Estimated absorbed dose rate, external and internal hazard index, representative level index, alpha index and annual effective dose.

No. of Soil Samples	D($nGyh^{-1}$)	H_{ex}	H_{in}	I_γ	I_α	Annual Effective Dose Rate ($mSvy^{-1}$)	
						Indoor	**Outdoor**
01	48.20	0.27	0.29	0.78	0.02	0.24	0.06
02	43.13	0.24	0.26	0.70	0.02	0.21	0.05
03	42.23	0.24	0.25	0.68	0.03	0.21	0.05
04	47.94	0.27	0.28	0.78	0.02	0.24	0.06
05	42.09	0.24	0.25	0.68	0.02	0.21	0.05
06	42.58	0.24	0.27	0.68	0.05	0.21	0.05
07	37.15	0.21	0.22	0.60	0.02	0.18	0.05
08	37.80	0.21	0.22	0.61	0.02	0.19	0.05
09	37.14	0.21	0.23	0.60	0.04	0.18	0.05
10	40.54	0.23	0.24	0.65	0.02	0.20	0.05
11	43.29	0.24	0.26	0.70	0.02	0.21	0.05
12	41.40	0.23	0.25	0.67	0.02	0.20	0.05

The potential radiological parameters are shown in **Table 2** which include absorbed gamma dose rate, outdoor and indoor annual gamma effective dose rate, both external and internal radiation hazard index, specific radioactivity index (gamma index), and alpha index and from the obtained data we can conclude that the region under study is safe in the health hazard point of view.

The estimation of radioactivity in soil has been carried out in numerous regions of the world. In India, the works on the radioactivity of soil and on radiation dose parameters are generally scattered. Pillai et al., surveyed natural radioactivity levels of soil samples from Tiruchirappalli district in Tamil Nadu through analysis of gamma ray spectrum of primordial radio-nuclides[4]. The average activity concentrations of ^{226}Ra, ^{232}Th and ^{40}K in the soil samples were found to be 6.5, 61.7 and 379.8 Bqkg^{-1} respectively.

Amanjeet et al., [11] made investigations on natural radionuclide distribution by the spectrometric analysis of surface soil collected from Panipat and its surroundings. The activity concentrations estimated for ^{238}U were reported to vary from14.82 ± 0.26 to 42.82 ± 0.84 Bqkg^{-1}, for ^{232}Th are range was from 12.94 ± 0.32 to 43.48 ± 0.96 Bqkg^{-1} and for ^{40}K it was from 238.05 ± 0.28 to 348.50 ± 0.95 Bqkg^{-1}. Radium equivalent activities were found in the range of 82.24 -108.49 Bqkg^{-1} with an average value of 92.21 Bqkg^{-1}.

Ravisankar et.al.,[14] conducted natural radioactivity in the beach sediment samples from the region between Thazhankuda (Cuddalore) to Kodiyakkarai along East Coast of Tamilnadu. The radioactivities of 20 samples using NaI(Tl) detector were reported to have average specific activities 3.67 Bq kg^{-1} for ^{238}U, 37.23 Bq kg^{-1} for ^{232}Th and 387.17 Bq kg^{-1} for ^{40}K.

Kansal et al.[18] have measured the activity and gamma dose rates of radio-nuclides in soil samples collected from Hisar district of Haryana by means of gamma spectrometry system. The mean activity of ^{226}Ra, ^{232}Th and ^{40}K were measured to be 17.79, 45.45 and 359.96 Bqkg^{-1} respectively. The total absorbed dose and hazard index for the soil samples were found to be within the permissible limits in the study.

Another investigation held in Punjab, India by Bangotra et al.[19] carried out the detailed study for measuring the level of radioactive element viz. ^{226}Ra, ^{232}Th, and ^{40}K in the Barnala and Sangrur region. The concentration of three primordial radio-nuclides (^{226}Ra, ^{232}Th and ^{40}K) in soil samples from studied area has varied from 25 Bq kg^{-1} to 48 Bqkg^{-1}, 28 Bqkg^{-1} to 47 Bqkg^{-1} and 356 Bqkg^{-1} to 598 Bqkg^{-1} with average of 37 Bqkg^{-1}, 40 Bqkg^{-1} and 451 Bqkg^{-1} respectively. It is claimed that the variation of activity concentration of ^{226}Ra, ^{232}Th and ^{40}K in the studied area was caused by different chemical and physical properties of radio-nuclides in soil in the region. The values from present study are in agreement with those reported in the literature.

4. Conclusion

Gamma ray spectrometry is used to measure the natural radioactivity concentration from the radio-nuclides, ^{226}Ra, ^{232}Th, and ^{40}K in the Poovar area of Thiruvananthapuram district. The obtained radioactivity concentrations of ^{226}Ra, ^{232}Th and ^{40}K were observed to vary from below detectable level to 9 Bqkg$^{-1,}$ 21 Bqkg^{-1}to 36 Bqkg^{-1} and 453 Bqkg^{-1} to 585 Bqkg^{-1}, respectively. The obtained radioactivity concentrations of ^{226}Ra are lower as compared with the world-wide average of 35 Bqkg^{-1}. Radioactivity concentrations of ^{232}Th is comparable with the world-average concentration of 30Bqkg^{-1}. Radioactivity concentration of potassium is above the average value of 400 BqKg^{-1}. It is observed that for all examined soil samples from Poovar area is far below the allowable limit of 370 Bqkg^{-1} since the estimated values vary from 76 Bqkg^{-1} to 101 Bqkg^{-1}. All the internal and external hazard indices are less than unity. The estimated data of annual gamma radiation rates fall under the advised safety range for the samples studied. Since all of the samples under investigation are within the advised safety level, there are no radiation concerns. Future radiological investigations and mapping of the study area will benefit from this research.

Reference

[1] Cochran J K, Bokuniewicz H J and Yager P L. 2019. *Encyclopedia of ocean sciences*. Academic Press.

[2] UNSCEAR (United Nations Scientific Committee on the Effects of Atomic Radiation, 2000). Sources and Effects of Ionizing Radiation. Report to the General Assembly with Scientific Annexes, United Nations Scientific Committee on the Effects of Atomic Radiation, New York.

[3] Pudjadi E. 2020. Assessment of natural radioactivity levels in soil sample from Botteng Utara Village, Mamuju Regency Indonesia. In *Journal of Physics: Conference Series* 1436(1), p. 012139. IOP Publishing.

[4] Sankaran Pillai G, Shahul Hameed P and Mazhar Nazeeb Khan S M. 2016. Natural radioactivity levels in the soils and human risk assessment in Tiruchirappalli district (Tamil Nadu, India). *Journal of Radioanalytical and Nuclear Chemistry*, 307(2), 1265-77.

[5] Kodama K, Ozasa K and Okubo, T. 2012. Radiation and cancer risk in atomic-bomb survivors. *Journal of Radiological Protection, 32*(1), N51.

[6] Cooper J R, Randle K and Sokhi R S 2003. Radioactive releases in the environment: impact and assessment. John Wiley and Sons.

[7] UNSCEAR 2008. Vol I, Annexure B. Exposure to the public and workers from various sources of radiation. *Report to the General Assembly*. New York, United Nations.

[8] Al-Jundi, Al-Bataina B A, Abu-Rukah Y and Shehadeh H M. (2003). Natural radioactivity concentrations in soil samples along the Amman Aqaba Highway Jordan. *Radiation measurements*, 36(1-6), 555-560.

[9] Ajayi O S, 2009. Measurement of activity concentrations of ^{40}K, ^{226}Ra and ^{232}Th for assessment of radiation hazards from soils of the southwestern region of Nigeria. Radiat. Environ. *Biophys.* 48 (3), 323-332.

[10] Aközcan S, 2014. Natural and artificial radioactivity levels and hazards of soils in the Kücük Menderes Basin, Turkey. *Environ. Earth Sci.* 71(10), 4611-14.

[11] Amanjeet, Kumar A., Kumar S, Singh J, Singh P and Bajwa B S. 2017. Assessment of natural radioactivity levels and associated dose rates in soil samples from historical city Panipat, India. *Journal of radiation research and applied sciences*, 10(3), 283-288.

[12] Bangotra P, Mehra R, Jakhu R, Kaur K, Pandit P, and Kanse S. 2018. Estimation of ^{222}Rn exhalation rate and assessment of radiological risk from activity concentration of ^{226}Ra, ^{232}Th and ^{40}K. *Journal of Geochemical Exploration*, 184, 304-310.

[13] Chowdhury M, Alam M, and Ahmed A. 1998. Concentration of radionuclides in building and ceramic materials of Bangladesh and evaluation of radiation hazard. *Journal of radioanalytical and nuclear chemistry*, 231(1-2), 117-123a.

[14] Ravisankar R, Sivakumar S, Chandrasekaran A, Jebakumar J P and Venkatraman B et al. (2014). Spatial distribution of gamma radioactivity levels and radiological hazard indices in the East Coastal sediments of Tamilnadu, India with statistical approach. *Radiation Physics and Chemistry*, *103*, 89-98.

[15] Senthilkumar G, Raghu Y, Sivakumar S, Chandrasekaran, PremAnand D and Ravisankar, R. 2014. Natural radioactivity measurement and evaluation of radiological hazards in some commercial flooring materials used in Thiruvannamalai, Tamilnadu, India. *Journal of Radiation Research and Applied Sciences*, 7(1), 116-122.

[16] Sharma N, Singh J, Esakki S C, and Tripathi R M. 2016. A study of the natural radioactivity and radon exhalation rate in some cements used in India and its radiological significance. *Journal of Radiation Research and Applied Sciences*, 9(1), 47-56.

[17] Eštoková, A and Palaščáková, L. (2013). Assessment of natural radioactivity levels of cements and cement composites in the Slovak Republic. *International journal of environmental research and public health*, *10*(12), 7165-7179.

IOP Conf. Series: Materials Science and Engineering 1263 (2022) 012034 doi:10.1088/1757-899X/1263/1/012034

[18] Kansal S, Mehra R, Singh N P, Badhan K, & Sonkawade R G. (2010). Analysis and assessment of radiological risk in soil samples of Hisar district of Haryana, India.

[19] Bangotra P, Mehra, R., Jakhu R, Kaur K, Pandit, P, & Kanse S. (2018). Estimation of ^{222}Rn exhalation rate and assessment of radiological risk from activity concentration of ^{226}Ra, ^{232}Th and ^{40}K. Journal of Geochemical Exploration, 184, 304-310.

Crystal structure and magnetism of rare earth intermetallic compound $Dy_{0.33}Ho_{0.33}Er_{0.33}Ni$

Abhaya Prasada Mohapatra[1], J. Arout Chelvane[2], A. V. Morozkin[3], S. Ramaprabhu[1] and R. Nirmala[1*]

[1]Department of Physics, Indian Institute of Technology Madras, Chennai 600 036, India
[2]Defence Metallurgical Research Laboratory, Hyderabad 500 058, India
[3]Department of Chemistry, Moscow Lomonosov State University, Moscow, 119992, Russia

*Corresponding author. E-mail: nirmala@physics.iitm.ac.in

Abstract. Multi-component rare earth intermetallic compound $Dy_{0.33}Ho_{0.33}Er_{0.33}Ni$ has been prepared by arc melting and characterized by powder X-ray diffraction and magnetization experiments. The sample crystallizes in orthorhombic FeB-type structure at 300 K and ferromagnetically orders around 40 K (T_C). The T_C is close to the average value of the ferromagnetic transition temperatures of DyNi, HoNi and ErNi compounds. Magnetization has been measured as a function of field up to 15 kOe and low field magnetocaloric effect around the magnetic transition temperature is computed.

1. Introduction

Rare earth intermetallic compounds with equiatomic composition of heavy rare earths (R) such as Gd, Dy, Ho and Er and nickel are known to exhibit large magnetocaloric effect near their ferromagnetic ordering temperature [1, 2, 3]. In an effort to tailor the magnetic transition temperature and the magnetic entropy change near the transition, rare earth site has been multiply substituted and it was found to be beneficial [4, 5]. A practical magnetic refrigerant should possess a large value of magnetocaloric effect that is widely spread over the temperature range of interest [6, 7, 8]. In the present work, three-component RNi compound namely $Dy_{0.33}Ho_{0.33}Er_{0.33}Ni$ has been synthesized and characterized. This compound exhibits a second-order paramagnetic to ferromagnetic transition around 40 K (T_C). From the isothermal magnetization data, magnetic entropy change around the transition has been calculated and a moderate magnetocaloric effect is observed near T_C. Despite the presence of three magnetic rare earths at the R-site, this compound exhibits a single T_C that is approximately the average of ferromagnetic transition temperatures of the individual DyNi, HoNi and ErNi compounds.

2. Experimental Details

Starting from stoichiometric amounts of pure elements (99.9 % pure), polycrystalline $Dy_{0.33}Ho_{0.33}Er_{0.33}Ni$ compound has been prepared by electric arc melting under argon atmosphere. The sample was overturned and remelted a few times in order to enhance the homogeneity. Crystal structure has been studied using powder X-ray diffraction (Rigaku, Cu K_α) at 300 K and the unit cell data were obtained using the Rietan program [9]. Energy dispersive analysis of X-rays (EDAX) has been performed to confirm the nominal composition. DC magnetization (M) has been measured using a vibrating sample magnetometer (VSM) (Lake Shore, USA) in the temperature (T) range of 15 K to 300 K in magnetic fields (H) up to 15 kOe. A few magnetization measurements have been performed down to 5 K using a SQUID based VSM (MPMS 3, Quantum Design, USA).

3. Results and Discussion

Powder X-ray diffraction data of $Dy_{0.33}Ho_{0.33}Er_{0.33}Ni$ obtained at 300 K reveal that the sample crystallizes in FeB-type orthorhombic crystal structure (Space group *Pnma*, No. 62, *oP*8) like the initial phases DyNi, HoNi and ErNi [Fig. 1]. The lattice parameters (*a*, *b* and *c*) of $Dy_{0.33}Ho_{0.33}Er_{0.33}Ni$ are 7.0137(4) Å, 4.1399(2) Å and 5.4349(2) Å respectively and these values are nearly equal to the arithmetic mean of lattice parameters of DyNi, HoNi and ErNi compounds [10]. Using energy dispersive X-ray analysis, the sample composition is found to be $Dy_{0.33}Ho_{0.30}Er_{0.35}Ni_{1.02}$. The EDAX spectrum is shown in Figure 2.

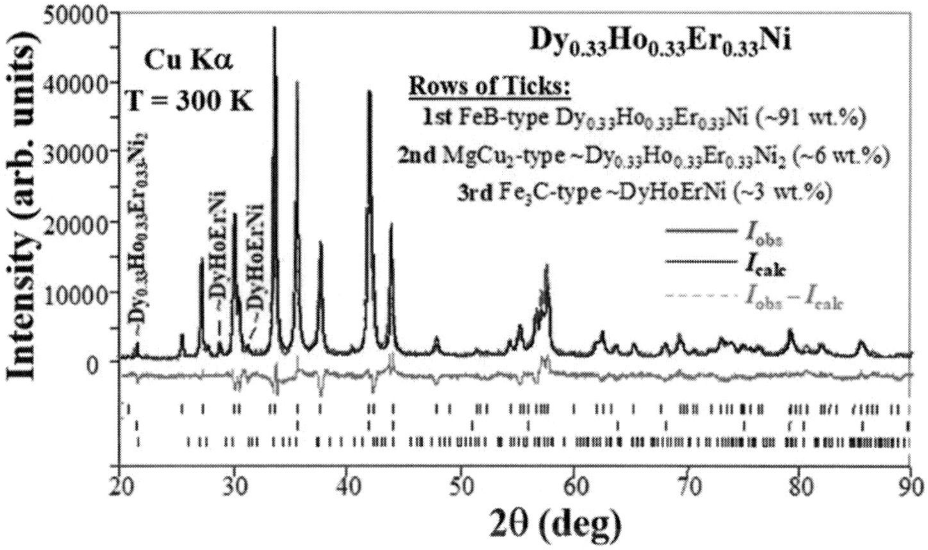

Figure 1. Powder X-ray diffraction data of $Dy_{0.33}Ho_{0.33}Er_{0.33}Ni$ compound at 300 K and the Rietveld refinement. The rare earth atoms occupy *4c* sites [0.1706(3), ¼, 0.1336(4)] and Ni atoms are positioned at *4c* [0.0614(5), ¼, 0.6266(9)] sites and reliability factor R_F is 2.8%. Rietveld analysis indicates the presence of ~6 wt.% of $MgCu_2$-type ~$Dy_{0.33}Ho_{0.33}Er_{0.33}Ni_2$ phase and ~3 wt.% of Fe_3C-type (DyHoEr)Ni phase. The reflections corresponding to these phases are indicated by vertical ticks at the bottom. The major individual reflections of the admixture phases are indicated in the main panel.

Magnetization vs temperature of $Dy_{0.33}Ho_{0.33}Er_{0.33}Ni$ has been measured in 5 kOe field in zero-field-cooled (ZFC) and field-cooled (FC) conditions during warming [Fig. 3]. The ferromagnetic order of $Dy_{0.33}Ho_{0.33}Er_{0.33}Ni$ sample at 40 K is evidenced as an extremum point in the dM/dT vs T plot [Inset in Fig. 3]. The compounds DyNi, HoNi and ErNi are known to order ferromagnetically at 61 K, 36 K and 11 K respectively. The three-component $Dy_{0.33}Ho_{0.33}Er_{0.33}Ni$ compound orders at a temperature of 40 K which is approximately equal to the average of the T_C values of the individual RNi (R = Dy, Ho and Er) compounds (i.e. 36 K). The predominant RKKY exchange interaction seems to be intact in the multiple rare-earth containing $Dy_{0.33}Ho_{0.33}Er_{0.33}Ni$ compound. A long-range order of moments at a critical temperature of 40 K is observed despite the statistical distribution of three different rare earth moments. The transition is relatively broad compared to that in the end members. The ZFC and FC magnetization demarcate at 11 K and there is a weak upturn in magnetization. This could possibly be related to a spin-reorientation transition. Similar spin reorientation transition has been reported in $Ho_xEr_{1-x}Ni$ ($0\leq x\leq 1$) compounds before [5].

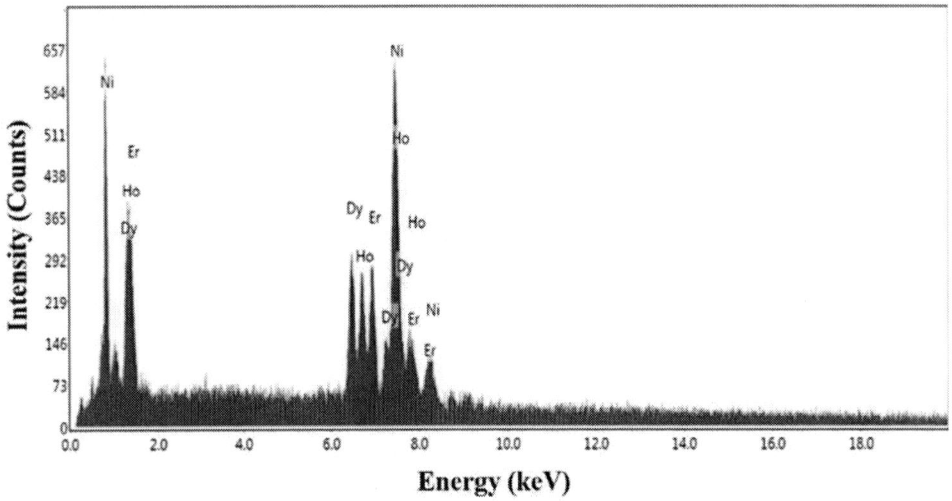

Figure 2. Energy dispersive X-ray spectrum of $Dy_{0.33}Ho_{0.33}Er_{0.33}Ni$ depicting various elemental peaks. Peak positions correspond to Ni K- line and rare earth (Dy, Ho and Er) L- lines.

The paramagnetic susceptibility is Curie-Weiss-like in the temperature range of ~150 K to 300 K and the fit yields effective paramagnetic moment (μ_{eff}) and paramagnetic Curie temperature (θ_p) values as 12 μ_B/f.u. and +13 K respectively. The positive value of θ_p confirms the presence of dominant ferromagnetic interactions. The $MgCu_2$-type, ~6% $Dy_{0.33}Ho_{0.33}Er_{0.33}Ni_2$ minority phase likely influences the low field magnetization subtly in the paramagnetic state of the $Dy_{0.33}Ho_{0.33}Er_{0.33}Ni$ sample. Therefore Curie-Weiss fit to the paramagnetic susceptibility is good only in the temperature range of ~150 K to 300 K. The other minority phase (~3 wt.% of Fe_3C-type ~DyHoErNi) is paramagnetic in the studied temperature range of 5 K to 300 K and hence is not expected to affect the magnetic data much.

Magnetization has been measured as a function of field and the M vs H data at 5 K shows typical saturation behaviour of a ferromagnet. The saturation magnetization value is found to be ~ 8.6 μ_B/f.u. [Fig. 4]. A weak hysteresis is observed with a coercive field value of ~ 575 Oe [Inset in Fig. 4]. The coercive field value is intermediate when compared with that of the single rare earth containing RNi compounds. The coercive field values are 0 Oe, 1100 Oe, 200 Oe, 90 Oe and 0 Oe respectively for arc-melted GdNi, TbNi, DyNi, HoNi and ErNi compounds at either 5 K or 2 K [2, 3].

Isothermal magnetization of $Dy_{0.33}Ho_{0.33}Er_{0.33}Ni$ compound has been measured as a function of magnetic fields from O Oe to 15 kOe from T = 15 K to 75 K at a temperature interval of 5 K [Fig. 5a]. From the Arrot plots [Figure not shown], one finds that the transition at 40 K is second-order in nature. Magnetocaloric effect around the ferromagnetic ordering temperature has been calculated from the M vs H data. The expression obtained from the Maxwell's thermodynamic relation (see below) has been used to calculate isothermal magnetic entropy change (ΔS_m).

$$-\Delta S_m = \mu_0 \int_{H_i}^{H_f} \left(\frac{\partial M}{\partial T}\right)_H dH$$

Here, H_i and H_f are the initial and final applied magnetic field strengths and μ_0 is the permeability of free space [11].

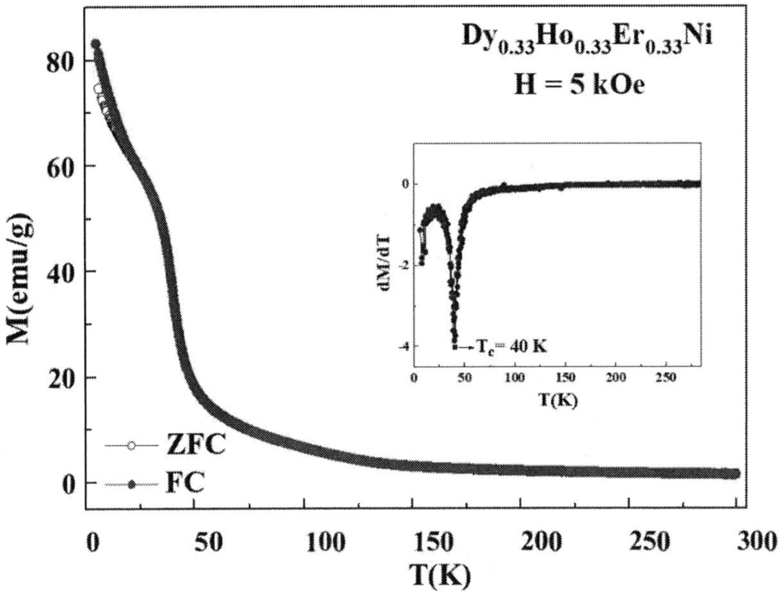

Figure 3. Magnetization vs temperature of $Dy_{0.33}Ho_{0.33}Er_{0.33}Ni$ in 5 kOe field measured in zero-field-cooled and field-cooled conditions. Inset: dM/dT vs T plot.

Magnetocaloric effect is large in the neighbourhood of the T_C as expected for a ferromagnet [Fig. 5b]. The maximum value of isothermal magnetic entropy change (ΔS_m^{max}) is about – 2.8 $Jkg^{-1}K^{-1}$ at 37.5 K for a field change of 14 kOe. The variation of ΔS_m^{max} value with field change (ΔH) is studied and it is found to be proportional to $(\Delta H)^n$ with n = 2/3 [Fig. 6]. This would suggest that the three-component rare earth compound $Dy_{0.33}Ho_{0.33}Er_{0.33}Ni$ is a mean-field ferromagnet [12]. The absolute value of ΔS_m is relatively small compared to the single-rare earth component RNi (R = Dy, Ho and Er) compounds [Table 1]. This could be because of the distributed exchange and broad nature of the magnetic transition. The slow change in magnetization around T_C could lead to relatively small values of magnetocaloric effect. In the case of 10% Ho-substituted ErNi compound, magnetocaloric effect is enhanced due to the overlap of spin-reorientation transition and ferromagnetic transition [5].

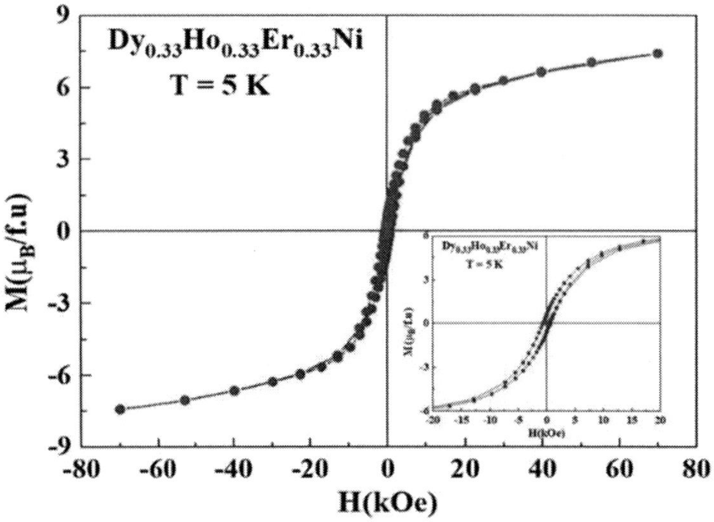

Figure 4. Magnetization vs magnetic field isotherm of $Dy_{0.33}Ho_{0.33}Er_{0.33}Ni$ at 5 K in fields up to 70 kOe. Inset: Low field magnetization is zoomed-in to show the weak hysteresis.

Table 1. Comparison of low field magnetocaloric effect of RNi (R = Dy, Ho and Er) and $Dy_{0.33}Ho_{0.33}Er_{0.33}Ni$ compounds.

Compound	T_C (K)	$-\Delta S_m$ ($Jkg^{-1}K^{-1}$)	ΔH (kOe)	Reference
DyNi	61	10.5	20	1, 2
HoNi	36	8	20	2
ErNi	11	14	20	1, 3
$Dy_{0.33}Ho_{0.33}Er_{0.33}Ni$	40	2.8	14	Present work

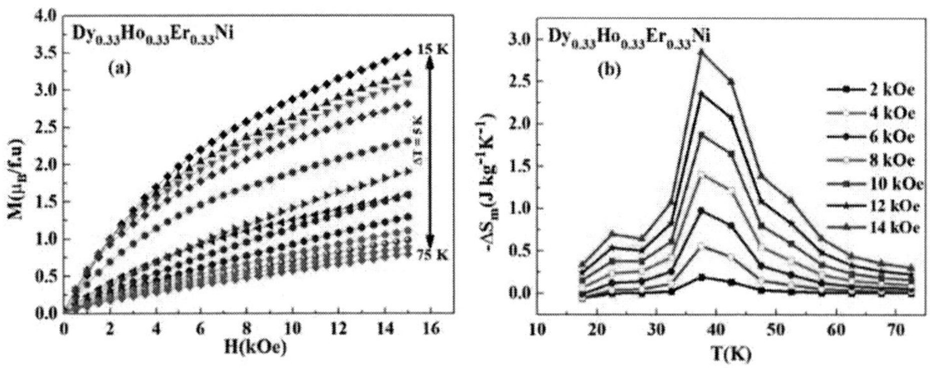

Figure 5. (a) Magnetization vs magnetic field isotherms of $Dy_{0.33}Ho_{0.33}Er_{0.33}Ni$ in fields up to 15 kOe. (b) Isothermal magnetic entropy change vs temperature of $Dy_{0.33}Ho_{0.33}Er_{0.33}Ni$ compound for various field changes.

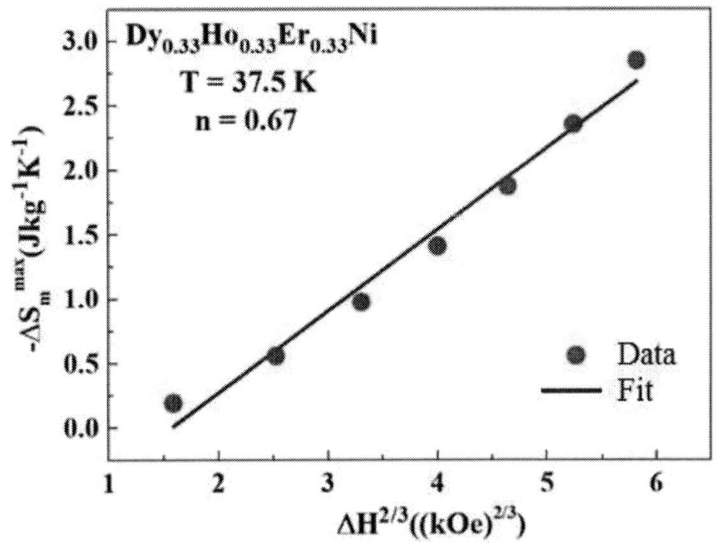

Figure 6. Maximum magnetic entropy change vs magnetic field change, ΔH and the fit to power law, $(\Delta H)^n$, with n = 2/3. Solid line is the fit to the data.

4. Summary and Conclusions

Three-component rare earth intermetallic compound $Dy_{0.33}Ho_{0.33}Er_{0.33}Ni$ (orthorhombic, FeB-type) has been synthesized and characterized. The compound orders ferromagnetically at 40 K which is roughly the average of the T_C of the individual compounds RNi (R = Dy, Ho and Er). Low field magnetocaloric effect around this transition has been calculated from the isothermal magnetization data and the maximum value of isothermal magnetic entropy change is found to be – 2.8 $Jkg^{-1}K^{-1}$ around T_C for a magnetic field change of 14 kOe. Substituting multiple magnetic elements at rare earth site of RNi compounds helps to tailor the T_C and the idea could be extended to design potential magnetic refrigerant materials.

5. Acknowledgement
Authors thank Sreejith P. K. for the help during a few magnetization measurements.

References
[1] Pramod Kumar, Suresh K G, Nigam A K and Gutfleisch O 2008 *J. Phys. D: Appl. Phys.* **41** 245006
[2] Rajivgandhi R, Arout Chelvane J, Quezado S, Malik S K and Nirmala R 2017 *J. Magn. Magn. Mater.* **433** 169
[3] Aparna Sankar, Arout Chelvane J, Morozkin A V, Nigam A K, Quezado S , Malik S K and Nirmala R 2018 *AIP advances* **8** 056208
[4] Chzhan V B, Tereshina I S, Karpenkov A Yu and Tereshina-Chitrova E A 2018 *Acta Mater.* **154** 303
[5] Zheng X Q, Zhang B, Wu H, Hu F X, Huang Q Z and Shen B G 2016 *J. Appl. Phys.* **120** 163907
[6] Tishin A M and Spichkin Y I 2003 *The magnetocaloric effect and its applications* vol. 6 (IOP Publishing Ltd., Bristol)
[7] Franco V, Blázquez J S, Ipus J J, Law J Y, Moreno-Ramírez L M and Conde A *2018 Prog. Mater. Sci.* **93** 112

IOP Conf. Series: Materials Science and Engineering 1263 (2022) 012035 doi:10.1088/1757-899X/1263/1/012035

[8] Pecharsky V K and Gschneidner Jr. K A 2006 *Int. J. Refrig.* **29** 1239
[9] Izumi F 1993 *The Rietveld Method* ed. by R.A. Young 13 (Oxford University Press, Oxford)
[10] Springer materials The Landolt-Börnstein database – Materials science data for 250000 substances, *http://www.spingermaterials.com*
[11] Pecharsky V K and Gschneidner Jr. K A 1999 *J. Magn. Magn. Mater.* **200** 44
[12] Franco V, Blázquez J S and Condea A 2006 *Appl. Phys. Lett.* **89** 222512

IOP Conf. Series: Materials Science and Engineering 1263 (2022) 012036 doi:10.1088/1757-899X/1263/1/012036

Structural analysis of $La_{0.7}Sr_{0.3}MnO_3$ manganite synthesized by sol-gel and solid-state route

Bhagya Uthaman, Akhila Prasad and M Hariram

Department of Physics, Fatima Mata National College, Kollam-691001, Kerala, India
Email: bhagya@fmnc.ac.in

Abstract. In this study, the structural properties of $La_{0.7}Sr_{0.3}MnO_3$ (LSMO) manganite synthesized in bulk and nano form have been analyzed in detail. The bulk LSMO was synthesized by the solid-state method whereas the LSMO nanoparticles was prepared using the sol-gel route. The structural properties of the prepared samples were examined using X-Ray diffraction (XRD). Rietveld refinement confirmed that all the samples crystallize in R-3c space group with a rhombohedral structure. Williamson-Hall (WH) Analysis using Uniform deformation model and Size strain plots (SSP) were employed to determine the average crystallite size and microstrain in the synthesized samples. SEM and TEM measurements have also been taken to analyse their size distribution.

1. Introduction

Manganites are an important class of compounds with the formula $RE_{1-x}B_xMnO_3$ where RE is a rare earth and B denotes divalent alkaline earth metal cation. Among the manganites, Lanthanum Strontium manganites are of scientific and technological importance with a wide variety of exotic properties such as magnetocaloric effect (MCE), colossal magnetoresistance (CMR), as catalysts, sensors, etc [1-4]. Manganites exhibit a strong interplay between the charge, orbital and spin degrees of freedom [4]. Double exchange mechanism in manganites is responsible for the ferromagnetism and metallicity exhibited by them. They also exhibit strong electron-phonon coupling which is attributed to Jahn-Teller effect [5-7].

$La_{0.7}Sr_{0.3}MnO_3$ manganites are of special interest owing to their high value of Curie temperature (TC), half-metallic ferromagnetic ground state which leads to 100% spin polarization, easy tunability of TC by changing doping species, concentration and pressure [5-7]. The discovery of CMR in Lanthanum Strontium manganites has made them potential candidates as magnetic field sensors [8-10] and magnetic recording applications [9, 11]. Hence, in this study, we have analysed the structural behavior of $La_{0.7}Sr_{0.3}MnO_3$ synthesized by sol-gel and solid-state route.

2. Experimental Details

LSMO nanoparticles were synthesized using sol-gel route. Stoichiometric amounts of Lanthanum nitrate ($La(NO_3)_3.6H_2O$), Strontium nitrate ($Sr(NO_3)_2$) and Manganese nitrate ($Mn(NO_3)_2.4H_2O$) were dissolved separately in double-distilled water and ultrasonicated for 30 minutes. Citric acid ($C_6H_8O_7$) and ethylene glycol ($C_2H_6O_2$) in the ratio 1.5:2.25 were added drop wise with stirring. The mixture was then stirred continuously on a hot plate at 80°C. The pH of the resulting solution was kept at 9 by adding small amounts of ammonia. Subsequently, the temperature of the solution was increased slowly to 100°and then increased to 300°C to form the sol. The sol then ignited to form the precursor. The precursor was then finally ground and pre-calcined at 400°C for 5 hours. The final product LSMO nano (designated as NANO) was obtained by calcining at 750°C for 5 hours which was then ground and pressed into pellets of diameter 10 mm and thickness 2–3 mm and sintered at 850°C for 5 hours. The bulk sample (designated as BULK) was synthesized by solid-state reaction using the corresponding

La_2O_3, $SrCO_3$, and MnO_2 with ethanol as the medium. The final bulk LSMO was obtained by a series of calcinations followed by sintering at 1300°C for 12 hrs.

Phase purity of the samples was analysed by X-ray powder diffraction using PANalytical X'pert Pro diffractometer with Cu-Kα radiation of wavelength 1.5406 Å and operated at 30 mA, 40 kV. The powder samples were scanned with a step size of 0.017° in the 2θ range 20° to 80°. General Structure Analysis System (GSAS)-EXPGUI software was used to carry out the Rietveld refinement of the X-ray diffraction patterns. The crystallite size was estimated using Scherrer equation. The β_{hkl} values were corrected for instrumental broadening by using standard silicon sample. The microstructural features were examined using Carl Zeiss Evo 18 scanning electron microscope (SEM) in secondary electron (SE) imaging mode. High-Resolution Transmission electron microscopy (HRTEM) measurements were done on NANO and BULK samples using a JEOL-2010 (Japan) electron microscope.

3. Results and Discussion

3.1. Structural Analysis

The Rietveld refined powder X-ray diffraction patterns at room temperature of the LSMO samples labeled as NANO and BULK is shown in figure 1 (a) and 1 (b) respectively. Both the samples were found to be in a single phase with rhombohedral structure and R-3c space group. It has been observed that certain peaks present in BULK are absent in NANO samples. In bulk samples, there are infinite number of planes and hence the XRD peaks are due to diffraction from these planes. But in nano samples, there are less number of atoms and hence less number of planes hence diffraction is not complete. Hence, the peak in nano samples gets broadened. Due to incomplete constructive interference, the diffraction from certain peaks may not be evident in the nano sample. However, in bulk samples, due to the presence of large number of crystallites oriented in all possible directions, all possible diffraction peaks should be observed.

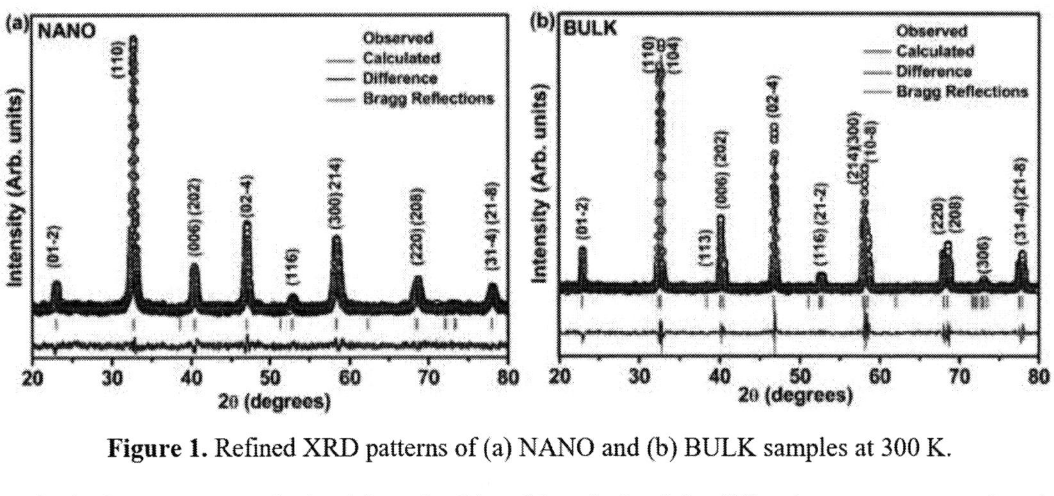

Figure 1. Refined XRD patterns of (a) NANO and (b) BULK samples at 300 K.

The lattice parameters obtained from the Rietveld analysis of the diffraction patterns were found to be a = 5.4875(3) Å, b= 5.4875(3) Å and c= 13.38(1) Å for the NANO sample and a= 5.5074(2) Å, b= 5.5074(2) Å, and c= 13.3644(5) Å for the BULK sample. It is observed that, there is a slight increase in the unit cell parameters along a and b axis as the sample changes from NANO to BULK, whereas along the c axes, it is found to decrease. The estimated cell volumes of NANO and BULK are 348.95(5) and 351.06(3) Å, respectively. The increase in cell volume is attributed to the increase in particle size from nano to bulk. In the present work, we have used sol-gel method for the synthesis of NANO sample. In this method, the growth of the grain is restricted due to the presence of surfactants and capping agents. Further, we have used a low temperature of 850 °C for the synthesis of nano samples. In case of bulk sample, high sintering temperatures of 1300 °C have been used for the complete phase formation which results in the growth of crystallites. Hence the crystallite size of the nano sample would be much less compared to the bulk. Lattice parameters, cell volume, atomic positions, bonding distances (Mn-O-Mn) and tilt bond angles obtained from Rietveld refinement are presented in Table 1. The flattening of the Mn-O-Mn tilt angles from 175.262° in NANO to 166.337° in BULK is attributed to the increase in the double exchange (DE) mechanism in BULK sample [5].

The average crystallite size (t) of both the samples have been determined from Scherrer's formula:

$$t = \frac{0.9\,\lambda}{\beta_{hkl} cos\theta_{hkl}} \tag{1}$$

where β_{hkl} is the full width at half maximum (FWHM), λ is the wavelength of the X-rays and θ is the Bragg angle. The FWHM has been determined by curve fitting the XRD peaks using Pseudo Voigt 1 function. The curve fitting of (110) peak for NANO and BULK sample has been shown in figure 2 as a representative of the series. Table 2 gives the parameters obtained from the curve fitting for determining the crystallite size (t) of NANO and BULK samples. The average crystallite size is found to be approximately 19 and 63 nm for the NANO and BULK samples sintered at 850 °C and 1300 °C, respectively. The crystallite size is found to increase with increase in sintering temperature.

Table 1. Refinement parameters obtained for LSMO NANO and BULK samples.

Sample	NANO	BULK
	Lattice parameters	
a (Å)	5.4875(3)	5.5074(2)
c (Å)	13.38(1)	13.3644(5)
Volume (Å)	348.95(5)	351.06(3)
	Atomic Positions	
La/Sr (0.7:0.3) x	0	0
La/Sr (0.7:0.3) y	0	0
La/Sr (0.7:0.3) z	0.25	0.25
O x	0.5146(0)	0.5422(0)
O y	0	0
O z	0.25	0.25
Mn x	0	0
Mn y	0	0
Mn z	0	0
Bond distance Mn-O (Å)	1.9389(10)	1.9550(5)
Bond angle (°) Mn-O-Mn	175.262	166.337
R_{wp} (%)	3.22	5.17
χ^2	1.107	2.730

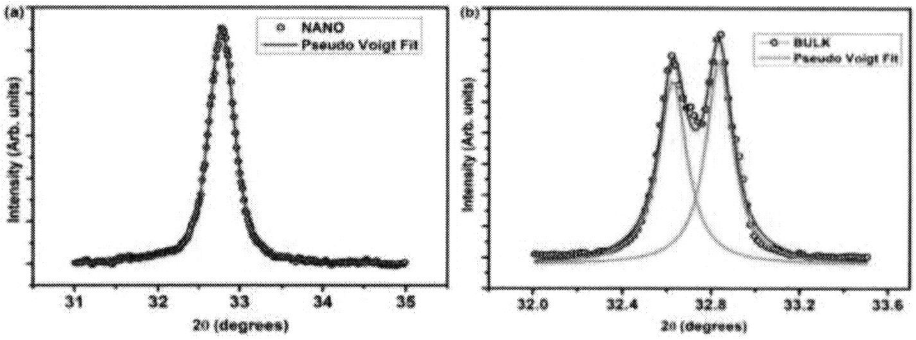

Figure 2. Peak fitting of (110) peak of (a) NANO and (b) BULK samples.

Table 2. Parameters obtained from peak fitting for determining crystallite size

NANO				BULK			
Peak	2θ (degrees)	β_{hkl} (degrees)	t (nm)	Peak	2θ (degrees)	β_{hkl} (degrees)	t (nm)
110	32.7827	0.3722	22.2581	110	32.62834	0.15423	53.6953
				104	32.83652	0.14782	56.0536
006	40.4393	0.4711	17.9802	006	40.24655	0.16183	52.3050
				202	40.61693	0.15977	53.0424
02-4	47.0061	0.4105	21.1097	02-4	46.88761	0.12209	70.9534
				122	46.9954	0.11285	76.7943
300	58.43049	0.61355	14.8406	300	58. 2104	0.13216	68.8235
				214	58.6319	0.1233	73.9207

The microstrain (ε) and crystallite size has been estimated only for the NANO sample using WH analysis and SSP. WH analysis using Uniform deformation model (UDM) has been used to determine the size and strain contribution to line broadening. In UDM, the anisotropic character of the crystal is not considered and ε is presumed to be homogeneous along all the crystallographic axes. WH equation is,

$$\beta_{hkl} cos\theta = \frac{K\lambda}{t} + 4 < \varepsilon > sin\theta \quad (2)$$

where β_{hkl} is the observed width, K is the shape factor, θ is the Bragg angle, t is the average crystallite size and ε is the root mean square (RMS) value of microstrain. By plotting $\beta_{hkl}\ cos\theta$ with respect to $4sin\theta$, the crystallite size is found from the y-intercept and ε is estimated from the linear slope of the line. The UDM plot for the NANO sample is shown in Figure 3 (a). The estimated crystallite size and microstrain is 43 nm and 0.00293 for the NANO sample from the UDM model. UDM model being less accurate for the calculation of t and ε, we have estimated them using the size strain plots (SSP). In this approximation, the crystallite size broadening is described using the Lorentzian function while gaussian function is used to estimate the strain broadening [12,13]. Hence we have used the equation,

$$\left(\frac{d_{hkl}\beta_{hkl}cos\theta}{\lambda}\right)^2 = \frac{K\lambda}{t}\left(\frac{d_{hkl}^2\beta_{hkl}cos\theta}{\lambda^2}\right) + \left\{\frac{\Sigma}{2}\right\}^2 \quad (3)$$

where K is a constant, d_{hkl} is the interplanar distance and $\Sigma = (2(2\pi))^{1/2} < \varepsilon >$ [12]. Here, the term $\left(\frac{d_{hkl}\beta_{hkl}cos\theta}{\lambda}\right)^2$ is plotted a function of $\left(\frac{d_{hkl}^2\beta_{hkl}cos\theta}{\lambda^2}\right)$ for the all orientation of peaks. In SSP, the particle size is determined from the slope of equation (3) and the square root of the y –intercept gives the value of ε [14]. Figure 3 (b) show the SSP plot for the NANO sample. The estimated crystallite size and ε

from SSP is 27 nm and 0.00255 for the NANO sample. The variation of average crystallite size and ε obtained from different methods is presented in Table 3. It could be seen that the average crystallite size obtained from SSP agrees well with that obtained from the Scherrer equation.

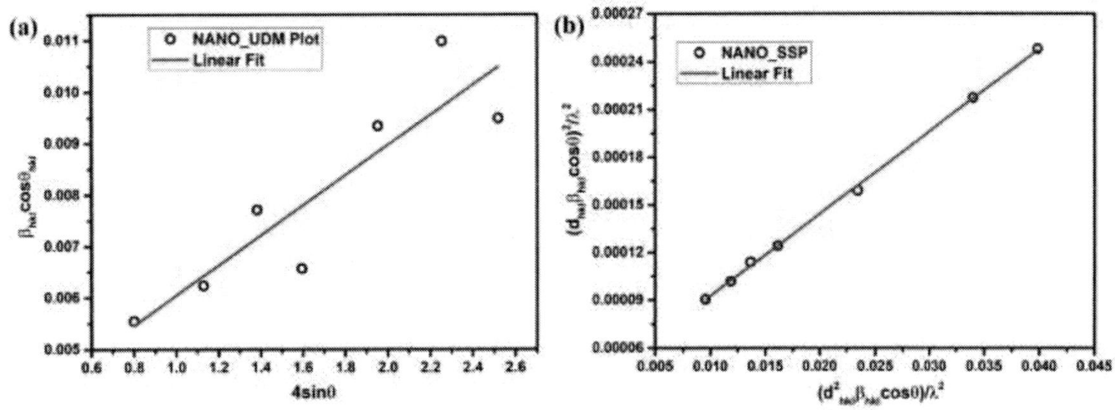

Figure 3. (a) UDM plot and (b) SSP plot for NANO sample.

Table 3. Average Crystallite size and microstrain obtained by different methods for NANO sample.

	Average Crystallite Size	Microstrain
Scherrer Equation	19.05	-
WH Analysis	44.44	0.00293
SSP	26.76	0.00255

3.2. Morphological Analysis:

Inorder to understand the surface morphology and microstructure of $La_{0.7}Sr_{0.3}MnO_3$ nanocrystals, SEM images of sintered, polished and thermally etched pellets of NANO and BULK samples have been taken and are shown in figure 4(a) and 4(b) respectively. SEM micrographs indicate that the surface of the samples are homogeneous with well-defined grain boundaries. The NANO and BULK samples has been further analyzed using HRTEM. Figure 5(a and b) represents the HRTEM images of the NANO and BULK samples and their corresponding SAED patterns are shown in figure 5(c and d) respectively. It could be seen that the particles are agglomerated both in NANO and BULK which could be attributed to the strong magnetic moment between the particles. The average grain sizes is found to be around 28 and 78 nm respectively for the NANO and BULK samples. It is evident that the crystallite size increases with increase in sintering temperature and the results obtained agree well with that obtained from Scherrer equation and SSP.

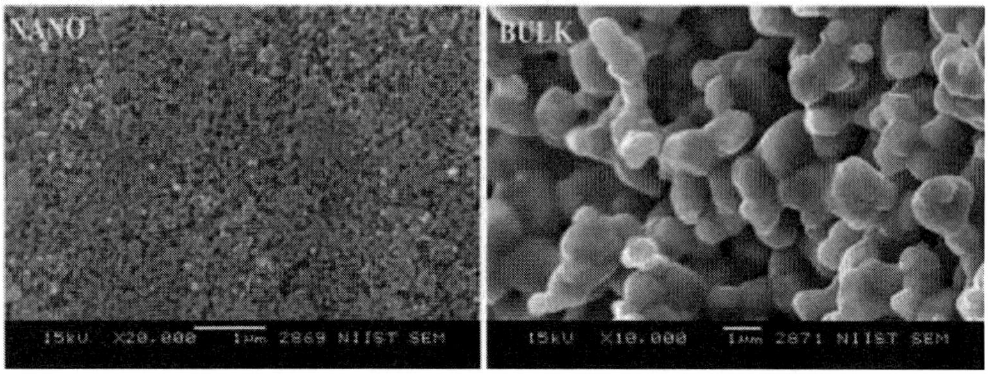

Figure 4. SEM micrographs of (a) NANO and (b) BULK sample.

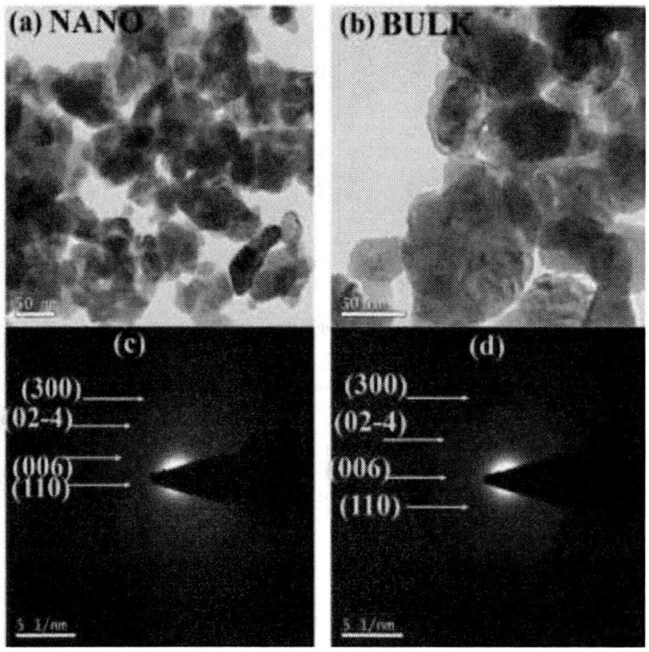

Figure 5. HRTEM micrographs of (a) NANO and (b) BULK sample; SAED patterns of (c) NANO and (d) BULK samples.

4. Conclusion

$La_{0.7}Sr_{0.3}MnO_3$ perovskite manganites have been synthesized by solid state and sol-gel technique. Powder X-ray diffraction technique was performed to examine the crystal structure and all the compounds assumed rhombohedral structure with space group R-3c. The crystallite size has been estimated from the Scherrer equation, WH analysis and SSP. The crystallite size determined from the SSP was found to be more accurate than that obtained from the WH analysis and agrees well with the results obtained by Scherrer Equation. Homogeneity of the compound was confirmed from TEM & SEM analysis.

Acknowledgements
The authors would like to acknowledge CSIR-NIIST, Trivandrum for SEM and TEM measurements. The authors would like to acknowledge Fatima Mata National College for partially supporting this work.

Reference

[1] Arakawa T, Yoshida A and Shiokawa J 1980 *Mater. Res. Bull.* **15** 269
[2] Phan M H and Yu S C 2007 *J. Magn. Magn. Mater* **308** 325
[3] Xia W, Pei Z, Leng K and Zhu X 2020 *Nanoscale Res. Lett.* **15** 1
[4] Zener C 1951 *Phys. Rev.* **82** 403
[5] Liao Z *Appl. Sci.* 2019 **9(1)** 144
[6] Tiwari A and Rajeev K P 1999 *Solid State Commun.* **111** 33
[7] Goodenough J B 1998 *Annu. Rev. Mater. Sci.* **28** 1
[8] Sadhu A and Bhattacharyya S 2014 *Chem. Mater.* **26** 1702
[9] Lau L N, Lim K P, Ishak A N, Kechik M M A, Chen S K, Ibrahim N B, Miryala M, Murakami M and Shaari A H 2021 *Coatings* **11(3)** 361
[10] Navin K and Kurchania R 2018 *Ceram. Int.* 44 (5) 4973
[11] Zhang C *et al.* 2021 *ACS Appl. Mater. Interfaces* **13 (24)** 2844
[12] Maniammal K, Madhu G and Biju V 2017 *Physica E* **85** 214
[13] Biju V, Sugathan N,Vrinda V and Salini S L 2008 *J. Mater. Sci.* **43** 1175
[14] Warren B E and Averbach B I 1950 *J. Appl. Phys.* **21** 595

AUTHOR INDEX